PI
THE T

I. Allan Sealy was born in
at La Martinière, Luckno
English literature at St Stephen's Co
an exchange student to the Honors College at Western ...
University. He then taught for some years at universities in the
United States, Australia and Canada. In 1982 he received a doctorate
from the University of British Columbia for a dissertation on the
Caribbean novelist Wilson Harris. *The Trotter-Nama*, his first
novel, was written for the most part in Lucknow, the city on
which his fictional Nakhlau is based. He has also written a second
novel, *Hero*. He is now a full-time writer but finds time to paint
and travel. He is married to a New Zealander and divides his
time between India, Australia and New Zealand.

The Trotter-Nama was winner of the Best First Book Section
(Eurasia) of the 1989 Commonwealth Writers' Prize.

PENGUIN BOOKS

THE TROTTER-NĀMA

1951 in Allahabad, India. He was educated
and Delhi University, where he studied
College. In 1971 he travelled as
Michigan

I. ALLAN SEALY

THE TROTTER-NAMA

A Chronicle 1977–1984

PENGUIN BOOKS

PENGUIN BOOKS

Published by the Penguin Group
27 Wrights Lane, London W8 5TZ, England
Viking Penguin Inc., 40 West 23rd Street, New York, New York 10010, USA
Penguin Books Australia Ltd, Ringwood, Victoria, Australia
Penguin Books Canada Ltd, 2801 John Street, Markham, Ontario, Canada L3R 1B4
Penguin Books (NZ) Ltd, 182–190 Wairau Road, Auckland 10, New Zealand

Penguin Books Ltd, Registered Offices: Harmondsworth, Middlesex, England

First published in the USA by Alfred A. Knopf, Inc., New York 1988
First published in Great Britain by Viking 1988
Published in Penguin Books 1990

1 3 5 7 9 10 8 6 4 2

Copyright © I. Allan Sealy, 1988
Map and genealogical chart copyright © Anita Karl and James Kemp, 1988
All rights reserved

Made and printed in Great Britain by
Richard Clay Ltd, Bungay, Suffolk

To
the Other Anglo-Indians

CONTENTS

PROLOGUE

Trotter

1

CHRONICLE

Trotter-Nama

11

EPILOGUE

Nama

563

MAPS AND
FAMILY TREE

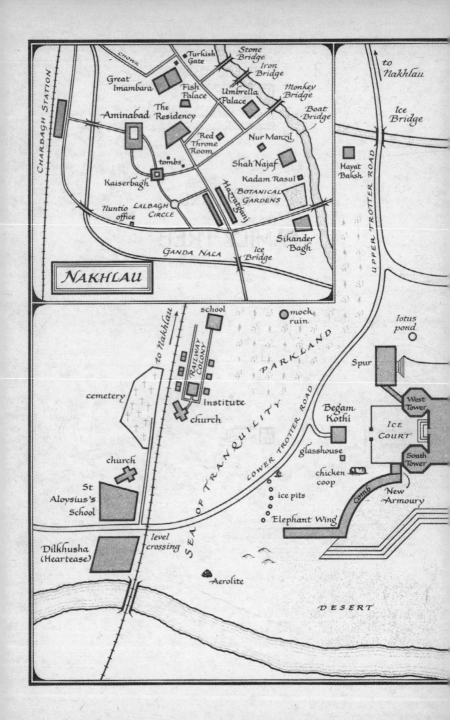

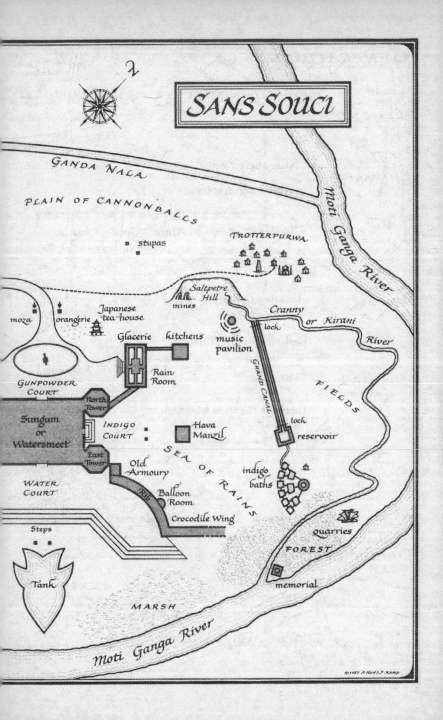

GENERATIONS

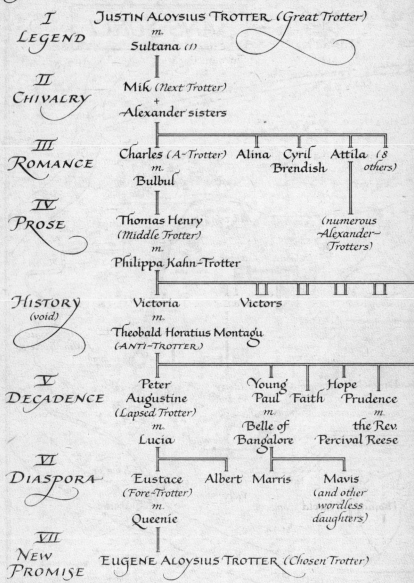

I
LEGEND

JUSTIN ALOYSIUS TROTTER *(Great Trotter)*
m.
Sultana *(1)*

II
CHIVALRY

Mik *(Next Trotter)*
+
Alexander sisters

III
ROMANCE

Charles *(A-Trotter)*   Alina   Cyril   Attila *(8*
m.   Brendish   *others)*
Bulbul

IV
PROSE

Thomas Henry   *(numerous*
(Middle Trotter)   *Alexander-*
m.   *Trotters)*
Philippa Kahn-Trotter

HISTORY
(void)

Victoria   Victors
m.
Theobald Horatius Montagu
(ANTI-TROTTER)

V
DECADENCE

Peter   Young   Hope
Augustine   Paul   Faith   Prudence
(Lapsed Trotter)   m.   m.
m.   Belle of   the Rev.
Lucia   Bangalore   Percival Reese

VI
DIASPORA

Eustace   Albert   Marris   Mavis
(Fore-Trotter)   *(and other*
m.   *wordless*
Queenie   *daughters)*

VII
NEW PROMISE

EUGENE ALOYSIUS TROTTER *(Chosen Trotter)*

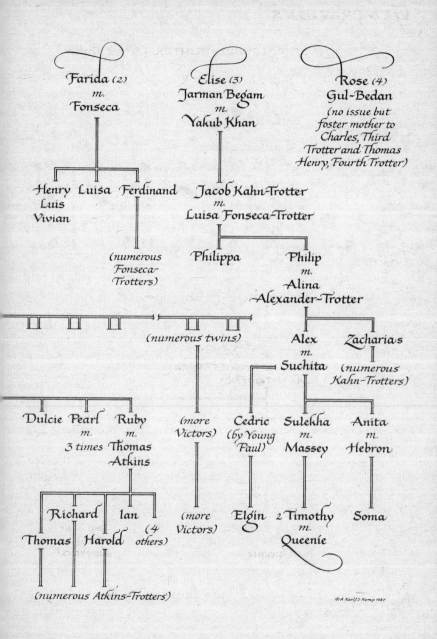

TROTTER

Take up the Grey Man's Burden,
To vie be nothing loth;
Where beauty calls or guerdon—
Stand up! Stand up! for both.

—HYMN

A good miniature is a sugarplum.

You know, I've been dreaming of gulab jamuns in warm syrup from Mansoor's in Nakhlau. Confectioners of Integrity Since (circa) 1763. Why can't Indians make decent sweets abroad? The gulab jamuns there are like stewed prunes. Is it something in the oil? Or in the milk? It can't be in the sugar, since sugar is constant across all borders, like carbon or hydrogen. Could it be in the air?

Have we taken off? I'm sorry I was late, by the way. Yes, I know the flight was held up—the looks as I came down the aisle just now! That one in the green sari, and she isn't all that small herself. But it's happened before and I suppose it'll happen again—the mad dash to the airport, the last call, the last and final call, the special bus spurring across the tarmac, the jocose mechanics at the front hatch, the ironical steward, the tight-lipped purser, the testy stewardesses, the long walk down the aisle, head bent, eyes scanning the seat numbers along the luggage holds, the blue looking left, the brown right.

"The Late Mr Trotter," my favourite dentist used to call me. His daughter was less charitable. "Lenten Trotter" was her choice, and when I asked her why, she said: Well, corpu-lent, flatu-lent, indo-lent. She thought the indo-lent was especially apt even though I said: I'm half Anglo, you know.

So. The Late Mr Trotter, Seventh Trotter, pleased to meet you.

Is the middle seat free by any chance? Yes I know the aisle seat's mine—and the window's yours, absolutely—but if the one in the middle is free? It is? Good. Now if I can just flip up the armrest, there, and put this cushion under the seat there'll be more room for everyone.

Well, yes, mostly me, I suppose, but there it is. Or here I am.

Anyway, a good miniature—ah, breakfast! Yes, madam, and one for the middle— my wife.

Well, I had to tell her something. No, I'm afraid, marriage is not for me. I can see you're off to a wedding, though, so I owe you an apology. The reason I was late back in Calcutta—in spite of three staggered alarm clocks—is that I was waiting for the icelight.

Icelight. *It's that slippery spermy light that comes just before dawn. We have no word for it—only the people of the Far North, who knew and valued the periods of light, spoke it and celebrated it in their glittering epics. It's the hour when their long ships, victualled by tallow light and pitch flare, set out eager and trim to cleave the back of the green sea. It's there in the opening bars of* The Sky of the North, *it's there in one corner of every canvas by that overpriced Munch. But what good is it, you may ask; does it pay the rent?*

It does, in a way. It freezes time, or rather, it traps it at that tremulous point just short of freezing, when time is neither solid nor liquid but simply a quality of light. It comes at the edge of sleep, when all those vivid fragments from the past float up to the surface hard and real but running away like lumps of ice. It allows you to get the past down, to copy it, after it's actually melted away. And the past alone is true. It's my livelihood anyway. Sans Souci, for instance—that's our ancestral home—I rebuilt it by icelight.

Sans Souci, Sweet Saviour! Ages since I was there, and yet I saw it this morning as clear as ever, unspoilt, preserved whole in ice. Like that woolly mammoth they found with fresh buttercups held in its trunk.

Incidentally, did you know we used to import ice from America almost two hundred years ago? Yes, half-way around the world in sailing ships. The British brought some over too. Somewhere down there in the Ganges is the wreck of one of their ice barges, the Mother Maturin. *Foreign ice! I like to think some of it got as far as Sans Souci.*

Now, a good miniature—ah, tea! Yes, madam, thank you. And one for the wife. She spends a lot of time in there, doesn't she?

The day—the day proper—has not begun until six to eight cups of lukewarm— never hot—milky tea have been absorbed. Sweet—*the spoon should stand upright in the cup like the plow in the Mississippi until the sugar melts. Fingers of scorched white bread, radically buttered, dipped swiftly and lofted—thus—into the waiting mouth before they sag. No matter if a curl of butter should slip into the cup and float there, sketching little fugitive arabesques—in fact a lump of yak's butter in there to start with would be ideal. Not that you can expect* that *at thirty thousand feet, even in First Class where I usually travel.*

See the Himalayas down there? Tibet on the other side.

My profession? You haven't been listening. You could say I was a writer. Aha! The look accusative—not really work, is it? Well, I used to be a writer, but in the old East India Company sense of clerk. All Anglos were writers until the railways came, almost all. Soldiers and teachers too—we're still that, though there aren't very many of us left. Maybe a hundred thousand, maybe two, counting bazar-side Anglos. The Sikhs are two percent of the Indian population—well, we're two percent of that.

You see that skinny chap across the aisle? Now there's a proper writer. West Indian East Indian, or maybe Fiji brahmin. Islander, anyway—see the pen in his pocket? The constant traveller. Same here, only I don't have ulcers. Cuts himself a large slice of worry. Now, if he took a little tea with it. But somehow I don't think he likes my tea ceremony.

Well, I'm afraid you're rather stuck with it. This is only my second. There are advantages to totalling tea—they can cut off the wine supply but they can't refuse you another cup of tea, not in India anyway. You see he's pressed the annunciator button. It'll be a dry white for him.

There you go—as if Indian Airlines would. Well, in fact I'm a painter. Ah! A mellower response. Why? Sentimental lot, you Economy types. You now, let me see. On special short leave, not your annual holiday. Off to your cousin-sister's wedding.

Yes, so, a painter, that's the truth. A miniature painter. Amusing? You wouldn't laugh if you had someone like Carlos on your tail for months at a time. I'm lucky to be here at all.

Not his fault, you could say. Just doing what Ivor paid him to. And he was fair about it. Whenever I laid off painting he laid off me. It was only when a new one came on the market that he returned, dutifully.

The first time I saw him was on the Burma railway—no, no, the first time was with Ivor. You set up on your own, Ivor was saying, and you're done for. Right on cue the door opens and he steps in. Tall, skinny, with a matchstick head and long vicious fingers. Carlos here will see to that. And Carlos snarls like the daytime-TV hit man that he is. That was the first time. But the first time I knew he was following me was on that train. Came and sat down opposite with his eternal newspaper. I was reading, I think, Shot'ha Rust'hveli's Joseph the Magnificent *from the Great Trotter's (peace be His) library when suddenly he looks up from his paper and says: They've spoilt Prague. Almost jumped out of my skin. All I could remember of Prague was a large old upper-storey room I shared with a Norwegian girl with elbows like tailor's chalk, and the late-night trams grinding by under the window, wires clicking. Brake-squeak, bell-clang, Unni asleep with her mouth open, shearing through remembered belts of northern pine, and the wires going click-click, click-click. But he didn't want conversation. Just went back to his dateless paper after scaring me half to death.*

And since then it's been Carlos in Argentina (we shared a ferry to Montevideo), Carlos in Luxor, Carlos by the pudding shops of Istanbul, Carlos by the rivers of Babylon, Carlos on the Trans-Siberian railway, Carlos in Sault Ste Marie, Carlos sitting with his back up against one of those glum Easter Island chins, newspaper open, as if either he or the stonehead could read. In his regulation fawn mackintosh with a bulge in the pocket. Happy to see me.

So miniature painting isn't just what you think—single-hair brushes and two parts zinc with one of lime-in the white of a duck's egg. Though that's the first step towards capturing the icelight. You can see it in the sky just above the elephant in my The Great Trotter Subdues a Rogue Elephant *(circa 1780) at the Clancy and Avril de Soto Museum of Oriental Art in Philadelphia. Where, incidentally, if you ask for cream cheese and bagels the waitress will look sadly at you and call out: Hash browns, double sunnyside, bacon parallel, pair toast. And coffee. Black.*

A good miniature, by the way, is an excellent investment. Would you like to see one? No?

There's also icelight in The Great Trotter Hunts the Boar *(circa 1780, V&A), but that's where the trouble started. Good money, though, while it lasted. Anyway, I think I've shaken him off—this is one country where he wouldn't follow me. Where it all began. Too many germs.*

No germs up on Baffin Island, where I had my fill of icelight—it bounces off the polar ice-cap and comes sliding across Greenland. I was doing artwork for a team of scientists on the trail of some former expedition—no cameras, no modern equipment, cricket on the ice with the Esquimaux. Strict naturalism for a change, with cloudberry, arctic poppy, saxifrage, rock tripe. Animal pictures too, including one I kept—the North American snowshoe hare, which is white in winter and dark brown in summer. Melts into its surroundings, instead of sticking out like me. I'm white here, but I'm brown back there—in addition to all this. It starts to happen at the airport, so I usually wait in the toilet till the change is complete.

There's one advantage to hiding in there. It's like this. The last call for Mr E. Trotter. You sit out ten minutes. Will Mr E. Trotter please report immediately to Gate 6. Stay put for another ten. Mr E. Trotter, you are wanted immediately at Gate 6. Then you count, slowly, to a hundred, and rush out. And after a little storm and stress they slap a First Class boarding pass into your hands because the stand-by crowd have filled up Economy. Then a whole bus, all to yourself, racing past the hangars with their beautiful jets, orange, green, royal blue. It works, usually.

I don't want you to think—though he does, Carlos—that he's the prime mover, the root cause of all this bracing mobility. No. That's safely here, under the seat. He thinks it's for sale, but it's not. I used to worry about losing it—all those years' work—but then I decided the safest way was to tempt fate. So it just travels with me in a brown paper bag. With my current address, so the bag is changed regularly. It's been left under bridges, on buses, in public toilets and telephone booths, on park benches, in Groppi's confiserie in Cairo, and it always comes back.

It's called the Trotter-Nama, *the Epic of the Trotters, or simply the Trotter-Book. Never quite worked out what* nama *means, but book is good enough. Means "name" in Hindi, but that's not the same thing. There are enough* namas *around—the* Akbar-Nama, *Abu'l Fazl's monumental piece of flattery of the Great Mughal; the* Shah-Nama *of Firdausi, the Epic of Persian Kings, not popular these days in Iran;*

the Babar-Nama, *written by the first Mughal himself, Akbar's grandfather; the* Sikandar-Nama, *or Epic of Alexander the Great; the* Ni'mat-Nama, *best of the lot, a medieval recipe book; not that the others lack recipes and all sorts of interesting odds and ends. Colourful too. But please don't confuse my nama with the* Tota-Nama, *the Book of the Parrot, a Hindu epic told by a talking bird that goes on and on.*

So, the Trotter-Nama. *The chronicle (not history) of the Trotters as set out by the Seventh Trotter. A mixed bag, prodigally illustrated as all those namas were, but this one by the author himself, not some lackey doing piecework at twenty rupees the page.*

That's the prime mover—the garnering of the past. And the result, for the chronicler, a paper-chase. Because we came from all over, not just England, and went all over, not just to England. Someone's got to do it, or it'll all blow away like half those old chronicles that came apart and were sold page by page, so that when you ask for them in any of the world's libraries your request slip comes back stamped, in violet, UNBOUND. *And so we forget. Past masters in the art of forgetting, my people.*

My people! I could have laughed up a storm when the words first struck me. Let my people go! Go where? *Trotterland? But one of the rules of the place where I sat said:* Documents the paper of which is brittle shall not be consulted under a fan. *So I just sat there and shook.*

The chronicle has a sequence, never fear, though the gathering was random. Montevideo to look for Peter, Fifth Trotter's grave (not found); the Falklands-Malvinas to check on Great-aunt Pearl who after she made good in motion pictures claimed to have been born there (though her mother, whom Albert called Mother-of-Pearl, was delivered—correction, delivered herself—of her and her twin sister right here in Nakhlau—well, we're almost there); Alexandria where the First Trotter (peace be His) was conceived and the Fourth Trotter bereaved when his wife, Philippa, broke her back in a fall from a camel that hadn't yet got properly up; Darwin, divisive name, for a recipe that was actually in Dehra Dun; Woolwich where the Second Trotter learnt about cannons, but not enough for his health; Isphahan, Naples, Turin, also in the Second Trotter's (Gipsy Trotter's) footsteps; Tunbridge Wells for leek pasties with the whilom Belle of Bangalore (she had turned Welsh); London, Weed, California, and Perth to try to get Queenie's secret out of Mavis; the Albert Hall where Dulcie the Diva, who taught me music, gave her first (and only) recital; though it was Soma, really, who brought out my voice.

But most of it happened here in India, in Nakhlau. In Sans Souci—Home of the Trotters. Trotters, Anglos, same thing. You'll see it in a minute. The plane goes over it just before we land at Nakhlau.

Hard work, the chase. Especially in the early years before the money from the paintings started to come in. The sour cheap airless hotel rooms with an ashtray always overturned at the same spot on the sand-coloured carpet. You lift it up and there is the ritual smudge of ash and butts and chicken-bones like one of those illustrations out of a child's Robinson Crusoe *with the legend:* Their horrible feast. *The waiting, the stillness, the unutterably forlorn chime of coat-hangers as you close the door on Room 23, closet witnesses to suicide, fornication, huge solitary pasta dinners.*

Not always indoors, because after a while you tire of hotels full of young tourists complaining about the tourists. What's wrong with tourists anyway? Are those who stay at home better? So you sleep on the beach north of Auckland (there was a Trotter policeman there, one of Eustace, Sixth Trotter's colleagues, who had been Gandhi's gaoler) and wake up with sand in your mouth and an armada of stranded Portuguese men-of-war for company. Or you settle for a park bench in Medicine Hat in October and find the Sunday edition of the New York Times much overrated as an insulator. Because you wake up with your head a block of ice on fire to find Carlos swimming towards you like a swordfish through the blue morning light, disguised as a park cleaner with one of those spiked sticks for picking up trash—what are they called? No way out but to burst howling from under the paper, tear it into a thousand pieces, scatter them around and run off stamping the earth and slapping your cheeks to get the blood going.

Freeway bridges are more sensible. Thoughtfully designed so you get shelter and a ledge just wide enough at the top of the slope on each side under the bridge. And no park attendants. You get used to the noise, the 22-wheelers thundering past, and it's a broad road shoulder in case you roll off the edge in your sleep—which can happen. You wake up to the sun rising behind two slender trees that could be Nakhlau minarets.

Halcyon wanderyears! The longest stop two months in Eugene, Oregon, where I was guru to the Family of Love—chubby brown gods were popular then. Afterwards fleeing south I was stuck for two days in the Arizona desert in the company of serrated reptiles and little hopping insects. Studio cactus-and-mesa that once framed the exquisite Pearl when she played opposite—and almost married—the sheriff who many years later, when he was President, ordered a whole naval fleet to stand by because she was caught up in the Falklands fiasco. On a flying visit from Hollywood to greet her fellow Falklanders. But that hadn't happened yet as I stood there on the abandoned set, waiting. There's a certain pleasure in standing on the freeway sucking jujubes and feeling the breath of those long cars as they flick by, always in packs, without slowing down at all. The longer the car, the sharper the lash—the Ford LTDs actually speed up when they see you, and the Cadillacs simply rocket past, zut, zut, zut. Then they're gone and you have the desert to yourself and you can watch the lizards cooking on red stones and count the dimpled rosettes of white thorn on the cactus until the joy of it sneaks up on you and you're trilling Che faro senza Euridice *in the original part and not as it was rewritten for the female voice to suit those squeamish Parisians. And at last the U.S. Cavalry in the shape of the trucker who pulls over and when you're on the road again says he passed a margarine truck which had collided with an eggplant truck in Death Valley and he could smell the fried eggplant clear down to the Mexican border.*

Slouching into Veracruz with the dentist's daughter on Peter, Fifth Trotter's trail, then haring across to Darien on the run from Carlos. The Pacific slams into you down *there—an insolent blue, rough as a grater. You can imagine yourself up a tree, gazing with a wild surmise. Stout Cortez, people seem to forget.*

I told her about Carlos. Just paint, she said. He's not chasing you. He's trying to get out. Giggling, because she was posing outdoors for Woman Bather with Watermelon *(circa 1690, not for sale). I almost put down roots. Her Mixtec pottery and onion-skin elbows could have furnished a home. Home! After the years of wandering, dreaming of that farm where I would live in peace, waking early, ploughing the mealies.*

But then He began to appear. Not him, the skinny one. Him. The Great Trotter Himself (peace be His). Saying: Eugene, write. I first saw him in the toilet at three in the morning. An eighteenth-century Frenchman sitting there, elbows on knees, chin supported, wig, stockings, buckle shoes. Face looked like myself grown old. Thought I'd ignore him but he kept turning up. Once we were doing ninety in the Studebaker and there he was, looking in at the window on my side, leaning down from his horse. Eugene, write.

One says paint, one says write, and the result is an illustrated nama. *If someone had said sing, you might have had a musical book, but no one did. Strange thing, jealousy.*

So the whole thing started again. Quebec to pay an old bill (the pond dry, the farmhouse gone), Edinburgh to call on the poet Cedric Trotter (he'd been dead ten years), Middlesex to tell Ivor what he could do with his The Great Trotter Hunts the Boar *(that was a mistake), Vladivostok for a change of air. Some change—fog, foghorns, the crash every half hour of a coal-loader down by the docks, a fat warm yellow musk of machine oil on the air, crunchy snow, a restaurant where the meal (Mongolian sheep's tail, curd dumplings, and pashka) was so rich you had to embezzle it, and outside, in the sodium glare of a streetlamp, reading or pretending to read the last issue of the* Catfish Farmer and World Agricultural News, *Carlos.*

To tell the truth, it wasn't all chase. One or two places out of interest—

The toilet? All right, hurry up, then. We'll be landing soon. Do I have to get up? OK, come on, then. I'll wait in the aisle—I'm not getting in and out again.

Happy? You were gone long enough—we're almost there. I was saying: One or two places out of interest. Art and all. Sam Palmer's Kentish copse, just to check on that Metafori; Kom Obo to adapt a watercolour by that fine man Edward Lear—bearded, but had a passion for chocolate turtles; the Tate because either he or Lyle invented the sugarcube. A quick walk, well, quickish, along Leadenhall Street past damp-cheeked brokers to St. Andrew Undershaft to wait for the ghost of that other fine Englishman, Charles Lamb, who gave forty years of his life to the Hon. East India Co. as a writer (old style), and whom Pater describes as having a, quote, clear brown complexion, eyes not precisely of the same colour, and a slow walk. And then a few side trips—to Sucre in Bolivia where I discovered with a sense of betrayal that they have guava cheese; to Windermere to see the marigolds lifting and dancing in the breeze (though I didn't have the heart to leave the station and took the next train back); to

Turin where at last, in the cathedral where they keep the Shroud, I understood. The thing in itself is nothing, a cipher. You *supply the figure. Even Carlos saw that before I did. The faith of the simple. And his figure's not much better than yours.*

So I finished it off. And here I am. You see before you, beside you, a reconstructed Trotter.

Ah—seat-belts, yes, madam. Seat upright, yes. Going down, are we? I'll go get the wife.

Snooty beauty. Now, if you look out on the right there in a little while you'll see Sans Souci.

Let the plane bank a bit. There. See how it all stands up? Flat, no perspective, like a good miniature. That's Sungum *in the middle, the main building with the towers. Means the* Watersmeet. *See the Crown on top? Over there are the old indigo baths. That's the Glacerie. The Cock Hall or Spur on the other side. The ice pits.* The people here are ice-making mad, *one traveller said in the last century. Fanny Parks—gave a nice recipe for jamun ice cream. That's a jamun tree there.* Eugenia jambolana. *Over there is Munnoo's mango tope. But where are the watermelons? And the jujube groves? The river seems to have joined up with the Tank. My God, Dilkhusha's under water! Looks like they've been having a bit of rain.*

Anyway, I'm going to give a fancy dinner when I get there. Brought all the stuff with me, and a few bottles of very late Sauternes. Had to pay duty on all except one. Don't think Fiji would be interested. Too sweet for him.

Yes, who knows, we might meet. Let's see. As they say every hour on All-India Radio: The next program follows.

Your attachy? You can get it when we've landed. Here, you hold on to this paper bag—don't get sick in it—I'll just get out a peppermint. Extra-Strongs. I hate landings. Taking off I don't mind so much, though they say that's more dangerous. Have one? Have two. OK.

CHRONICLE

TROTTER-NAMA

On the poop of the Mandalay,
Where the owl and the petticoat play,
Full seldom is whirred
The shuttlecock bird—
For the crannies row grimly
Past banks hung with imli—
As the ice in the hold runs away.

—NURSERY RHYME

CONTENTS OF TROTTER-NAMA

The chronicle	19
Lines in praise of Nakhlau (*from Qaiyum*)	24
INTERPOLATION: An Apology	26
Frontispiece	26
INTERPOLATION: Concerning an alleged painter, one Zoffanij	27
Frontispiece continued	28
Entry in Jarman Begam's diary for June 21, 1799	29
The Great Trotter considers the heavens	33
The Great Trotter considers the earth	34
The Great Trotter considers what is in between	35
The black partridge (*Francolinus francolinus*) praises sugar	36
What the Ganda Nala offers	38
A note on the crocodile of Hindoostan	40
A word about ocean currents	41
What remains?	41
Fonseca's letter of resignation	46
How the gypsonometer is made	51
Kirani	55
Mango-fool	68
How the smoked glass is made	73
Etc. e.g.	76
How immaculate bleach is made	77
How suspense is made	82

VERSE: By Moti Ganga Heron sits (Catch)　　　　　　　　　84

Nil　　　　　　　　　85

On the correct manner of harvesting ice in Quebec and Massachusetts,
　　North America　　　　　　　　　95

Khas-khas-tati, thermantidote　　　　　　　　　99

A stalking—and a confession　　　　　　　　　106

A meditation on Indo-Greek sculpture　　　　　　　　　110

COMMENTARY: Who　　　　　　　　　113

Justin Aloysius Trottoire to Mme Trottoire (1)　　　　　　　　　114

COMMENTARY (passim)　　　　　　　　　115

Justin Aloysius Trotter to Mme Trottoire (2)　　　　　　　　　116

Justin Aloysius Trotter to Mme Trottoire (cont'd)　　　　　　　　　117

Brown Bess　　　　　　　　　119

How Trotter gunpowder is made　　　　　　　　　121

Concerning the Great Trotter's guns　　　　　　　　　122

Dinner invitation from the Governor-General to the Nawab　　　　　　　　　124

Reflections while netting in the East Tower　　　　　　　　　129

Journal entry in the Great Trotter's Green Book　　　　　　　　　133

INTERPOLATION: Concerning certain miniaturists, chiefly Mughal　　　　　　　　　135

VERSE: Who will praise (Quatrain)　　　　　　　　　139

On the correct method of mining curry powder
　　(*Memb.* III *Sect.* 2 *Subs.* 2)　　　　　　　　　140

Advertisements　　　　　　　　　147

How a fortune is made　　　　　　　　　150

Day's-end jotting in the Great Trotter's Blue Book　　　　　　　　　156

On the muster of horses　　　　　　　　　157

Pankha　　　　　　　　　160

Concerning the Great Trotter's Din Havai　　　　　　　　　163

Breakfast at Dr Bellows's School, Madras　　　　　　　　　169

Breakfast for nilchis at Sans Souci　　　　　　　　　169

A kahani　　　　　　　　　170

Another kahani　　　　　　　　　170

Preamble to the last will and testament of Justin Aloysius Trotter　　　　　　　　　177

Concerning the generation of heat and its transfer　　　　　　　　　182

With regard to the oiling of camels and the injecting of oil
　　into their nostrils　　　　　　　　　188

The dairy cattle 188

On the correct handling of contradictions in the manufacture of ice 197

A resolution 201

A command 202

A proverb 203

Journal entry in the Great Trotter's White Book 208

A note on winds 211

VERSE: On the late destruction by storm of the sugar-cane crop (Elegy) 214

The grooms' dung-gatherers wish to ventilate a grievance 216

Monies outstanding to Qaiyum Beg, master poet 217

The order 219

The battle of giants in the south (after Firdausi) 220

A warning 222

Some remarks on the monsoon of Hindoostan 225

VERSE: The beautiful boy (Couplet) 226

COMMENTARY: A lacuna: Problems relating to the text of an earlier
version 236

How the hot-air balloon is made 239

Great Trotter &c. &c. &c. (Panegyric) 240

Proceedings of the inquest into the death and bequest of Col. Justin
Aloysius Trotter held at Nakhlau, 23 June 1799 245

INTERPOLATION: Concerning Henry Salt (1780–1827) and others 250

An artistic passage 251

A rejoinder on coincidence (so-called) 261

How Trotter ice is made, these days 262

Extract from *Gipsy General: The Life and Adventures of Michael Trotter,
Irregular Soldier*, by Maj-Genl Victor Cholmondley, VC, London,
John Eames, 1911 266

Extract from *The Military Memoirs of General Mik. Trotter*
(translated from the Persian) 272

Plain English 273

Seersucker 275

INTERPOLATION: Concerning the art of the miniature 276

The Harp of India (Henry Louis Vivian Derozio) 283

Petition of the Anglo-Indians at Calcutta 287

A further extract from *The Military Memoirs of General Mik. Trotter*
(translated from the Persian) *290*

Reflections on self-portraiture *296*

Extract from minutes of evidence taken before the Select
Committee on the government of Indian territories *307*

Theses on the gulab jamun (1844) *314*

Who Says the Great Trotter was Great? by P.U.N.D.I.T. *316*

The salamander *321*

How red tape is made *323*

A note on ghi *325*

The jakfruit *332*

The siege of the Residency at Nakhlau *336*

How a mine is sprung *339*

How History is made *343*

Extracts from *My Path to the Victoria Cross*, by Thomas Henry Trotter
(Nakhlau Trotter) *344*

INTERPOLATION: Concerning Mr T. Jones Barker's painting
The Relief of Nakhlau *348*

VERSE: The Trotters of Sans Souci (Limerick) *362*

How Trotter Curry is made *363*

Forecast of a plague of dust (Proceedings of the All-India
Pantheosophical Society, Nakhlau Chapter, 1873) *366*

T. H. Montagu *368*

Interloper, Snake in the grass, Dust devil *383*

A headline (from the *Nakhlau Nuntio*) *387*

How jaggery (or gur) is made *388*

VERSE: Unmake the Ruinous Tempter (Hymn) *390*

INTERPOLATION: Who killed the miniature? *393*

VERSE: Arrack Room Ballad (Chorus) *402*

Another headline (from the *Nakhlau Nuntio*) *411*

Aspects of the World-Historical Water-Spirit
(*Weltgeschichtlicher Wassergeist*) revealed *413*

Table-talk *422*

A memorial *430*

The mango *446*

What is wholesome *462*

VERSE: Romantic haven, trysting sward (Couplet)   470

Conceptio   472

VERSE: O Eugene, Thou Art a Great Master of Fame!
    (Couplet, after Nizami)   478

VERSE: Merciful showers (Hymn)   483

In which I introduce literary echoes   484

A further note, very brief, on the crocodile of Hindoostan   493

VERSE: My shoes they are Japani (Marching Song)   496

A sermon—cut short   498

How the doolie is made   505

VERSE: Sweetest of Aunts, Dark Moon (Couplet)   509

INTERPOLATION: OT   512

The Commercial Service of Radio Ceylon (31m)   517

INTERPOLATION: The Kirani School   526

An engagement   539

INTERPOLATION: *The Great Trotter Hunts the Boar*   543

How ice cream is made (these days)   545

How the Raj is done   560

THE TROTTER-NAMA

being
the Chronicle of the Trotters
as set out by Eugene
Seventh Trotter

On the twenty-first of June, 1799, from ten minutes past ten in the morning until the stroke of noon, a man not much above four feet tall, portly, handsome, eighty, alive and well, floated in the sky above Sans Souci, looking down in unspeakable wonder upon the dwarfed features of his château and the lands about it.

How came he there, Narrator? Once more, how came he there?
Bring me first the cup.
Will you start with a dessert wine, Narrator?
My own Cup-Bearer! Better still a liqueur.
Here is a potent little Mexican blend, wheedled from ripe cherries and the cocoa bean.
Oh heavenly! Now answer me. Which is the most perfect of days?
The twenty-first of June, it being the longest of days, when the ice is dearest.
Well said. Now listen. I have heard from the cranny bird, sometimes called the writer bird, that it happened in this way.

Justin Aloysius Trotter rose late that morning. He passed the night's water, its dark soil, purified his hands and rinsed his mouth, stood under his watering-can on a pallet of mango wood, towelled his bulk, put on fresh clothes, and composed himself for breakfast. Before him there appeared his customary eight chapatis spread with ghi, a pigeon curry, and a cliff of white rice topped with three pats of unsalted butter. He ate. Satisfied, he turned to his toast, which he dipped in a bowl of tea neither seasoned with cloves nor sweetened with honey. Sated, he called down for his shoes. There being no guests at this morning's breakfast, he did not need to excuse himself, for he was not at table in the Rain Room. His breakfast tray had been brought to his rooms in the West Tower where he sat on a patterned rug to eat. In its place now appeared his walking shoes, a pair of closed-in black Jodhpuris filigreed with gold. They were sadly worn, but the master of all Sans Souci slipped them onto his illustrious feet and made his way downstairs to the Audience Hall. Flapping aside the servants gathered there, he crossed the inlaid floor and descended the flight of steps into the Indigo Court on the northeast side of *Sungum*, sometimes called the *Watersmeet*. Stooping, he threaded the eye of a massive iron gate though he could have gone around, there being no fence on either side. He walked unaccompanied but not unseen between the Glacerie and the Hava Manzil, past the kitchens, past the music pavilion, between a row of mulberry trees and the indigo baths, and up the slope of the saltpetre hill. At the top, which was not far from the bottom, he came upon a wicker basket lined with blue-and-green silk cushions. The Great Trotter stepped into this basket.

The basket was capacious. It might have held forty chickens or twelve dogs or mangoes without number. Instead there were, besides a rug and the cushions: a spyglass, an astrolabe, an horologe, an horoscope, a barometer, a gypsonometer, one hundred and forty meteorological instruments, four sheets of writing paper of the Great Trotter's own manufacture and bearing his watermark, an inkhorn, three pens, two curried doves, and a partridge in a covered dish. There was also a skin of iced water.

Into this basket the Great Trotter stepped. The watching crowd of Sagarpaysans tensed, held at bay by a cordon strung fifty feet all round from the basket. They had collectively abstained from work, knowing that today it would not matter, and turned out for the floating. Since five o'clock that morning, the stream of servants that ordinarily flowed from the hutments near the mines to Sans Souci had turned the other way, running uphill like the water in the Great Trotter's fountains. They fell silent as the bamboo ladder by which the master entered the basket, leaning on Yakub Khan as he climbed, was taken away. This was a sign for the ropers on the three platforms to begin their work, two teams pulling and one paying out. When the huge yellow bladder of close-silk stuff was swung into place above the basket, it at once bloated out. Its mouth, stiffened with whalebone, gaped over a firebucket intensely hot from its freight of living coals. The bucket, lined with clay, hung from a tripod whose base was the gondola in which the old man stood. At the top of the tripod was a hoop whose diameter matched the balloon-mouth. To the hoop were secured both balloon and firebucket, the bucket suspended by chains five feet above the Great Trotter's head.

One week earlier, the First Trotter had all but left the earth when the balloon collapsed onto the firebucket and was singed. In a flash of inspiration the old man had made good the damage with a large patch upon which he caused to be embroidered his crest. All that week Zuhur Ali, bespoke tailor, laboured with silk skeins, blue, green, and orange, on his ear. Today the balloon rode proudly above the flame, tethered by its net to the hoop. On one side it wore, in place of last week's scar, a sun of orange above a castle of yellow, a ship of blue upon a sea of green, the whilom Frenchman's fleurs-de-lis coupled with the fishes of Tirnab, and a scroll to complete the device with the motto: TERTIUM QUID. On the other side it wore in black letters the name: SALAMANDRE.

If a cry went up from the Sagarpaysans, the Great Trotter did not hear it. *For why?* Because he was jolted off the earth with a suddenness he had not anticipated. *For why?* Because no allowance had been made for a mooring rope. *What a marvel is this man!* Thereafter the Great Trotter floated in peace. The balloon rose rapidly above the toddy-palm trees and he watched them shrink into bent pins pricked into the tawny pincushion of the saltpetre hill. Above, the sky was cloudless. Its indigo grew deeper as the horizon dropped away. Nor were there any gusts to buffet the *Salamandre*, though the month of June is plagued with fiery winds called loo. *Thanks be to God. But He has further given us Intelligence, which when applied brings Knowledge, which when ordered is Science.*

It was not for nothing that the First Trotter had chosen the month of June. He knew of a cool circuit of air which flowed during this month in an echelon apart, far above the fume and fret of loo. Once latched onto this current, he reasoned, a balloon should describe a calm and constant orbit about Sans Souci until its fires cooled. He had demonstrated the surmise to his own satisfaction with a smaller, unmanned craft in the June of 1798.

At the height of two thousand feet the First Trotter did a strange thing. Standing among his one hundred and forty meteorological instruments, he brought the tip of his finger to his mouth. As if he were about to turn a page of his Bible or his writing paper, he moistened the fingertip with a furtive tongue. But he had not brought the great black Book and he had written nothing in the past quarter of an hour. Instead he held the finger up this way and that until it caught a cool breath from that same upper current. There it was! At once he began to operate a rope which connected, by a system of pulleys, with a broad vane suspended below the gondola in which he stood. Once set, the vane would deflect the current of air at a constant rate and the *Salamandre* lock onto the inner track of the current's course. The balloon began to list, and in a few moments was drawn into its chosen course. Now the

Great Trotter glided in the company of those kites whose effortless flight he had often marvelled at when, some hot afternoon, the promise of rain set them wheeling about the sky.

His course fixed, Justin Aloysius Trotter had nothing to do but gaze down upon the earth he had so lately trod. It passed beneath him like a dream. *And is it not?* First his eye was drawn to the four towers of *Sungum* with their joint crown, then with a wrench of especial possessiveness to his own West Tower. From there it shifted a finger's width to the domeless South Tower. On the earth it was his practice to look the other way when passing this tower. Now, at so great a distance, it did not seem to matter if his eye strayed. And having once looked, it seemed he could look at nothing else. Was she at her window? But why should she be? How should she know? He had told her nothing. Nor did he ever now: they did not speak or even meet. He ate in his tower; she had the dining table to herself. He imagined her there, sipping the endless glasses of water that were her sustenance, the table companion he had longed for in the old days, the only one of his wives he had ever talked to, until he made the mistake of sharing her bed. The one in the East Tower, now, was fierce in love and prayer but spoke little and took her meals in seclusion. He never saw her now, not even on moonless nights. The one in the North Tower did nothing but weep. Only the German's daughter was interesting and, latterly, interested. Why then had *he* lost interest? Why had he not left it at table-talk?

But—wait! Was that a speck of white framed in the uppermost window of her tower?

He sprang at his spyglass and, fumbling, put it to his eye. What was this? All *Sungum* reduced to a grain of sand! The South Tower to the tip of a needle! Did his angel dance there? He saw he was looking down the wrong end of the telescope. Impatiently he spun it about, but as he did so it slipped from his grasp and fell, the kites swooping after it, until it parted the ripples of the Tank far below and was swallowed up.

For fully one circuit the Great Trotter was sunk in the profoundest gloom. He sat among the cushions heedless of all that passed below, feeding only on his sorrow and rage. As this mood began to abate, he cast an eye about the gondola over each of the objects with which it had been furnished. It alighted upon the luncheon dish which kept company with the gypsonometer. He lifted the lid of the dish. Abstractedly he tore off the leg of the tandoori partridge and ate. He tossed the bone over the side of the gondola, where a kite caught it up. His disposition much improved, he fondled the gypsonometer. He traced with a thumbnail the calibrations of its brass arc. At the forty-fifth degree he stopped: he must waste no more time. There were measurements to take, a piece of writing to begin, and here he sat idling! He got up, clutching the rim of the basket to steady himself. It was then that the beauty of the earth spread out below struck him. The gypsonometer slid from his grasp. It followed the telescope over the edge of the gondola and fell into the desert south of the Tank. He let it go.

Looking east, Justin saw littered the fallen new moons of a dozen ox-bow lakes—his lakes!—stretching out towards the horizon. There, to one side, ran the crystal waters of the Kirani river, a tiny winding stream. Further out, well beyond the lakes, sprawled Nakhlau's river, the Moti Ganga, broad, silted, indulgent. Far away on the horizon glinted the mother of rivers, the Ganges, into which the Moti Ganga emptied. Together the three rivers gave the king-dom of Tirnab its name. On the far side of the Kirani river squatted little villages where the land showed brown on ochre. His villages! From them white dust tracks led to open fields, purple with sugar-cane, green with chick-peas, yellow with mustard. His fields! All ripening together in June, but he did not think it strange. A dozen mango topes stood out of this mosaic, embossed in a darker green. His mangoes! Here and there a gulmohar tree shone red. His trees! His forest, his quarry, his desert, his stream! His plateau—the saltpetre hill where it all started. His indigo baths—spread out like a bracelet at the edge of the plateau—the product of his science! His gardens—here formal and pleasing, there rambling and sweet—the product of his art! His fountains, his parklands, his groves, his canal, his Tank, his château! His *Sungum*! His Sans Souci!

The Great Trotter's breast swelled with satisfaction. All this was his. He spread his arms. He turned around. All, all, his. All good and fat. Would that Mama were alive—and poor Papa! And what should his former mates think could they but see him now from the France to which all had safely returned?

A thought struck him. *Could* they see him at this moment? Might he see them?

He looked west. France was there, a film of green on the horizon. Fighting some fruitless war, no doubt. Losing the New World. Concluding some base treaty. He lowered his eyes. When he left America it seemed certain that France would inherit Spain's empire. Britain had won. When he arrived in India it seemed certain that France would succeed the Mughals. Britain had won. Well, let it go. What had he to do with either France or Britain? This was his home—all this. Here he would die—an event that could not be far off, for he was old—here he would be buried.

The *Salamandre*, travelling south by east from the plateau, was passing over the jujube groves that fringed the desert. From here the Great Trotter could look down and see the towers of *Sungum* reflected on the face of the Tank. He recalled the accidental beginning of this lake, the result of the artificial hill on which *Sungum* stood. It had occurred to him that there was no reason why the widening hollow should not take a definite shape. Accordingly the Tank was designed. It was to take the shape of a fleur-de-lis stretching outwards from the Grand Steps, its elongate head pointing between south and east. It was served by a gate, the Water Gate, which lent its name to the court at the top of the Steps, the Water Court. As work proceeded on the buildings, the cutting of the lake was neglected. Divided between Tank and *Sungum*, the Great Trotter came to sacrifice the cause of the one at the altar of the other. So where the gate and head were done with care, the lyrate scrolls on either side were indifferent things. Twenty monsoons had reduced them to a sorry pair of fins. Looking down now, the Great Trotter was astonished to find swimming far beneath, not his firangi fleur-de-lis but the fish on the seal of Tirnab.

Swayed by this consideration, Justin Trotter turned his gaze upon the Nawab's capital. As if sensible of his intent, the balloon, which had been travelling south by east, bucked and broke loose from its circuit. It struck out westward, bisecting the circle it had so far calmly described. No matter which way Justin worked his pulleys, no matter how many instruments he jettisoned, the balloon held its new course. The Great Trotter soon found himself directly above *Sungum* and travelling northwest. He stared down into the funnel that was the South Tower. Her tower. He watched the château recede as the craft swept on. At the opposite side of the circle the *Salamandre* returned to its course with a second twist and flourish that brought him Nakhlau. What a glittering of domes and minarets was there!

Lines in praise of Nakhlau (from Qaiyum)

Well is it known to all the peoples of the earth that the city of Nakhlau (which the vulgar and rough-tongued call Lakhnau, or One Hundred Thousand Boats) stands without equal for the beauty of its gateways, the majesty of its walls, the grace of its towers, the sheen of its domes, the lustre of its meanest dwellings washed with lime and shimmering under an indigo sky. Who has not heard of Chowk, with its heaven-embracing markets loaded with silks and incense, sugar and mangoes, its colonnades festooned with peacocks, its fragrant stairs washed hourly with crimson juices? Here, veiled, pass heart-expanding women with chaplets of flowers and comely boys with languid gait. Here are bejewelled elephants and haughty eunuchs, there frolic charioteers and vegetable lambs. Here are pannikins of crushed pearls, trays heavy with sweetmeats, the mouth-rejoicing gulab jamun, the tongue-delighting jalebi, the tooth-vibrating kulfi, the universe-arresting Sandila laddu; there are love philtres, a thousand roses distilled in a vial; here again are gossamer bodices, chikan-worked, of which a courtesan may put on twelve and still not be modestly clad. You who have feasted on the coconuts of Cashmere, who have lolled upon the nag-phan of Ceylon, who have slumbered beneath the kamchors of Thibet, and found no peace, stop in these scented gardens. Pause by some twilit lake whose ripples finely slice the clove-of-lahsan moon, whose shores are fringed with rubber trees and broad-leaved grasses where some dark lady clothed with the night plays on her flute a solemn air and one rapt bird stands unmolested by a company of pythons. And when, borne on cool breezes, the laughter of the citizenry wafts to you down some perfumed canal, voices so mellifluous that the traveller Kuo Chin-wu once asked where were these heart-easing bells that he might buy one, board you your sandalwood barge and hope to leave. Alas! There is no leaving. Have not visitors from Constantinople and St. Petersburg, Toledo and Tashkent, Peiping and Aleppo, Bokhara, Kon, and Mandalay, stood speechless on the top of Lakshman Tila? And do they not then burst into tears and coming down disband their retinues, paying off their assherds and muleteers, their cooks and compote factors, their masalchis, sutlers, food-tasters, scullions, guides, guards, unguent-mixers, herbelots, mustard-oil-pressers and masseurs, because after this there can be no more travel?

(CHRONICLE RESUMED)

At the edge of all this magnificence Justin Aloysius Trotter had set his fleur-de-lis seal. And now it was turned fish. He squinted at the city. Its domes winked back at him: the Nawab's domes. Its whitewashed towers shimmered in the sun: the Nawab's towers. From the city wall a road ran east towards Sans Souci, but it was not Justin's road. It did not become the Trotter Road until it reached the Ganda Nala, a sewage canal which divided Nakhlau from Sans Souci—and then not until half-way across the bridge which spanned the canal.

Meditating on this injustice, the Great Trotter was visited by an old passion. Often it had seized him when he stood of an evening at his favourite window in the West Tower, an urge deep and hot for enlarging his domain, by main force if need be. Had he not been the Nawab's Commander-in-Chief? And who else in Tirnab could match his cannon? Who better for military survey, for teaching ballistics, training up troops? This passion he had confessed to no one, man or woman, and as he grew older he locked it away in his breast, examining it but rarely. Lately when he took it out he found it shrivelled into a contentment that he might do much if he wished. But now—here—in the air above Nakhlau what swept over him was the original lust, that suzerain impulse which once shook to his vitals a younger man. Take this city, then all Tirnab, and who was to say what else might follow? Install the Nawab in some petty principality. Drive the British down the Ganges into Fort William, thence into the Bay of Bengal. Invite General Petitjohn up from his Deccan pasture. Recall Dupleix—was he alive? Wipe clean his disgrace. Appoint these men his deputies. Recruit, train, rearm, fortify, advance, annex, consolidate. Drive deep into the south. Pacify the northwest. Send an embassy to the Czar with Easter eggs. Dispatch an emissary to China complaining of her maps.

Borne from height to height, the Great Trotter leaned over the edge of the gondola now sailing far above the Ganda Nala, which marked the westward limit of his demesne. Lips chumbling, he made to encircle with his arms what he could no longer hope to win with a confection of strategy and gunpowder. In a younger man the gesture might have passed for a rush of hot blood, had any been by to observe it. In an octogenarian—a man already half angel— the cacoëthes was strangely moving. The effect did not escape Justin himself. A man once given to irony, he pictured all that happened next before it came to pass, the whole of his future flashing before his eyes as the past is more commonly said to do when death comes suddenly.

(INTERPOLATION)

An Apology

Peccavi! The chronicler has sinned and you have every right to complain. Half a dozen pages of this *nama* and still no frontispiece! Mea culpa, mea culpa, me a Mexican cowboy. The bed of nails tonight. Not one illustration from the master painter of the age—certainly for the late yellow period of the Kirani School—giant among miniaturists, darling of auctioneers, envy of collectors, copyist par excellence, his work highly prized but modestly priced, hung in the great museums of the world, everywhere sought, nowhere sufficient. Let me then make good the omission.

Frontispiece

A ruled border of alternating fish and fleurs-de-lis in blue and green on a pink ground. The border dusted with silver.

In the upper centre, a balloon in shape like a papaya, in colour like a ripe papaya. Its crest as given above, in orange, blue, and green; the name SALAMANDRE also visible on the other side but upside down along the upper edge. Dependent from the balloon a gondola, tilted. In it, or perhaps just outside, a figure in white, a halo about its head. The head, exact centre, shewn in three-quarter face. All other heads in the picture appear in profile.

The figure. The Great Trotter wears on his head a wig. It is the only item of Western dress he has retained and it assorts well with his white kurta, being powdered daily by Fonseca. The kurta is embroidered in white after the Nakhlau chikan style. Lesser painters cannot achieve this effect, white on white. The face is that of an old man, but a stout old man and therefore devoid of unsightly hollows. Its curves are honest, the cheeks rounded and nowise haggard. Such wrinkles as might have distressed a thinner man have been smoothed away from beneath by a warm and generous unction. The forehead is regular, receding perhaps, sweating certainly, the nose prominent and slightly upturned at the tip, its nostrils inclined to flare. The eyes are round, famished, but not unduly large, and—wonder of wonders!—the left more blue than brown, the right more brown than blue. The hands, one upraised, are podgy, with short blunt graceful fingers such as a painter or singer might covet. One of the fingers might be brought to the tip of the tongue. The skin is that of a Gaul, with some slight Nilotic tint, after forty summers at the twenty-fourth parallel. The discerning viewer will find the chin touched with a tarbrush of pig's bristle. One moment.

(INTERPOLATION)

Concerning an alleged painter, one Zoffanij

Two other portraits of the Great Trotter exist, oils both, by that relative wisp of a man, Zoffanij. What his contemporaries saw in him I don't know, but it's said they queued for hours outside his studio, ladies of quality too. Well, I too have had my sitters—but let us look objectively at the portraits.

The first shows a frail Justin lost in a vast concourse of men gathered for a cock-fight. There are some firangis in the foreground, but the great mass are Indians, courtiers and hangers-on to the Nawab whose own august presence fills the centre of the canvas. Bets are being laid, a circle drawn, and the air is thick with dust and cries. The supposed Justin is seated on a European chair, one bony leg crossed over the other, and a prissy look on his gaunt face. It's not clear whether he's examining a cock held out to him by a lean pencil-bearded half-Turkish steward-and-cocksman or just gazing feebly into the air, reckoning up his millions. In the right foreground sits a virile fellow in a mince-pie hat and curl-toed shoes, the picture of plump good health and doubtless modelled on the real Justin until the painter in a fit of malice or faint-heartedness put the Great Trotter further back. Zoffanij himself is off to one side, staring dully at the viewer, with one hand waving at his own imagined scene. Romantic fiction! Conjured up by an envious man who saw the Great Trotter once and then at a distance. And doesn't distance diminish? Here is a painting very likely done from memory in London on the celebrity's return from his Grand Oriental Tour. And doesn't memory thin?

The other, even less reliable painting is entitled *The Great Trotter and His Friends*. It shows three friends—among whom Zoff not only numbers himself, but, in a forgivable lapse, places himself squarely in the centre—and of course the great man. The putative Justin is squinting at a worthless miniature by Tulsi the Younger or one of those insipid Mughals and turning his back on some exquisite bananas. Zoffanij—let us give the man his due—could do a banana. Though judging from his one self-portrait, in the Uffizi gallery in Florence, he might have profitably eaten a couple after. As it is he remains, if not gaunt, visibly wanting. In the Uffizi self-portrait he hopes to distract the viewer from his unfortunate face by posing as a kind of clownish Hamlet. His only endearing feature is a gap between his two front teeth—unless some later visitor inked it in while passing through. He leans on one elbow, holding up a skull which can't help but make his own look lively. ARS LONGA, VITA BREVIS on the spines of nearby books. You can see him there leaning in front of a mirror with his skull, then making a dash for the brushes, then back to the skull, then back to the canvas and so on until the travesty is complete. Ars longa? Zoffanij's! God forbid. The only thing long about this bounder, fingers apart, are his teeth. Vita not brevis enough by half, or the world might have been spared this piece of middle-aged dementia.

But to return in calmness to his so-called Justins. There is a conceivable excuse for these fleshless representations. The paintings, if genuine, may date from the summer of 1789 when the Great Trotter was recovering from a grievous illness and much reduced thanks to an ill-considered vow. But if so, he filled out again shortly after, perhaps not to the old Justin, but enough to make him recognizable, respectable, lovable. And portraiture, let me remind the admirers of Zoffanij and all his works, is a plunder of the general character, not a petty pilfering of some specific and transient frailty.

Jealousy, you say? Very well. Let someone else speak. I draw your attention to an Italian engraving which, though not exactly of the Great Trotter, closely resembles him. It is of the famous eighteenth-century castrato, Carlo Broschi Farinelli, in his classic role, *The Great Mogul*. Look it up some time.

But, the frontispiece.

Frontispiece continued

Above the balloon the sky is first blue, then indigo. There are no clouds, but one is being born in the upper or indigo sky.

Beneath the balloon stretches an ochre plain cleft by a canal, the Ganda

Nala. The canal flows into a broad river, the Moti Ganga. A small winding stream, the Kirani or Cranny river, which arises in the saltpetre hill, also empties into the Moti Ganga. On the near side of the canal is spread Sans Souci, its buildings of mixed stucco and sandstone. Its crown and glory, *Sungum*, sits with its towers upon a man-made elevation. The result of this mound is a hollow that has formed a lake or Tank in which *Sungum* is reflected. To the right of *Sungum*, two fingers' width above, is a low square tableland, the saltpetre hill. On it are raised three bamboo platforms around a launching pad. Beyond are a jungle, a small stream, villages, several ox-bow lakes, and a broad river. On the far side of the canal is the city of Nakhlau.

Birds and animals fill the parklands and jungle. The peacock is one. The pigeon is another. The black partridge is another. The dog is another. He is a crafty beast. The tiger is another. The camel and elephant are others. The horse is another.

Trees are many: the jamun (*Eugenia jambolana*), the mango, the guava, the jakfruit, the imli or tamarind, the English tamarind, the nim, the pipal, the silk-cotton, the gulmohar or flame, the laburnum, the oracle, the papaya, the banana, the Chinese orange.

Flowers are some: the canna in rows, the rose in beds, the lotus in ponds, the daffodil, the bougainvillea, the Persian rose, phlox, and on the banks of the Kirani stream, the rat-ki-rani or queen of the night.

Men also abound, and women. On the tableland is a crowd of persons in ragged dress. These are the Sagarpaysans or camp-followers or simply ocean-of-peasants. They gaze in rural idiocy at the sky, some pointing. Among them, in richer dress, may be told a baker-and-Chief Steward, a head-poulterer, and a folk-doctor-and-dentist. Apart from the crowd, a dhobi-and-dyer is at work by a pool, beating a white gown on a rock by his hut. Beside him is an indigo vat, full. At a lower window in *Sungum*, an aged man sits bent in half at his desk. At another, lounges a man once fat but still handsome, a book of verse in his hand, a cup of wine resting on his belly. At another window, a middle-aged man, pock-marked, looks in a mirror. A crack in an East Tower window shews two women, one pink and one purple (the pink in truth a girl), singing. At an upper window in the South Tower is a woman in white gazing also at the sky. She is the colour of ice. In her hand is a quill, a drop of ink fresh upon the tip.

This was the frontispiece.

Entry in Jarman Begam's diary for June 21, 1799

I awoke at five o'clock this morning, the sky being neither dark nor light. It is my favourite hour at this time of year—small respite from the sun's wrath, which is already mounting at breakfast—but today is of especial note—and not for that it is to be the longest and hottest day of the year—for today Trot is to go up in his *Salamandre*. He has not said a word, of course, but the servants are all abuzz with *zulmundur, zulmundur*. I must watch at the window when the time comes. Shall I be able to see him? Had I only his spyglass—but he would not leave that behind. I wonder how Yaqoob Khaun has provisioned the craft, for Trot is sure to be hungry. Heaven knows how long he will be up there. He must eat—he has been looking so [*illegible*] of late. And his parasol—if Fonseca has not had the good sense to fetch it there I shall scold him most severely. It will be hot at ten and can only become hotter as he is borne nearer the sun. He will be able to see France from up there—and America too, Fonseca says. That will mean Germany, which is on this side, will show more clearly still. Could I get but one glimpse of the fatherland! Would that I were going up instead! I flatter myself I should not be in the least frighted though I were tossed most handsomely by the loo. It would be infinitely more diverting than cutting paper, which Fonseca has of late been distracting me with and which he says is the best ton in Calcutta. Yesterday he made a great many Japanese lanterns and hats and Canton doilies. I asked him to fashion me a balloon, but he answered—"Madam, a balloon with holes is like Lord Swan with Mister Chicken's feet!" I thought this a most elegant jest and asked him Whether it was original? He simply smiled in his enigmatic way and inclined his head sagely.

Today it is still Thursday's white, with a yellow kerchief, because that scoundrel Dhunee Dass is late with the wash. "Memsahib," he declares, "in this season I must go *very* far to find good water." As if he dipt my cloathes in Himalayan streams! His wash dazzles only because he pilfers indigo dust from the factory.

Will Trot see me, I wonder? If I stand at the window and wave, he is sure to look. I am smaller than America but not so far away. What would Fonseca say to that! I shall try it on him. But for his company, which I confess most agreeable, I should be much vext with solitariness, for the women here are such vapid creatures. And since I write for myself I might confess a little more—for am I not at liberty to digress as I chuse? He is a handsome enough creature with his beetling forehead and lively eyes, though I did not think him so when first I saw him in Trot's tower. Then I noticed only the pock marks and the irresolute chin. I forgive him his finical hairdresser's manner, for there is nothing effeminate in his speech. He has the gait of, I should think, a peacock—but he would be much teazed if I told him so, being not a little vain and therefore anxious to conceal his vanity. His hair is not in the least grey though he cannot be less than forty, and his teeth are not in the least yellow though he is inordinately fond of tobacco—not that he would smoak or chew it in my presence. He cannot play chess, but he is full of extravagant tales, told so rapidly one might lose one's way with a smaller talent. He is clever, for a man, though in a different way from Trot or Moonsheejee. They say Father was a wit, but then a travelling seller of inks must be quick if he is to profit in a foreign land. What brought him here? He never spoke of his travels except curtly, and of Germany not at all. Had he already a wife there? Have I sisters and brothers walking cobbled streets and sleeping under pointed roofs? Fonseca declares that Europe is paved from end to end so that carriages may cross it in a week, but he has never been there or seen the Portugal he prates of. He would see it, in purple, if he went up with Trot—this side of Florida with some little blue in between. He has seen only Bombay, and now his heart is set on Calcutta. He would fain go there this day were there not a surfeit of hairdressers that side. I fear he will never get there, for all that he cuts and dresses to perfection. If he should go, there would be none to entertain me when I am tired of pure mathematics—which I confess is often of late. To think that I ignored him these many years! Doubtless his travel tales of Thugs and Mahrattas and Ranas could be spun out endlessly. "Madam," he will cry—though he well knows my birth—seizing a lock from my shoulder, "a hair-breadth 'scape, madam!" Lately he has taken to coming here on the smallest pretext. Rekha has begun to make eyes when she announces him, and she has a loose tongue, that one. I have seen her behave most familiar with Yaqoob Khaun. Why do I mistrust this baker-man? Could it be a clew that he appears to cultivate the saucy girl for some design she cannot know? Desire her person he surely cannot—it is alien to his temper—handling her as if she were a key.

I must resolve to be more faithful to the pages of this journal. Moonsheejee must be my model—the good man unbends from his desk only to send me the volumes I ask for, and always one more which he deems necessary to my education. "Too much numbering will congeal the fluids of your brain," says he. Last week it was Kautilya's *Discourses*, Aboolphargius's *Dynasties*, and the *Tota-Nama* of Kapildev. Yesterday it was Ibn-i-qasim's *Mirror of State* and *Cup of State*, Englished some forty years ago by Colonel Townshend and bound up in one volume. There are some few things in it of interest, but little that I could not have counselled myself. In the afternoon he sent up for my inspection (I think he must allow me sense) through Fonseca—who professes not to understand the man, or to be out of sympathy with "all your statecraft" says he—the first fruits of his own labours in translating from the Turki a fragment of the *Babar-Nama* beginning with the three hundred-and-eighty-third folio. There are another seventy-two, widely supposed lost, which he has dredged up from Trot's chambers of unsorted books and manuscripts. He bravely proposes to classify every last item gathered there, and swears he would translate all such as wanted translation—were he not besieged with requests for formal odes and qasidas from all the grandees of Nakhlau. God grant the old librarian a long and quiet life! His deputy, Qaiyum, is a [*illegible*] wastrel.

But here it is already eleven—Trotter will have gone up—and I had meant to watch at the window—

(*CHRONICLE RESUMED*)

The gondola rocked sharply upon Justin's tilt at the city that would never be his. As if abetting him in his desperate enterprise, the *Salamandre* tipped him into the air in the direction of Nakhlau. With a crash the horologe, the astrolabe, the meteorological instruments, and the luncheon dish slid into a corner of the basket. The horologe began to strike the hour of noon but got no further than one silvery chime when its mechanism froze, the hands stopping at twelve.

Without a word the Great Trotter fell. The crash and chime alerted him to a state which had earlier escaped his notice: he was wrapped about in a sheet of silence. The invisible current of air played on his cheek but made no sound. He looked up but the heavens gave him no answer; the sun's gong hung mute. And in the silence long chains of mathematical problems cannoned through his brain, effortlessly resolved. Numerical figures of every description—the dimensions of Sans Souci, the distance to the pole, the weight of the earth, an imbalance in the ice account, the specific gravity of lead, the survey tables of Tirnab, an unpaid dhobi's bill—all rippled into crystal tropes and streamed silently before his eyes. This was curious, because on earth he had been unable to proceed beyond long division, a source of much amusement to his prodigy of a Burgher mistress. He was marvelling at the transformation when his eye was held by a still greater wonder: the sky was empty of the stars which he and he alone saw by day below.

Justin stared. Until yesterday, his nights were starless while the daysky tormented him with a dazzling display of heavenly bodies. Now the clock was turned back and all was blue again. What did it mean? The sky's colours changed subtly, but where the blue ran into the indigo, or where the indigo received the blue, he could not say. Nor could he point to where the colour was purest. To an indigo manufacturer the realization was a blow. At the zenith, where the colour seemed true, seamless, and virginal, where purity was most insistent, there it was that Justin longed with a fierce longing to install the absolute. But he could not. For was there not a purer spot just beside it? Falling, he searched for the elusive point, but now the sun which had reached the zenith stood in the way. It was noon.

In that elastic moment Justin examined his perplexity.

The Great Trotter considers the heavens

There it goes. The space of my finest hesitation filled with blinding light. Complete uncertainty, complete knowledge! A sky with stars, a sky devoid of stars: one or the other, all or nothing? But tell me, Trotter, have you not seen those stars that one sees only by indirection, only by looking beside them? And by the same token, might there not be infinitudes of blankness one can know only by looking at stars? Blanknesses not to be confused with those wider spaces of vulgar blue that distinguish star from star, and exist only to serve the stars, so that each might enjoy quality and particularity. These other spaces the stars in turn serve, being harbingers of a void mightily small, a space neither in them nor behind them but other than them, a scruple which their faint light invokes by shedding darkness. Here is knowledge of a kind, for though it does not announce itself, whether as common darkness or as specific light, yet it has considerable being. The blue is too fickle, and as for the sun, it drowns the shy signal in an unending torrent of light.

(*CHRONICLE RESUMED*)

Justin remembered the first trial of his indigo. After an hour's simmering in the vat his bolt of cloth had come out white—if anything, more dazzlingly white than when it had first gone in. He cursed the indigo, ladling some of the dye into a bowl for inspection. The liquor was true blue. Then what was the matter? He examined the cloth once more: it was ordinary cotton, unwaxed. He was on the point of flinging it back in when before his very eyes the cloth began, very faintly, to darken. He took it out into the sunlight and watched it go from pale blue through an infinite number of stages to a dark and fast indigo. The secret, it seemed, was neither in the dye nor in the cloth but in a third place. It was in the air.

Above him, Justin's *Salamandre* righted itself, and the lid of the luncheon dish slid back with a clink. The sun struck him full in the face and he turned over as he fell, looking downwards now at an earth that flew towards him at a terrifying speed. Yet his senses were more alert than at any time since he entered the world.

The Great Trotter considers the earth

It seems I am to exchange one vat for the other: out of the blue into the brown. So be it. I make no complaint.

That, directly below me, is the Ganda Nala, there is the city, there is the river——but hold—hold—*hold!* The canal is flowing *backwards*, running from the river to the city! Or why would the trunk of a toddy palm drift that way under the Ice Bridge instead of this? Or the scum run against the stream? Wait—the parklands are turning green—in June!—when they should be the colour of bread. On the hottest day of the year! Where are the dust storms down below? Why are sands by the river turning black when there are no clouds? Why is there a swamp where my indigo fields should be? Who has torn up the baths? Where are the mango topes? The river has changed its course. The sugar-cane is early, the wheat is late—no, there's wheat in the sugar-cane fields, but now again sugar-cane! It goes from yellow to green to purple and back again in the twinkling of an eye—merciful heavens, what is happening down there? The grass flickers orange, the trees are blue, the colours shift and ripple as if some lunatic wind were scattering the pages of an illustrated book. Can it be true after all, as Timur Beg wrote, that in Hindoostan everything is backwards, the elephants' trunks being their tails carried in front? Look! The smoke from my brickworks is being sucked back into the chimney, and it's the same with those wisps curling back down over the city. That blue cloud is sinking, yes, back onto the many dung fires of the Sagarpaysans, and there above the forest a milky green strand returns to some charcoal-burner's stump fire—in *my* forest! But where are the trees? My tamarinds are gone, my avenues retreating into saplings and seed pods. My gardens lie all unravelled, the shrubs pulled under by the fuse, the flowers closing up and turning into buds. The wrong birds are singing—where is the cranny bird?—now they are not singing at all; now they fly backwards to their nests, climb into their eggs, tender beaks remaking their shells, sealing themselves in; buildings are coming down everywhere, my *Sungum* is undone, where is the Glacerie, why is the West Tower half finished, who has put the scaffolding back on, but what do the workers think they're doing, the stonemasons' bullock-carts are hauling slabs to the quarry, the bricklayer returns mortar to his hod, removes a brick, takes his hod to the trough, where bhistis extract the water, mazdoors separate the sand from the lime, unslake the lime, the tiler comes down the ladder with tiles on his head, the sawyer dislodges his saw, the sawdust rising to heal the cut, the painters are stripping the walls, the carpenters taking out windows, the glaziers restacking their panes, the grinders and finishers breaking up the floor, the sealers exposing the foundations, women carry away baskets of earth on their heads to the Tank, its waters have dried up, the hollow filled in, the hill eroded; holes, then blank spaces appear where the other buildings stood, then other, prior structures take their place, mud huts, twelve villages, then these too give way to fields, the fields to a fort, the fort to mean dwellings, these to a river, a jungle, a jheel covered with ducks, a swamp full of crocodiles.

There—now the colours begin to run the other way. My vat is muddied. I must scold that Munnoo—what am I saying! I'm a dead man. Where is my son who went from brown to blue? There, in France? There, in the Deccan? Might he see me now? Would he turn away? Well, let it come—his father is beyond help. I will suffer nothing, simply a change of identity—and what of that? Did I not ask for my stone to read:

JUSTIN ALOYSIUS TROTTER

WHO

LIVED AND DIED

The Great Trotter considers what is in between

For that matter, if at every stage in my descent I am at rest, can I be truly said to fall at all? Is there nothing in between? Is the third thing nothing?

> *Excuse me, Narrator. But could we have a little less speculation and a little more story?*
> *Impertinent Cup-Bearer! Could I have a little more patience? And a little more of that Mexican blend. In a little while you shall have more story than you could wish for.*
> *I take it on faith, Narrator.*
> *Believe me, I have a mystery brewing for you, told me by the Did-you-do-it. But first some praise of sugar and then a very foul smell.*

(CHRONICLE RESUMED)

Justin Aloysius Trotter drew at a constant speed towards the earth. There fell with him, on either side, his wig and his masak of ice-water, the one a little higher than the other. Below, to one side, he saw his lands swiftly accumulate details not visible from the *Salamandre*. To the other side of the canal, and still through the pincer of his clasped arms, he observed a like multiplication of Nakhlau minutiae. A parkland with tombs/a city with tombs. His/the Nawab's. Blades of grass now returned to brown/blades of grass now returned to brown. His/the Nawab's. The earth on both sides was scorched.

Hot, Justin felt his throat rowelled by thirst. His white kurta billowed out and flapped at his shoulders, but it gave him no comfort. He reached for his masak but it danced away at his touch, and the ice cubes gave a liquid chuckle. Exposed to the sun, his scalp prickled. He stretched out a hand for his peruke. Easier to snatch a dandelion boll: a cloud of talcum came away on his hands.

And now it was not only thirst that distressed him. Justin was hungry. Might the *Salamandre* have sent down the tandoori partridge? He looked about him: it had not. The bird was wasted, his lunch floating away. But it was not a tandoori partridge he craved, nor was it the curried doves. It was nothing savoury; rather, a taste he had almost forgotten thanks to a hasty vow. It flashed through his mind that today was his birthday, and this recollection only made the absence the more poignant. He felt a quivering of taste buds at the utmost tip of the tongue, an ungovernable tickling at the root, neither salt nor sour nor bitter. It held promise of a sensation intensely pleasurable— sinfully, maddeningly, cripplingly, suffocatingly pleasurable; it was a siren song calling one to an endless debauch, inviting surrender to pleasures un-speakable, to a long sweet slavery, to sweetness without end.

Sugar was Justin's present and most abject craving. Had only Yakub Khan sent up, instead of those spiced birds, a baker's dozen of his sweet roggen loaves—a poulterer's dozen—a single loaf—a slice—a crumb! Partridges— pah! Did not the king of partridges himself trumpet his surrender?

The black partridge (Francolinus francolinus) *praises sugar*

Shir daram shakrak. With this sound the durraj (black partridge) of Hin-doostan greets the dawn. He is the size of a dog's head, and his plumage is of many colours, the body between black and green, the neck green without black, the gorget purple, the head rufous, the bill yellow, the wing brown above and black beneath and speckled black on white at the tip. He is a handsome bird, as road-travellers (poets) know. Hear him in the sugar-cane fields, his head turned towards the east. He has run careless of snakes (ill-natured poets, senior librarians) among the purple stalks. He pauses on the bund, looks this way and that. See him lift his head. See his purple throat swell. See his beak open. Sing, bird, sing. Hear now: *Shir daram shakrak!* The first syllable is quick: *shir*. The rest is measured but not slow. *Daram* is voiced with care but not conviction; to tell the truth, it is thin (ugly, spoken without elocution). But there is more: see the proud bird's eye glaze, feel the pulse quicken in his jugular. Hear him redeem himself. *Shakrak*—sugar! It comes quickly at the end, climbing to a peak. *Shir daram shakrak*—"I have a little milk and sugar." Who has told me this? The emperor Babar records it in his *nama*. The good Englishwoman, Annette Susannah Beveridge (sharbat, sorbet) has put it in English. The Frenchman de Courteille renders it: "*J'ai du lait, un peu de sucre*," but on what authority? Why "a little sugar" and not "a little milk"? Effrontery, the bitter (the Gaul); Hazard, the salt; Envy, the sour; or Indifference, the bland. Cowardly de Courteille, no friend of India, enemy of Nakhlau whose sugar once travelled as far as Cathay. Sugar gives courage: let us follow the greater heart. Padshah Babar the Brave writes more: "The partridge of Arabia and those parts is understood to cry, *Bi'l shakar tadawm al ni'am* (with sugar pleasure endures)!" Wants there greater proof?

(*CHRONICLE RESUMED*)

Justin fell. As he fell, he felt a surge of regret. On his mind's tongue he knew again the kiss of sweet roggen. He recalled breakfasts past when the baker-and-(then still)steward reserved for himself the honour of waiting. The future baker-and-Chief Steward would glide into the barsati or Rain Room on the roof of the Glacerie, where breakfast was customarily taken, one hand held high above his head in the French waiting fashion. In place of a tray there floated, just above the baker's hand, a basket of varnished reeds lined with a green napkin. In it nestled a covey of soft brown loaves. These he would offer first his master, then the favoured Jarman Begam, then any others who happened to be at table (which was rare). Taking one, Justin would preserve a short silence. Then he would lean over his plate and inhale deeply. Lastly, he would break off a piece, dip it in his tea (which he took with a lump of yak's butter), and sticking out his tongue a short way he would ferry the morsel into his impatient mouth. The ritual was respected even by the literal Jarman Begam from whose recipe the loaves had first been baked. The Great Trotter had himself undone it, forswearing sweetness in a fit of abstract piety (*Headstrong Trotter, Senseless Vow*). Every morning thenceforward the First Trotter had his breakfast brought to his chambers in the West Tower. No longer did the first sunlight flood the barsati; undrawn, the Rain Room curtains grew brittle. The breakfast table stood cold and joyless, its mitred napkins gathering dust. The ovens baked common bread, the baker-and-major-domo glowered and spat into the ashes and gave the making of Justin's chapatis to a cook, the same who specialized in pigeon curries.

Today, as he fell, after an eternity of unleavened, unsweetened bread, Justin longed for a crumb from his own table. An infusion of tea-red sunlight, the face of his transparent mistress, a loaf of her sweet roggen, all newly risen—ah! here was bliss sufficient. He leaned forward in the silence and inhaled deeply, expectantly.

What was this? A stink, foul and sewagey, was coiling in his nostrils, an odour to which every pestilential thing in India seemed to have contributed its part.

What the Ganda Nala offers

The brimmings of cesspits, the green rot of markets, the scum of sewers, the swill of gutters, the refuse of gullies, the stench of offal, the vapour of privies, the crust of drains, the sweat of bird-catchers, the lime of seducers, the lint of navels, the foulings of footpaths, the footbaths of postmen, the leakings of oilmen, the oilings of lechers, the slime of ruttings, the scalecakes of fish-stands, the mire of fowl-houses, the squirtings of cats, the grime of urchins, the dribblings of ancients, the pap of infants, the navel-cords of outcastes, the flickings of brahmins, the swabs of morticians, the sweepings of barbershops, the flushings of abattoirs, the slops of stews, the slab of neat-sheds, the parings of pariahs, the dressings of doctors, the wipings of cooks, the findings of ear-cleaners, the leavings of surgeons, the muck of mullahs, the waterbrash of lalas, the scrapings of tanners, the mange of muskrats, the pressings of beauticians, the rootings of scavengers, the semen of eunuchs, the shavings of padres, the spittle of mendicants, the turds of soldiers, the pickings of schoolboys, the scabs of traitors, the piss of bullies, the blisters of tabla-masters, the phlegm of palki-bearers, the ordure of chamberpots, the dung—

—Narrator—

of bats, the rummage of middens, the sludge of sluices, the dunnage of pyres, the rankling of boils, the rakings of gutters, the guttings of butchers, the gougings of taxidermists, the disjecta of ragmen, the rags of acrobats, the bones of hunters, the hair of criminals, the ears of informers, the eyes of spies, the stools of sentries, the droppings of politicians, the lather of courtesans, the glow of wrestlers, the emptyings of yogis, the heavings of gluttons, the hawkings of vendors, the retchings of beggars, the warts of harlots, the chan-cres of students, the rattle of consumptives, the matter of sores, the armpit hair of cowards, the oozings of sweat-shops, the cuckings of cloaca, the cotton of monthly-pads, the voidings—

—Narrator!—

of cretins, the discharge of pimps, the lavings of lepers, the spewings of drunkards, the effluvia of pickleworks, the ebullitions of smelters, the slag of armourers, the acid of carters, the moultings of reptiles, the crackling of corpses—

—Narrator, do you hear me? Your eyes are rolling!—

the bedding of incontinents, the bile of oil painters, the gall of historians, the swaddling of infants, the stillbirths of virgins, the scribbling of weavers, the weaving of scribblers, the betel-juice of bicyclists, the chewing-gum of motorcyclists—

Enough, Narrator.
What is it, Cup-Bearer? Where am I?
It's past, Narrator, there now, there now. Here is a little rice wine from Japan. It will calm you.
O my sweet Ganymede! For a moment I thought I was—no it is too horrible . . .
Then leave it. Let us go on.

(CHRONICLE RESUMED)

The smell of these things, channelled by the Ganda Nala, rose to meet the Great Trotter. Other things too, but who will record them? *Life is short.*

Justin well knew it as he drew to his life's close. Falling, he looked southward. At a stone's throw was the Ice Bridge, with whose central arch he had now almost drawn level (for he had been falling some time). The bridge was bare: men do not go abroad at noonday in June unless on an urgent mission. The Trotter Road was untrafficked as far as Sans Souci, the Nawab's road unpeopled as far as Nakhlau. Then what was this new sound, sharp and repetitive, pecking its way through the heat like a woodpecker? It was no living thing; rather it seemed the report of some engine to come, a chatter of pistons pumping furiously. And shortly a machine did appear from the direction of Sans Souci. It had two wheels and a lamp in front, and astride the belly was a man in uniform who stood racing his motor, once, twice, three times. Then, chewing calmly, he threw the machine into motion and hurtled towards the Ice Bridge. Half-way across he disappeared and angel voices sounded, rising to fever pitch and ending abruptly. In the stillness there appeared from the direction of Nakhlau another man. His kurta-pyjama was dazzling in the midday sun, almost blue with whiteness. His lank hair was freshly oiled and might have hung to his shoulders if it hadn't streamed out behind him, for he rode a machine not unlike the other. It had two wheels and a lamp, but no engine. The man glided along silently, his feet pedalling in circles. As he crossed the bridge he spat a merry curlicue of betel-juice into the Ganda Nala. The spittle turned the water a brief red, then it was gone. Then the man himself vanished.

Justin was amazed at these apparitions. So many wonders in one day!

Might it all be some exotic romance, a tall tale trotted out? He shook his head. It felt strangely light, and he remembered his peruke just in time to see it fall with a chalky plash into the canal, tail first. It floated a little way, then was sucked under. Faithful creature! Ten winters, summers too, it had covered his pate, fitting snugly, hatching notions, conjuring youth. Well, let it go. Youth had fled; the stars played tricks; summer and winter were unpinned. Did anything else of substance remain? The masak: his leathern flask of ice-water had fallen behind in the race, being heavier. For an instant it hung above the turbid waters, its skin purple like one of those dark plums remembered from his boyhood. It wore a fragile bloom of moisture, and for a moment Justin saw behind it a shade of green not to be found in his adopted land. The masak met the water with a smack, the ice cubes gave a last mocking chuckle and went down. What could they mean? A jostle of cubes . . . three syllables of ice. Man . . . da . . . The *Mandalay*! His ship had not come in: his Quebec ice was late. Never again would he taste of those distant ponds where once, in the fire of youth, he had gone skating in May. The pity of it! Now when his thirst was greatest, now when his senses were so keenly awake. That he should feel most alive when life was no longer his to command!

A note on the crocodile of Hindoostan

The crocodile is a freshwater reptile, amphibious and wily. He is the length of one dog when small, two when grown. He feeds on fish and birds but has been hearsaid to prey on humans, prizing especially the pancreas or sweetbread. A washerman was taken from the Moti Ganga near the Bridge of Boats, a young girl lower down in the same stream. Crocodiles wait in muddy waters, floating like toddy palm logs. A story attaches to this beast. Once Crocodile said: "Monkey, the jamuns (*Eugenia jambolana*) in yonder tree are purple and sweet." Monkey replied: "But who will ferry me across the river?" Crocodile said: "I will." So Monkey got on Crocodile's back. Halfway across the river he grinned and said, "Now I will eat you. Already I can taste your pancreas. It is purple and sweet." Monkey was greatly alarmed, but said, "O Crocodile! You are my best friend. I would happily give you my pancreas, but my liver is still better. Only, I have left it in that fig tree on the bank whence we came. Take me back and I will exchange it with you for one of those sweet jamuns." "Very well," said Crocodile, and he carried Monkey back to his bank. To this day Monkey has not tasted the jamuns of that tree, but he has his pancreas. This shews the wile of the Crocodile. Another proof is that he will sometimes snap at the bird which cleans his teeth. The Monkey story is told by the mendacious Indians. Another concerns the Elephant. For that you must go to the deceitful British. But who will trust either? Trust me:

I will tell a better tale than both. The wonder is I do not know it yet myself. A further remark about this beast. When about to die, or when his mate is killed, he is said to shed a single tear in the shape of an egg. Within, you will find a tiny creature made in the image of the parent. Thus is the crocodile species propagated. He is best killed from under, for from above you will not. His flesh makes poor eating, being flat, cold, and lengthwise.

A word about ocean currents

The ocean does not stand still. After wetness, motion is its chief attribute. It is just always coming and going. Boats upon its surface and living creatures below may each avail of this shifting, going when it goes, coming when it comes. What is the first cause of this motion? Whose hand rocks this cradle? The hand of God. But directly? No, not directly. Indirectly. God has made the sun and the moon, his instruments and his glory, the one to chafe the earth (and its waters) and the other to chill the earth (and its waters). The warm attracts, the cold repels, and currents follow. Winds help them and rivers hinder. The warm are red, the cold blue: every schoolboy knows this. Currents have names from their discoverers, their navigators, their neighbouring land masses, their fish, but not their reptiles. Such as: the von Humboldt, the Quiros, the Labrador, the Eel; but never the Crocodile.

(CHRONICLE RESUMED)

Justin saw his end had come. He raised his eyes towards Nakhlau, meaning to look his last, but an embankment of earth stood in the way. Sorrowfully he turned and looked towards Sans Souci, but there too a curtin was built up; the Ganda Nala's banks are steep in June, the waters having run low. The First Trotter closed his eyes. He wished to sleep the long, still sleep of the tomb. Left bank or right, it did not matter where he fell. Let it be in Nakhlau or in Sans Souci, so long as his grave was dug deep, his sleep unbroken. Here Yakub Khan would find him—no one crossed the Ice Bridge as often as he—and follow his orders. Where he fell he was to be buried. *Vanity of vanities!*

What remains?

Neither bank is to be the Great Trotter's resting place. All solid things have deserted him: his *Salamandre*, his wig, his ice, his *Mandalay*. What remains?

The lust that engorged his heart, spurring him to rashness, has run its course. His pincer is undone: the hands unclasped come apart, obeying no centre, the feet drift together unbeknownst. The Ganda Nala's surface is broken by the slippers of Sans Souci, whose pointed toes slip noiselessly into the stream. Without a splash, without so much as a ripple, Justin Aloysius Trotter passes from air to water. One last vision is his: reflected on the glittering surface of the canal he sees, opening his eyes, a tawny sky spread with stars. I am still alive, he declares as life is taken from him. When the head has slipped below, there remains an arm upraised, and after the arm a finger, the same whose tip not two hours ago the tongue moistened. Escorted by a toddy palm log, the newest cess to the Ganda Nala is swept downstream to the Moti Ganga and thence into the mother of rivers. In a muddy stretch patrolled by crocodiles the body is unpicked. God's will be done. One part alone continues downriver, whole and unhurt, and at last out into the sea. It is jellylike, purple and sweet. It is the pancreas. Coaxed by the action of a warm current, it inches with a flopping rise and fall along the ocean floor, staining with its dye the Bay of Bengal.

(CHRONICLE RESUMED)

No one but Justin himself witnessed the fall. The Sagarpaysans who had raced along below the balloon, chasing a shadow that slid down the glacis of the saltpetre hill, sailed around the indigo baths, and skirting the Tank on the east side, shot across the desert, tired once the front runners got as far as the jujube groves and fell back. Hooting, they watched the *Salamandre* sweep westwards along the edge of Dilkhusha or the Heart's Ease (tracing a path which the railway would follow when it came to be laid by their children's children) and curve back towards Nakhlau.

After three further revolutions about the hub of Sans Souci, the *Salamandre* descended upon the plateau, its fires at last cooled. It came to rest within the triangle formed by the bamboo platforms at a point equal in distance from each. Its vane folded gently under the gondola, and the gondola met the earth without the jolt with which it had left. For a moment the vessel balanced there, trembling like a creature possessed of supernal intelligence. The Sagarpaysans, gathered once more at the cordon, sensed this presence and respected it with silence. Then the balloon, which in that space had preserved the dignity of its crest, gave a sigh and sank with a silken murmur. Released from awe the Sagarpaysans surged forward, breaking the cordon, and ran to the gondola meaning to carry off the Great Trotter in a triumphal palki.

There was another space of dusty silence when the crowd, which had had eyes only for the balloon, discovered the gondola was empty. Then Yakub Khan, baker-and-chandler and balloon master, who had the keeping of the ladder, vaulted into the basket and began to toss the particoloured cushions about as if he expected to find his master hidden in some cranny. Upon this sign—the baker-and-victualler might have been tossing sweets among them—the crowd began to heave and babble.

Yakub stood up and looked wildly around, sensible in spite of his surprise of the danger in which he stood. Sunya the egg-brahmin, he saw, was looking not at the *Zalmandar* but at him, and his eyes were heavy with mischief. He must act at once and with all the authority he had so sedulously shaped over the years, kneading into the lump of his advancement minute yet ever increasing measures of a yeast fermented in the still of his patient breast.

—*Wah! Metaphor, Narrator!*—

He found his voice. "Some of you run Tankside! See if he has fallen there. Sunya, you lead them! Scatter them about on every side. Send one as far as the ber grove. You, Salim, go to the zenana. Ask if any saw him fall. No—wait! Yes, go. But do not speak of it before Jarman Begam, hear me? Ask the other two. Gunga, you search the marsh down to the river. Rekha and you children go home quickly. The women also will please return to the village and shut themselves in. I say so. Zuhur, you run to the Gunpowder Gate and stand duty. Wazir, you go and get any stragglers and comb the parklands. And, hé Wazira, send one to the house-servants to look on the rooftops and between the buildings. Rouse that slugabed Qaiyum, but leave the old librarian. Ré Munnoo and Nankoo, silly fools, you two scan the heavens. Go to the top of the Crown, one, and the other to the roof of the Rib above the Balloon Room. Hakimji, it is best if you wait with me."

The men began to move off, but Yakub called after them.

"And, ohé, listen well. *No two must search together*, and no one is to wait for another. Split up when you reach your beat. If anyone finds the Master he must report at once to the Audience Hall, where Hakimji will be waiting. Do not on any account touch the body. Cover it decently if you can, but do not move it. Go."

When the crowd had dispersed, Yakub turned to Hakim Ahmed.

"Brother," he said, "this is surely the most fateful hour of our lives. We must act boldly but calmly as befits worthy men. That is why I have asked you to remain. You are a responsible man, unlike that Sunya. Here is what I want you to do. It's very simple. If someone has found the body, you must detain him. You are a hakim; you know about herbs and suchlike. He will have come running in the heat. Give him a cool green draught. Lock him up somewhere, somehow. Then go at once to Tartar Sahib's tower—making sure that barber doesn't see you—and hang out the flag—the blue-and-green standard—at the uppermost window. It is kept in the chest in the vestibule of his chambers. Here is the key to the chambers, here is the key to the chest.

That will be a sign to me and I will come without delay. As you know, I cannot leave the *Zalmandar*."

Hakim Ahmed nodded his head slowly. He was a somnolent giant with a slack, bearded jaw, the beard dyed red with henna. His puffy eyes were solemn and generally upturned, giving him an air contemplative and idiotic. He liked to mull things over as he ground his roots and herbs, scanning the roof of his brain for stray wisps of intimation that might happen to drift by. He disliked haste, but he liked a scheme, and the prospect of one made him submit to the present urgency. It made a folk doctor, a man given to pre-scriptions and pronouncements, himself wholly biddable. The hakim had al-ways suspected that some day Yakub, many years his junior, would give him an order. Unable to decide how he would respond, he had postponed the decision. Now it was taken from him, and he hurried away wordlessly, tucking the keys into his cummerbund. As he went he comforted himself with the thought that his patients, who knew less about certain things than he, took his twists of mauve powder and pellets of ear-wax without question.

When the hakim had gone, Yakub Khan wiped his face on his pocket handkerchief and scoffed into the damp cloth.

"Simple physician!"

He looked about the gondola in which he stood and kicked aside a cushion. "And you, precious metaphysician. Where have you fallen?"

He was a tall slender loosely knit man, with a camel's neck and sound teeth. Coming at the top, his head might have been an afterthought, a dot on an inverted question mark whose drift was a constant torment. The face was lit by a pair of hazel eyes burning fitfully two inches above a wick-moustache that Yakub trimmed twice a day. He noticed the covered dish. He bent down, removed the lid, and with a turn of his wrist scooped up the one-winged bird and crammed it into his mouth. Then, with a curried dove in each fist, he jumped over the side of the gondola and began to lope softly towards Nakhlau.

When Jarman Begam broke off her journal entry and ran to the window she saw no sign of a balloon in the sky. She reproached herself for having sat dreaming with a pen while such a memorable journey was in progress. She had meant to catch the first possible glimpse of the *Salamandre*; instead she had been fussing with words while the world, or a significant fragment of it, went by. "A window is worth a thousand books," Fonseca had said the other day, opening one. She remembered his illustrated lecture on the subject, and with a guilty twist of the head dismissed him.

It was past eleven, and the sky remained blue and empty. She craned out of the window: there was no one to be seen either on the ochre earth or in the sky above it. Then, as if issuing out of a window in the East Tower, the yellow bulb of the *Salamandre* hove into view and sailed silently, with scarcely a tremor, around the Tank. On the glassy black waters its image, inverted and unbroken, glided like a ghost. Elise screwed up her eyes and scanned the gondola for any sign of movement which would show her husband busy with his instruments or signalling France. But there was no silhouette, idle or busy. Shall I wave, shall I shout, she wondered, stepping from one window to the next in her tower as the balloon travelled west by south. Perhaps he is asleep or resting, she said. No—he has lost something and is sulking. The *Salamandre* disappeared from view behind the West Tower.

There was nothing to do now but wait at the first window while the balloon completed its circle. Elise stood at the window-sill careless of the sun. Once she glanced over her shoulder at the octagonal turret room. It looked unnaturally bright. Ordinarily at this hour all the windows would have been doubly secured against the sun, the green louvre shutters on the outside and the pane windows within bolted and latched. The heavy curtains of twilled cotton would snuff out any stray beam of light or dust and the room would be steeped in a cool subaqueous gloom lit only by a tube of mirrors opening onto the escritoire. On the hottest days Elise withdrew to an inner chamber or descended to lower and lower refuges in her tower. Today she was in the uppermost room, with all its windows thrown open. Each was a harsh rectangle of blue, and at the first of them Justin Trotter's consort stood, a little before noon, awaiting the return of the *Salamandre*.

In the silence a crow rasped from the banyan tree below. Now and then there blew a ripe gust from the elephant stables. A fine rain of sand fretted away at the rock and stucco pile of *Sungum*.

At last the balloon drifted past the edge of the East Tower and began once more its double track around the Tank. This time Elise fancied she saw a figure lean over the rim of the basket, looking out towards the ox-bow lakes. The figure spread its arms and turned around. Elise bent her head back and shaded her eyes with a hand that might have been made of glass. The glare was fierce all the same, and she found it easier to follow the inverted figure of the *Salamandre* reflected on the blue-black sheet of water. She had fastened her eyes on this image, when it appeared to halt in its track and return the way it came. The brief illusion, she saw, was created by the balloon's becoming larger: the craft had in fact stopped, but it was not returning the way it came— it was coming her way!

Elise began to wave first her handkerchief, then both hands at the approaching balloon. She saw the Great Trotter tug furiously at a set of ropes like a rebellious puppet. Next, a row of missiles began to punctuate the surface of the Tank, the sound of each splash—*bhut-oosh*—carrying dimly to her as the newest ring of ripples criss-crossed the last. *Bhut-oosh! Bhut-oosh!* When the *Salamandre* was past the Tank and above the Water Gate, she began to call: "Just-in! Jus-tin! Ju-stin!" But her voice was hoarse at the best of times, and she was used to calling him by another name. The tiny figure, enmeshed in ropes, did not respond. The gondola swept overhead, surely grazing the Crown, and the *Salamandre* disappeared from view.

Elise did not see the Great Trotter look down into her tower, nor could she follow his flight around to the West Tower, window by window, as before. He simply shot over the Crown and was gone. The next time the balloon appeared, the gondola was empty, and so too the time after, and the time after that. Then it did not appear at all. Forty minutes later Rekha ran into the room, burst into tears, and ran downstairs again without uttering a word:

Fonseca's letter of resignation

June the 21st, 1799

Honoured Sir,

Sensible as I am of your kindnesses to me past and present, it cannot be with other than profound anguish that I address you on a matter which, since it grieves me to distraction and will be forever a thorn of remorse, I dare conceive will cause you some little concern—though never so much, I pray, as will not be forgotten the instant it so pleases you. This I confidently trust, having known so well the natural largeness of your heart, extending even to slaves of your purchase, that I quickly came to count myself less your slave than your son, albeit unworthy of those gifts showered on me during that little time in which it has been my good fortune to serve you. A double sunrise, good master, has been my daily privilege in your service—and a double sunset. When you rose, cheating the sun of its rays, I shaved you dutifully but never close enough. When you retired, outlasting the sun's light, I talked you to sleep, but never long enough. Your sun's son asks forgiveness, but now more especially in the light of this dark matter. It grieves me more for that we are, every one at Sans Souci, much beholden to you for our preservation in a state of careless well-being such as none could enjoy but for the Mechanick genius which has brought you riches and the Organick goodness which prompts you to share them. Sir! I am all unworthy, but what chiefly troubles me, more even than the matter I speak of, is that my unskilled hand cannot shape the letters of my heart's gratitude. Not a few years have passed since I addressed myself to the troublesome business of writing—tho' for your sake I consider it no pain, recalling in modesty that I was judged at Mrs. Bidwell's school in Bombay (I told you of it) to have some talent that way and given a book and silver medal struck at the Mint in token of a good round hand—so I will beg your patience with such inelegancies as crowd this page and ask that you impute them rather to a want of custom than to a lack of wit. I will not remind you of the happy hour in which I came to you, needing myself no reminder of that moment of deliverance from the Hell that is a string of cruel masters. Sir! Could the vilest ingrate look complacently upon a matter so dark as this? Have I not turned it over in my mind these eleven months without bringing it to a conclusion? Prudence ever watchful roams the stage. For how does the Bard put it? No sooner doth Will resolve to act than that vixen hath her way. And I doubt not when you have heard out the matter of which I speak you will forgive me these stammerings, seeing in them not the irresolution of a coward who loves none but himself, but rather the hesitations of a child who loves you too well. Can a man of feeling entertain so gloomy a prospect (as that held out by the matter of which I speak) without a measure of indecision? Sir! A matter of far less consequence would fret the stoniest heart, yet I hope there is not so little flint in my breast as cannot strike a single spark of compassion in yours, my noble master. Let them that will, speak ill of me, Sir, I remain your loyal servant even in that hour when I must press you on a matter which concerns my very servitude. Nor will I conceal from you that there have been lately noised about your estate certain rumours, rumours so vicious and unfounded that to treat them with contempt—as I trust you will—would be to honour them with a notice that they undeserve. To be brief, Sir, the matter of which I speak (one which I have given much consideration) is this—but here my spirit quails. Then let it remain innocent of the black remainder of this imperfect letter. Sir, I have decided (after giving the matter due thought) that it were best to beg you to discharge me from your employ at the end of this same day. You start, my lord! I see your kind hand tremble. Could you but see mine as it forms these unkempt words, words that were better penned in the darkest night of Erebus than in the bright noontide of this noble pile. Long may its happy towers stand firm against that most cunning of worms, Rumour, who now raises his grewsome head. But for his blight, which touches, good Sir, the very heart of *Sungum*, I should have no cause to leave your service, far less for so charmless a city as Calcutta. Bombay, good master, is my home, but return there I cannot for reasons privy to you. Calcutta, then, it must be. I fear the fashions change there so quickly that my old sheers will be laught at,

but what else so please your Honour can a hairdresser do? Unless he
carry some introduction to the quality of that city, he is obliged to turn
cranny. You are known, Sir, in Calcutta—indeed far beyond. I ask you
only for a letter which, joined to those by which I came to you, will
smooth my way in a strange world. If it make not my fortune it will be
my solace in the days when I come to rue this rash but—so help me—
never dishonourable act.

> Your honour never had so loyal a servant as
> *Wilfred Ignatius Albuquerque Fonseca*

(CHRONICLE RESUMED)

Fonseca wiped the nib of his pen and read the letter over. He smoothed
back the four pages on his tabletop, admiring the large round hand. Once he
had had to cross out a *will* where he had written the word twice, but it was
a small blemish and at the edge of the second page. One couldn't waste
another sheet on that. Not that there were any to waste: he had taken the
last four sheets of Trotter paper from the library where by Sans Souci custom
all blank paper was to be stored. The Great Trotter alone could keep paper
out overnight.

Reaching the end, Fonseca's eye strayed through an open window to the
South Tower, and he felt the muscles of his thighs contract. He rose and
picked his way through his scattered belongings to the almirah mirror, a tall
cheval glass bought from his master who imported curiosities from Europe
for those who could pay. Fonseca had paid a little each month for years. It
was a handsome glass, framed in dark wood, bevelled at the edges and swung
on the almirah door.

A man past forty stood there, his face so black it shone blue at its points
and in the pits marked there by smallpox. The eyes were unusually large and
had the effect of reducing a face that was in fact generously fleshed. The tip
of his tongue showed pink between his lips.

Fonseca drew close to the mirror until his breath clouded its surface. His
eyes roamed over the face which appeared each time the vapour lifted.

"Elis-se," he sobbed. "Elis-se!"

The barber-and-raconteur swung back the almirah door and felt among
the cool silk shirts. From the back of the shelf he drew out a wig of white-
gold hair and stroked it. Carefully, he put it on, swung the mirror door shut,
and looked at himself again. Then he unstopped a jar of cold cream whose
label read: ALPINE SNOW. He dipped two fingers in it and dabbed the cream
on his forehead, his cheeks, his chin. He spread it gently, evenly. A solemn
grey face stared back at him. With shaking hands he rummaged in a drawer

and produced a red crayon. Peeling bare the point, he coloured first his cheeks lightly, then his lips a heavy red. It's no good, he thought. It looks nothing like her. His throat was dry. He came so close to the mirror it stroked his belly. At once he tugged the shirt up and pressed his skin against the glass. A little gasp escaped him and he kissed the glass.

"Elise!" he moaned. "My Elis-se!"

He did not stop kissing until the mirror was covered with rosebuds and his trousers had fallen about his shiny black boots.

As the Sagarpaysans, shaken and disappointed, dispersed on Yakub's orders, Sunya made his way down the slope of the saltpetre hill. The aged poulterer-and-brahmin waved on those who had been placed in his charge, directing them to various Tank-points. Stunned by the Great Trotter's disappearance, he was troubled to find that as he walked the face that went before him in his mind's eye was not his master's in the slant perspectives of the past, but another's, lit by the vertical sun. It was the baker's. He saw once again Yakub's antics in the gondola. He heard once more the silence of that long moment when each man stood undecided. He smelt Yakub's fear in that eternity before the baker-and-factotum found his voice. Yet the face Sunya saw now was that of a young man—the young Yakub, the apprenticed baker of fifteen years ago. What was the Muslim up to now? He had watched the wiry youth advance from post to post, improve the ovens, outclass the chief baker, perfect past recipes, introduce new ones, oust the chef, trespass on the cooks' duties, encroach on the bearers', perfect a new and sensational bread, create offices where none existed before, appoint cronies, unlock forgotten godowns, restore empty functions, dust off old uniforms, and fill every void with his mercurial presence.

"Well and good," the poulterer muttered. "But what has a baker to do with chickens? Eggs, perhaps, one sees a link: but at one remove. There is a khatik whom I depute to gather and deliver the eggs. But chickens? Where does a baker come in? Since when did flour and chickens mix? Flour and water, yes: let him scold the bhistis. A water-carrier is a contemptible thing—look at that Gunga Din. Flour and salt, very well: can one respect a salt-panner? Flour and sugar: why, gur merchants are known scoundrels. (*Honest Sunya*) Why even flour and hair: doesn't that firangi barber, whose shadow polluted me last Thursday, mix it in with his talc to dust on the Great Trotter's hair? But flour and feathers? No. A thousand times, no."

Sunya stopped in the dappled shade of a pipal tree. A bulging brown parcel of a man, speckled with leucoderma, he was easily camouflaged. He stood on one scrawny yellow leg with the other tucked up in reserve. The tension in the lifted foot betrayed a man who trembled at the future and brooded on the past. He looked back to the top of the tableland, where he made out the figures of the baker and the herbalist in a huddle. As he watched, the hakim strode off, tucking into his cummerbund something that had changed hands. Then Yakub bounded off the other way, towards Nakhlau. To his cock-fighting comrades, no doubt, bloodthirsty Muslims all. Not content with rearing fowls—honourable profession—they must incite peaceable birds to violence, spurring them on to shed blood. Unnatural sport! Did God mean fowls for bloodshed? Is there even a speck of blood in an egg? No. And if there is—even the minutest trace—does one not fling it away in horror as an unclean thing, fit for sweepers? Yes. But a goodly egg, a godly egg: what is there in that? Do the scriptures proscribe it? No. Who, then? A handful of fanatical pure-brahmins, a lunatic fringe, and on suspect authority. They refuse to eat with me: let them. But what do the old codes say? A miser, a convict, a thief, an eunuch, an actor, a bamboo-maker, an evil-doer, an usurer, a public woman, a physician, a person in trouble, a cruel king, a washerman, a butcher, a panegyrist, a blacksmith, an adulterer, a drunkard, a vain man, an angry man, an enemy, a wily man, an eater of broken bread, an armourer, a goldsmith, an ingrate, a wine-seller, a husbandless or sonless woman, a multitude, an oilman, a liar, a faultfinder, a common priest, a weaver, a dog-seller—do not eat with these. There! Not a single harsh word about poulterers, nothing hurtful of eggs.

No, an egg is a noble thing. Consider its shape: there is the sunya, the zero from which all things spring, to which all things tend. Consider its colour: there is the whiteness of the sun, of cows, of milk, of pure ghi, of goddesses, of all good things. An egg is blameless. An egg is smooth hairless and unbegotten. It is firm, it is fragile, it is flawless, it is just fine. Pure-brahmins are mistaken; more, they are envious of us egg-brahmins. But at least they respect the bird that brings forth this wonder. They would not take its life. Can such a bird be plumped for slaughter, its male muscled for sport? The handsome cock, the haughty quail, the black partridge (*Noble Creature*)—these are the innocents those men teach to fight and kill. Tartar Sahib too, but was it not at that Yakub's instigation that this barbarous sport from those countries was first begun at Sans Souci? Poor cock! His throat torn by some hand-sharpened spur, he rises and throws himself again into the fray. And some of his number have come from my coops. How else to explain that snooping baker, his prowling henchmen, and—until last year—Tartar Sahib's own permission? Unquiet baker, fowl-thief, usurping fox, sly mongoose, hairy biped, bad character, flat villain! At what remove from the wholesome, chaste, and lovely egg, the true, the noble, the good egg!

So absorbed, the poulterer found his feet had led him to the southern shores of the Tank, where it abutted the jujube groves. He cursed himself for having unconsciously obeyed the baker's command, and was turning away when, despite his fastidious high-stepping gait, he stumbled on a curious object. He stopped, squatted, and stared at it. Made of brass, it looked like a fragment from the workings of some mechanical bird. Sunya picked it up and examined its many angles and joints, some of which appeared to have worked loose. He ran a horny yellow nail along the graduated arc. He prodded a ratchet that looked like a cockscomb. It rocked briefly, then stood still. Turning it about, Sunya made out an eyepiece, its glass broken. Might this be one of the Great Trotter's instruments? But who would wantonly destroy it so? And what was it doing here?

He took off his red turban and wiped the sheer dome of his head.

Unless—why, that was it—unless it had fallen from a great height. Before, with, or after—*the Great Trotter himself!*

Sunya gave a start and looked involuntarily upwards. At his feet was the hollow where the instrument had struck the earth before turning over. Tiny pieces of glass shone in the crater, and a sugary stain was spread like lace beside it. But elsewhere the sand was undisturbed. He widened the circle of his search, peering into clumps of the prickly pear called snakehood cactus, but still there was no sign of a body or the mark of one on the sand. He had begun to search the thorny jujube-plum bushes when a notion took him. Here was a chance to discover what the baker and his herbalist friend were up to. He could return to *Sungum* as instructed and declare the search at an end. If the body had already been found, Hakimji would impute his claim to the excessive heat, or the poulterer himself could cite one of those mirages not uncommon in the desert region beyond the Tank. And if they required to be led to the spot, he would comply and simply claim that the body had been moved by some spy—after all, the country swarmed with agents. In either case the baker's plan would be nudged into the open.

Sunya turned his steps towards *Sungum*, hurrying a little. Soon he found himself jogging (*Incautious Sunya*) despite the weight of the gypsonometer.

How the gypsonometer is made

I wish to shew how the gypsonometer is made. The adept will in the left hand take metal, brass when it is available, some other when not. Bend it with the right, first applying heat, then hammers of various weights. When a cup (P) is formed, seal its mouth leaving only two holes (Q, R), neither too large nor too small, but just medium, the width of the little finger perhaps. To one of these he who is skilled will fix first a valve (S) and then a tube bent into the shape of an S (T). To the other he will fix a tube that is straight (U). In another place, stout adept, bend you a brass rod into an arc (V). This flatten, mark with calibrations long and short by rule of thumb, and hold in readiness. Take an amphora, lota, or other kettle (W) such as are sold for fifteen rupees in Chowk. But the ones sold by J.c. Solomon & Son are best. They are across from the Rangili Manzil just where the road turns away. Do not go past the corner for then you have gone too far. Take off the lid (X) and place the cup, valve, and pipe within, attaching them with arms to the inner sides of the vessel. The nether end of the S-tube you will introduce a short way into the spout (Y) of the kettle from the inside. There is now a vessel within a vessel. The larger fill with ice-water through the mouth, the smaller with lassi, sharbat, or another sweet drink through the upright tube, using a funnel. The esteemed guest is served first cold water. When the outer vessel is empty, it is tilted sharply backwards. The valve on the inner vessel opens and *through the same spout* the adept pours lassi, sharbat, or another sweet drink. Thus is the guest amazed. The invention is also of use to secret drinkers. Another use to which the invention is put is in surveying. For this purpose the adept must insert an eyepiece into the knob (Z) on the lid. He must then remove the handle to the kettle. With the Solomon kettle this will not be difficult. He who is cunning will replace it with the calibrated arc. Readings are taken when the lid is swung back on its hinge and the spout aligned with the desired object. Surveyors in hot climates find this a most useful instrument. This is what I wished to shew. So do that. In some parts the gypsonometer is called a dipsonometer, but the making is the same. Do it as I have shewn and praise God. And if he who is ignorant follow not my directions he is hapless. God is great.

(*CHRONICLE RESUMED*)

At his desk, Munshi Nishan Chand, master of fourteen languages; student of the rishi Vasudev at Mathura; member of the 1724 expedition to Lhasa; librarian to the Maharaja of Kon, the Raja of Paltan Bazar, the Governor of Bengal, and the Nawab of Tirnab; author of learned treatises in many fields, including philosophy, mathematics, botany, politics, medicine, glass-making, and astronomy, of histories of Mexico, Louisiana, Java, Armenia, and Tibet, of books of verse in epic, elegiac, and lyric modes, of sonnets, quatrains, couplets, and other forms in Sanskrit, Persian, English, and French; calligrapher, connoisseur of painting, music, and maps; sometime tutor to the renowned scholar-princess of Tehri; traveller to the Levant; compiler of the first Uzbek-Urdu dictionary; recorder of Toda folk-songs, Nicobarese creation myths, and Annamese harvest hymns; numismatist, critic, editor, archivist, cataloguer, codicologist, occidentalist, night-filler, and present librarian of Sans Souci, sat in a trance.

The time was just before noon, but that was of no consequence. Some forty minutes ago, the munshi had pushed out a decimal and watched it float down a stream of ciphers, washed to and fro as the river widened, now riding a choppy current of figures, now breasting the tides of unreason, now caught up in an eddy at the shores of possibility; always shifting, changing all it touched, jewellike, serene, minuscule, infinite. In its presence one was past pleasure, past care, past age, past rheum, past failing light, past sight itself. Here evil, love, compassion, cowardice, loyalty, cunning, goodness, truth itself, were naught; their several quantities totalled nothing. Before the decimal—into the decimal—even the zero must collapse, for the zero was the crystalline iris which ringed the unfathomable pupil of nothingness. The decimal conducted one past the zero of the rishis, the vanishing circle of the horizon. It was the black pearl without price which comes after a string of lesser pearls, the last zero, magical, potent, impregnable, yet fertile. This seed, source of the Ganges, wisdom of forest sages, *they* had stolen, and with it its nine membranes, so that the world now called these after the interlopers, *Arabic* numerals. Arabic indeed! Did the Ganges flow in Arabia? Through Arabian forests! Chance, trade, and feckless scholars had borne this precious cargo there to men who grubbed for Hindu calico. Desert barbarians! Tent-dwelling buffoons, sunstruck plunderers, idol-breakers, they had come galloping to the source and stayed to drink. And who would not exchange a wilderness of stones for so fair a country as this? But to come in war, laying waste what they could not understand, razing what their artisans could never hope to build, snuffing out the sacred flame with the sand of their oblivion—and all this in the name of God! These are the savages who rule us now, converting wretches from the meanest castes, preferring rice-Muslims to deserving Hindus, meat-eaters to devout men, pressing foreign labels on sons of the soil—or what self-respecting historian should call himself *ghulam*, or what writer of esteem *munshi*?

"*Munshi* Nishan Chand," the librarian repeated. "The name has stuck in this godless city. The other day a letter came so addressed from the village. Well, wear it you shall, but not without cause. At every step recall your mission. Study the circumcised foreigner, barbarian though he be; learn his roughcast languages, school yourself in his childish arts, trace out his tactics, duplicate his strategy, mirror his guile, best his success. Scorn no means to turn his crescent blade eventually upon himself. This is the way. Patience, humility, cunning, until that day when you are more skilled in his own arts than he. Then overwhelm him, and with him his house. And after he is gone, restore once more the bright ancestral home, sweep clean the hearth, rekindle the pure flame. Avenge the violate zero."

Nishan Chand woke from his reverie and watched the decimal drift away.

Its eye looked quizzically at him, and for a moment he too was disappointed in himself. He smiled sorrowfully at the blank page before him and it gave back his crumpled face.

"You! What could you do, poor munshi? Pillar-to-post scholar, hired scribe, nonagenarian liberator! Write a memorandum? Turn Tirnab upside down with a stroke of your pen?"

The munshi rose stiffly, a task that required only the straightening of his knees. Bent in half (his legs bolt upright, his back a cross-beam) he looked like a walking gallows. Yet the face he thrust at the world, though square and wizened, was endlessly vital. His bones cracking like pistol shots, he stretched himself into half a dozen shapes of fatigue. He took off his cap, a Turkish cap, and fanned his scalp with it. A few wisps of white hair fluttered there. He looked down at his shoes: their toes curled upwards, Baghdad fashion. His legs were involved in Sultanpur pyjamas; it had been many years since he had worn a dhoti. His kurta was cut in the Nakhlau style, and over it he wore a Persian cape. Was he turned Muslim, then? Had his life's scheme rebounded on him? Did any trace of the Hindu remain upon his person? Or would one of his village passing say: "There goes one of them"?

Nishan Chand felt again under his cap for the knot by which Vishnu would pull him up to heaven. A strand of hair, longer than the rest, and knotted, still graced his crown. He was comforted by the mere touch. The foreskin too was intact. Good, good. Both are concealed, precious signs. Go disguised among that lot, but keep the heart pure.

The librarian looked once more at the page where his reflection hunched. One point alone, shining there in silver, would single him out from the crowd, but it was not a Hindu mark. On his cape he wore a button. The button, though plain, was more an ornament than a device, and yet precisely its function occasioned its display. Today you saw buttons here and there among men of taste and sense, but when the Great Trotter had first given it him, giver and receiver were the only men in Nakhlau—in all India, who was to say?—with buttoned balabars. Not without vanity had the librarian first shown it, and even at the height of summer he wore with pride this badge of Europe. It was a token of the Frenchman's esteem, a token also of his own cosmopolitan bent, the same that had first led him to experiment with Muslim dress. For the rest, his pyjama-kurta was roiled and sweaty, his cap ringed with shiny dirt, and he did not care.

Nishan Chand took off and polished his spectacles. Here too was a gift from the Great Trotter, another example of Europe's plastic ingenuity. The munshi smiled sadly. For a moment he wished he had not stopped at the Levant. "That youngster Abu Taleb is said to be going to Britain; let us see what he reports. Little does he know my mind, though, God help me, I love him like a son. Those firangis might be capital allies for Hindustan: resourceful soldiers, crafty merchants, birds of profitable passage. Enlist them to the cause with their guns and gunsights, their buttons and bioptics."

He held the glasses up against the light.

"Trotterji could wear a pair himself if he didn't set so much store by his profile. What if the Nawab did strike medals of it? True, he knows *Sungum* well enough to need no lenses, but he might read more in certain faces if he took to spectacles. All that hocus about stars by day when he can't tell earthly friend from enemy. *She*, now—she could. But only thanks to my instruction. She is apt, apter I would swear than the Tehri princess (God grant her soul a man's form next). This misbegotten daughter of the German ink-vendor is wise beyond her years, but wilful as the wind. Never a care for order, degree, no notion of system, sequence. Yet keen as a razor and flashing fair—no wonder the others fear her. Or so it is said, if one can trust servants. To credit their tales one would have to believe it's not only the curls of her head that that black Portuguese barber singes. Hairdresser indeed! I know a kirani when I see one; I too have lived by my pen."

Kirani

see CRANNY

CRANNY, n. Originally Indo-Portuguese clerk using English; secretary; miserable scribe; mere copyist; dull accountant; harmless drudge; simple scrivener; one who works in an office; pen-pusher; slavish hack; nook; member of caste neither here nor there; country-born Christian; some of the above (pl. *crannies*) whence all of the above applied to Anglo-Indians generally, this community having supplied the bulk of English copyists (see WRITER) f. Skr. *karan*, *karana* (see also RAT-KI-RANI)

"Hairdresser to a bald head!" the librarian scoffed. "Just as well there's *her* hair or he would have little else to do except manage the ice. Mister Ice Manager Sahib. Cannot ice manage itself? And what child couldn't powder a wig? Or play three notes on a curled horn—at all hours, when there's reading to be read, sleep to be slept? This one is finical, cares for nothing so much as turning a phrase, when his duty is to copy, poor scribe. Well, copy he does. Never a man quicker to learn: his dress, his manners, his whole person modelled on his master—before the master himself became a native! Whom will you copy now, kirani?

"Still, he is harmless. At most a cecisbeo. Look at that one now: baker with horse and carriage, baker with his fingers in the butter dish, baker in the pantry, baker in the kitchen, baker in the arsenal, baker in the indigo works, baker in the stables, baker in the cock-hali (which he renames the Spur), baker in the balloon room (has he gone up too?), baker in all but her bedchamber— the kirani beat him there! Baker in the doldrums. Let him try the library, he will see what Hindus are made of! My lump of a deputy will sleep through it all. There is something at work inside that baker's loaf, but it cannot be a brain or else one could approach it through the eyes. Lately it has begun to crank out some base instructions for the hands, the feet, the double-roti nose.

"Well, it's no concern of mine. But you, my friend," the munshi addressed his absent employer, "had best be on your guard. Never mind hot-air balloons: this one will never get off the ground. You saw what happened last week. Reread those stars. You wish me to write your biography. It is in progress, here." Nishan Chand tapped his head. "But if you are not careful an enemy will do it for you. He will sum you up in stone, and at no great length. Yes, yes, I recall your will—it's somewhere here—WHO LIVED AND DIED. Very good, most continent. But," and Nishan Chand smiled a smile toothless and conspiratorial, "why then bother with a biographer?" He held up a hand. "No matter, we are men of the world. But if this bread is to be buttered on the underside you must pay the butterer. Friendship is one thing, but I must live to value it. Consider my plight: at ninety-nine, with all my faculties, my senses firm, my writing never better, I look about me for one who saw me honoured at the court of Kon, but none remain; their very sons are dead. You know the expedition to Lhasa: it was the journey of the age and I its literary lion. Yesterday I met a learned historian, a man of grace and culture, who had not so much as heard of it. And such as do honour me honour my reputation, or the *shade* of that reputation, as if this *body* were a spirit which lingered on beyond its natural term. It is not, and I say to you one cannot live on honour, Trotter Sahib. The Nawab's pension would not feed a bulbul. And now that he is failing, so they say, will his successor remember me? And when *you* die, who will pay your biographer, the one who circumvents your marble continence? Mere talk of codicils is not enough; you must sit down and write: *To Nishan Chand, I leave such and such.* I have much work to do, and I do not speak of biographies alone. Keep your testimonials: have I not a boxful? Letters from ghosts addressed to ghosts, while their subject lives on—on stiff chapatis. Halva and ghi-puri for upstarts, brown rice for the munshi. Better to have been a baker."

The librarian hawked and shot off a ball of phlegm at a spittoon in the shadows beyond his desk. The exercise, far from clearing his throat, brought on a coughing fit and further volleys into the dark. Afterwards he sat in silence with his eyes tightly shut and his tongue threshing about in his mouth. When he spoke again it was in a new tone altogether.

"My dear sir, the Great Trotter will owe more than a life to his biographer. True I must await your death before I can commence your life, but after death you will have more to thank me for than that bookly life. A man's line is worth a shelf of lives, and for its preservation in Sans Souci you will thank not your friend the biographer but your employee the librarian. Any ass can write a book, but only its dispenser can direct its fate: bind it, catalogue it, translate it if need be, and above all place it in fit hands. Writing—ha! That half-Portuguese barber of yours can write. This paunchy wine-bibber I have for a deputy librarian wrings out an intelligible line from time to time. *He* is the munshi. Kirani or munshi, foreign writers both, brainless mimics; but Hindustan has another word which does not fuss with scribbling, taking all knowledge for its province. It is my proper title, though you and the whole world call me munshi. *Pandit* Nishan Chand has spoken."

Nishan Chand took a turn in the aisle that ran past his cubicle. Standing, he looked tolerably secure; when he walked he seemed in perpetual danger of toppling over. He would totter along, gathering speed until he reached an angle in the passage, whereupon the hands that rested on his knees would slide up and clamp themselves on his hips, and his progress would be checked. Swinging around just short of the wall, the munshi would resume his headlong career, his head swivelling briskly as he picked up the scent of various half-forgotten scholarly trails. His cubicle was at the Water Court end of the library's northeast wall, where the astronomy shelves met the mammoth collection of works, ancient and modern, on refrigeration. An underground floor had been chosen for the library, the better to preserve the books from the yellowing effect of the sunlight. The narrow windows that looked out on the Indigo Court were high even for a man of average height, yet Nishan Chand was well supplied with light. Directly above his desk there opened a funnel which extended by a series of tubes along the ceiling to a broad window in the northwest wall; here was that fretwork of mirrors and crystals with which the Great Trotter had contrived to store and transfer light, causing it to turn corners undiminished. A bluish haze filtered down from the funnel, washing the desktop on which there lay a single sheet of blank paper.

From the opposite direction to the pipes the munshi heard, counting off the hours, the water-clock strike noon. He broke off his pacing and returned to his desk. No sooner had he sat himself down than he felt a chill creep along his crooked spine. Reflected on his page he saw a face. It was not his own. And it was upside down. Struggling to keep calm, the munshi gripped his kneecaps and began to rock. The front lobe of his brain sent urgently to the seat of memory for aid, but the identity of that face eluded him. He took off his glasses and put them back on. Then his rocking slowed to a halt and

Nishan Chand sat rigid in recognition. He had seen, for the first time, and the last, the Great Trotter, wigless.

Yakub drew near the Ice Bridge. It bulked before him washed with lime and burning in the afternoon sun. Its very name offended the baker-and-Chief Steward, needling him with the one office that had so far proved beyond his reach: Ice Manager. The black topassa from Bombay had been quicker, speaking English and dancing attendance on the old hermit. Yakub would rather not have used the Ice Bridge at all, but he had frequent business in the city, and the next bridge across the Ganda Nala was a mile to the south, well past the hunting lodge. So cross it he must, but when he did he preferred to think of it as the Barfi Pul or Coconut Ice Bridge (*Gentle Yakub*).

He sat down on a ledge to regain his breath, and found the seat so intensely hot it might have been unbearably cold. The thought unsettled him momentarily; he liked to be sure. He eyed the dreary parkland he had just crossed, with its frayed babul trees and blazing gulmohars. Trees and earth were covered with a fine coat of dust, and he congratulated himself on not having returned to the stables for a horse. Anybody in the South Tower might have seen him riding away, especially since the loo seemed unaccountably to have stopped. He could always borrow a mount from the halvai on the other side of the bridge.

He looked intently at the towers of *Sungum*, shrunk in the distance to the size of a dog's head. Then he frowned. Already! He screwed up his eyes to make sure. A particoloured flag of blue and green was hung out of the topmost window in the West Tower. So soon!

He ground his teeth. How could it be? Gawping oaf of a medicine man— if you have blundered, Yakub will draw every tooth in your muscle-bound head. Two-pice dentist! Mecca-returned magician!

Yakub got up. So there was no time to lose. Why couldn't the old spark have died quietly in his bed—or hers—instead of falling out of the sky and setting all Sans Souci ablaze? Ostentatious ass: a showman to the end. A profligate who never learned that power, not splendour, is the proper end of riches. Splendour is outward: and how does it multiply? By ciphers—and a cipher the rich man remains. But power is always one and indivisible, suffering no subtraction. Take away from one and what remains unless some vulgar fraction? But on the other side: add to one and the sum must still be one. One, my fallen master, absorbs utterly; its gain is the other's loss. Let there be no alternatives—an end to *or*! No more conjunctions—away with *and*! Down with the hyphen!

The baker-and-philosopher unclenched his fists and tenderly picked the flesh off the curried doves. When he was finished he leaned over the side of the bridge and dropped a nest of bones into the Ganda Nala. The waters had run low and they were covered with a fine dust like talcum powder. At midnight a sheet of ice would crust the surface and by four o'clock in the morning the canal would be frozen solid, but Yakub had no time for signs. He took up a pinch of dust from the side of the road and rubbed his long lean hands. Purified, he made his way down the Nakhlau slope of the bridge. Through a sparse hedge on the left, just above the Nine-Foot pir's shrine, he could already see the halvai's shop.

"But I *want* to see the balloon!"

Rose Llewellyn Bibi gave her curls a petulant shake. The curls were really flaps, little irregular wads that made her look as if she cut her own hair. In fact it was cropped for her by her only friend, who had just forbidden her to go to the saltpetre hill. Rose was close to tears and began to beat on the arms of her chair.

Farida Wilkinson Bibi put her hands to her ears in mock exasperation. She was sitting on a padded divan in the East Tower (to which Rose had brought her own chair) and leaning with one elbow on a long indigo bolster. The room was blue-washed and the floor covered with Mirzapur rugs.

"O-hoa, little sister, you're becoming more of a savage every day! Soon we'll have to feed you roots and berries and who knows what."

"Why? Just because I want to go and see the *Salamandre*? Everyone's gone. Naz has gone, Parveen's gone, all the servants have gone."

"Are you a servant? All those low people running to see his sinful machine. Do you want to join that sinful tamasha? You want to tease God, no? Do you know what *Salamandre* means?" Farida was leaning forward and her bangles shook.

"What does it mean?"

Farida was not sure herself, though she knew flames had something to do with it.

"There you are," she pounced, "you don't even know that and you want to go running. It's a hell-fire machine anyway—Parveen said Hakimji was saying so. I'm surprised she's gone herself, knowing that. Do you want to be like her?"

"Yes."

Farida sat back again. "If God wanted us to fly He would have given us wings. As it is, our husband is a man, not an angel, and men should keep their feet firmly on the earth. There will be time enough for sky-walking when he dies."

"*Farida!*" Rose began to cry. She did not much like the Great Trotter, but if he died there would be no more ballooning.

"Yes, and if you don't want to go to hell you had better start to pray and forget about all his wicked toys. They say he reads philosophy all day."

Rose, who did not know what philosophy was, had a terrible vision of wickedness and began to cry harder than ever. Her friend was pained by her own harshness. It was not that she was unaccustomed to Rose's tears; the girl had cried ever since she arrived at Sans Souci. It was just that lately the flood had abated and this seemed to have something to do with the large yellow silk balloon which had been taking shape in the balloon room. Farida had it from her servant-girl that Rose stole there each day along the roof of the Rib. And the more often she went, creeping along past the obelisks and other wicked shapes in the Great Trotter's observatory to kneel at a window in the dome of the balloon room for hours on end, the less she cried. For the sake of her own peace (her tower was just along a balcony from Rose's), but also because she liked the girl, Farida did not want the outbursts to resume. She crossed the rug on her hands and knees, knelt beside Rose's chair and slipped an arm around her shoulder. Pleased with the unexpected rush of sympathy, Rose cried on. The older girl kissed her softly on the forehead and, undoing her fists, on the palm of each hand.

"Come, little sister, this is not the way. We'll finish our game—"

"I don't want to play." Rose half turned her face away. Farida looked down at the scattered tamarind seeds.

"All right then, just close your eyes and think of something else, something colourful and bright. Now tell me what you see."

"A balloon."

"Stupid girl! You think you see a balloon but it's the devil. So actually you don't want to see him at all. Besides, you know who *else* will be there."

"Who?"

"*She.*" Farida nodded her head slowly.

Rose at once buried her face in Farida's bosom. She was not really afraid, but it was a ritual that bound her to her friend.

"And that Hindu munshi of hers, the old man who looks like half a table."

Rose burrowed deeper, drying her tears on Farida's shalwar.

"So you see it's best if we stay where we are and leave them to their sin. We'll see if God lets this thing go up. You know what He did last week— yes, a big hole burnt in the very centre. We should be praying to Him to spare our husband's life."

Again Farida saw her mistake. Rose's lips had begun to pucker and her violet eyes filled with tears. Farida noticed for the first time her ugly nose and was pleased; she was filled with love for her little friend. She began to plait her long hair in a single rope behind her.

"Never mind the silly game. We'll sing a song, little sister." And she named a Bihari hill song she had sung at home while waiting for the monsoon to break, "This way Rain Cloud, dear."

"No, let's sing 'Ring-a-ring.'"

"All right, we'll sing both. First yours and then mine."

She stood up and began to clap her hands. The two sang and fell among the cushions, then stood up and repeated the song and fell down again. Then Farida began to sing, looking from time to time in a tiny wall mirror rimmed with pastework stones and remarking her handsome nose. Her eyes too were beautiful, almond shaped and not in the least light, and her hair hung long and rich and black. She hugged Rose tightly in her arms rocking and kissing her as she sang. When she stopped, both girls—in fact Farida was long past girlhood—found they were locked in a close embrace and staring gravely into each other's eyes. Rose began to giggle.

"Now we must pray to God," Farida said sulkily, "to forgive us for the sin of singing."

Sunya approached *Sungum* by the southwest gate, on the other side of the Audience Hall from the gate by which the Great Trotter had left not six hours ago. He was no longer hurrying. Cautiously he threaded the gate within the gate, crossed the court, and mounted the apron of broad low steps leading up to the hall. He was relieved to pass into its cool darkness, but the sweat on his palms was less from the heat of the afternoon than from an unease which having begun with doubt had condensed into a kind of fear.

Was it wise, the poulterer asked himself, was it prudent—and Sunya was a prudent man—to meddle in this matter? Had he not been a little hasty? After all, it was no trifling affair: Tartar Sahib was missing, presumably dead; this was not a time for petty rivalries, much less for lunatic plotting. Such things savoured of bets and cock-fighting. If others wished to scheme and hatch intrigues, that was their business—his was hatching chickens; gathering up the eggs in their season (or appointing one to gather them up); selling some; incubating others in one of Tartar Sahib's improved solar boxes; rearing proud, placid, productive birds. Leghorns, Rhode Islands, Corsican bantams, Madagascar pullets: these were his domain. Chickens were his business, eggs his proper sphere; politics, power, string-pulling, pushery, rope tricks, were for that gaunt funambulist. If he wished to confront Yakub Khan, the time to have done it was six years ago over the dung affair. The quarrel had been trifling in itself, but the cause just, and the baker not yet Chief Steward. That time had passed, the balance of power had shifted, a pecking order been established. If the baker-and-politician wished to rule the world, let him; a sorry end awaited all such.

"What has a poulterer to do with politics?" Sunya demanded as he removed his shoes. He padded across the cool marble, resolved to ask rather than give information. The desert plan had been an idle fancy, best abandoned.

The herbalist-and-dentist was waiting ensconced in a niche at the south corner of the Audience Hall. Sunya did not see him and walked straight on. At the centre of the hall, by the fountain, he paused, uncertain.

"Sunya bhai! *Hoi*!" Hakimji called. "What news?"

Sunya looked about him in confusion. The voice, whose first report had sounded like a rocket, came from every side: *Sunya-nya-nya-NYA!* The Audience Hall dome had an echo.

"Here, bhai, here!" Hakimji bawled, setting up a new series of echoes which the whispering gallery above caught up and shuffled. Sunya looked all around, his eyes still unaccustomed to the dark. Every niche in the hall seemed to announce the herbalist's presence, and there were forty-eight, tucked behind a pillared arcade. At length the echoes faded, and where the last one died a bearded figure was waving to him. He strode towards it determined to say nothing.

"But what have you there, Sunya?" The red beard drooped with curiosity and the folk-doctor-and-dentist displayed a row of uneven teeth.

Sunya looked down at his hands: between them they carried the gypsonometer. In his running debate with himself he had quite forgotten it.

"It's nothing," he said hotly.

"Nothing? Well, nothing comes in strange shapes, brother."

There was a pause during which both men regarded the machine.

"But what exactly is it?" Hakim Ahmed asked, inserting the *exactly* so as not to appear stupid.

"It's a new egg-generating machine devised by Tartar Sahib."

"New! My teeth are in better repair. But Tartar Sahib—what news do you bring of him?"

"None."

"None!"

"No. I know nothing. I have heard nothing."

"Nothing! You come carrying nothing. You know nothing. You have heard nothing. Yet you have come. And in haste, so it would seem, bhai." The herbalist shook his head. So Yakub was right to sense something afoot, cunning devil. "Sit, brother," he went on, gesturing at the niche to his left just beyond the corner door where the southwest wall began. "You must be tired, a man of your age. Today is surely the hottest day either of us can remember." He lifted his black skull-cap and scratched underneath. "What do you say? What a day for him to have chosen for his sky-ride! No wonder it came to grief. Fortunately there's no loo to speak of—dust on top of such heat would have been the limit. Thank God, who is One."

God is many, meat-eater, Sunya thought, but took his perch silently in the adjacent niche. The two men sat regarding the marble vistas to either side. The door between them opened into the South Tower; the vestibule behind it was sparsely furnished, being simply a landing for the stair that led up to Jarman Begam's quarters.

"Nobody else has come in yet," Hakim Ahmed said, "aside from those two fools, Munnoo and Nankoo, with some absurd tale about a giant bird. I sent them smartly off. Yakub is at his post by the *Zalmandar*—as you know, he cannot leave it. I wonder what he'll do now. Never at a loss, the rogue. With him, one plus one is always one. Let's see now what he does with this new problem: one minus one."

"Nothing," Sunya was tempted to respond, but he held his peace. He was not going to be drawn.

"He's up to something," the herbalist continued. "And what he does will rebound on us, you may be sure."

Sunya looked up: here already was cause for alarm.

"You mean our jobs are in jeopardy?"

"That they are in any case. Tartar Sahib is dead. Well, missing, at any rate. The problem is how long we can keep them before we are all swallowed up. Then that rooster of yours will be of no further use to you." Hakim Ahmed pointed at the gypsonometer.

Sunya winced. "The bibis will keep us on," he hazarded.

"They will do as he says."

"Jarman Begam too?"

"Let us see."

"Matters will run their course."

"They will go the way he directs."

"It's not the end of the world."

"It's the end of ours—if he chooses."

"What are we to do, then?" Sunya was now genuinely distressed. He saw his snowy leghorns, his spotless eggs, again menaced by the old marauder, but in a new and total way. How would he feed his family, his wife? Now she would know hunger, the water-buffalo—refusing eggs!

"There is one way," the herbalist replied. He paused, stroking his beard with great composure and scrutinizing the gypsonometer. "We must find Tartar Sahib before he does."

Sunya inspected the frescoes on the ceiling. They were strange foreign conceptions, the work of that Italian cripple. The faces, the arms, seemed wrong, but they were the colour of goddesses.

Hakimji persisted. "If someone could lead us to where he might be found."

Sunya drew a breath and looked down at his calves. The leucoderma was spreading. He said, letting out the breath slowly: "I went to the desert. I found this contraption there. It's one of Tartar Sahib's machines, I don't know what for. It must have fallen with him."

"Him? With whom, Sunya?"

"Tartar Sahib."

"Tartar Sahib!"

"By the ber grove, on this side. Between the Tank and the aerolite."

"You found the body?"

"It must be there."

"Must be! Bhai, Sunya, either you saw it or you didn't."

"Look, it was hot. It might have been a mirage."

"A mirage?"

"They appear in deserts—you should know, you're Arabia-returned. They're there but not there."

"Sunya. You're babbling."

"This, *this* is no mirage!" Sunya shouted, brandishing the gypsonometer. "He's there. We must find him. I saw him. He must be there, he is there!" The poulterer was on his feet.

"Very well, Sunya. There's no need to tell the world about it. If you saw him, you saw him. You did, did you?"

Sunya was no longer in any doubt. "I tell you I saw him with these eyes. What do we do now?"

"We must go there at once. But you're all upset. Let's refresh ourselves before we set out. I have a cool drink here—there was no Rooh Afza, but I persuaded the head cook to make us some mango-fool. He was only too happy. Poor fellow has little enough to do these days. I should have offered it to you before. How ill-mannered of me!"

Yakub entered the halvai's shop and was blinded at first by the sudden darkness. Mansoor, who was busy frying jalebis, saw him but did not get up. Sitting cross-legged, he was a perfect globe of flesh, a purple sphere suspended in the void like some auspicious planet. A wide brass bowl of gulab jamuns was evidence of the morning's work, and beside him on a tray was a pyramid of pink barfis; now he had turned to making jalebis. He held his muslin pouch above the hot kadhai and spun a twisting thread of white batter into the oil. A chain of loops and curls and rings formed there, floating on the oil and sizzling gently as it went from white to gold (*Cunning Craftsman, Masterly Mansoor*). At last the halvai looked up.

"Welcome, brother Yakub! I am honoured. Make yourself comfortable. Boy! Clear that bench. How many times must I tell you not to use that cloth? You'll eat a rap from me next time. So, Yakub! Welcome again. It must be pressing business that brings you here at this hour. The very crows have folded their wings. Only a wasp or two about—they know where to come. You think it's hot outside? Try sitting over a fire all day with smoke and oil clouding the air around you. If there weren't two weddings to cater for tonight, I would leave this job to the boy. And he wouldn't start until the sun had gone down a little—would you, you thieving scoundrel? Tell me then, Yakub— no, let me guess. It's another wedding! No? A party for some Calcutta bigwigs! No? Tartar Sahib has some firangi guests? All right, you tell me.

"A horse? That's all? The Chief Steward of Sans Souci, keeper of the stables, master-gelder, comes to *me* for a horse! No, Yakub, you imagine me an ass, or you wouldn't take me for a ride like this. Ha! Take me for *a ride*! Just a moment."

The halvai took up a slotted ladle and scooped the golden chain out of the oil. He placed it on a mesh and let the oil drain into a second kadhai. Then he seized the rings and plunged them into a bowl of syrup. When the jalebis had plumped up, but before they had lost their crispness, the halvai broke off three rings and pressed on them a tissue of beaten silver (*Worthy Confectioner, Exquisite Artist*).

He handed the jalebis to Yakub on a leaf, and laughed out loud as he did.

"Sorry, Yakub! I misheard you. For a moment I thought you said *no*!" His eyes bulged. "You *did*? Yakub, bhai, what are you saying! Surely you mean yes, yes? No? Yakub, reconsider, I beg you—the offer is free, no strings attached. Shun this foolery. Look, here's gold beneath the silver—see the precious liquid running in these veins? You're not well, that's it; the sun's gone to your head. Do I need to remind you that the finest sweets in Nakhlau— I won't say the whole of Tirnab, because who knows: one must keep an open mind—issue from this shop? Even Hindu halvais concede that. The Nawab himself sends to me for halva when the British Resident is coming to tea. These are the jalebis that Tartar Sahib himself bespoke in the old days before he took that imprudent vow. Look, bhai, the leaf is fresh and green—none of that dried leaf business that these heathens go in for: we aren't worried about its soul. Compose yourself, my friend. When you say no you mean yes—I once knew such a case from the last solar eclipse. The woman was found wandering in circles just here by the bridge—the Barfi Bridge!—ha!— very good, Yakub—anyway, she was found wandering by the grave in the noonday sun, frothing at the mouth. You would have thought a mad dog had bitten her but she took water. Water! You would like a glass? My God, then it's the same trouble! Yakub, look at me. I'm going to ask you one last time, please concentrate, try to help yourself: is it jalebis you want or water? Or even jalebis *and* water—or water and jalebis? Just water? And a horse—oh my God, she was in a hurry too. Your mouth, Yakub—is that a trace of froth?

"All right, all right, calm down—the boy will fetch you a cup of water. Boy! You see, he's already gone to fetch it—here he comes. Well trained, na? And I will untether the horse for you. He's a little thin, but one can't fill his trough with jalebis. You're *sure*—? All right, all right. The price of sugar these days. Don't ride him too hard in this weather and keep away from his ears. There's no saddle, just the harness; not that a good horseman like you ever needed one. Never mind payment. Are there debts between friends? Just try to persuade Tartar Sahib to give up that absurd vow, then we can have the old days again, when a river of sweets ran across the bridge to Sans Souci. And here, wait, take him something to weaken his resolve: I have some special almond barfi here. No? On your way back, then? Well, no matter, some other day."

Yakub drank out of the clay cup and politely smashed it. The halvai nodded courteously, but he could not recover his good cheer. He began to unpin a foot from under him and when it did not respond, slapped a vast thigh. The report echoed around the shed and set off a dark billowing of flesh below his belly. Still the foot would not respond; its toes peeped like jamuns just out of reach, and Mansoor gazed at them, disconsolate. He rocked his head and, turning slowly on his axis, snapped his cloth at the boy. The boy ran off to untie the horse and brought it around to the front where Yakub was waiting (*Insipid Messenger, Unhoneyed Tongue*).

Sadly the halvai watched Yakub mount. Astride the meagre salt-and-pepper creature, the baker-and-master-gelder's spindly legs trailed in the dust. He went off at a trot and the halvai gloomily watched the dust settle on his gold and silver. He could not bring himself to eat the jalebis on the leaf, though Yakub had not so much as touched them. He sighed and took up his ladle. The oil had begun to smoke and his eyes stung. The next time the boy passed that way, the leaf vanished.

Fonseca reeled from his almirah mirror and sat down heavily in an old wicker chair. For several minutes he stared at the louvre shutters that kept the afternoon sun from spilling in at the window. Where the sun did slip in, it slashed a bold exclamation mark on the floor, surrounded by two long dashes where the jalousie slats were loose, thus: ----- ! ----- . Fonseca watched this figure inch across the floor and fatten as it slanted up a wall. The only sound apart from his breathing was a reedy squeak from the chair each time he shifted. If it grew dark outside for a moment, he did not notice. At length he rose and began to pack. As he opened his trunk a bitter scent cut through and cleansed the air, the scent of dried nim leaves strewn among the clothes to keep away moths. He worked steadily for an hour, arranging, removing, and rearranging his things, crossing and recrossing the small room. His silk shirts, gifts from the Great Trotter when he took to Muslim dress, he placed at the very top in the wooden trunk. Beneath them was a box lined with red velvet, which held his shears and combs and curlers. He had stared a long while at those inert silvered tools before snapping the box shut and winding his barbersheet about it. Fitted into a space between his pressed breeches and his cravats (also the Great Trotter's gifts) lay a well-thumbed copy of the letters of Alexander Pope, his prize at Mrs. Bidwell's school for a good round hand. Other nooks and crannies he had plugged with tobacco, a jar of pomade, and a dozen trinkets. In a black box beside the trunk was coiled an old French horn.

As the barber-and-Ice Manager finished packing, the lid of his trunk fell forward with a crash. Fonseca drew back sharply, blowing on his fingertips; not a good omen for a journey. He glanced at the shuttered window. How was that other journey progressing? Fonseca saw his master bumping along at tree-top level, getting his wig entangled in the branches of some toddy palm. His arm leapt out to shield the old man from punishment and he uttered a broken cry: "Father!" But the vision faded and he was left stranded in an operatic pose. Fonseca could sing, but there was nothing to sing about. He had remained behind to write his letter, but equally he had not gone to the launching because this morning—almost as if he had sensed betrayal—the Great Trotter had not rung downstairs for his barber-and-man. A day could not begin without Fonseca's razor, his strop and towel, his steaming basin, his dish of talcum powder. Today had so begun. Fonseca had watched the steam die on his basin, wondering whether his master knew that his slave meant to desert him. He dropped his extended arm and laughed mirthlessly. It was too late for suppositions of that kind; the letter was written, the trunk packed, tomorrow he would be on his way at dawn. Two things remained: to pay a last visit to the Glacerie, seat of his exaltation, and to bid Jarman Begam goodbye. Fonseca noticed he used the servants' name for her, and wondered briefly whether she saw him as a servant or as a respectable if penurious attendant whose dress and speech set him apart from the common run of employee at Sans Souci. Did she know he had been bought with his shears and horn? Abstract notion! In another day he would be hairdresser at large, nobody's man.

The thought parched his throat and he wondered whether he shouldn't call in on Qaiyum, the deputy librarian, and drink a last cup of Solomon wine with him. But no, it was midafternoon and the ample astrologer-and-bibber would be asleep. O for a glass of mango-fool! But the kitchens had made none for a year.

Mango-fool

MANGO-FOOL, n. Cooling hot-weather drink made from green mangoes boiled, mashed, and mixed with milk and sugar. Water in various proportions may be substituted for milk, thus varying the colour from greenish white to whitish green; the sugar is invariable. Ice is frequently mixed in, but should not crowd the surface. Silver tumblers are frowned upon by connoisseurs, the acids acting upon the metal to produce effects ranging from the unusual to the bizarre.

Pondering his future, Fonseca made for the Glacerie with a prickling in his mouth. Although he did not expect anybody to be about in *Sungum*, he chose the way through the tahkhana, Justin's underground retreat of a summer's day. That way he did not need to brave the sun at all; he simply stepped out at his door, turned the corner, and without leaving the West Tower descended two flights of steps, the first to the library and the second to the tahkhana. The tahkhana was little more than a cellar, cool, dark, and damp, with a plinth of white marble in the centre; it smelt faintly of bat droppings, and with its sloping black inner wall it looked like a cold fireplace. It was the Great Trotter's exclusive domain; here he had had his vision of Quebecois ice, here he had invented and installed the first mirror tube. Fonseca came down often enough as far as the door to deliver a book or manuscript from the library. But only after he was appointed Ice Manager had Justin shown him the passage to the Glacerie.

The passage was in fact an air vent that sloped gradually upwards until it reached the northwest wall of *Sungum*. From there one travelled within the wall itself, just below ground level as far as the North Tower, beyond which stood the Glacerie. One came out into the ice godown, an underground hall where Sans Souci ice was stored. To find the entrance to the passage was an act of faith in an ill-lit tahkhana whose irregular walls were a honeycomb of deceptions. The secret was simply to find and keep one's face to the draught of cool black air that flowed down from above.

Fonseca entered the passage, startling a colony of bats and sucking in the moist air as he went. Enveloped in immediate blackness, he kept his eye on a faint glow of icelight in the distance. He ran a finger along the mossed wall to steady himself but desisted when he remembered there might be centipedes. He ignored the dry scuffle of cockroaches on stone. Once before, he had struck a match and in the bare second before the draught blew it out he had seen them on the wall beside him—burnt orange, dark yellow, date brown, almost, it seemed, in formation; they might have been mounted in a collector's cabinet, except that their feelers were swaying gently like living clockwork. At the end of the passage he came to a door that responded to a high note sweetly held.

The Glacerie godown held no surprises; after all, he kept the only key. Its shelves were bare of ice and stood in desolate ranks. It had been a hard summer. Fonseca wandered aimlessly among them repeating, "Mr. Ice Manager Sahib." Then he saw an open window and frowned; it was against all rules for Glacerie windows to be left open. Someone would have to answer for it, he thought, and immediately smiled at the academic nature of his response: in the first place he was leaving tomorrow, and in the second there was no ice that might suffer anyway. On an impulse he decided that he did not wish to return the way he had come. He climbed through the open window, jumped out into the blinding sunlight and made his way back to *Sungum*. He had remembered his second duty: Elise.

Elise stood at the window absorbing Rekha's wordless message. She had on occasion admitted but never dwelt on the possibility of Justin Trotter's death. He was many years her senior, and would precede her as a matter of course—not that she could take either departure seriously. It was enough to allow that at some comfortably remote station death would put an end first to the Great Trotter's labours and then, still further on, to those of his chief consort; for the present there was enough to occupy both lives many times over. The multiplicity of his tasks in particular seemed sufficient reason for a special dispensation in the matter of death. Why, latterly he had even shut himself away from her. Was he at work on an engine that would be in perpetual motion? He had caused light to turn corners, water to run uphill—might not such a man perfect the anti-gravity boot? Was there a future for frictionless mercury-borne chairs? Was the perfect dye at hand? The perfect bleach? No man, surely, who so earnestly dedicated his life to these ends could ever run out of so vulgar a commodity as time. Yet here was Trot dead (she was sure).

Should she weep? What would the learned Ibn-i-qasim say? That men were mortal, that life was uncertain, that Alexander, Darius were clay to stop a crack with. Homilies which tragic events such as this should stamp with conviction; yet more than ever she felt inclined to doubt their worth. Could she, for instance, be carried off before she had finished Ibn-i-qasim's own *Cup of State*? It was inconceivable—in the face of the evidence—to leave a book half read.

Elise noticed that once more her thoughts had come around to herself. She set about examining the case. Justin Trotter is dead. What does the

statement mean? She was unable to proceed beyond simplicities: he will not
speak again (but he has not spoken for a year); he will not come to me (but
he has not come for a year—nor has he gone to her). She glanced at the
fastened windows of the East Tower. Is that all? Already I have exhausted
his meaning, returned to myself—*he* is empty of speech, of seed; he is only
to be sown, to be spoken of, and always in a new and complete tense. And
I? What must I do?

Jarman Begam stood very still, her arms pressed to her sides, her white
Thursday gown hanging from her shoulders like a tent. The eyes set in her
narrow face might have been made of glass, and her elbows were smooth and
cold. What must I do? she repeated, and did nothing. After an eternity she
seemed to thaw, first creaking as she stooped to pick up her fallen handkerchief,
and then inching across the room in a crystalline trance. She shut the door
behind her and went downstairs, stopping at the gallery level and turning into
the corridor that overlooked the Audience Hall on the southwest side. She
arrived at the West Tower breathing audibly, her progress no longer glacial.
This was Justin Trotter's tower, but she did not mean to climb its stair. Instead
she went down a flight of steps and began to knock softly, insistently, on a
green door at the Audience Hall landing.

It was some time before she realized that Fonseca was not in.

It was past three o'clock when Yakub arrived at the Nawab's palace, but the
heat was more stifling than at noon. The road through the city had been bare
and drained of colour, the buildings and shopfronts edged with black. Nearer
the Fish Palace there were blots of shade under the garden trees, and the river
steamed a greenish ochre. For fear of being laughed at, the baker-and-Master
of the Horse tethered his borrowed mount a short way from the palace. In
the river's shallows a small pot-bellied girl was splashing a water-buffalo
which shook its nose in the air from sheer pleasure. Yakub called to the girl
and promised her a copper coin if she would tend the horse as well. The girl's
eyes widened and she nodded solemnly. Relieved, he left her to it and turned
up the broad way to the palace. Above the scalloped archway of the main
gate were moulded in stucco two fishes, the Nawab's symbol.

"Where so quickly?" A blue-turbanned guard stood at the gate, barring
entry.

"I must see the Nawab on a matter of great urgency."

"To you or to His Highness?"

"To His Highness."

"But it is not yet four. His Highness is asleep."

"Then he must be woken."

"Do you say so?" The guard looked past Yakub as if for a palki or a nobly caparisoned horse. He took in the stranger's embroidered yellow tunic and the gold threads in his turban.

"I say so." But there was a quaver in Yakub's voice.

"And who may you be?"

"I am Chief Steward of Sans Souci."

"The French firangi's house?"

"The same."

"A message from across the canal?"

"A most urgent one."

"Very well, but I warn you, the next gate will be harder, and there is another, harder still. And then you are only at *our* steward's gate."

"I know. I have been here before."

Yakub spoke the truth. He had twice been to the Nawab's palace, once on the occasion of the British Governor-General's visit from Calcutta, and again when the Nawab had given a breakfast followed by a cock-fight. But he had never entered alone. On both occasions he had merely accompanied the Great Trotter, and he himself had sat at a lengthy remove from the grandees. He had eaten in another room altogether, long after the rose-water bowls had been taken away from the chief table. Only at the cock-fight had he been in the foreground, crouching over Sans Souci's prize cock, Heaven's Vengeance, and stroking its throat with a ringed finger. The Nawab had noticed him, even spoken a word of ironical encouragement to his opponent's trainer. Then the Great Trotter's cock had won. The Nawab was courteous, full of smiles, and furious. At the next match, Heaven's Vengeance fought the Nawab's cock on home ground in the Cock Hall or Spur, and won again, against all the rules of etiquette. The Nawab's fury mounted. Before the next match he sent a man to the French firangi's trainer with an offer. Heaven's Vengeance lost the fight and was barely patched up after. Yakub bought himself a horse. At the final venue, Heaven's Vengeance lost again and was destroyed. Yakub bought himself a carriage. Today he wished he could have ridden in it to the Fish Palace.

On his way to the second gate, Yakub wondered whether he should not have given the first guard a coin. He seemed to remember his master pressing a rupee into a darban's hand, somewhere. Or should he have been more peremptory? What was the correct style in these matters? There was still so much to learn that for a moment he felt dizzy with confusion. What was the proper way to seek an audience with the Nawab, he wondered, forgetting for a moment even the motive of his audience. He resolved that a greater disdain with guards was in order, and had no sooner assumed a mask of immense hauteur than he looked up into a face which was clearly not that of a guard.

A small concourse of silent nobles and flunkeys surrounded the face, a party evidently bound on some excursion, though why at this hour was not clear. The puzzlement showed in the flunkeys' bleary eyes. At first Yakub supposed this to be some dandified petitioner who had brought his partridges out for a walk. The figure on the topmost step did not resemble the man who had bent over him at the cock-fight. True, he was black verging on purple, and his skin had the tight smooth glossy look of an aubergine, but there was a strange otherness about this figure, and it was not that he looked squat where the other had been stately (*Niggling Yakub, Needless Finesse*). It was like a word misspelt or turned around. And suddenly he saw it: the Nawab looked exactly as Trotter Sahib had looked before he gave up his firangi garb—the Nawab was dressed as a European. He had heard about the switch; it happened about the time Trotter Sahib began to wear Indian clothes. Today the Nawab's lime-green frock coat was fastened with gold knobs along a bulging meridian (*Earthly Master, Shapely Lord*). A lavender scarf fronted with white lace graced his neck. His breeches were of bunched purple velvet, tied at the knee with black ribbons; below the knee, the calves were encased in white hose. The shoes, of highly polished leather, with a curious block at the heel, were secured with silver buckles. On his head this ebony Frenchman wore a wig of tight white curls. In his hand he carried a piece of smoked glass. He fixed his small round eyes on Yakub.

"You!"

Yakub bowed deeply, gratified.

"I know you from somewhere. You are of my court?"

Yakub's pleasure contracted; he had supposed himself instantly recognizable. "I am from Sans Souci, Highness."

"Oho. The master cocksman."

Yakub bowed again.

"Come. You too shall witness this extraordinary event. There's no match today. My quails are at rest, and as for these handsome creatures, you shall not molest them." He called the birds to heel. "News? News can wait, my good fellow. This business cannot."

The party moved out into the hot sunlight and began to descend the steps.

"First, and in passing," cried the Nawab, "every man will observe his own shadow as it goes before him down the steps. It proceeds stoutly, forthrightly, without cant or crookedness. Next, every man will notice the shadow of his neighbour. Consider how it snakes and creeps and twists."

"Wah! Wahh! Wahh! Bravo!" A chorus of praise came from the red-eyed flunkeys. The Nawab was pleased and prodded a pale young man in the chest.

"You, Hussain the Ear-Waggler, will write a verse on the subject and see if it can match my sentiments."

The young man's nose twitched and his red eyes filled with terror. He simpered into his muslin cap: "Match *your* sentiments, Highness!"

"No. Let it be. You are a puling rhymester. I will ask that renegade Munshi Nishan Chand to make a couplet of it. Your job will be . . . to carry the message to him."

"Surely, Highness, your shadow is the slim exception that proves the rule." Yakub had been wondering how to begin.

"Then I must appear crooked to myself," the Nawab rejoined. "Or stout to you. Which do you intend, cocksman?"

"*Stout*, Highness! Why, I would never—"

"I am *pleased* to be so, cocksman. Cocksman, you had best stick to quails: a flatterer you will never make. Not for you the sugared breath, the honeyed tones. Your tongue has more barbs than a cock's foot!"

"Wahh! Bravo!" (*Wahh! Bravo!*)

Yakub hung his head, smarting at the snub. Or had he mistaken the spirit of the Nawab's riposte? What if it were no snub at all? Perhaps the highest circles delighted in exchanging insults, and the breach of etiquette was the only etiquette. He looked enviously at the courtiers. How easily these silken men wore their refinement, how little they had had to fight. They simply were, all came to them, while he was forced to go and grasp and get.

"*Be*!"—the Nawab cried—"that as it may, this was not the wonder I wished to demonstrate. I did not rouse you from your afternoon beds simply to show you your neighbour's shadow or your own. Other, infinitely greater shadows are stirring—and I do not speak of my own, for these others are not on earth but in the heavens—though the earth has a role to play. Wherefore I have brought this." He held up the piece of smoked glass. "Today, as you know, there will be an eclipse of the sun. Was that why I had some trouble flushing you from your apartments? Perhaps Hussain here had his pots and pans ready to beat upon like some ignorant old biddy? However, here he is in the dreaded sunlight, winking like a frightened rabbit—and he is right to blink. Let no man look upon the sun's face at this hour without a smoked glass. Insanity, impotence, blindness: this triumvirate await the heedless. Taken by itself each is bearable; together, what havoc they wreak upon the healthy! But the far-sighted man, the prudent man, the well-prepared man, the gentleman, brings with him his smoked glass."

How the smoked glass is made

I wish to shew how the smoked glass is made. The adept will take in his left hand a mirror such as courtesans affect, and in his right a stone. Any stone will do so it be solid, sharp, and rough, but the mirrors sold by J.c.

Solomon & Son are best. They are across from the Rangili Manzil just where
the road turns away. They open early and close late, and remain unshuttered
through the afternoon be the sun fierce or mellow or wholly or partially
eclipsed. The proprietor is a handsome man, generous with credit as with
wine. Good adept, scrape well the silver from the back of the mirror. With
the Solomon mirror this is the play of children. Meanwhile, light a candle and
hold it in readiness. Candles are plentiful and cheap at the Solomon establishment; it is cheaper still if you buy in bulk. Lucifers, quick match, tinder-
boxes, flint, and other incendiaries are always in stock. They also sell pyjama
drawstrings, tape, ribbons, banyans, collars, buttons (these are a European
device, samples of which are being offered free during the month of June),
buttonholes (these are supplied at a moderate charge), and all your haberdashery and hosiery needs. When the glass is clear it is ready to darkle. Hold,
good adept, it over the candle, neither too far above nor in the flame but just
where the flame turns to smoke. When all is grey, but not lampblack, the
glass is considered smoked and may be taken to eclipses whole or partial.
However, if the adept be a noted prankster without much to do, and if he
wish to deceive his courtiers on the hottest day of the year, let him choose a
mirror with a flaw in the glass (he need look no further than J.c. Solomon &
Son). A bubble in the glass when smoked gives the illusion of a shadow
crossing the face of any bright object, heavenly or not, viewed through it.
Pane or plain glass may also be used, but a mirror is more shapely. This is
what I wished to shew. So do that. Praise God.

(CHRONICLE RESUMED)

"Very rarely," continued the Nawab, impatient of interruption, "does the
eclipse coincide with the midsummer's day. And never before has a total
eclipse occurred on the midsummer's day of the last year in any century. An
auspicious moment indeed."

"Highness, the century has just begun."

"Who spoke?"

It was Ibrahim, an ancient noble who had been tutor to the present and
the previous nawab. He knew about this one's practical jokes, and was particularly aggrieved at having his afternoon nap cut short.

"By our calendar, yes, Ibrahim. But I need hardly remind so learned a
maulvi, a man who has read Al-Biruni's *Chronosophy*, that there is another
calendar in Europe—where time is measured with clocks such as this." The
Nawab produced a watch from his fob and held it up for inspection. Then he
pocketed it and held up the smoked glass.

"Attend, all of you! The ingress begins. Each will get his turn. You, cocksman, look first."

He handed Yakub the glass. "Mark how it encroaches upon the light, this envious shadow, like the snout of some foul camel."

Yakub drew near the Nawab and spoke softly.

"The eclipse has already occurred over Sans Souci, Highness."

"Observe its hesitant advance—what do you say, cocksman?"

"Trotter Sahib is dead, Highness."

There was a lull in which the light turned grey, every object in the outer court taking on a smoked look. The Nawab's own frock-coat went from green to muddy gold.

"Give the glass to Ibrahim, cocksman. Let us walk a short way together. Where might she be waiting?"

"*She*, Highness? It is Trotter Sahib who is dead!"

"Still, where is she?"

"Highness?"

"You are unaccompanied?"

"I came at once, sire."

The Nawab regulated his displeasure. "At once and without the German's daughter. The greatest chess player in the land. That is bad news, cocksman. Do you see that modest dome by the river, cocksman? It was to have been my French commander's resting place. And you have left him in Sans Souci. Him and her, cocksman. Sad tidings, sad indeed, cocksman. Do you know what they do to such messengers in Europe, cocksman?"

"But this is good news, Highness. Sans Souci is yours."

"With you as its Wazir, I suppose."

"We can make a clean sweep of these firangis, Highness. The heir is missing, Jarman Begam—if wife she be—can be persuaded to sell."

"Do you know her?"

"I am her steward, sire."

"Then you cannot know her. Or you would have brought her here at once. In that carriage I believe you have acquired."

"She knows nothing of it yet, Highness."

"Cocksman, your simplicity is touching. You prize your own brain so highly, you cannot imagine intelligence existing outside it."

"Sire, she cares for nothing but books."

"She has continued her studies?"

"She does little else."

"What has she been reading, steward? You are in every room."

"Old histories, musty books, sire, best used for heating bath-water. But concerning Sans Souci, Highness—"

"We *are* concerned with Sans Souci, cocksman. We have talked of nothing else so far. It was to have been my summer palace, my Versailles, the solace of my declining years. And you have left her in it." He looked directly at Yakub and spat. "Weightless wretch! Toothpick! Marrowspoon! Bone in the kabab!—*oh*, et cetera!"

Etc. e.g.

Skewer without the kabab, Poker, Spare rib, Pullthrough, Clyster-pipe, Skeleton key, Male key, Dry wicket, Pinhead, Pin without the head, Eyeless needle, Scarecrow, Starveling sliver, Vexatious splinter, Stick, Stalk, Beanstalk, Twig, Straw, Last straw, Stamen without the head, Flowerless climber, Thorn without the rose, Venomous fang, Upright reptile, Weathercock, Spoke, Streak, Rake, Wraith, Lath, Drumstick, Bitter nim toothbrush, Beesting, Armpit hair, Trunk without the elephant, Sitar without the gourd, Cane without juice, Desiccated coconut, Shred, Slip, Wisp, Wafer without the ice cream, Fibre in the mango, Thread in the tamarind, String on the banana, Stick without the kulfi, Minaret of folly, Spindle, Thincompoop, Stick cinnamon, Fool without the cream, Foil, Silver leaf without the jalebi, Slippery carbon, Etc.

(*CHRONICLE RESUMED*)

Fonseca crossed the Audience Hall and rapped on the South Tower door. He had no wish to be seen loitering there at an unaccustomed hour and hoped Rekha would be in to show him upstairs. There was no answer. He knocked again, louder, and then realized that Rekha would be with the rest of the servants chasing the *Salamandre*.

He hesitated, then let himself in. As he placed his foot on the stair, he heard a curious sound, a sort of guttural residue like a bubble of air pushing up past a voice-box that might already be untenanted. He could only have described it as a *cluck*. It came from inside an almirah that stood in the recess under the spiral stair. He had often noticed this cupboard, identical with his own except for the mirror. Crossing to it, he tried the knob, and then his own key. The key turned, the door swung open, and Fonseca saw a sight that stopped his heart. Crammed into the hanging side of the almirah was a man, staring at him. It was the Great Trotter, dead.

The next thing he knew, Fonseca was half-way up the South Tower. His flight was checked by a thought: might it have been an illusion, a mirage? Curiosity overcame caution, and he tiptoed back down. The Great Trotter was still there, pale and motionless and staring.

The barber-and-man's next impulse was to throw open the hall door and shout: *He's dead! He's dead!* That would bring all Sans Souci running, because the echoes in the Audience Hall carried: at a certain pitch they grew louder instead of dying away, and could last for fifteen minutes together. Fonseca had once returned from a summons to the top of the West Tower to hear himself playing over and over a run on the horn.

He decided he had better make certain his master was indeed dead before announcing the fact to the world. "But you're up in a balloon!" he whispered. "What are you doing here?" He approached the body gingerly and felt for a pulse at the wrist. Only when he had assured himself that it was in fact a corpse did he realize, letting the hand drop, that the corpse was not that of the Great Trotter. Yet it was the body of an old man, bald, bulky, and white, and no other at Sans Souci met that description. The clothes, he now noticed, were not Muslim clothes, the cut of the shirt being Hindu, and a dhoti taking the place of the pyjamas. He looked hard at the face, at the staring yellow eyes, the beaked nose. It was a face he had seen—where? Fonseca scanned his mental jigsaw map of Sans Souci for a gap where this piece might fit. Of an evening, looking west? No, it was a morning face, an early morning face, a southward face. The piece went home: it was the poulterer, the egg-brahmin! Each morning before breakfast he would watch in the distance (while he shaved himself) the poulterer strutting between the coops and the stables like a grenadier, his leucoderma spots flashing in the sun. Up and down he marched, with ferocious little jerks of the head, as if daring anyone to come near. Now, strange to say, his white patches (they had been spreading of late) had all joined up, and the egg-brahmin sat pale and dead. He was not yet cold, and the realization brought Fonseca back to the present. He now had every reason to see Jarman Begam, and he must do so at once.

He ran up to Elise's quarters three steps at a time.

How immaculate bleach is made

I wish to shew how immaculate bleach is made. Here is one way; there are others, less sure. The results are to be seen to be believed. The adept will use a good pot of brass, dung fire, dyes to be specified, hair tonic, and much patience. Brass pots are to be had from J.c. Solomon & Son who are across from the Rangili Manzil, just where the road turns away. Another branch is to open beside the new Residency, beyond the banyan tree. Good adept, go to J.c. Unburden your sorrows, unchest your woes, enumerate your needs. A good purchase, even on credit, soothes the heart, dulls pain, cheats anxiety. The terms are fair, and a small deposit will secure you brass pots, pans, lotas, thalis, utensils of every kind, foreign crockery, Sheffield knives, toast racks, and many bright and useful things that have begun to come from that side. Having found his pot (the large are best) the adept will mount it on a dung fire. With the Solomon pot this is easily managed; it is light, the brass being thin as muslin. Look for the Solomon mark on the bottom (before filling). Into the pot pour water. When it is simmering add a packet of indigo dye with the Trotter label (be wary of imitations) and also packets of red and green dye. When the three have neutralized one another, the liquid will be of a grey colour. Simmer, good adept, for a further six hours. Do not stir. You may wish to drop a smooth pebble into the pot; do so if it helps pass the time. Then remove the pot from the fire. Take now in the left hand a bottle of *Mrs. Fernandez's Patent Hair Tonic and Grey Remover* (the label shows one of the misses Fernandezes with her hair unpinned and parted in the centre; it is grey to the left of the parting). Empty the contents into the pot. Do you wish to add nard, gum arabic, fenugreek, black salt, rhinoceros horn (powdered), civet, mirror silver, Alpine Snow, fair-and-lovely, rat-ki-rani, soapwort, baby's tears, bison milk, hailstones, leek, honeydew, liquid paper, soma, monosodium glutamate, and Himalayan Bouquet talcum powder of the sweetpea scent? Do not, fair adept. Resist the decorative impulse. Let the bleach cool and strain into bottles, or else pan, sun, scrape, and powder. Empty bottles are available free of charge at the Solomon establishment; caps and stoppers are reasonably cheap there. The wine is just fine. Hold the mixture in readiness. It will be found to resemble mango-fool. On the other hand, cunning adept, take another pot. In it immerse all articles to be bleached, using well water. Bring to the boil in a third pot more water and add to it a modicum of ordinary bleach from J.c.'s shop, following the directions on the label. Transfer all articles from the second to the third pot and allow to bleach. Just before removing, add a few drops (no more than three) from the milky green mixture in the bottles and see the difference. This is what I wished to shew. So do that. In all things praise God. *Do not take the milky green mixture.* If taken, induce vomiting and give milk. Fresh milk is available in the usual places, such as the halvai's beyond the Ice Bridge, but you may not wish to go so far. Go modestly.

(CHRONICLE RESUMED)

Elise sank unceremoniously in a heap at the foot of the green door. Of course! Fonseca would be up on the saltpetre hill or in the parklands searching for the *Salamandre*. She leaned back against the door. It opened with a long slow groan, and she stood up at once, too distraite to be embarrassed. Seeing nobody there, she stepped inside. Though she had never been in Fonseca's room she knew to turn left upon entering because it corresponded exactly in its spiral shell shape to an identical chamber at the bottom of her own tower. The room was empty not only of its occupant, but of any trace of his possessions except for a large trunk and what looked like a hat box beside it. In the general bareness, the room seemed to oscillate around the trunk. Without knowing what she did, Elise went up to the trunk and lifted the lid. She shrank back at once.

"Fonseca!" she whispered incredulously. "Packed and leaving—today of all days!"

She ran her eyes over the contents of the trunk and fingered one or two of the trinkets. Then she stood up and looked rapidly around the room. Walls, table, and shelves had been stripped, a wardrobe stood empty, one of its doors left open. Elise was crossing to inspect the almirah when the lid of Fonseca's trunk fell shut. She leapt forward, clutching at the almirah door. When she saw what had happened she stood there breathing lightly until her heart was quiet. The almirah held nothing of interest; turning away, she mechanically shut the door. As she did, she glimpsed a face in the long mirror. Again she drew a sharp breath. It was not her own face, though she stood directly before the glass: through a forest of red she made out the face of Fonseca himself. The face hovered just beneath the surface of the glass, caught in a kind of vapour, the dyed black curls crowned with a gold wig; in place of the habitual ironic mask was a look of earnest entreaty. Before she knew what she was doing, Elise bent and kissed the glass once, twice, then repeatedly, without restraint. Coming to herself, she found the mirror covered with rosebuds and began to scrub them furiously with her handkerchief. When she was done, the glass was clear and the beseeching face gone.

Softly she ran from the room. The Audience Hall yawned coolly at her and from the roof of its marble mouth she heard over and over again a fugitive echo, *I saw him. . . . He must be there. . . . He is there. . . .* , and under it, now very faint, the trace of another echo, *-NYA! -NYA! -NYA!* Her gaze swept the hall, but there was nobody there.

She descended another flight of steps and entered the library. The pollen of a hundred thousand books sent a thrill through her as she made her way among the dark-varnished shelves, scores of them, radiating from the empty centre. At the far wall a bluish glow showed where the librarian's cubicle was, and Elise groped towards it through a jungle of bark scrolls and leaf manuscripts, books bound in lizard-skin and goathide, vellum-bound tomes, parchment folios, papyrus cylinders, clay seals, books of brick, of stone, of sand, of bark, of bone, of cloth, of paper, of wind, of copper, of glass—every last one of which Munshi Nishan Chand could have fetched without a light. The old man was sitting at his desk hunched over a page, and he did not stir when Elise entered.

"Munshiji!" she whispered, then a little louder, "Lhasa lion!"

The librarian turned sharply in his seat, his whole body swinging out like a wicket-gate. A luminous globe of spittle which had been gathering on a thread at the corner of his mouth broke off and flew into the void.

"You! I thought for a moment it was *him*." His gesture took in the sky, the West Tower and finally the page lit by the mirror tube.

"Munshiji, he's dead."

"So you know."

Elise stood amazed. "But how did *you* know?"

Nishan Chand waved at his desktop and turned away. His student bent her slender neck over the page. There, ghostly as a watermark, upside down and wigless, hung the figure of the Great Trotter. Above him in the cloudless sky, a cloud no bigger than a split pea was being born; below ran the murky waters of the Ganda Nala.

When she could speak, Elise asked without looking up: "But how . . . ?" Her voice trailed off as her hand stroked the page.

"The mirror tube opens to the west," Nishan Chand answered drily. "It looks out through the clerestories in the hall."

Elise bowed her head. "What am I to do, Munshiji?"

Nishan Chand turned away again. "A librarian, madam, dispenses books, not advice."

"But I am your student."

"And I am simply a conduit."

"You have taught me all I know."

Nishan Chand took off his spectacles and waved them at the shelves. He stared unseeingly and spoke into the gloom. "They have taught me all I know. I hope I have been of some use."

"But you must help me now."

"I see you have misread certain lessons. You must help yourself. Or ask that young—" The historian-and-bookman bit back his spite; he was in fact a little jealous of what he took to be the barber-and-man's success with his student.

Elise ignored his unspoken jibe and said simply, in the hoarse voice that he still found exciting: "There's trouble brewing."

"When is it not? The brew is history: without it I should have no job."

"This is not history, Munshiji, this is politics."

"The moment it sees light, madam, politics becomes history."

"But we are still in the dark, Munshiji. And it will touch us both."

"I am too old to care. And you are almost too young. But you are right. It is to be faced, I suppose."

"So what am I to do?"

"I have already told you." Nishan Chand waved his spectacles again at the shelves.

"The old lessons?"

"The same."

"For today?"

The munshi inclined his head and smiled. "Yes, for today. The solutions never change. Only the problems are new."

"Then the answer is already in my tower?"

"Best of students."

"Panditji."

Elise returned to her room and sat in silence at her escritoire, meditating on the future and running an eye absently along the bookshelf nearest her. On an impulse she reached across and took down a banana-leaf manuscript kept in a turmeric-coloured napkin. It was Aditya Muni's *Forest Discourses*, which she opened at the famous passage beginning: *O daughter of the sky-city* and ending *weep, for weeping consoles the heart, bathes the eyes, and purifies the crown (royal mind)*. Jarman Begam felt a stirring of sorrow in her belly. It rose in convoluted reams, mounted to her throat, and she began to weep for her lost husband, for her lost father, for a certain packed trunk, for an unfinished Sans Souci. For thirty minutes she wept, dabbing her eyes with a rose-stained handkerchief and marvelling at the new and not unpleasant sensation. Then, much relieved, she bent over a basin, splashed her face with water, and patted her forehead with cologne.

Next she took down a rice-paper scroll of the fourteenth-century Suko-Thai commune called Sangwat or Songwat, in which every other line was written by a fresh hand so that no work might be attributable to any one author. The work had no title, as befitted the product of a convent without a head, beginning simply: *the task divided is the task made light/ the sister who has not learnt trust/ wishes to become a mother-superior (she-dog) in the barn/*. Elise was advancing to the fourth line when she heard a sound like the stropping of a razor. She looked up. There was somebody outside her door. A sharp knock followed.

Elise's fingernail made a nick in the scroll and she bared her teeth instinctively in a snarl of fear. The thought—ludicrously inapposite—flitted through her mind that her nails wanted cutting, and immediately she recalled that Fonseca had left behind a pair of nail scissors the last time he was up; she could see them on the dressing table from where she sat. But who could it be out there? Rekha was not in the habit of knocking. Should she pretend she was not in? But today was a day for breaking down doors. She must take courage in her hands, brave the enemy; he might even prove an ally. She stood undecided nevertheless. Then she crossed the room, took up the scissors, and going to the door, drew back the latch.

How suspense is made

I wish to shew how suspense is made. Fear not, good adept. For this experiment you need no materials from J.c. Solomon & Son, who it is true are no longer in the main bazar but conveniently located all the same across from the Residency, just where the road turns away. Do not go farther, for then you will fall into the clutches of that evil bania, Rakesh, who sells clanking chains and creaking doors. For this experiment you need only that which you draw upon first entering the world. For suspense, good adept, this God-given material—namely breath—is either held or drawn sharply. That is all. The heart will be found to rise as far as the mouth, but do not be alarmed, not excessively. This is what I wished to shew. So do that. Do it and praise God. However, if this recourse should prove inadequate, J.c. Solomon & Son have a wide variety of Gothic, Visigothic, and Gosi-vathek novels which are cheap, glossy, and guaranteed to have the desired effect. Praise God.

(CHRONICLE RESUMED)

Fonseca stood in the doorway. He had lost the jesting face he customarily brought upstairs with him, and in its place he wore the look of a cornered bandicoot, his black cheeks gone grey though he had just run up two hundred and forty steps.

"Madam!"

"Fonseca!" (*Where were you, Fonseca?*) "Oh, Fonseca, he's gone!"

"Madam?"

"Dead, Fonseca, dead! Don't you know? Weren't you there?"

"Then you've seen him?" Fonseca pointed down the stairwell.

There was a charged silence in which Jarman Begam absorbed this piece of news.

"What do you mean, Fonseca—my husband *there?*" She coloured at the word *husband*, and Fonseca, who had hitherto only read about the phenomenon in novels, regarded her cheeks with a moment's aesthetic detachment.

"The Colonel, madam? No, no—I mean the body downstairs—*him*. He's *dead*." It was the first time Fonseca had seen a corpse.

Another silence travelled down the stairwell.

"Fonseca, the *Colonel* is dead, dead and gone. What is all this about his body?"

It was now the barber-and-man's turn for astonishment. "Colonel Trotter? *Dead?* But how—then it *is* him down there?" Fonseca was so terrified his cheeks took on a yellowish mottling. Could he have failed to recognize the face he had shaved every day until today—four thousand times at the least—until he knew every pore and follicle and fold on its surface?

"Colonel Trotter," he mouthed. "*That*—down there?"

"Down where, Fonseca? Please compose yourself."

"Madam, he's changed somehow, changed in death. He looks more like that poulterer, that egg-brahmin."

"Fonseca, have you taken leave of your senses?" (*Oh, Fonseca, why are you leaving, have I been unkind; has Trot?*) "Will you kindly explain once and for all what you mean?"

The hairdresser drew himself up and pointed with one hand.

"Madam. There is a body"—his fingers played a downward arpeggio in the air—"a dead body—at the bottom of your stair. It is at the landing that gives onto the Audience Hall."

"But it can't be. He fell into the canal. That broad one at the edge of Sans Souci."

"The Colonel fell out of his balloon?"

"Yes. I thought you were there." A note of accusation crept into Jarman Begam's voice.

"Madam," Fonseca replied, "this body has not fallen. Much less from a balloon. And not at all from a balloon into your tower."

But already Elise was on her way down. "Come with me, Fonseca," she ordered, and taking his hand, hurried down the South Tower for the second time that afternoon. She had not descended twenty steps when she stopped and, brushing past Fonseca, mounted them again. Returning to her bookshelf she took down a massive volume bound in crocodile-skin. It was Ibn-i-qasim's *Mirror of State* and *Cup of State*. With it under her arm, she rejoined the barber-and-man, who was standing there in utter disarray.

It had just come home to Fonseca, despite his burning hand, that he would never carry to Calcutta a letter of reference from the renowned Colonel Trotter of Nakhlau.

A barge worked by fifteen oarsmen was making its way up the Moti Ganga. The boat's owner, who was also its pilot, stood at the prow frowning attentively at the dun expanse of water ahead. Somewhere here was a wrinkle in the current which marked the approach of a shelf of rock. Beyond the shelf the river turned a corner, and it was at that corner, on the other bank, that the Kirani river flowed into the Moti Ganga. The boat must cross over to the deep water just beyond the rock shelf or face a tiresome hour in the shallows trying to double back without being swept past the mouth of the lesser river. There was also the risk of an encounter with the Nawab's river patrol. Formerly, an understanding had existed, but in recent years, as the Nawab and his former Commander-in-Chief grew older and apart, the tax-collector had turned greedy.

The crossing was made and no Nawabi boat appeared. Slipping into the Kirani river, the oarsmen felt the current slacken and leaned gratefully on the oars.

"Don't stop there, you loafers!" the captain bellowed, but his voice could not conceal his pleasure at having arrived.

The men, their minds occupied with money and food and wives, ignored him. They began one by one to sing, not the tuneless rowing chant—*chal ho ama-ho kheench, chal ho ama-ho kheench*—that had brought them all the way from Calcutta, but a local catch sung by the fisher-folk of these parts.

(VERSE)

> By Moti Ganga Heron sits
>   Daylong making plunder,
> Barbed Tengan fish lets loose his dart
>   Dingdong both go under.

The boat drew up against the Sans Souci jetty, and the crew, raucous with laughter and singing, began to unload the cargo: seven large pinewood crates. The captain leapt onto the jetty and walked up and down humming. Above, the sun had declined and the sky was a doubtful colour neither white nor gold nor blue. Around the jetty the sandbanks suggested rubbed bronze, and the marsh beyond still wore a rippling heat haze through which the distant stones of *Sungum* danced and shifted. On the other bank an arm of silt was stippled with newly planted sugar-cane; beyond it the Moti Ganga ran like treacle, and even its tributary had taken on the strange yellow half-light of the sky.

"Watch the sacking there, you! Leave it on!" the captain called. He turned to another man who had clambered up onto the jetty and was pretending to direct the operation. "Sutli, there won't be any horse-train. They've given up expecting us. Run over to the village and borrow a couple of bullock-carts. Say Tartar Sahib will pay."

He looked again across the marsh at *Sungum*. It glowed a cheerful quirky grey. In the sky above it there hung, no bigger than a dog's head, a white cloud. He hummed a little louder. Hari Om was looking forward to ringing the Ice Bell. He turned and walked to the end of the jetty, looking the other way now. Where the rivers joined, a long purple stain had come into the water. He laughed out loud. "The crop must have been a good one if they have enough *nil* to throw away."

Nil

NIL (see also ANIL), n. Indigo; the colour blue; the colour between blue and violet; blue dye extracted from plant of genus *Indigofera* (see INDIGO, INDIA); indigo cake or powder or other blue substance used by washermen (see DHOBI) in washing white garments or in dyeing white cloth blue (or indigo); aniline dye. 16th c. Hind. *nila*, blue; f. Sansk. *nili*, indigo.

1593 "Wee trust y^r Worshyppe will see ye profytte to bee hadde from ye sylke, pepper and *nil* trade." Terence Traherne to Lord Culver, *Letters*, p. 12.

1601 "Fulle rightlie doe the Portugeese call this substance Indigo, for *nil* contayneth all ye numbers of Indian profytabilitie." Terence Traherne to Lord Culver, *Letters*, p. 212.

1694 "Negres coupant l'*Anil* ou Indigo." Illustration in Pierre Pomet's *Histoire Generale des Drogues*, Paris, 1694.

1695 "*Nil desperandum.*" (conjec.) Lady Culver to Terence Traherne, *Letters*, vol. II, p. 12.

1799 "The crop must have been a good one if they have enough *nil* to throw away." Boatmaster to himself, *Trotter-Nama*, p. 85.

"Trot!"

The cry had no sooner escaped Jarman Begam's lips than she saw her mistake. She checked her impulse to smooth the puckered forehead beneath her hand, and took a step back, brushing as she did against Fonseca, who had been peering at the body in the cupboard from behind her. He gave a little jump which he turned into a gesture of protection.

"You see?" he whispered. "It's not the Colonel. It's that egg-brahmin, what's-his-name."

"Sunya." Jarman Begam knew the name of every inhabitant of Sans Souci.

"Sunya, of course. But it doesn't look like him either. I mean, he was brown—well, brown with those white patches he had developed. This man is all white. It *is* the poulterer, isn't it?"

Sunya's maculation was gone.

"It was."

"It's like—someone—completely *new*."

Elise looked out through an embrasure in the tower. The surface of the Tank was glassy again; it might never have been disturbed by a row of instruments jettisoned from a balloon. Its midday black had softened to violet, and the blanched floury dust on its banks had absorbed some evening gold.

"That's history for you, Fonseca," she murmured. She seemed to have lost interest in the body.

"Madam?"

"The problems are always new."

"The—problems—?"

"The solutions remain the same."

"Madam," Fonseca bowed. To himself he said, she's come unhinged with grief, poor girl, a realization that seemed to improve his own spirits. He was growing accustomed to the corpse now, and the presence of another person with him in the room turned his awe to irreverence. He began to regard Sunya as a present but junior party in the deliberations, a party to be seen but not heard, dumb rather than dead, the death a sham.

"All the same," he continued, "what is our friend doing dead? And why has he chosen your tower to do it in?"

Elise did not reply. She stepped across to the door, opened it, looked into the hall, shut it again, and drew the bolt. Then she sat down on the lowest step but one and, leaving Fonseca to pace in a semicircle between stair and cupboard, opened Ibn-i-qasim on her lap. She ran the tip of her finger down the index with which Townshend had thoughtfully furnished his translation, and coming to the word *succession*, read after it the page numbers, in Indian numerals: 6, 21, and 1799. The first two of these referred to a youthful Qasim's *Mirror of State*, the last to an older man's *Cup of State*. Turning to the nearest of the references, Elise found it uncut and tore along the fore-edge with a glassy little finger. She read: *Even as the cup passes from hand to hand, so each king, drink he never so deep, is but its steward* (Elise trembled at the word) *the vessel greater than he, outlasting him, passing to the next in line and then the next, until the banquet hall itself be empty, blown leaves its shifting royalty*. At page 21, she read: *for who but a ghoul would inhabit a charnel-house, who of the Faith dwell in a mausoleum?* And at page 6: *Look long in the obedient glass, O Sovereign; when you are gone the palace ape may command in it his royal portrait. Death is a tardy leveller; the mirror is more quick (lively)*.

Fonseca brought his arcuate pacing to a halt half-way between the still heads of Sunya and Jarman Begam.

"Madam," he began, "we cannot—any of us"—he gestured all round with a nervous scissors-finger—"remain here indefinitely. And since it is not in our friend's power to go, I would suggest—"

"Fonseca, can you have forgotten? Colonel Trotter is dead."

Fonseca had forgotten: the fact was of such awkward proportions that, unable to accommodate it, he had simply shut it out and turned to matters in hand. Conscious of a larger unease, he had slipped into the levity of a polished hairdresser; rebuked, he became irritable.

"Madam, I have not forgotten. But if he is dead, not all the magic in a hundred books—supposing you could read them before nightfall—will bring him back to life."

"I cannot bring him back to life, Fonseca, but it is just possible we can make his rest a peaceful one."

"Then we must set about finding *his* body and leave the poulterer's to its fate."

"I've told you, the Colonel fell into the canal five hours ago. If anything remains of his body, it will be on its way down to the sea."

Fonseca's eyes began to widen again. "But how did it happen?" His voice ran up high. "And how do you know?"

"A sudden turbulence in the upper air." Jarman Begam remembered the little joke about America she had meant to try on the hairdresser. It was like flat soda-water on the tongue. "The balloon was swept off course," she continued. "It came directly over this tower instead of continuing in a circle around Sans Souci. The same wind's ceasing must have upset the gondola over the canal. Trot fell out of his balloon, but he died of drowning."

"Madam." Fonseca's voice was a rush of wind. "You saw all this happen?"

"I saw one half of it. I saw him pass over my tower."

"And the rest?"

"Munshiji saw the rest."

"He alone?"

"Yes."

"Then there are only two who know?"

"All Sans Souci knows he is dead. But only we know how."

"And him?" Fonseca indicated Sunya's corpse.

Jarman Begam looked at Sunya as if it was he who had spoken. "He," she replied, addressing the dead man across immeasurable time, "is the first casualty of a minor struggle at the edge of insignificance. If we are careful, he will be the last."

Fonseca turned from the bleached cadaver and looked at Jarman Begam with a new respect. "Madam," he repeated, without a trace of his habitual banter. "I am at your service."

"Then you must go without delay to the Colonel's tower and fetch down a suit of his clothes—the usual ones. Don't trouble with a wig."

"Yes, madam." Fonseca spun on his heel and made for the door. Death was absorbed into duty, and for some reason his heart had begun to sing. He longed to obey, utterly and without question.

"Wait, Fonseca."

"Madam!" The hairdresser stood at attention.

"There is something we had better do first."

Jarman Begam opened wide the almirah door. Peering in, she saw a silver tumbler placed beside Sunya. She picked it up, passed it under her nose, and handed it to Fonseca. He examined the contents, a ring of milky green at the bottom.

"It's mango-fool!" he exclaimed.

"With a pinch of something added, I would think—by no friend. It's a silvered tumbler, and Sunya who is—who was—a Hindu, would have used nothing but brass."

The barber-and-galiant nodded knowingly. He sniffed at the tumbler and said: "It smells like my green pomade!"

"Fonseca."

"Truly, madam. In Goa I have known ladies—clients, you understand, in the line of business—who insist that their hair be treated with a lotion that smells very much like this. It is distilled from green mangoes."

"That is most interesting, Fonseca, but we must now attend to Sunya. Before the owner of this tumbler comes back to claim what is his."

"But why do we need to tamper with this body? It's none of our doing, none of our business. Leave him here: he'll be found."

Elise looked at the barber-and-adventurer and shook her head.

"Fonseca, whom do you suppose the suit of clothes is for?"

"Which—oh that!—oh—*Oah*—" Fonseca let the scheme sink in; in his eagerness to be of use he had not understood. He returned Jarman Begam's level gaze, one of his eyebrows rising slowly. He did not know whether to be afraid of this woman.

"Come," she said. "We must now conceal Sunya from his concealer. We cannot carry him upstairs unassisted." She paused. "Do you know the way to the tahkhana, Fonseca?"

"Of course, madam. I was up and down there with books for the Colonel a hundred times a day until I invented the dumb-waiter. There's nothing down there. Apart from a marble plinth. It was there, you may recall, that the Colonel had his ice epiphany. The room connects with the Glacerie."

"Then we must take Sunya there. It's down your stair, is it not? We shall have to risk the hall, but we must keep to the shadows and remember not to speak."

———

Yakub tossed a coin at the buffalo-girl who was frolicking in the river and swung a spindly leg over the halvai's pony. Shaken out of an afternoon nap, the creature would not budge. The baker-and-master-gelder leaned over and whispered two sinister syllables into its ear, and the animal broke into a terrified gallop. In less than half an hour it was standing rigidly outside the halvai's shop as Yakub picked himself up out of the dust. The halvai did not detain Yakub with offers of sweets (*Prudent Mansoor*) and without waiting for a cup of water, the baker-and-Chief Steward crossed the Ice Bridge and made his way to *Sungum* along the Trotter Road.

He was nearing the sunken garden (where the water in the fountains no longer flowed uphill) when a voice hailed him from the saltpetre hill just below the *Salamandre*'s launching towers. A muscular figure in a white cotton tunic and cloth cap to match was waving excitedly as he half ran, half tumbled down the glacis.

"Yakub! Yakub! Ama-hoi, Yakub!"

It was the herbalist. His dyed beard wobbled and his breath came in spurts.

"Yakub! Tartar Sahib is still missing. I know, I know, I hung the flag out but what to do—that illegitimate Sunya came to me and lied about having found the body. I tell you, he's nowhere to be found! In the desert, he says, between the Tank and the aerolite, but I swear there was nothing there. And what do you think—he himself has gone and disappeared. I gave him some mango sharbat with a bit of powder and he lay down happily enough. Then I put him in the nearest almirah and went to hang out that flag. Hai! my poor legs—not what they used to be. Kushti, kabaddi—you name it, I was champion. But now. *He is there*, he says, *I saw him with these eyes*. So I run God knows how many steps up to Tartar Sahib's quarters. Then down again, then two miles, four maybe, to the painted rock. Nothing, I'm telling you, nothing. No Tartar Sahib. Looking here, looking there—in every thicket, every tree. Not one shoe, not even a button—oh—just a strange hatching machine. Gave it up. Two miles, maybe four, running all the way back in case you were waiting, my lungs like cactus. I tell you I was ready to kill Sunya. But when I get back to the almirah, what do I see? Nothing. Where I left him—nothing, no Sunya, not even my tumbler. So I run straight to his house in the village. His wife says she hasn't seen him since he went looking for Tartar Sahib— going to teach him a lesson when he gets home. What a woman, my God! Then I ran back up to Tartar Sahib's tower to take down the flag— in case you hadn't seen it yet. When I get to the window, what do I see? Nothing—no flag. What could I do? I came running to the *Zalmandar* to look for you—you said you couldn't leave it—running uphill, my legs, my God, and then—*nothing*! Even you were not there. So I waited and just as well I looked down this way. What heat! It was cooler in Arabia. To think I wasted that mango sharbat on that infidel. But Yakub, you're covered in dust! What's the matter? You look as if it was you that fell out of the balloon. Surely you didn't trip just getting out of the basket? Sorry. Well, there's nothing left but to find that lying poulterer. We'll rattle his eggs till he tells us where Tartar Sahib is."

"Tartar Sahib, Tartar Sahib! The devil take Tartar Sahib."

"Yakub!"

"Must we track him down to hell?"

"*Yakub!*"

"Look, Hakimji. Tartar Sahib is not our quarry."

The herbalist was too taken aback to reply. He looked at Yakub and then back up at the *Salamandre* as if trying to put the two together and start all over again.

"Did you call off the hunt?" Yakub asked shortly.

"Well, I thought—"

"No matter."

The men passed under a giant silk-cotton tree and instinctively slowed their pace in its shade. The ground beneath their feet was strewn with tufts of white silk and crushed scarlet flowers of a heavy narcotic odour; a sparrow lay drunk in the dust.

"Bhai, Yakub. One minute you—"

"Never mind. How are things with the bibis?"

"They have learnt about it. There's weeping in both towers—it could be heard up on the hill."

"And the other one, the *Begam* so-called?"

"She could not but know. Yet the South Tower is silent."

"So. Nawab Sahib may have been right."

"*Nawab* Sahib!" the herbalist repeated. His eyes said: *You* know the *Nawab* Sahib! and rolled up as his jaw went down.

"Yes," said Yakub lightly. "We were conferring just now—he sent for me. That's why I was not at the *Zalmandar*." He quickened his pace once more, and the herbalist fell into step with him, a shoulder's width behind.

"So," Yakub continued. "You've drugged a son of the soil and lost a firangi. Let's see if you can catch something in between." His tone had the vibration of a taunt.

Hakimji frowned uncomprehendingly. "*Me?* But *you* were the one— what—how do you mean, Yakub?"

A stoop that had nothing to do with the sun on his back had come into his manner.

Fonseca ran trembling up his master's stair. The portage through the Audience Hall had been a hair-raising business, every careless footstep drawn up into the vaulted ceiling and dropped with a clatter on the far side, as if somebody were bursting in at the Indigo Door. When the little party reached the West Tower, Jarman Begam had again shocked the hairdresser. Still smoking in his memory was the sight of an ankle which flashed like a razor from under her gown, drew back, steadied itself, and with a quick thrust sent Sunya tumbling down the stone stairwell to the tahkhana. Fonseca had turned and fled, the sound of a reedy voice reverberating in his head, rising above the flesh-and-bone thuds of a body rolling down sixty steps: "Remember, he has fallen from a great height, Fonseca!"

Fonseca had never travelled so swiftly to the Great Trotter's chambers. He mechanically brought together the suit of clothes of his errand, his breath coming and going like a wrestler's. For the first time he had not knocked when entering; leaving, he might have been a thief. At his own landing he hesitated. A desire swept over him to turn left instead of right, to return to his room, take up his trunk and horn box and flee. The stables would be unattended. In his hands was a suit of Muslim clothes; a quick change and he could slip away unrecognized. Through the hall door he heard his misplaced footsteps roam the vaulted ceiling. He looked down at the blue Nakhlau cape in his hands and wondered with a shudder how he should look in native dress. Darker than any man at Sans Souci, Fonseca had yet never worn anything but a frock-coat and breeches. He could change back into them once he got to Calcutta. He looked out through a slit in the turret wall. The drive wound through the dusty gardens, past the dusty maze, and out through the Gunpowder Gate to meet the Trotter Road. The evening sky was what he imagined was a Mediterranean blue, the blue of that sea where it meets the Atlantic, but Fonseca had never seen the passage to Lisbon.

A voice spoke in his ear: Go, Fonseca! Sail away! Leave these changeling bodies: you are an aesthete, not a mortician. Beauty calls, all Calcutta waits. They have not heard of beauticians: you, Wilfred Ignatius Albuquerque Fonseca, will found the first modern beauty parlour in the Orient. Ladies will flock to your door, throng your porches, swoon in your verandahs. Take Fortune by the forelock—clip it for your keeping. First an hirsute establishment in Chowringhee to rival Andretti's of Bombay, then the parlour, then another parlour with ice cream and strings and horn on Sunday afternoons, and why stop there? A Bow Bazar theatre, a concert hall, with troupes of Lisbon dancers, Hungarian gipsies, Peking acrobats, actresses from London, sopranos from Vienna; a Fonseca ballroom, a Fonseca skating rink, Fonseca billiard rooms, a Fonseca band pavilion, and on until the very name means quality entertainment, and a verb is born: *to Fonseca, to have Fonsecaed, let us Fonseca this night away.*

Fonseca turned left and made for his room. The door was open though he had not left it so. He peered in, feeling more than ever like an intruder. The door of his almirah was shut, though he had not left it so. (*Go back, Fonseca! Take trunk and horn and go!*) He crossed to the empty wardrobe. The mirror was wiped clean. He looked in it: it gave back a narrow pale reflection, nothing like his own, and incredulously he rubbed his cheeks. Then he saw a pair of eyes, pale like the face, and ice-green. He took a half-step back and in one bound made the door. When he shut it behind him, the trunk and horn box were on the inside.

"Later," he whispered. "Tomorrow."

"It's nothing. Simply give her this message from the Nawab Sahib: that he is grieved to learn of his Commander-in-Chief's death; that he has been building, ever since Colonel Tartar's illness of ten years ago, a tomb with which to honour his friend when the lamentable hour of his death should arrive; and that it having pleased God that that hour be upon us, the Nawab's chief wife wishes to comfort the Jarman Begam and open wide the doors of the Fish Palace to her. That is all. A child could remember it, and you are a learned doctor."

Yakub was being especially courteous, as was his practice when in a rage. He addressed the herbalist with the politest forms, as *he* instead of *you*, though he would have liked to *thou* him and more. As his temper rose, his manner became increasingly formal and his speech waxed exquisite.

"Boon companion, I cannot possibly go to her so begrimed."

"Yakub, look, it's best if you go." Hakim Ahmed had begun to sweat again though he sat in the cool of the Cock Hall or Spur, where Yakub's quarters were. "She sends for me only when she needs some arrowroot or something," he pleaded.

"Indeed, and who but an herbalist to spread balm on her present sorrow?"

"Yes, but it's you who know the Nawab, not I."

"Certes. But, esteemed friend, surely you know of her aversion to me. It is proverbial—unjust perhaps, but constant. Nor does she trouble to conceal it from me, while for you she has always a fair word. *That erudite physician*, she said the other day when I chanced to drop your name."

"Well," the herbalist said. He looked this way and that, then directly at Yakub as if an idea had just struck him. "I'll go." He was anxious not to appear browbeaten and spoke carelessly. "But there had better be something in this for me. Already—"

"Vintage friend, of course there will be. As a token, you shall have the use of a carriage whenever it pleases you. The Nawab himself will be eager to meet his nuntio."

"Very well. How does it go? *The Nawab's chief wife wishes to comfort the Jarman Begam . . .*"

". . . *and open wide the doors of the Fish Palace to her. That is all.*"

". . . *and open wide the doors of the Fish Palace to her. That is all.*"

"No, no—*to her. That is all.*"

"That's what I said, Yakub. Never fear, leave it to me." The hakim tossed his head, wishing to buy back his independence with a show of resolution. "Where is she?" he demanded breezily.

Yakub beamed. "Where she always is: in her tower! Have you known her to leave it?"

"There is one more task for you, Fonseca," said Jarman Begam, "before we summon the others."

She stood by her handiwork in the tahkhana, regarding it with a dispassionate eye. The Great Trotter lay between them, serene despite the bruises of his fall, and shrunken from the loss of his wig and slippers.

It was dark in the room. The mirror tube, although switched on, was fading, and the only other light came from a candle. The high marble plinth in the centre of the tahkhana was spread with the Great Trotter's blue-and-green standard, which had been found flapping out of the topmost window in the West Tower. Laid out on the flag was the Great Trotter himself, his hands folded on his breast. The candle, set in a brass stick, burned at his head, illuminating the pale crown and forehead; when its flame leapt in the watery darkness, it caught the rims of the coins that weighed down the eyelids, and a button at the right shoulder. It flickered on the folds of a jacket whose silk border flashed kingfisher blue. The white muslin kurta-pyjama floated greyly, its chikan embroidery not visible at all. Already the cell smelt of death.

"You must go to the Glacerie to fetch some ice. It's your preserve, is it not? It does not matter if you are seen—in fact you might wish to show yourself to anybody who happened by."

"Madam," Fonseca replied. "I'm sorry to disappoint you. I was there this very afternoon. To say the stocks had run low would be to misstate the case. It's been a bad year. I'm afraid the last of the ice went up in Colonel Trotter's masak."

"So much the better, Fonseca. Your task is made lighter."

"I need not go?"

"Indeed you must."

"To the Glacerie, to fetch no ice?"

"Precisely. I wish it known that the Colonel is to be buried this same night. That the heat will not allow delay. And while you are there, making the lack of ice plentifully known and visible—some witnesses would be in order—you could send to the village for Yusuf the carpenter. And to the city for Father Angelico—no, leave that to me."

"Excuse me, madam, but Colonel Trotter was a—was he not a Moslem?"

"You mean because he kept—because he had four wives?"

"I did not mean that, madam, but as you know he had ceased to practise his childhood faith."

"He had not replaced it with Mohammedanism," Jarman Begam replied slowly. "You are thinking of his clothes." She waved a hand. "One does not simply put on a religion, Fonseca, or one might just as easily take it off."

"I was thinking of the popular impression. His servants would have it so. And then there was his new faith, the Din Havai."

"I did hear something of it from that Qaiyum. *An amalgam of half-doubts*, he called it. A mixture of many faiths, at any rate, not just one." Elise started to go, as if closing the issue. "But perhaps you are right," she said, turning. "Let us have an imam present, and read both services over this unfortunate man."

"It will look well," the barber agreed softly.

"It will do more, Fonseca. It will placate certain quarters, and strengthen our position."

For the first time that day Fonseca saw Elise smile. It was an odd smile, and the hairdresser, who had been looking for courage to dip his practiced hand in the corn-silk tresses so familiar to him, retreated. "Madam," he bowed. "I shall send for Hakim Ahmed. He is not an imam, but he has been to Mecca and can officiate."

"Very good. Precedence can be found for it, I'm sure. And I will send for Yakub Khan and have him announce that Tartar Sahib's body is found and lying in state."

Elise began to mount the stair, hitching up the hem of her gown and stooping short-sightedly. She seemed to the barber-and-Ice Manager to have tapped some buried lode of energy that gleamed in her eyes and crackled in her hair. Her manner of tucking in her kerchief at the wrist as she left was alarmingly practical. Fonseca, who was not a practical man, had an idea and at once called after her. She stopped a short way up the curving stair and turned, peering down at him. In the half-dark she looked like a stalactite.

"We will want gravediggers, madam."

Something like the hoarse chuckle of ice-cubes in a masak made its way down to the barber-and-entertainer.

"The grave is already prepared, Fonseca."

"Already?"

"Yes."

"But where——?"

"You are standing in it, Fonseca."

*On the correct manner of harvesting ice in Quebec and Massachusetts,
North America*

I wish to shew how ice is harvested in Massachusetts and Quebec, territories of North America. Good adept, choose any sweetwater pond. If a road
go by it, so much the better. If there be a Hudson's Bay Company store
nearby, that is good also. To transport tools from J.c. Solomon & Son (who
are in their new premises beyond the Residency banyan tree, just where the
road turns away) is no little affair. It can be managed, but until negotiations
are completed and what is called a *mail-order catalog* put out, costs will be
high. Meanwhile, the tools you need may be had from the store mentioned,
but be warned that they are not cheap. You cannot expect Solomon prices in
exotic parts. Better to canvass the local farmers, Québécois or Massachusettsians, and rent or borrow their tools. Do not fear competition; they will think
you mad. They know wheat, hops, oats, beet, and barley. If it be winter, you
must bide your time though deep in ice. Divert the farmers, entertain their
wives, tickle their daughters, dandle their infants, wallop their brats. Many
have never seen a dark man before; use care. Test their justly renowned
patchwork quilts, try the maple fudge of December, the pralines of January,
the sugarplums of February, but refuse the black puddings of March. When
spring is one month distant, bundling time is done. Do not delay, for once
the wife with fervour switch the feather-tick it be already spring and the
farmer will not be parted from his tools. Borrow from one a saw, from one
a groover, from one a snath, from one a sled, from one a spokeshave, from
one a cold chisel, from one a crow, from one a rope, from one a chain, from
one a ramp, from another mules. (At home, all may be had from J.c.) On a
sharp clear day before the thaw, helpers being present, remove all snow from
the pond's surface. When the ice is bare make there a grid of squares, neither
too small nor too large but just medium, and commence to cut. Begin at the
corner nearest the road, if a road go by; if not, at that corner nearest the sled.
When sawing, sharp adept, stand on the white side of the blade, viz. not on
the chosen block. Old hands have made this fatal error. Gather up the blocks;
sled, dray, or ferry them to the nearest port. A wide selection of maps may
be had beforehand from J.c. & Son. The ships in port there have stones for
ballast in the hold. Do not reason with the captains; they will think you mad.
Your ship holds no stones; its captain, the redoubtable Daud Dickason of

Rangoon, is smiling secretly. Fill it with Quebec ice (or Massachusetts ice), insulate with hessian, pelts, or wood-chips, and having packed also the customary temperate produce, such as apples, strawberries, etc., just above the ice, set sail for Calcutta. Do not linger, stout adept, at the Equator; do not linger in Calcutta. Load the cargo at once onto a barge and hie you upriver. And this is what I wished to shew. So do it swiftly and praise God. Ponds, like sunshine and air, belong to Him. In Calcutta local ice is two rupees a seer and gone by July; upriver it is even more, and yours is foreign. Praise God.

(CHRONICLE RESUMED)

"Oh good, Hakimji, you have come."

"You were expecting me, memsahib!" Hakim Ahmed's jaw slackened. He had trusted the advantage of surprise to be his.

"Yes, of course. Fonseca sent you here, did he not?"

"Fonseca, memsahib? You mean Yakub—that is to say—the Nawab Sahib—I mean—it having pleased God . . ." The herbalist-and-dentist's voice trailed off into a yawn. When he was nervous he yawned and snapped his fingers in his mouth.

"Hakimji, what's the matter? Is something wrong? You look as if you've seen a ghost. Can I order something for you to drink—some mango-fool perhaps? I'm sorry to have troubled you on such a day. But, tell me, what is this about the Nawab Sahib and Yakub and God?"

"He's here—that is—I was just talking with him—"

"Which of them is here, Hakimji? With whom were you just talking?"

"Memsahib, the Nawab Sahiba has been building—she would like to express her—Yakub says—the Nawab Sahib would like to open the doors of his tomb—it having pleased God . . ." Hakim Ahmed's message hung in wisps, a frayed web spun by an inexpert spider. Even as he toiled he was ashamed of his performance; Yakub would never have faltered, but his tunic was muddied and he was unpopular.

Jarman Begam preserved a long silence. The hakim, with the faith of a petty schemer, began to persuade himself that his guile was after all invisible, that his words had not reached her: they had blown about the room and he was free to start again as if he had never spoken.

"Memsahib—"

"Hakimji," Jarman Begam interposed. Her voice was brittle, as if she were the older party. Hakim Ahmed fell silent. He was a strong man with a good digestion. Unlike Yakub, who was dyspeptic and morose and inclined to blame his wind on mental agitation beyond his control, the herbalist knew to find relief, on those rare mornings when he woke belching, in a few strategic sips of raw milk. Now he felt a bubble growing in his tube which would want a sterner remedy.

"Concerning the Nawab Sahib and Sahiba," Elise continued, "it is best if you do not exercise yourself unduly. Medicine is a noble profession; that is your proper sphere. Concerning Yakub Khan, I should like you to send him to me when you leave. I have an announcement for him to make; that is his proper sphere. Concerning God: now that is why I have sent for you."

Instead of going at once to the Glacerie, Fonseca paused again at his landing. He did not have his trunk and horn box in mind, but he was drawn back to his room all the same. The Elise who had just left him seemed so transformed from the figure in the almirah mirror, he had begun to doubt whether the two were one and the same person. He knocked softly at his own door, he did not know why, and when there was no answer, let himself in. The crossing to the almirah was an eternity, each footstep sinking into the flags until he stood before the mirror rooted in stone. No trace remained of the green eyes or the pallid face. The mirror returned his own image: a man of forty with sunken eyes and a borrowed shirt.

A bell is ringing somewhere, thought the barber as his eyes roamed the glass. That's the beginning of a paunch, Fonseca (*it's a bell you've heard before; it touches you, unlike the vulgar clang of the breakfast bell which you routinely ignore, or the brass din of tiffin or the solemn dinner gong*). Ah, a grey hair missed in your eyebrow (*it's not a clock or a church bell*); the nose might have been better done (*it's not a cowbell or an elephant bell*); tobacco will spoil those teeth, Will (*it's not a tocsin or a plague clapper*); that was your master's shirt (*it's not his call bell or his hall bell*); you're bathed in sweat, Will (*it's not a winter bell or even a monsoon bell*).

What is it then? the reflection asked. It's a once-yearly sound (*but it's been longer than a year*), an early summer sound (*but this is late*), a May sound (*but this is June*). It has a sparkling note (*where ordinary bells are dull*), it is sharp cold crystalline pellucid, between a tinkle and a splash, a mirror shattering on stone and leaving a pool of silvered sand.

"The Ice Bell!" Fonseca spoke out loud. He shook his head free and looked out of the window. A ledge of cloud lay just above the horizon, level on top and jagged below; underneath, the last of the sun glowed like a cockscomb. "So the *Mandalay* did not miscarry. There'll be ice all summer."

Then he remembered his mission, and a chill crisped the wet folds of his shirt.

————

Yakub and Jarman Begam stood in silence, their faces turned to one side in an attitude of listening, as in a frieze. An oblong of gooseberry-green sky hung between them with two stars pricked into its upper quarter. When the bell stopped ringing, Yakub spoke first.

"It seems we shall have enough ice after all, memsahib." His voice was calm and stroked with satisfaction, though the sound of this bell had always been painful to him.

"If it *is* the Ice Bell, steward." Elise knew very well it was. "And," she struggled on, "if what you say of the required burial practice is correct—though I would not have called my husband a saint. These villagers are easily misled. I shall have to verify the business from Munshiji." She had no sooner spoken the name than she repented of it. She did not want another corpse, much less that of her mentor.

"He is a Hindu, memsahib. You are deceived by his clothes."

"But he knows the Koran and a great many Moslem texts by heart. Still, on second thoughts, we will not trouble him." She looked out into the gloaming. "He will in any case have gone home. I shall ask Hakim Ahmed of it; he is a devout Mussulman and has been to Mecca. Stay—he is not here. I have just this minute despatched him to the White Town to fetch Father Angelico, the Roman Catholic priest."

Yakub bridled. "Memsahib, Colonel Trotter was a Muslim."

Jarman Begam looked at him. "Perhaps you were deceived by his clothes, steward."

Yakub shifted again. "I had better go and supervise the ice delivery," he said.

"Fonseca is already there, steward. I believe he keeps the key to the godown."

"The carters will want paying," Yakub persisted. "Usually it is my horse-train that fetches the ice from the river."

"The ice account is managed by Fonseca, is it not?"

"Mismanaged, I would say."

Jarman Begam knew her steward spoke the truth. Yakub's own affairs were conducted with scrupulous correctness, the accounts balanced and never a coin mislaid. Monies that accrued to him, or which he deemed and deducted as his due, were not excessive considering the amounts that passed through his hands. Power, not profit, shone at the back of those part-Turkish hazel eyes. The further the baker-and-Chief Steward extended his reach, dismissing servants, shunting others, turning all he touched to iron, the more frugal he seemed to become. The horse carriage was simply a conveyance; it brought him to a new site for his ambition without the distraction of having to fuss with reins while getting there. If it looked impressive, that was not a bonus to be enjoyed but an advantage to be pressed home. Beside this man, Fonseca was a smiling muddler, careful of nothing but his cravat, scented, extravagantly dressed for a man of his station, smoking expensive cigars, drinking (so Rekha had it) foreign liquors, forever buying curious ornaments from Armenian pedlars and itinerant jewellers. A strange assortment of trinkets had met Elise's eye when she opened his trunk—wind-chimes, cut-glass cups and polished stones, some valueless, some of inconceivable worth. Then there were the gifts he left in her tower, trivial but exotic, anonymous but certainly his: how should a barber come by them?

"Had this boat not come in," Yakub was saying, "the rest of the month would not have borne thinking of."

"You mean," Elise replied, "our cool drinks should not have tasted so well?"

Yakub did not blink. "True, memsahib. Nor the water. It would have been a painful summer, khas-khas-tatis and thermantidotes notwithstanding."

Khas-khas-tati, thermantidote

KHAS-KHAS-TATI, n. Screen of fragrant khas-khas (or cuscus) grass which set in doorway or window and sprinkled with water allows a cool moist draught pleasing to some.

THERMANTIDOTE, n. 1. Cooling hot-weather draught ("Phew! I could do with a *thermantidote*.") 2. Waiter serving or device generating this ("A fine pickle we're in—d'you suppose there's a *thermantidote* handy?" "Bearer!") 3. Sail fitted into window and flapped continuously to create a breeze; close relative of the punkah (see PANKHA) but westerly. 4. (rare) Delaying apparatus used in summer burials when waiting for priest (or priests) to arrive.

"Yes, the thermantidotes," said Jarman Begam.

Darkness had fallen. As if from a history book she remembered: Trot is dead. She rose from her chair.

"Well, steward. Hakim Ahmed and Father Angelico will be a while coming. Even if the ceremony is to be postponed there is enough to do. To begin with, you must announce the death."

"The death is already known, memsahib." Yakub made a laconic gesture at the window nearest him. From the East Tower came a broken keening, echoed in the North Tower.

"Even so," Elise said. "It must be formally announced. And also—what is not known—that the body has been found and is lying in state. You may use whichever bell you like—or the gun, *Urban*."

"It might confuse the populace and cause needless consternation."

"None that a speedy burial will not mend. But you are right—use the Audience Bell. That will summon them without ado. When they are gathered, cry it three times from the parapet. Those who wish to pay their last respects below must make themselves presentable. Children are to be left at home. It will be a brief viewing, as space is limited and time short. They must file down the stair, pass singly around the catafalque, and leave. No more than ten at one time on the stair. The doors will be shut when the priest and Hakimji arrive, and I will confer with them concerning the time of burial. If the ladies are not too disconsolate to budge, they may wish to attend. I will leave the asking to you; I believe you have their ear. Now I must go down to the Glacerie. Please light my way."

At the bottom of the stair, Jarman Begam took the candlestick from Yakub. She stepped briskly past the almirah where Sunya had been hidden earlier in the day, and entered the vast hall. The darkness was total except around her person; evidently the lamplighter, like all the other servants, had gone home.

Left in the dark, the baker-and-Chief Steward watched Elise glide across the marble floor, the candle held before her so that she threw back a silhouette gilded at the edges. At the centre of the hall, near the fountain, the candle guttered and Elise paused; the flame rose up brighter than before, and she went on her way, a white, black, and gold figure repeated on the polished floor.

Yakub turned away, congratulating himself that he needed no light to guide his way around Sans Souci. The darkness around him was so black and thick it stroked his skin like velvet when he moved. As he took a step away from the door of the South Tower, he heard behind him a throaty sound like a *cluck*. Then, much closer, another *cluck*. A voice squawked at his shoulder.

"Baker!"

Yakub spun around. He felt about him but there was nothing there. He turned again and looked the way Jarman Begam had gone. Two points of yellow light, one above the other, marked the spot where she stood on the other side of the hall at the Indigo Door.

Elise raised her voice and called again, setting up a chain of echoes near and far.

"If you see the poulterer—what is his name?—send him to me—*Sunya*!"
From every side came the haunting mockery: *-nya! -NYA! -nya!*

———

Hari Om, the boat's captain, had rung the Ice Bell as soon as the first of the bullock-carts drew up by the Glacerie. It was a rite he took immense pleasure in every year; he had even jumped off the lurching squeaking cart and run on ahead the last fifty yards to where the bell hung. The bell—it was actually a gong—hung outside the godown door on a slight eminence, a giant lens in which he enjoyed seeing himself reflected upside down. He thought of it as a cold sun whose rising marked the profitable end of a long journey, tedious in spite of its sudden dangers, worrisome in spite of his faith in·a barge for which he had paid good money. This particular evening, though the day had been long, the light had all but failed by the time he fronted the bell. He could barely make out the path of the mallet as it curved through the air—held by the right hand in the flesh, by the left in the image—and struck the translucent metal. The bell gave a glassy shudder, as if drawing in a breath before singing its note. Again and again Hari Om struck at an image that shivered and faded with every stroke. When he stopped, the image had split in two: Fonseca stood beside him.

The two men touched each other at the elbow formally, like colleagues who if they met oftener might be friends.

"Captainji."

"Manager Sahib!"

"Welcome." Fonseca's voice was strained, but the captain did not notice. Except to shout at his men, he had talked to no one since Calcutta.

"What a journey, what a journey, hé Ram, hé Ram!" Hari Om cried. "Longer than it's ever been, and that after waiting three weeks in the river's mouth just drifting up and down waiting for Tartar Sahib's ship, the men too getting restless, demanding pickles, chapatis instead of rice, I thought this time it's surely sunk, *Poor souls*, I was saying just at the moment when we spotted her flag, you ask Sutli, at the *very* moment I said that, *as* the words were leaving my lips, in comes the *Mandalay*! The men began to dance and wave, I tell you Managerji it was like the rains breaking! Not that we waited, no, loaded up the crates, here, check the firangi captain's bill of lading, loaded up the same afternoon and left, after paying the taxes, of course, firangi taxes, Nawabi taxes, taxes, taxes, at every bend in the river, even right here just now, the Nawab Sahib's men, and the heat, hé Ram, I tell you if ever an honest boatmaster worried about his cargo, I did, then I told myself, those foreign people that side they know how to pack their goods, straw, sawdust, wood-chips, who knows what, even animal skins, chhi-chhi-chhi! anyway, after that I didn't worry, not too much, I tell you, though, towards the end, actually after Benares or so, something was stinking in the crates, the men starting to complain, but nobody would touch the skins, so I gave them a good yelling, I said, You just pull a little harder and we'll get there sooner, you think I don't have a nose? so hurry home, hurry home, and here's Hari Om at last, thank God. Look at these scoundrels, will you, collapsing under the weight, Sutli, you rogue! Just look, you'd think he had the world on his shoulders, Managerji, maybe you'd better get some of your men to help."

"Captainji, one thing—Trotter Sahib is no more."

Hari Om's smile froze. He looked dumbly at Fonseca while his hands groped for the mallet hook. Behind him the grunts and shouts of the oarsmen-and-coolies sounded like a distant battle.

"Dead! *Tartar* Sahib?"

"Yes, Captainji. And what is more, your ice could not have arrived at a more awkward moment."

"But the payment, Managerji, all that freight, the taxes! I will be a ruined man." Hari Om steadied himself. "Forgive me." He wiped his upper lip. "When did he die?"

"This very day. That is the problem. It would have been better if you had come tomorrow."

"But already things are rotting. Two tons of ice were not enough to keep them fresh."

"Well, let us see. There's nothing we can do. They've opened a crate there."

Fonseca and Hari Om walked across to the Glacerie steps where a ramp had been laid down and a crate stood open on its side. The coolies around it were whispering. The barber-and-Ice Manager bent and looked into it. A pile of fur and wood-chips lay in the middle with a slack coil of rope wound aimlessly about them. Surrounding the island was a yellowish mulch of pears. The second crate was opened: another heap of pelts and wood-chips rose out of a bubbling lake of apple sauce. In the third crate was a kind of evil-smelling blackberry compote, in the fourth a porridge of strawberries, in the fifth a pool of rancid cheese, in the sixth a volatile puree of salmon, in the seventh a mess of chocolate. Hari Om darted from crate to crate, his amazement turning to oaths.

"Now you see," he shouted, "you sons of pigs, this is what comes of slacking at the oars, stuffing yourselves with chapatis, pickles, chutneys! Here's chutney for you piglets!"

The men, divided between awe and indignation, began to mutter.

"Who is he to talk?"

"Fat chapatis."

"Mildewed pickle."

"There was a spare oar."

"Rice!"

Grumbling, they made way for a slender figure in white carrying a candle.

"What is the matter, Fonseca?" said Jarman Begam.

Hari Om bowed. "Namaste, memsahib," he greeted her, instinctively changing his tack. "Memsahib, this cargo has been rotten ever since we loaded it on the boat." He turned to Fonseca to clarify a point. "It may have begun to stink *horribly* at Benares, but long before that it was already bad—no?" He turned to his men.

"Long before."

"Horrible it was."

"I would say at Patna."

"Patna? *Krishnanagar*."

"Calcutta."

"I could smell it even when we saw the sail coming in," confided Sutli.

Jarman Begam paid no attention to the chorus. She said, in her hoarse voice: "There is one crate left unopened, Captainji."

The last crate was opened. There were no pelts in it, no wood-chips, no rope. A small block of ice, no bigger than a dog's head, stood there glowing in the dark. Elise stooped and picked it up herself. She held it up against the candle and read its crystals, threaded longitudinally.

"Massachusetts," she pronounced, with the air of a diamond cutter.

"I would say Quebec, madam," said Fonseca. He took the ice from her and laid it on its side.

"Massachusetts, Fonseca," Jarman Begam repeated with some asperity, and she stood it upright once more on the barber-and-dialectician's palm. She looked at him. "Take good care of it, Mr Ice Manager—Sahib." And she turned and walked away.

Fonseca made as if to follow but stopped at the top of the steps leading to the godown. His hands parted a fraction and the ice block fell and smashed on the flagstones. The oarsmen gave a cry and Hari Om knelt at once and began to pick up the bigger pieces. A Sans Souci man rushed for a bucket. Hearing the commotion, Jarman Begam halted and came back. She ignored the pool already forming at her feet.

"Captainji, please don't bother. You will be paid in full. It must have been a hard journey. Your men will get a bonus from the Ice Manager Sahib. Meanwhile, take them to the kitchens and ask for all the chapatis and pickle you can eat. No—say I have ordered you puris. Steward, is that you?"

Yakub had come up.

"Will you see that these men are fed?"

Elise turned to Fonseca and walked him a few paces aside. "The crates are not to be touched tonight," she said. "Tomorrow before dawn you and the boatmaster must see that this mess is disposed of in the river. I think Sunya may be allowed a proper funeral after all." She looked down at where the hem of her gown felt chill and wet, and as if forgetful of Fonseca, she kicked an ice-chip down the steps to the godown. Once more Fonseca saw the ankle flash; in the moonlight it seemed an overture, and the barber-and-man was moved. A lump rose in his throat.

"And when you have paid these men," Elise continued, "will you bring the entire ice account—every ledger—to me?"

Holding up her candle once more, Jarman Begam returned the way she had come, leaving the men to wonder at their various fates.

The Great Trotter was buried that same night. Father Angelico came to sprinkle water and dab holy oil, and Hakim Ahmed read aloud from the Koran. Looking on were Rose Llewellyn Bibi, Farida Wilkinson Bibi, Yakub Khan, Fonseca, and Jarman Begam. Gathered around the plinth in the wavering yellow light, they were a curious company: Hakim Ahmed, muscular and earnest, his henna-dyed beard glowing as he recited scripture; Father Angelico, rubicund and robed in black, except for a starched white collar which fretted a matching band of red around his ample neck as he fussed with chrism and aspersorium while following a line of prayer with one finger; beside him, Rose, sleepy and bewildered in as dark a gown as could be found in her wardrobe; Farida, in mourning white, holding her little friend's hand, tears of silent rage running down her cheeks as she struggled to shut out the Christian part of this mockery of a burial ceremony; to one side of the table, Yakub, his dusty tunic unchanged, his eyes locked on his former master; to the other, Fonseca, his head bowed over a black cravat in what was either prayer or embarrassment; and at the foot of her improvised catafalque, Jarman Begam, changed into a gown of plain black bombazine, her cool eyes greenly sweeping the circle of mourners. In the centre of the circle the Great Trotter lay composed as before, except that a lead-lined coffin had been slid under him. There was a small stir when Rose, who had begun to fidget, shrieked: "He's crying!" But it was only a trickle from a piece of ice resting on the Great Trotter's forehead, and the Massachusetts pond-water did not reach the egg-brahmin's lips. The service concluded, the coffin lid was put in place, but as a concession to the Muslim party, it was not made fast.

"It will be nothing for him to sit up when the angel calls," Jarman Begam assured Hakim Ahmed, who nodded his assent and rolled his eyes up piously.

The mourners filed up the winding stair.

"You see," Elise pointed out, touching the Roman priest's arm, "it is more than six feet."

Father Angelico ran his prayer-book finger around the starched collar. He was anxious to change into his nightshirt. The Audience Hall was lit with lamps and tapers, grouped chiefly around the Gunpowder Door. The air was less morbid than down in the cellar, but close nonetheless, and smelt of churchly tallow and jasmine incense, a mingling which did nothing to alleviate the priest's distress. Blue smoke rose to the ceiling where Marazzi's indecorous angels swooned in a firmament of voluptuous pink. Father Angelico found no succour there; he had viewed them at leisure one pleasant winter afternoon when the sun sloped in at the westerly clerestories and was reflected off the roseate marble floor. Tonight he shifted accusingly, rapping his missal and worrying his beads. Elise turned to him.

"I am sorry to have inconvenienced you at this hour, Father, but it could not have waited till tomorrow. You see how hot it is even in the middle of the night. But here is something for your pains. I trust all is well at the mission compound. The coach is waiting; Hakimji will see you home."

She called Hakim Ahmed back from the Gunpowder Door. He had watched the purse change hands and in his excitement moved away, expecting her voice.

"Hakimji," Elise murmured, "I thank you for your services. You will be better paid tomorrow, but there will be refreshments waiting when you return tonight."

When the coach had clattered off down the drive, Jarman Begam put the stonemasons to work sealing the door of the tomb. Coming to life, Yakub gave orders and bullied the masons' labourers who were already sliding blocks of stone across the floor on sacking.

"How many came to pay their respects, steward?" Elise asked.

"Two, memsahib. The bhisti, Gunga, and a widow whose husband the Colonel Sahib shot with a fowling piece some years ago. She was compensated at the time. The fat one from the library threatened to come, but of course he is late."

"Was the poulterer there?"

"No, memsahib. I sent to his house to ask and heard there was much sorrowing there. His slippers have been found and the wife believes he may have gone off on a sudden pilgrimage. He often speaks of going to Benares, but never gets further than Sultanpur. A pious man, but capricious. They are all that way."

Elise listened with interest to this account, then remembered aloud: "The chickens will want looking after while he is away."

Yakub's bow was fractional, little more than a tightening of the diaphragm. "I will see to it, memsahib," he said, though his lips did not move. There was bile in his mouth. Defeat he could take; in a few days it would look (as his retreat from the Fish Palace had already begun to look) like a tactical withdrawal. But generosity in the victor irked unbearably. And the gift a trifle that would have come to him as a matter of course!

Elise turned to Fonseca, who gave a nervous start.

"Now, sir, the ice account. Munshiji will be here shortly about the will and there can be no sleeping tonight in any case. I gather there has been some mismanagement."

Fonseca shot a pained look at Yakub. A timid confused smile broke on his face.

"That will be all, steward," Elise added.

"Very well, memsahib." Yakub had not expected relief to come so soon, but he was no sooner conscious of it than his bitterness returned. The grandest of my schemes has come to naught, he said as he walked away, and I find solace in the prospect of a fresh intrigue. Mr Ice Manager Sahib. A considerable office, true, and one that I have bid for with hot heart in the past—but why? When ice amounts to nothing, runs away in no time?

He stepped out at the Gunpowder Door under a brilliant canopy of stars. Why had he run to the Nawab? What had he hoped to gain? He was already Chief Steward, sole steward. Could he have supposed the Nawab, who wanted a summer palace for his declining years, would hand over to a useful cocksman all Sans Souci? Install him as wazir simply because he knew the grounds? Not for a moment. Then why his errand? The nobles, the eunuchs, the very poet-and-jester had overheard the Nawab's remarks and laughed him to scorn. He knew no one at court, none of those gilded men, not even the friends of friends. Yet in Sans Souci he passed for a power; indeed in its closed world he was one. He had come far. With each advance he stood amazed at his timidity; men of higher rank invariably turned out vulnerable, even clownish; mysteries proved empty, laughably prosaic. He had thought boldness sufficient; now his audacity taunted him with an indefinable lack. What if there were nothing underneath it all? A fatter man might have helped him to that knowledge.

A stalking—and a confession

Yakub walks uneasily down the Gunpowder Drive. He is not accustomed to examining his motives. Meeting little resistance, he has had no need of introspection. The storm in his brain is always wild enough to evoke a kind of analytic awe, but it is an awe of details, not causes. He acts by instinct, went to the Nawab on impulse. The impulse was right, the method wrong: he misjudged the woman, she beat him. This much is plain to the baker-and-cocksman, as is the sensation of pleasure in the exercise. Is that all that runs ahead of him—his running? Yet he knows he will sleep an anxious sleep tonight.

He looks back up the dusty drive brushed white by the broad moon. He looks the other way. Three giant nim trees shake their heads noncommittally at him. Instead of going directly to his bare quarters in the Spur, he walks as far as the Gunpowder Gate. From here he can see both the Spur and the Glacerie. When will the sight of the Glacerie cease to cause him pain? He turns away and looks out across the flat powdery plain which a later generation will call the Sea of Tranquillity. Its tremulous grey and white and umber suggest a moth at rest.

Yakub pricks up his ears. Is that the sound of a knife drawn in stealth? He steps casually past the gate, then dodges behind one of its pillars and stands flat against it, holding his breath. He too carries a knife, a small one with which he pares his nails.

Who stalks the baker tonight, Narrator?
Are you there, Cup-Bearer? Consider:

Fonseca is with Jarman Begam studying arithmetic; Hakim Ahmed is on his way to White Town with Father Angelico studying theology; Nishan Chand is hunched over his desk studying the will (or is he?); Qaiyum lies drunk studying the back of his hand; Sunya lies dead studying nothing. Who, then? Who has followed the gaunt Yakub at a fixed distance, stopping when he stops, now pressing up against the wall of the Spur, now holding back a low branch, now using this boulder of cloud to whet a sharp curved silvery edge? Who is this man's kismet, sailing above him radiant and round?

Witless Cup-Bearer! Who but the Seventh Trotter? I cast no shadow: I am the light. I can come up close, squawk at his shoulder, make him jump, knock him about the ribs and run off. Or shall I be generous, large-hearted, handsome, big? Pity poor Yakub: friendless, fleshless, flat? Cancel his anxious sleep, give it to somebody else? Very well.

Yakub will sleep as usual tonight, an orphan's blank precipitous sleep. His customary six hours; he allows himself no more. Tomorrow he will brush his long white even unpitted teeth with a bitter nim twig, thirty strokes on every surface. He will have fresh eggs for breakfast, boiled, not fried in butter, eggs fetched for him by a new man he has appointed to gather them up in future. He will have the chicken run swept and garnished. He will begin an ice scheme. Wanting a plan, he must live by schemes; lacking breadth, he slips in where he can.

Let him go, Narrator.
No. Let him stand there a while.

Hakim Ahmed slept poorly that night. It was his practice to avoid sugar at night (*le dix-huitième siècle stupide!*) and on his return from White Town Jarman Begam had given him some mango-fool. The tumbler was his own. Then she had sent him home and advised a diet of fresh milk. Luckily the Hindus next door had a cow; Sunya's wife went around to the cowshed and coaxed some milk from the indignant creature. The herbalist-and-folk dentist's dreams involved a red cow in solemn debate with Father Angelico concerning reincarnation. While he tossed, snatching shreds of metempsychotic sleep, the stonemasons working by lamplight sealed the door to the tahkhana. They were paid by Jarman Begam and returned to the village while it was still dark. They dreamed ordinary dreams, of falling from rock faces, of wells, of women. The Sagarpaysans dreamt chiefly of balloons. Zuhur Ali, tailor master, did too, but his dream was in colour, in orange and green and blue on a yellow cloth. Yusuf the carpenter dreamt he was buried alive and could not die until the resurrection day. Munnoo dreamt of Garuda, Vishnu's bird-chariot. Nankoo dreamt of a roc. Munshi Nishan Chand, with a will to declare on the morrow, merely dozed; his sleep was ordinarily in the nature of a trance. This night he revisited Tibet and was valorous in battle. His deputy, Qaiyum, dreamed between bouts of senselessness of a bottomless cruse of wine stolen from a Persian poet. Rose Llewellyn Bibi dreamt of dolls that sat up and cried in the middle of the night. Along the corridor in the East Tower, her sworn sister-and-ally Farida Wilkinson Bibi dreamt of her dead husband's uncircumcised flesh and was mortified, even in her dream. Her dreams were usually complicated with sin. In White Town, Father Angelico dreamt of ox knuckles in gravy, fine white bread, asparagus and new-dropped lamb, spinach noodles swimming in olive oil, anchovies in tomato sauce sprinkled with fennel, breaded veal, ginger wine, and a giant egg flan which unaccountably refused to set and kept transferring itself into new vessels. At two o'clock Yakub put away his little knife and returned to the Cock Hall or Spur. He climbed stiffly to the roof where it was his practice to sleep in summer. From there he could see the roof of the Glacerie. He felt sure it was a cooler place to sleep. In the guest room of the Glacerie, Hari Om dreamt of a far country he had never visited across the Black Water for fear of losing caste and for want of a sufficient reason. He was late starting out across a certain river, and the spring ice began to break up under his feet. The small ice floe on which he balanced looked as if it might at any moment be swept into the middle of the river and over the falls. He woke in a sweat, his heart hammering. Jarman Begam sat awake in her tower before a sheet of paper with a ghostly watermark. The candle running low, she lit a fresh one, opened a speckled notebook, dipped her pen in ink, and wrote: *June the 21st, 1799*. Then, realizing it was already tomorrow, she crossed out the words and wrote: *June the 22nd, 1799*. And then, breathlessly: *If it were some romance, yesterday would be scoffed at. Howbeit, Sungum is now a tomb. No Nawab would dream of living here*. It would be the last entry in her diary. In the Fish Palace the Nawab dreamt of living in *Sungum*, but woke frustrated. In the tahkhana, Sunya lay empty of dreams. His last vision, of Marazzi's frescoes, remained imprinted on his eyes, but he could not see it. He did not taste the ice-water that trickled down his cheeks to the corner of his mouth, he did not hear the lid of his coffin lifted, he did not feel himself lifted out, he did not smell the barber's sheet in which he was wrapped. He made no objection to being wheeled on an ice trolley up a gentle gradient with a cool black draught of air flowing against his feet, or to being shot up a ramp and into a pinewood crate that smelt of high cheese. No sooner was Sunya in than Fonseca began to hammer back the prised planks. Awakened, the boatmaster rose from his damp sheets and came downstairs. The oarsmen-and-coolies who had been dreaming dreams now tender, now violent, were aroused and put to work. Before dawn the bullock-cart train reached the river. The barber-and-Ice Manager doused the first crate with oil and set it alight. As he watched it burn, he murmured a line he had often heard Hindu pallbearers chant: *Ram nama satya hai*, God's name is truth. Before the pyre collapsed, he pushed it down the bank and into the stream. The other crates followed. Sutli, whose dream had been especially tender, thought the business could have waited until morning, and said so. His mates agreed, but said nothing for fear of displeasing their so lately generous Ice Manager. Fonseca, who had not slept, heard nothing but the echo of Elise's scolding revolving in his head. Sunya's ashes floated off in a froth of temperate offerings that sizzled and now and then spurted flame. The Moti Ganga was no longer purple, but the Ganda Nala remained frozen until noon of the day following the Great Trotter's death. During this time it smelt of talcum powder and was spangled with stars. Children from both sides played on its surface, and in the thaw a girl who had dreamed she was going to drown, drowned.

The oarsmen-and-coolies dispersed, their captain Hari Om going to a friend's village to lodge. Six rupees to a wandering pujari bought Sunya his last rites. The bullock-carts were returned to the village and full payment was made. The villagers were astonished; they had dreamt of taxmen. Fonseca then gave, in advance, half a rupee to one of them for a ride back to *Sungum*. The man goaded his bullock ecstatically and the cart bounced away at a jangling bone-rattling trot. As the sun came up behind him, Fonseca levitated at the back of the cart, reviewing his dreamless night and wondering if he had not sufficiently atoned for embezzling from the ice account, somehow, forty thousand rupees.

A thousand pardons, Narrator, but do I sense an ending?

You sense a beginning, Cup-Bearer—the odour is the same. I propose to take you through the tombstone to the womb.

But the fable for our times, Narrator, that deep gothic tale?

Yes, that is past, its unities spent. The fit I laboured under when I wrote it lasted two days and a night. I took nothing but sherry and truffles. But fetch me now a beaker full of something Greek, Cup-Bearer—is it Taki or Sake?

Not sake, Narrator. We have had that. Here is a peach brandy, round, moist, and fruity.

My Saki! Now listen to the koel's song—ku-O, ku-O, ku-O!

A meditation on Indo-Greek sculpture

Consider O my soul the land called Greece. It is crab-shaped, Attic, and salt. Yet it produces honey-baklava, long poems, broken statues, and warlike men. Not all the warriors are called Alexander (Achilles is one). Of those who are, some go east, some west, and some remain. This is a law, Trotter's Law: *Of men called Alexander, some will go east, some west, and some remain.* Of those Alexanders who go east, some stop at the Oxus (which the unreliable Indians call Jhelum) in the Punjab, others go as far as the Kirani river (which the noble Anglo-Indians call Cranny) in Tirnab. Two thousand years may separate them, and much courage. The first Alexander, by some called the Great, did not tarry in Ind. He left behind him a satrap, a sheet-anchor, blue eyes, and statuary. The statuary, of heads, of busts, of torsos, such as full-round Buddhas, he caused to be buried in shallow trenches all over his conquered province. The satrap he placed on a curule chair, the sheet-anchor in a lake (where it was found by one of the wily British, an historian), and the blue eyes he scattered through the villages. But the statuary is of essence. Keep to the straight path, my soul. Ever after, the sculptors of that part of Ind used the Greek model, marrying to it native charms (or marrying to Greek charms the Indian model) and burying the finished work according to the custom. Dug up by archaeologists and assembled in a room, the pieces are called the Gandhara School. High Seriousness, Beauty, Delight: the aesthetic virtues, O my soul, mark the Gandhara School. Truth sits on every soapstone lip, Grace smooths the oleolithic brow.

Tread carefully, my soul, for here with sword and chisel drawn, creeps the other Alexander. He bears no surname, unless de Lesser be one. Do not confuse him with Alexander of Hales or Alexander of Minos or Alexander of Aphrodisias, though he is descended from the last. His eyes are blue as the Aegean, his lips drop sottish tales of war and busty wenches. He it is who stopped at Sans Souci, who won over the Great Trotter, who raised up pagan effigies (Achilles is one) on the parapets, who turned the head of the Great Trotter's only son with blood and thunder, who thus incurred the great man's wrath. Who was banished to a far corner of the Crocodile Wing, who swore his innocence, who in his banishment wandered the deserts and jungles of Sans Souci, who skulked in the quarry, covering its face with edicts and carvings martial and erotic. Who took a widow of the gipsy-blacksmith caste. O impurity! Who filled her belly with the Aegean. O sin! Who brought forth Gandhara images. O idolatry! Who before his banishment had begun the Great Trotter's monument, after the Great Trotter's own prescription: *Justin Aloysius Trotter, who lived and died*. Who before he completed it fell from grace. Who got no further than:

JUSTIN ALOYSIUS TROTTER

WHO

(COMMENTARY)

Who

Who indeed! Confusion surrounds his very birth, this rash but handsome Gaul (*Light of the World, Nectar of Sans Souci*). The when, the where, lie wrapped in antique mists; even the whether is open to doubt, though he came and dwelt in Nakhlau, leaving the monument that all may see. The birth date, 27 December 1729, assigned by Mr Montagu (*Proxy Trotter*) is conjectural, based on an astrologer's chart drawn many years later showing Mars and Venus rising. The place, Al-Qahira, Egypt, is assigned on the slenderest evidence. Remy Trottoire, weaver of Marseilles, is said to have been pressed into sea service, to have jumped ship in Alexandria, and to have found his way to Al-Qahira. There, so the fable goes, he got with child a Copt and returned, with wife and son, to Marseilles. The boy, frail and sickly, showed no aptitude for the trade which his father resumed. Instead, he spent his time idling at the dockside and being by turns whipped by his father and cosseted by his mother. At thirteen he ran away to sea, thirsting for adventure and exotic sights.

Tissue of lies! Transparent concoction! Mr Montagu, let posterity note, was a man of the wick, with an appetite for travel never requited. A man, can we doubt, cosseted by his father and thrashed by his mother. A dried-up quill of a man with a sharp nose and a measurable imagination. An historian.

Let us then dissipate this academic dockyard fantasy and seek out the real Justin.

He is born on the twenty-first of June, 1719. So far from being premature, as the historian's version has it, he has spent ten months in the womb and arrives in the fullness of things. A glistening globe, he greets the world, like all great men from Akbar to Zoroaster, with a laugh. The ship's doctor-and-accoucheur, accustomed to cries, screeches, whines, and caterwauling, stays his spanking hand. Young Justin, roaring all the while, tears off his caul and seizes the medical finger with a grip the doctor will never forget. Outside, a storm has been raging, but at the auspicious moment it withdraws to vex some other quarter of the Mediterranean, leaving a looking-glass sea. The mother, Miriam (*Cupola of Chastity*), who insisted on making the voyage because the price of cotton was falling, dies within sight of land. The father, Joseph Trottoire, a merchant of Lirey, is of Franco-Swiss stock, descended from a certain Jean Petitot. His father, Jean Petitot's son, changed his name to Trottoire to avoid religious persecution in Geneva and later emigrated to the country of his Catholic ancestors, settling in Lirey. Joseph has spent the year selling dear and buying cheap (looms and cotton are his business) in Grand Cairo. To further his commercial interests, he has married the daughter of a Coptic merchant from Alexandria with whom he has regular dealings.

He refuses to allow his wife a watery grave; she must have her monument, a heroine of industry, a martyr to the cause of free trade, of which Joseph is a staunch and busy advocate. The ship docks at Dijon, and the merchant hastens with his son and his dead wife to Lirey. There, Miriam, said to have been uncommonly devout, is buried in the tiny foreigners' cemetery, the Cimitaire Ste Fatima, where her stone is visible to this day. The name, it is true, is worn away, but the date reads clearly: 1719. The Coptic lady, for all her virtue, could not have been delivered of a child, even one as mercurial as Justin, ten years beyond the veil. So there can have been no coddling for the First Trotter unless *ab ovo*. Or unless by the second wife. A retired soprano, she teaches the growing boy to sing. By his fourteenth year, the lad has determined on a career in the Italian opera, spending his nights in company which distresses a father too meek to either scold his son or reproach his wife. When Justin does a strange thing. In a desperate bid to join a travelling company of Florentine castrati, he severely wounds but does not permanently damage himself. Humiliated by his failure, he waits only for the wound to heal before enlisting in the French force bound for Quebec.

Justin Aloysius Trottoire to Mme Trottoire (1)

Mama dearest,

Have you forgiven your darling son? He loves you very much and is always thinking of you. Twice his life has been spared through your prayers. All the way across the Atlantic it was very rough with waves like alps and we were separated from the convoy. I was almost swept overboard when I was sent to cut some rigging. I got stuck in the ropes and was held by God's grace, but swallowed a good deal of sea-water. Mama dearest, I know it is a great sin but I did not call on Him in that moment. Your son was thinking only of his dear mother and her sweet face. The stench was horrid from the start. Once the bilge tubs overturned and slopped into our galley as we ate. At the end we were on short rations of water and biscuit and if a ship going the other way had not given us a bale of leeks it would have gone hard with us. They say the tables of the upper deck were well spread for all that and some dainties were even unloaded at Quebec. We are drilling all the time and learning the use of a new musket whose name I cannot mention. Yesterday three of us went skating. The ice was thin and the farmers warned us off but my good friend Joseph—he is from Lyons—simply laughed at them. Such a quick, noble, and generous heart—I owe him my life from yesterday—but pray do not fret, for I am well. I will tell you of it some day. My dear Mama, if you could only persuade Father to forgive me my rash act my exile will be bearable. He will speak to me again, I know it, if you ask. I do not know when we return. I have an eczema on my back which is troublesome at night, but everything else is well. The houses here are of wood, the squirrels large and red. The Indians are handsome and go dressed in skins and furs. I have learnt some words of their language, such as *kalamazoo*, which is a saucer of honey, and *saggamite*, which is a porridge of cracked wheat with cream and maple sugar. Our commander says the ground is very white for May. My kisses to Mathilde and little Sophie but especially to your dear self. His son salutes my father and showers kisses on you.

Justin.

(COMMENTARY)

The reader can put only one construction on the *rash act* which prudence prevents the boy soldier from giving a name. With what delicacy does this young man elide any reference to his thwarted vocal ambitions!

One other letter home survives. It is written at a much later date, some ten years after the first. Betweenwhiles, Justin has served in Quebec, Providence, and Louisiana, narrowly escaping capture at the fall of Louisburg, and taking part in the joint French and Indian attacks on New York during the next few years. He returns home to find his father dead and his stepsisters married. He lives in Lirey with his dear mama, measuring out her laudanum, ministering to her needs. These are the Great Trotter's Lost Years; we may only guess at their substance from the formed tastes of the maturer man. Doubtless he eat hearty, sang high, and read everything that came his way, from scurrilous broadsheets to astronomical treatises, from a great black family Bible to the lucid texts of the Enlightenment which glowed in the hand like books of ice. His sometime singer mother would have gone with him to churches and lieder-rooms and public halls to hear the oratorios of his beloved Handel, whose *Fireworks Suite* was, after a year of odium, being grudgingly applauded this side of the English Channel. And no doubt the theory of war, of gunnery and ballistics, picked up from the current surplusage of military works, was a soldier's solace in that time of unlucky peace. Then one day he reads of the exploits of a certain M Dupleix in the East Indies. Kissing his mama, he enlists again and sails away, this time around the Cape of Good Hope.

Justin Aloysius Trotter to Mme Trottoire (2)

Madras
June the 21st

My dear Mama,

I have this minute been allotted my bed in a barracks that will sleep
forty men. The mattresses and pillows are stuffed with some coarse
fibrous husk and the pillow being flat as a biscuit does good service for
a writing desk. A ship sails for France today or tomorrow, having waited
on us two weeks while we limped around Ceylon with one mast down.
When we arrived this morning we had to wait three hours within sight
of the port on account of a fierce tide. Two of the advance party were
drowned within thirty yards of land, so the gloom is upon us. It is so
very different, Mama, the town, the trees, the creatures, the inhabitants.
The men are as black as the sand is white and wear many yards of
untailored cloth. The women are still more encumbered but their garments are brightly coloured. They keep their heads covered and their
faces hid, so I cannot tell whether they be beautiful or not—though they
could never hope to match my dear mama. We have been ordered to
keep clear of the bazar, which was called Black Town by the English,
so I cannot hope to describe them further for you until the next ship.

No sooner were we ashore but we saw a most curious sight. A large
bird, grey and erect, was tossed a bone by one of the old hands here, I
surmise for our amusement. The bird, which they call the adjutant-bird,
caught the bone readily in his bill and himself tossed it several times in
the air, catching it again and again until he had it lengthwise. Judge of
our surprise when he swallowed it whole—though it was longer than
this hand! He was none the worse for his greed and seemed to say, *look
you, here is the first of many wonders in this land.* The sun is cruelly hot,
and though there be some relief in the shade, the moisture in the air
undoes it.

Our commander is a kind and sobre man who has served in India
for many years. He has twice shown me favour before others, being
himself fat and well-favoured; if I am apt and alert I think I may expect
promotion before long. The English are said to be making preparations
for an attack. Their ships patrol the coast to the north and south (though
we sighted none) but do not dare come close or we should send them
off in a hurry. We are expecting reinforcements from the port of Pon-
dicherry. I feel certain I will distinguish myself in the fighting that is to
come, but pray do not distress yourself on my account. Your son will

conduct himself with every regard for the honour of our family name. We are called to mess—

(COMMENTARY)

Here the letter is broken off and remains so for more than a month. Much happens in the interval, but Justin does not distinguish himself in battle. Hostilities commence that same day—one can imagine an interrupted meal— and in a series of engagements the British, outnumbered a hundred to one, win. The French lose and Justin is taken prisoner (although it may be that Justin is taken prisoner and the French lose). But distinguish himself he does, in peace. His account of the incident is curiously underblown, but I will let him speak for himself, noting only that the name of the ship that is the sinking site of his heroism is incorrectly transcribed by him as *Fath-i-Islam*, an error Mr Montagu (*So-called Trotter*) perpetuates. The Calcutta Register of Vessels has *Fatty Salaam*, and considerations of euphony alone should compel respect for this fine specimen of English orthography. Justin's letter continues from Calcutta in a darker ink (or so it appears beside the ink of the first part, which is almost washed away) and an altogether different hand, the work almost, one might say, of a new person. The *o*'s and *a*'s are nobler, the loops of the *g*'s and *y*'s have a new generosity to their sweep, and the *b*'s have bellied out finely, ostents of a shape to come.

Justin Aloysius Trotter to Mme Trottoire (cont'd.)

My dear mama—I scarcely know whether I should begin anew or continue this letter, begun it would seem a lifetime ago. And indeed it has pleased God to grant me a second life (though if the American ice-skating mishap be counted, then it is a third). You must know the outcome of the war with England so I will not dwell on it. How this letter is to be carried to France I cannot say. But I must tell you that I was taken prisoner in the fighting and shipped with forty-three of my fellows to Calcutta. The bottom, called the *Fath-i-Islam*, miscarried off the coast of Bengal, and we were cast into the sea. There is a story abroad that the *Fath-i-Islam* was once the French ship *Insulaire* sunk in the Ganges some ten years ago but secretly refloated by an enterprising merchant. Well, after a nasty ducking I managed to turn over one of the boats and pluck from the water some of my remaining companions who faint from battling the waves had begun to lose their hold on the mast to which we clung. For this I was cited by the English in Calcutta, another of their ships having picked us up the next day. Now that peace has been concluded I may use the distinction to gain preferment in their Company. I fear it is all washed up with our side in India, and a man must make his way. For this reason I have altered some few letters in my name so as to have it read *Trotter*. I do not know that I will remain long in Calcutta, for there are many opportunities up-country and fortunes to be made in war and trade.

I have now had greater opportunity to examine the country in which it seems fate has cast my lot. It is not at all like America. One marvels that the Spaniards called those people Indians, for those people are primitive and handsome. This country is old and feeble, being hot and wet and hot and dry by turns. It is everything we are not, so that any object you are like to touch upon at home might be fairly argued to have its opposite here. Their cats are thin where ours are sleek, the rivers muddy where ours are clear, the bread flat where ours is risen. Winter is their pleasant season! Our washerwomen beat the clothes with a paddle; their washermen beat the paddle with the clothes. A tobacco pipe which with us is short and straight is here long and sinuous and pliant, being called a *hookah* (but I do not yet smoke, Mama). It is much the same with the native's temper. Where we are accustomed to dealing forthrightly he prefers the roundabout way, now obsequious, now remote, for no man will trust another who is not of the same *caste*. This is a word from the Portuguese, meaning pure. For all that, he is easily managed and brought round. I conceive it is not impossible to amass a fortune in any trade soever, the soil and climate being conducive to culture all the year round and the people most tractable.

Is my dear mama keeping well? The Saarbrücken waters at bedtime, with a nice little dish of lamb's brains? Have Sophie bring you a dressed quail every week, or what does her Inspector of Markets count for? I wish you would marry again, Mama. Perhaps a change of name would suit you too, and M. d'A—— bids fair to become mayor! As for me, the company does not encourage its junior officers to consider marriage. The English look less favourably upon alliances with native women than we do in our territories, though at one time they paid the sum of one pagaoda for every child brought for christening out of such a marriage so that their soldiers might be encouraged to take Indian wives. Not but what every man has his mistress and some indeed do marry. The women here are more slender than those of the south (where rice is eaten) but none so pretty as my dear mama.

(COMMENTARY)

The letter is unfinished and was never sent, although the son preserved it in his trunk. By winter Justin had word of his stepmother's death and began his lifelong search for a woman who should take her place. None was to be found among the paler Anglo-Indians of Calcutta, and within the year he was billetted up-country with a Brown Bess by his side.

Brown Bess

BROWN BESS, n. Rifle issued to British soldier (or foreign national carrying British arms) in 1758. Bright Sea Service. Musket barrel 42 inches. Calibre .75. Weight 9 lbs. Effective range 200 yards; accurate to 100 yards.

(*CHRONICLE RESUMED*)

The new weapon was manufactured in Bristol and fired in a different way from the one Justin had carried to Madras, so for some weeks he found himself reaching for an imaginary pin at the muzzle. Ensign Trotter's coat was also new—unless from his ducking in the Bay of Bengal the old one had gone from blue to red by the action of a warm current. What was certain was that there came to be inscribed on the rolls of the Hon. East India Company's Bengal Army the name Justin Aloysius Trotter (*Elephant-Bodied Warrior, Radiant Powder-Keg, Dread Cannonball*).

Fortune smiled on this Frenchman-turned-Englishman. In his first engagement he was noticed by the Commander-in-Chief of his adopted army. During the afternoon's fighting he fired accurately and with effect into a group of enemy soldiers whose cannon, perched on a knoll opposite, might otherwise have caused considerable havoc. Promotion to lieutenant followed upon a transfer, irregular enough, to an artillery regiment where the young officer applied in the field his impressive theoretical knowledge of ballistics. *More highre! Much!* he would yodel at his bewildered gunners, expounding the art of the surprise lob to men who held with swift and modest trajectories. Round and round went the elevating screws, higher and higher flew the balls, until the enemy no longer knew where they came from: were they surrounded by Company cannon, did the sky rain thunderbolts? A puff of smoke showed straight ahead; they ducked behind embankments; the ball came down upon their heads.

"We are aiming not at the enemy but at an ideal, at the apex of the triangle isosceles which us divides," the First Trotter explained to his commander after the enemy had surrendered. "The two points of the base are interchangeable, but the third is of essence. The gunner who finds the apex can the earth move." Peace came, but the axletrees of British guns grew taller; Justin Trotter cannoned from lieutenant to captain to major, from Chandarnagar to Clutterbuckganj to Kon on the border with Tirnab. Then he escorted an envoy to Nakhlau. There, one August day, he rode his roan out past the market-gardens and pleasances and sugar-cane fields, across a broad canal and up a square hill whose flat top was not far from the bottom. Looking down, he saw a dun plain watered by an inconsequential little stream which issued from the tableland on which he stood and ran into a larger river just beyond a forest at the horizon. He was at once in thrall, and stood gazing at the prospect until the light began to fail. As he rode back he saw his horse's hooves strike sparks off the flinty slope of the hill. The sparks danced and swarmed like fireflies.

Returning to Kon, Justin Trotter found that the red in his military coat had faded, whether from the sun or the damp he could not say. "Give me but a captain's pay," he wrote to the Governor-General-and-Commander-in-Chief, "and let me go to Nakhlau." The men in Calcutta agreed, and the First Trotter took his coat across the river into Tirnab. A little accident at the ford saw his coat come up blue again. The young Nawab of Tirnab was delighted: he knew Paris and spoke French, his axletrees were miserably stunted, his own Commander-in-Chief was ailing, and the French artillerist's reputation ran ahead of him.

On the strength of his reputation the First Trotter asked permission to stage a display of rocketry and firepower. The Nawab consented. The dun plain across the canal was made ready with mock huts, canvas forts, and straw redoubts. The soldiers of Tirnab were drilled for manoeuvres after the French mode and responded well. The cannons of Tirnab were trundled over the East Bridge, their barrels pointing at the sky, and the First Trotter cast a giant gun to follow in state. Caught up in the spirit of the occasion, the Nawab gave orders that gunpowder be issued to the French firangi in any quantity he desired (but on no account balls or shot). Colonel Trotter, for that was his new rank, respectfully declined the offer. For a month he supervised the manufacture of shotless cartridges and ball-less shells. The best firework-makers in Nakhlau brought with them their red pepper, their turmeric, their mint, their cobalt, their rose essence, their betel-nut. On the chosen night, huts, forts, and redoubts exploded in an inferno of red and gold and green and blue and rose and crimson. Blue-and-green-turbanned troops charged across ravelins, into ditches, and up the glacis of a hill daylit with cannon fire. The Nawab rocked in his seat with glee (*Global Sovereign, Geoid*) and was beside himself when the big gun thundered a final salute. "All this land," he cried, "from the Ganda Nala east as far as the Moti Ganga, we grant in perpetuity to our new Commander-in-Chief, the French firangi." The First Trotter bowed a courtly bow and then, digging his heel into the square hill on which the marquee was pitched, saluted. A tiny spark flew up from his boots.

The next day a firman was issued from court ratifying the grant. It was stamped with the seal of Tirnab. Firman in hand, Justin returned to survey his demesne, climbing the littered glacis to where the empty marquee flapped. He scooped up a handful of gravel, rattled it in his palm, and smiled. Carelessly he tossed it over his shoulder. The gravel, white and pungent, was saltpetre.

How Trotter gunpowder is made

I wish to shew how Trotter gunpowder is made. Choose a hot day, good adept, but not too hot. Gather in one place saltpetre, sulphur, charcoal, curry powder, and a mortar and pestle. For the saltpetre you must first find a square hill or tableland such as crop up in dun plains. It is best to look at night, for saltpetre is a most wholesome food to fireflies. A fireworks display will win you such a hill, but for this manoeuvre you must already have the gunpowder. In the market saltpetre occurs in sacks but is costly. The cheapest is at J.c. Solomon & Son, who are in the usual place, just where the road turns away. For the sulphur, good adept, look next to the saltpetre: the two are found together in nature (God is good) and at reliable chemists (J.c. Solomon is one). Where saltpetre attracts fireflies, sulphur repels mosquitoes. A spoonful taken with honey will keep them away; more will keep friends away. Charcoal is partially burnt wood. Where there is smoke there is usually charcoal, but do not tarry for then there is ash. Curry powder occurs in yellow lodes between the saltpetre and the sulphur, partaking of the nature of both but lacking the radical moisture of the one and the costive properties of the other. It is not to be confused with chilli powder, which is vegetal. There are two ways of mining curry powder, the *correct* and the *incorrect*. (*Vide. Memb.* III *Sect.* 2 *Subs.* 2.) Grind with mortar and pestle the various elements separately. The pestle is the club, the mortar the bowl—or is it the other way? (This is the two-option bind—a third thing would resolve all perplexities.) A vapour will be seen to rise from the saltpetre; this is the radical moisture departing, from the action of the sun. In cold countries where the water is heavier by four ounces in the pound (*vide*. Burton, Magister Robert Shafer, Machometes Bragdedinus, Ibn Sina, *et alia*) and the sun more gelid, the process is longer. When the saltpetre is thoroughly dry, not before, sift the dry ingredients together. At this stage, good adept, smoking is hazardous, as any surgeon will testify. Store the gunpowder in a cool dry place, away from sunlight, spectacles, and the like, perhaps in a magazine called the Hayat Baksh Khana, or Life-Giving

Place. This is what I wished to shew. So do that. Hold fire and water and praise God.

(CHRONICLE RESUMED)

During the first year of his residence in Nakhlau, Colonel Trotter lived in the marquee on the saltpetre hill. While the Tank was being hollowed out and an artificial plateau raised up to the south of the hill, the new Commander-in-Chief of Tirnab fired a variety of experimental guns the other way across the plain. The big gun, called *Urban*, and a hundred others of various barrels and bores spat prodigious quantities of fire northwards, their muzzles belching creamy puffs or violet plumes or jagged green tongues, depending. Chain-shot, hook-shot, grape-shot, balls of iron, brass, stone, naphtha, and crystal rained down upon the tawny plain, battering targets natural and man-made, including three Buddhist stupas which had crumbled in peace for two thousand years.* At a time when the Austrians had begun to cast their projectiles as near to spheres as possible, the First Trotter was experimenting with a rub to each ball. From the pattern of a stray firecracker he developed the devastating spiral-track shot which he would combine with the surprise lob with terrifying results in a later campaign.

In the second year, when the Gunpowder Court and the West Tower were completed, Justin Trotter moved out of the marquee and into his new home. By the third year of the Trotter era, a regular train of newly struck cannon was rumbling across the Ganda Nala and along the Nawab's road to the Fish Palace and its environs. The smoke from the foundries by the Gunpowder Court was dense enough for its pall to run two hundred miles east till it leaned over the border that divided, with a broken purple line, the pink of John Company's Bengal from the blue of Tirnab.

Concerning the Great Trotter's guns

"Guns are wonderful locks for protecting the august edifice of state; and befitting keys for the door of conquest." The great historian Abu'l Fazl, who

---

* Forty years later Napoleon's artillerists would riddle the Sphinx in much the same way. A delightful Egyptian sweet of the time was *qand*, or candy, made of highly refined sugar. This is perhaps the place to note that the Pyramids hide a secret quite as tantalizing as that of the decayed Sphinx. At least one medical authority has remarked (from an inspection of the mouths of mummies) on the general excellence of the ancient Egyptians' teeth. Sir Thomas Browne, who draws a parallel with the teeth of the "*Bannyans* of *India*," concludes that dentistry must needs have been a "barren profession" in those happy days.—E.A.T.

was quite fat, has put it so eloquently that I can do no more than echo him. Machiavelli, too, speaks well of guns, and there are some others.

The Great Trotter, who is the soul of generosity, has guns without number in his arsenal. They are of two categories, *short* and *long*, but some divide them otherwise, such as *native* and *foreign*, and sometimes *of iron* and *not*. All are either plain or ornamented, and though many are heavy some are light.

The Great Trotter has himself cast a gun so terrible that it defies description. Others he has cast, which may be described, are beyond number so the listing would be tedious. Some are cannons; others, shoulder-guns; still others, pistols. Naturally, these are not to be confused with the matchlocks.

The Great Trotter's favourite weapon, purchased from a Franco-Gaelic cook-and-deserter, is the Brown Bess, a short foreign gun of iron, of forty-two inches' length, .75-inch calibre, and nine pounds' weight. This weapon therefore falls happily into the category of guns *purchased*. Then there is a French fowling piece with which he caused great slaughter in the field. Like the other it is a naval model, but it is so transformed by his genius that to class it among the purchased would be folly or petty-mindedness. Experimenting constantly with its parts, the Great Trotter contrived an earless concealed hammer and a tongueless concealed trigger (by the cunning expedient of multiplying trigger-guards and inserting false triggers) which connect with a series of locks and false locks. Thus it might equally be classed among guns *manufactured*. The whole is so overlaid with nacreous whorls and florid beading that it is impossible for an enemy to discern where ornament ends and function begins. Thus only the Great Trotter or a close friend can fire this gun which astonishes the whole world.

The Great Trotter, who is a just paymaster, is also an excellent marksman and cuts a fine figure with his gun of the moment. Clay pigeons without number lie at his feet. What is this body but a toy of travail?

Then there are the carabins, arquebuses, fusil or firelocks, mousquetons, flint-, spring-, and wheel-locks, wheel-cum-matchlocks, chiselled firing swords covered in Brescian work, snaphauns, snaphaunces, fowl-snatchers, birding pieces, pistols with globose butts, scroll butts, fish-tail butts, lobe butts, pear butts, sack butts, pistols with globose butts and brass stocks, globose butts and silver stocks, globose butts and wood stocks, pistols with scroll butts and brass stocks, scroll butts and silver stocks, scroll butts and wood stocks, pistols with fish-tail butts and scroll-work, pistols plain, hand cannon, a combined hand cannon and pistol, an Utrecht-type blunderbuss with a folding spring bayonet, an ordinary blunderbuss which doubles as a speaking trumpet in parleys, another which retracts into a pair of opera glasses, two- and four-barrel Turkish pistols, single-barrel Moroccan pistols with dog locks, not to speak of cabinets full of dogheads, dags, pyrites, pyrite-holders, sears, searlugs, luggs, combs, tumblers, steels (which is to say, hammers), frizzens, flash-pans, sash-hooks, primers, fusees, touch-holes, patrons of brass and steel, patrons of gold, ramrods, monkey terminals to ramrods, butt-caps masked, butt-caps unmasked, barrel keys, turnscrews, strikers, scabs, ring-necked cocks, pommels, horns, powder flasks of ivory, of leather, shells, bolts and pans, cherry shot, case shot, cartridge paper in immense sheaves, cartouche caps, and one or two other things.

The Great Trotter has invented a machine that will clean all his guns at once. The wheel is turned by a camel which comes and goes.

The Great Trotter also makes sophisticated weaponry for sale. Purchasers include ordinary citizens as well as princes of the earth such as the Nawab of Tirnab, who was a most generous patron, once.

> *Narrator, this is all very well, but tell me how in the generation of myth the First Trotter came to be a gourmand.*
>
> *Put wine not words into my mouth, Cup-Bearer. An aperitif now, and you will not doubt me?*
>
> *When have I doubted?*
>
> *You have had your reservations.*
>
> *Forgiveness, Narrator!*
>
> *Very well, the cup. Now listen. I have heard from the Great Indian Bustard that it happened in this way.*

(CHRONICLE RESUMED)

Before long the smoke from Justin Trotter's foundries had reached Calcutta, where it became impossible to ignore. Within a fortnight an invitation arrived for the Nawab of Tirnab from the Governor-General and was delivered by the British Resident in Nakhlau.

Dinner invitation from the Governor-General to the Nawab

Monday, the 1st of June

The Nawab of Tirnab
Fish Palace
Nakhlau

Dear Nawab Sahib,

Word has reached us of your French table and the excellences of your French chef (who we gather was one of the Queen's Own Volunteers who left suddenly during a skirmish with Dupleix's forces in the Deccan—but no more of that). We hear also that you have often expressed the desire to have the British Governor-General (ourself) for dinner, and are happy to accept. We are certain that the famous Colonel Trotter, who is drawing a Commander-in-Chief's salary from you and a Captain's pay from us, would wish to attend. We will be passing that way on the 21st inst. on our way to subdue certain recalcitrant southern princes. Would 8 o'clock be all right?

Sincerely,

Fort William
Calcutta   *The Governor-General*
R.S.V.P.

(*CHRONICLE RESUMED*)

"Merde!" said the Nawab, but he gave orders to Gaston.

"High-handed!" advised the Prime Minister, looking forward to the feast.

"Diction!" sneered the poetaster, who knew he would not be invited.

"Grammar!" winced the maulvi, who did not want a Governor-General for dinner.

"Tough!" agreed the Resident, whose digestion was poor.

"Trouble!" thought Justin, but sent his coat to be pressed.

Was the Nawab perhaps preparing for war? The Governor-General launched a smiling question through the steam of Gaston's tortoise soup. The Nawab put down his spoon. War! But of course not! He was, au contraire, busy securing peace. The Governor-General looked out of a window in the banquetting hall. That pall of smoke, for instance? he nodded. The Nawab followed his gaze: outside, the stars were hidden. By strength alone is peace secured, he answered. He would rather have been eating alone. Good enough, the Governor-General said, making a pellet of his bread, but certain ill-advised princes—southern princes, of course—had made a practice of enlisting French armourers to their cause and hanging out provocative black flags. The First Trotter began to hum in his high sweet voice. The Nawab made rapid passes at his soup. Colonel Trottoire, said the Governor-General, pointedly using Justin's discarded name and staring fixedly at Justin's coat, which was now bleached white—the sun is harsh on foreign dyes in these latitudes, is it not? No doubt you have considered indigo. The First Trotter smiled an enigmatic smile which could have signified: I have considered indigo, or: Indigo? Well, continued the Governor-General, returning to the Nawab, the Nawab was welcome to visit Bengal—and of course to dine at the Company's table and sample British fare. The Nawab looked glum (*Exquisite Eater, Palate Extraor-*

dinaire). And afterwards, the Governor-General-and-joker went on, he could review the might of British arms, sufficient to lay waste a dozen principalities. He was speaking, naturally, of *southern* princes—and their French lackeys— not loyal, reliable, trustworthy northern ones. Northern princes knew very well that diplomacy, like haute cuisine, was a matter of subtle alliances. *Hot* cuisine! the Nawab cried, exactly so! Diplomacy is too piquant a matter to be left to bunglers. And he sent for his master chef. Gaston entered, the virtues of his tortoise soup were extolled, and he bowed deeply, his ginger head dipping. But, whispered the Nawab to his chef, and his next words amazed the man. Hot cuisine. Blinking, Gaston withdrew. Thereafter the courses came and went like singed cats, each dish, whether from Provence, Brittany, Loire, or Alsace-Lorraine, more fiery than the last, until the very petit pois glowed like tiny red coals. Only Colonel Trotter's appetite seemed unimpaired (*Great Trotter, Foremost Among Gourmands*). The Nawab looked disappointed, almost pale; the Governor-General looked distressed, almost purple; the other guests were merely puzzled at the odd alliance. The last few dishes were Indian, and both the Nawab and the Governor-General ignored them, but Colonel Trotter ate on. When at length the finger-bowls arrived, strewn with rose petals and garnished with a wedge of lemon to cut the grease, the Governor-General raised his immediately to his burning lips and drank. An embarrassed silence fell on the company until the Nawab, schooled in old Nakhlau politesse, made the gesture that would live on in legend. Looking each way down the table, he took up his own finger-bowl and drank. The lesser guests followed suit, and the gaffe was smoothed over.

Each side gave and took a point. The Governor-General returned to Calcutta to cool his temper; Colonel Trotter returned to the Gunpowder Court to cool his furnaces. The pall of smoke over Nakhlau disappeared; that over Government House, Fort William, thinned to nothing. The Nawab thanked Gaston O'Leary, but begged him to continue as before; the Governor-General never again strayed from boiled beef and pudding. But Colonel Trotter's desire for red chillies grew ever more intense. Although his military ardour was dampened, Justin's heart was hot within him, and one day a new column of smoke stood over Sans Souci: it was white and issued from the kitchens.

This was a formative period in the Great Trotter's career. He gathered around him cooks, Muslim cooks from Nakhlau, Hindu cooks from Benares, Parsi cooks from Bombay, Christian cooks from Goa, Daman, and Diu, Jewish cooks from Cochin, cooks from Assam to Gujarat, from Kashmir to Kerala, cooks from Trans-oxiana and those parts, free Brahmin cooks, bound Pariyah cooks, bellicose Jat cooks, egg-brahmins from Rohilkhand, fish-brahmins from Bengal, non-garlic Jains, chapati Punjabis, rice Madrasis, Gujaratis who use sugar in their curries (*Admirable Race*), Goans who use vinegar,

Pahadis who use fruit, Burmans who use coconut, turmeric-grinders from Malaya, Cambodian gingermen, Javanese peppermen, Bangkok onionmen, Cuttack macemen, drifters from the Cardamom Hills, curry-powder miners from the Sagarpaysans, muscle-bound masalchis, footloose spice-tasters, shapely oilmen, good-looking deep-fryers, dashing rice-factors, jobbing boners, stringy kneaders, rakish stokers, brawny strainers, tetchy peelers, stodgy griddlemen, suave rolling-pin artistes, smarmy pot-stirrers, avid tasters, Tibetan marrow-men, Szechuan noodle-winders, Kazhaki pemmican-traders, Georgian gou-lash-turners, Armenian cinnamon-shakers, Iraqi date-mashers, Phoenician confectioners, Persian tandoori-masters, and a half-Turkish baker's apprentice with eyes like living coals.

A man who sits on a saltpetre hill can command much.

As Sans Souci took shape around him, Justin grew into his château, filling out with gusto, his every surface advancing symbiotically with his house, a dome appearing there, a belly here; there a turret, here a fold; here a palpitating buttock, there a gibbous barbican. And as his appetite for curries deepened, his tastes widened to take in mint chutneys, cauliflower pickles, cucumber salads, green mango achars, tomato kasaundis, lotus-root, tamarind, pepper-water, pastes, purees, preserves, curds, raitas, and a thousand accompaniments of rich and satisfying food.

There was one lack (*Ignoble Deficiency, National Scandal*). Justin longed for dessert. But the Indian cooks, who held sway in the kitchens, one and all looked at him askance: sweets, certainly, they allowed, but in their place, not with meals. Justin was not appeased. How to shake off a habit instilled in him by a stepmother who having failed in song found succour in desserts? And to the horror of the young baker's apprentice-and-waiter who regularly brought him a saucer of digestive anise seed to conclude a meal, the First Trotter sent for and broke a pomegranate of crystal sugar and mixed its kernels in with the aromatic seed. In this modest way, soon to be refined, was born the first true Indian dessert: a sweet eaten directly following the other courses and not at some casual remove (*Path-Breaker, Sweet Outrider*).

Having perfected his menu, the Great Trotter looked about him and found a banquetting hall risen at no great distance from the unfinished North Tower. Down the length of the hall, between pillars of aqua marble, ran a long table, varnished and buffed to a gloss that concealed the many leaves by which its length could be increased depending on the number of guests expected. High-backed chairs upholstered with maroon leather stood along the walls, ready to be drawn up should the occasion arise. Chandeliers cut and worked by Bohemian craftsmen hung in festoons waiting for the brilliant dinner parties that would last far into the night. The walls beyond the col-onnades were lined with tapestries depicting revels of bygone ages in far countries; the pictures in between showed wedding scenes with wine and food in plenty and riotous guests convivially entwined. But Justin ate alone.

The First Trotter dined in solitude. His gigantic meals took up a fraction of the table, being carried to him in relays of ascending complexity, the covers shifted nearer the Nakhlau end as he progressed, sinking ever deeper into his upright chair. At length the First Trotter would sigh and call for his finger-bowl, indicating that he was done with preliminaries. The sigh would twine about the marble columns, creep down the corridor, and slip in at the kitchen door. At once another and louder sigh would come back out. Puri fryers would get up and stretch, curry-factors mop their armpits; a few hours' rest was theirs, for now the sweetmeat brigade were busying themselves with trays of halva, hefting bowls of laddus on their shoulders, unfurling sheets of beaten silver for the jalebis. When Justin saw out of the corner of his eye a dozen bearers making for him along the corridor in Indian file, his heart would leap up and go out to meet them and he would count himself the most fortunate of men. I will call this place Sans Souci, he breathed; and he did.

The last sweet gone (*Evening Raga, Dark Pavan*) Justin was yet conscious of an unnamed anxiety that roamed the table, hovering like some disconsolate wasp. A knowledge he had been dimly aware of all along began to coat his tongue and for a moment cleft it to the roof of his mouth. Justin was bored. He was tired, not of life, not of eating (*Hair-Splitting Narrator, Quibbling School-man*), but of eating alone. Justin was lonely. Not that he was ignorant of the pleasures of secret food-hoards, solitary feasts, private rumination; nor were the giant banquetting hall meals devoid of charm, and their advantage over communal meals did not escape one who had known the privations of a regimental mess. It was simply that he could not, he knew, always and forever eat alone. On such occasions Justin would have liked to lift his head and see at the far end of the table a face, soft and contemplative, regarding him with, if not motherly devotion, wifely love.

Justin fixed his brown eye on the past. He saw Job Charnock, founder of Calcutta, snatch a woman from her husband's funeral pyre and make her his wife. Their descendants would populate the space, as yet blank, between Park Street and Dhurrumtollah, Chowringhee and the Lower Circular Road. But that was Calcutta: how to do a Charnock *here*? Wife-burning was rare in these parts; Nakhlau was a cultured city. (Now Delhi was another matter, he saw, his blue eye scanning the future.) But what to do in Nakhlau?

The First Trotter applied to his master-and-friend, the Nawab. The Nawab knew of a certain family with three daughters, beauties all, it was said (though no man had looked upon them and they had never seen the world). Already in their twenties, and past marriageable age, they continued to refuse prospective offers because no men of their own kind were available. They were of the Prophet's line. In straitened circumstances, the family kept its proud resolve: when had one of them married an outsider? They heard with horror the Nawab's offer on behalf of his Commander-in-Chief, communicated by a lady of the court. A refusal was given and the daughters lived on as before, by prayer, embroidery, and fasting. A year went by in which the offer was repeated with each new moon and refused the same night. The sisters kept up their netting and lace and chikan work, the Nawab returned to Molière, and the East Tower of Sans Souci was completed. Justin, always intrigued by resistance, persisted. Then, without a word, the second sister, reputedly the most beautiful of the three, disappeared. Along with her there vanished an old woman who had served the family as cook-and-slave for many years. The pair were met at the bridge across the Ganda Nala by the Great Trotter's men (led by the young baker's apprentice-and-condottiere) and conveyed to Sans Souci, where the East Tower was given them. Word got back to the family, the brother swore blood-vengeance, the two remaining sisters stared long and accusingly at the door, the father was broken-hearted, and the precinct was outraged. But the marriage was solemnized and Sultana Trotter refused to return.

Reflections while netting in the East Tower

Let them howl! What's done is done, though I still wonder if it was not all a dream. What was that long blur of light that began at our back door and ended here? What were those strange shapes in the street? I had no idea houses were built so high—and all this just outside our house, it can't have been more than a few paces away. And those strange jutting wooden ledges on our own house, with railings and pillars, overlooking the street—what were they for? That was my last glimpse before Her Ugliness tugged me away saying, Chal bitiya, hurry. One building I seem to remember, it must have been a mosque, with a dome so high and beautiful it must have taken a hundred years to build, blue as the sky and glinting like a ringstone. That must be where Father and Jafar go to pray, because they used to say it was just ten minutes away. But father and brother they no longer are—Jafar, they say, threatens to kill me—and the Frenchman—to avenge the dishonour. As if he could kill a rabbit! Was that a rabbit which Father brought home for us as a plaything when we were little, or is that also a dream? Everything's confused. No, it was real—I remember the trail of hot pellets it used to leave as it hopped about. And in the afternoon, after our rest, I was always up first to feed it carrot sticks. Once Jafar, with that strange devilish look in his eye, threw it high in the air and let it fall. I remember the sound as it fell on its side, like a masak. Maybe he'd like to do the same to me—I think he loved the rabbit too. He was, I remember now, always afraid to let us hold it: we were too silly, we would choke it, it would bite off our ears. When Father came home from his hajj and told us all about the strange and holy sights of Arabia and the road through Persia, Jafar took up the staff and said when he was grown up he would make the same journey. Naz, Nafiza, and I sat watching quietly. How proud we were of him, though he was younger than any of us! And Father smiled and nodded. What is a dome, Father? I asked him, and he cupped his hands on high and brought them down in two curves. And what is a bridge? Ever since I was little I wanted to see a bridge. He held both arms straight out in front of him. And what does a river look like? One hand moved forward weaving in and out. But that's a snake! I shouted, and Mother was angry, and Jafar began to scold me as though I wasn't older by two years and three fingers. Of course he grew fond of me later, but that was because he had a wife to scold, and then two. And when Naz whispered to me one day that she would like to marry soon because she was already eighteen, and I whispered it to him like a fool, he got terribly angry and told Father and Father came and shouted at all of us, saying we were shameless creatures who wished to ruin his good name. A poor man he might have become, he said, but a good name was worth great riches. Sooner or later, he said, calming down, a man of the line would be found for each of us, and until then Naz was not to give the rest of us ideas. From that time on Naz doubled her fasting and prayers and studied her Arabic for an extra hour and worked twice as hard at her netting. She must have known from Mother what flour and oil cost, though Mother hid such things from the younger ones. I used to envy Naz her quickness—I had trouble enough with Urdu, and my embroidery was never very good, I think. I was always dreaming of rivers and bridges. When Mother died it was even harder because her work was best of all and used to fetch more. And Father became irritable, poor man, and scolded me if I got the least letter wrong, saying, This is how you repay me!—I should have let you grow up ignorant and unlettered like the neighbours' daughters, like the women in every other zenana, their heads full of gossip and tattle, slandering even their own menfolk. I suppose you will be talking about me next. As if any of us would have dreamt of it! True, Nafiza did her share of gossiping, even though she was the youngest—never a tongue as cruel as hers. Always scheming with one sister-in-law against the other. This one has a secret stock of jewels which she hoards while her husband's family want, that one is a sullen deceitful flirt. So that Jafar would come home from prayers and beat one wife or the other, and they would come to me and show me their bruises. And Naz looking at all of us as if we were filth—though she never let her eyes rest on me too long. She knew I was prettier, and sometimes it was as if she was afraid of me. Not that I would have challenged her, with her Arabic and all that. Yet the more she studied, the more she prayed, the more bitter she became, refusing to talk to the rest of us, heaping the most unpleasant tasks on Nafiza because she was the youngest. What is the good of all this fasting and study if it makes you sour? Jafar is almost as stern and regular as Father, yet he pulls his wives' hair, and at mealtimes there was hardly ever any food left when he was finished. And that Khurram who came every other day, God's name forever on her lips, but also all the mean tales of the town. I laughed too sometimes, she had such a droll way about her. Father—have I begun to judge him?—his was only a blindness to his son's faults. Yet it was not always so. Before Mother died we were happy. But what a fuss when the offer came! The tray sent back, the scenes, the scoldings. Naz already committed to a life of fasting, to God; Nafiza moody and watchful. It would have blown over had the offer not come again and again—and even then it would have come to nothing if Her Ugliness had not grown tired of living on scraps. So thanks to her I'm here. And what have I gained? A husband who is twice my age, whose language I do not speak and who speaks Urdu like a foreign bird; servants—even Her Ugliness has a maid!—; rich food; a tower. And what have I lost? My father, who will die, whom I loved unstintingly and who loved me best, I think; the company of my sisters, whose faults seem daily less important; my brother, who seems to have had my interests at heart; our friends. It's like being in another country. But so was the street outside our house. What a journey, Allah! So this is how Father felt in Persia and Arabia. To think I envied him his rivers and bridges! Well, now I have seen a dome and crossed a bridge, and from here I can see, in the distance there, a river.

(CHRONICLE RESUMED)

The brother headed a deputation to the Nawab. The Nawab, accustomed to deputations, said, I will see. Come back in a week. And touching the purse, he allowed the Prime Minister to take it. The precinct's wrath cooled, but the brother returned to court. You must go there yourself and ask, the Nawab advised. See what she has to say. Sultana, Her Ugliness standing guard, said: What's done cannot be undone. I am married. And the brother was escorted away, returning to his patient wives. The father died and his errant daughter set up a new zenana into which she retreated with relief. The spirited bid of that one journey had left her exhausted. Her beauty drained away down hamam sluices and brass spittoons, her hair grew brown and stringy and came away in the comb, her sap-green body thinned with each waning moon. She saw her husband rarely, and ate with him not at all. Only one person seemed to have profited from the exercise. Her Ugliness, eating rich food and waited on by a maid, grew younger, unbent, and held her head up as servants never do. Her ancient breasts, which for years had hung like empty panniers, filled out, her shrunken calves grew sleek, and her one ornament from the lean days, a wedding ring, had to be cut off her big toe.

In due course there came a child. A sickly shred of a boy who lay there trembling like a filament of coiled metal in a laboratory yet to come. From time to time an erratic charge would shake him to his atoms, his bulbous eyes would flash and start from their sockets, and his five extremities would thrash about, but no sound escaped him. He will be a soldier, pronounced Alexander, the first foreign artisan to arrive at Sans Souci. A great lover, said a beardless Hakim Ahmed, pinching the blue foreskin as he put away his bamboo stethoscope. A pilgrim, said his mother, gazing through the window at a picture-book world. A wrestler, said Her Ugliness, slapping an oily thigh. A corpse, said Justin, turning away.

Not one of them was wrong. The boy flickered on, suckled by Her Ugliness in whose bounteous breast there ran an inexhaustible supply of milk. It was as well there did, because otherwise he should have drained every cow and buffalo and mother-goat and elephant and nursemaid and mahua tree in Sans Souci. Before long the strength took root, and although his khaki limbs remained wiry, especially the legs, it was plain that many years would pass before he was a corpse. His mother smiled weakly at him, the jade moons darkening under her eyes, and he stared back, but neither made a sound.

Each day when she had finished smiling, Sultana would take a little vermicelli pudding (*Fatal Continence*). Next she did an hour's netting or embroidered her bedsheet green on green in chikan-work so fine it caused her delicate skin no discomfort. Afterwards she would turn her son over to an ayah and ask Her Ugliness to carry her downstairs. There, at the perron that led down to the Water Gate, a glass-bottomed palanquin would be waiting, and she would climb, veiled, into it. Go, she commanded the palki-bearers, and every day the question came back: Where? Settling in, she replied: Just go. And the palki wandered over Sans Souci while Her Ugliness, who sat opposite, called out directions following Sultana's random finger. Now left! Now right! Now straight on! Now wheel! And every now and then, *Stop!* Her Ugliness would climb out, careless of purdah, ogling perhaps one of the palki-bearers, and stooping under the palki with a great show of leg, pick up the object which had caught her mistress's eye. Then the palki would move on until another object was sighted or the command came, Enough!

In this way Sultana brought home a feather, or a leaf, or a blue stone, or an eggshell, or a snakeskin, or a shoehorn, or a tamarind seed, or a sticky balloon, or a dragonfly, or a footprint, or a fig. She made no attempt to classify the things she gathered, a matter of great frustration to Justin on his permitted visits, but simply set each object down after long scrutiny beside the last one found. A kite might chance to fall beside a piece of string, but the string lay beside the nozzle of a watering-can, and that beside a rat-poisoner's conscience and that beside a tea-cosy. Day by day Sultana's hoard grew until all the niches and mantelshelves in her room were filled. Eventually the windows were blocked up with cabinets to make room for the tiger's claws and tailor-bird's nests, while cannonballs and clouds lay in heaps on the floor, finally spilling over into the cradle where a silent babe rocked. Justin would enter at the outer door, having first asked Her Ugliness if his wife were seemly, and tiptoe through the jumble to where his son lay. He looked down into the cradle at the boy whose breath came and went softly among rusty arrowheads and monsoon toads. The boy stopped rocking and returned his father's gaze with equanimity, until his bright eyes flicked away and met his mother's, and the two exchanged a look of deep unsmiling love.

"What about a name for the boy?" the First Trotter broke in one day. Coming up he had tripped on a python-skin.

"A name?" Sultana murmured and lapsed into silence.

"Yes, nama, nom, name. For the boy."

But already she had drifted off, picking up an arrowhead and pressing its tip into the heel of her fragile palm. She dropped the object with a cry as a petal of blood appeared on her hand.

"What is that?" she shivered.

Justin gave her the name in three languages. While she repeated the words, he leaned over and fastened a Sans Souci locket around his son's neck. ☞ *The locket is fastened.*

Then he picked his way across the carpet, casting as he went a despairing eye over the room's disorder. That night he sat musing at his marquetry table with the turned barley-sugar legs. Presently, aroused from his meditations by the snapping of a strand of cane in the seat of his chair, he took up a pen and opened his journal.

Journal entry in the Great Trotter's Green Book

She is daily more frail, more distracted, if distraction be the word for her malady, and if indeed her malady have a name. Our son also lacks a name, though he grows bigger and stronger with each day. The Moorish ayah will make a wrestler of him yet—I no longer fear for his life though he has yet to cry or smile as healthy infants are said to do. His mother has already begun to teach him to recognize objects and he appears to respond with intelligence, though he cannot yet be brought to repeat the words she mouths. Her collection grows ever greater; it is as well she inhabits a lofty tower. Next month

I will suggest she move up one further storey since she will not be persuaded to give up her collecting until she has reproduced the world. But what chaos there! It is like the Nawab's army—gunners marching with swordsmen, spahis rushing in pell-mell, an elephant preceding a horse. Nothing in its proper place—that place continually invaded by a host of ill-assorted identities. Each object warring with the next, yet every creature accommodating its neighbour, the substantial trafficking with the insubstantial, the contrary rubbing shoulders with the same, that which agrees seducing that which clashes, change surprised by permanence, exclusion and concurrence running together, effect stealing a march on cause. What is one to say of a world put together by some giddy tailor-bird? Our very magpies are models of order beside this hotchpotch happenchance nest. And yet cohere it does, the whole cemented with an invisible native glue. In all that welter my wife knows readily enough where any object is to be found. And though she may not know its function—inhabiting as much as I do a new world—she has an inexhaustible appetite for names. Does the proliferation of labels subtly change the nature of a thing? Is it a weakness, this fluidity of names disguising a rigidity of functions? Strength is a single name cloaking a multiplicity of functions—France at war, France making peace; England taking Bengal, England pacifying India. But what is this India? Is it not a thousand shifting surfaces which enamour the newcomer and then swallow him up? It allows him the many titles of victory while obliging him to accept a single rigid function, that of conqueror. The very divisiveness that allowed him in enmeshes him. How is he to grasp what cannot be held—what in fact holds him fast? Is this a perverse and passive strength? How is he to fire a weapon whose triggers are so numerous and interlocked? This man is a Gentoo, that one a Moor; this stray beast is sacred to one, is freely slaughtered by the other—who will consider himself polluted by still another creature; other sects delight in sacrifice, still others wear masks across the mouth and nose lest they unwittingly kill the smallest germ. How am I to forge an army of these multitudes—I who not a year ago dreamt of even greater things? Can I hope to find my wife unveiled or am I condemned to see her always through a gauze of ideas that I bring with me, notions that are not of India but of France? Yet if I endeavour to put aside these ideas I am lost in a maze of particulars. Their scriptures do not help; there, so I am told, the one concept that unites these disparate objects—Hindoostan—is defined simply as the land where the black buck roams. The nearer I approach this land the further I am driven back into my already formed ideas, and I conclude by studying—despite my intentions, my love—not India but Europe, or Europe's India, which is the same thing.

    My intentions wilt, my love is tediously irresolute—only force will take this variegated India. The British know it; Bengal is theirs and it is only a matter of time before they find a pretext to take Tirnab. The last Nawab was called Rangila, the Colourful, for his sensuality, his dissolute enjoyment of things that he might have spent a little energy ordering. The British will simply invert the proposition, substituting order for enjoyment, but their control will partake of pleasure for all that. After the first spoliation will come restraint, regulated pleasure, a profitable deferring of the moment—and postponement is the strictest bliss. But what child will come of the union? Pray God my son live. I would give my life for him. Lately I have been studying, with the help of Qaiyum, who knows Persian and some Arabic as well as Oordoo, certain *namas* which tell the story of this land. I have also purchased many hundreds of miniature paintings, some of which are exceptionally [*illegible*].

(INTERPOLATION)

Concerning certain miniaturists, chiefly Mughal

Drawing the likeness of anything, says Abu'l Fazl, flatterer-and-platitudinarian, in his *Akbar-Nama*, is called *taswir*, picture. The Great Trotter (peace be His) collected taswirs indiscriminately, large-hearted man that he was. For instance, his librarian's shelf list includes both the original Indian *Tota-Nama* and the Persian translation of it, the *Tuti-Nama*, trifling things to judge by either taswir or text, romantic intrigues and far-fetched stories told by a dirty parrot. And as for pictures per se, the good man seems to have surrendered his judgement altogether. The library was crammed with indifferent work by such names as Basawan, Daswanth the Suicide (speaks for itself, that), Ranthambhor (who helped illustrate the *Akbar-Nama*), Miskina or Mushkin or Mushkil the Difficult, Madhu the Elder, Tulsi the Younger, Kanha, Kesu, Lal, Govardhan, etc., etc., et so painfully cetera. Even someone called Zarrin Qalam or Golden Pen, who specialized in calligraphy. These are the twerps the Third Trotter (who passed for an artist) would model his early work on, and we can be grateful that few of either the originals or the copies escaped the fire of 1857. But I'm running on ahead. If you want a specimen of their work, there's a painting of some emaciated opium-eaters that was sold and made its way to the Red Fort museum at Delhi (entrance free). The Third Trotter admired it; you'll see him—he didn't even eat opium. Enough; I rest my case. Prejudice? All right, I'll name an exception—Khwaja Abu's Samad rose above the general mediocrity. He was called Shirin Qalam or Sweet Pen, and came, noteworthily, from Shiraz.

Tell me now, Narrator, how Sans Souci was built in the fat days.
You wish to know, Cup-Bearer?
Most heartily.
You will not scoff?
When have I scoffed?
In the tuck-shop, Cup-Bearer. But fetch me some Shiraz wine, go. What?
*   So quick!*
The Khyber Pass was open, Narrator.
Marvellous, but now listen. I have heard from the tailor-bird that
*   it happened in this way.*

(CHRONICLE RESUMED)

Barred from his fading wife and nameless son, Justin turned his energies into stone: he began to build in earnest. The makeshift bridge across the Ganda Nala by which the Nawab's cannon and the Nawab himself had rolled for the French-style manoeuvre-cum-fireworks, the same by which Trotter cannon had rolled in the opposite direction during the year of the black pall, and at whose centre the First Trotter's posse had met Sultana and Her Ugliness, he had demolished. In its place was set a lime-washed slab which would in time come to be called the Ice Bridge. The new bridge was opened and traffic doubled across its wide false arch, wagons of foodstuffs clattering towards Sans Souci from the city, the bullocks snorting, and camel-carts of Trotter gunpowder moving leisurely the other way.

Other wagons brought the building materials of Sans Souci. Until now sufficient grey stone had been found in the quarry that abutted the jungle to the east, but as the plans for the château and its surrounds grew more complex, materials from other parts of Tirnab and beyond began to arrive. There came marble, red sandstone, teak, crystal, black sand, aluminium, shale, beryl, jade, adamant, mica, lead, iron, ash, reddle, glass, tinsel, stucco, cork, tin, china, leather, hemp, mallow, chalcedony, brick, cedar, bamboo, cane, pine, balsa, rice-paste, wood, wire, nails, rope, schist, gypsum, ash, zarrinmlamin, chrysoprase, cast iron, angle-iron, and jaggery, or raw sugar, which when mixed with lime and ash makes a mortar stronger than rock. Caravans, elephants, bullock-cart trains and crocodiles of coolies beat a path that would come to be the Trotter Road. Many of their consignments might have been more conveniently unloaded at a jetty east of Sans Souci on the banks of the Kirani river, but the jetty was not yet built, nor was the road to the river, and in any case the Nawab required all imports to pass through his taxman's hands. In later years the firangi Commander-in-Chief was able to persuade his master that Sans Souci warranted its own dock, but by then the building was virtually complete. As for white sand, lime, clay, and mango-wood, all were in abundant supply in the First Trotter's domain.

After the carts there came on foot, by boat, by yak, and on horseback, rock-breakers from Cape Comorin, tilers from Peiping, earth-movers from Cooch Behar, dome-dressers from Petersburgh, gipsy blacksmiths from the Thar desert, spirit-levellers from Isphahan, a plinth-master from Tibet, rampart-setters from Benin, a Scottish mason, plasterers from Cochin China, steeplejacks from Hradcany, master-builders from Ellora and Elephanta, stylites from Memphis and Corinth, Malayan dog-men, terracers from Macchu Picchu, and strawmen and thatchers from the surrounding villages. Already hard at work was a Macedonian sculptor. They came without being called; word spread like windblown sand and in each place where it entered a man kissed his children and his wife, took up his tools, and set his face towards Sans Souci.

Workers' villages, dormitories, brothels, and canteens sprang up on three sides of the existing structure, where as yet there stood only two towers, kitchens, and a banquetting hall. By day a hundred pillars of grey smoke stood over lime pits and blacksmiths' furnaces that had once been a foundry. Vapours from shale tubs stung the eye, and the hot June air sang with the smack of pitch. By night the same fires wore cooking pots, brass for the Hindus, zinc for everyone else. A maze of tracks was beaten from the campsites to a thousand workplaces, and in the spaces in between there grew up dense thickets of scaffolding. Along the tangle of lines, Justin, watching from his tower, saw ten thousand workers darting to and fro, purposeful as ants. And among them moved by fits and starts an inquisitive queen—a black palki that now scurried left, now right, now straight, now stopped to scratch in the sand.

At night there drifted across the dark plain the smell of beet borscht and chapatis, of roasted yams and parched corn, potato pancakes, noodle soup and okra fried crisp in olive oil. After a space in which the dotted fires shrank to twinkling points of red, there rose the belch of tablas, the clink of blacksmiths' songs, a thrumming of mandolins and balalaikas, and from halfway up the saltpetre hill the drone of a lone highland piper. Not a hundred years later the bagpipes would play another tune on that same ground, but tonight the sound twined nasal and melancholy, complaining of a love without return. And Justin's heart swole with longing for a wife whose arms grew frail as cobwebs, her breasts lighter than moonbeams, her legs a single strand of silk. Far into the night he lay awake, touched by the sounds of darkness, of jackals howling in a jungle clearing, of pi-dogs barking back, of one young woman screeching her despair from a brothel door. Turning over, Justin explored the cracks in the canvas weave of his bed until he fell asleep and woke in the morning with dark-ringed eyes and a coated tongue. After breakfast he threw himself into the business of building Sans Souci, pretending to control what he could hardly credit, hurrying from site to site as if hoping to outrun the black palki whose forays became more frantic with every passing day.

"Press on!" the First Trotter pleaded with the gipsy lohars, and the splendid Indigo Gate came to lack a fence on either side. "Leave off!" the First Trotter screamed at a shameful huddle of Corinthians, and twenty-four white columns were left without pediment or roof as the builders moved on to a new task. "Let it be!" the First Trotter begged a kneeling Chaldean, and the sundial forever lacked a gnomon, the astronomer shambling off with many oaths. "Can you not hurry?" the First Trotter called up the scaffolding to the Malayan dog-men who were busy knotting twine around bamboo, and that afternoon four plasterers fell a hundred feet to their deaths. "A little haste!" the First Trotter urged the Tibetan plinth-master, who was conferring by signs with the spirit-levellers of Isphahan, and the Cock Hall or Spur got its tilt from north to south. "Time is short!" whined the First Trotter within earshot of the Cooch Behari earth-movers, and the fleur-de-lis lake was set upon a course that would end with a fish Tank.

Work went on, stopping nowhere long enough to finish. Every day mock windows multiplied, mock shutters standing in for the glass panes sent to enclose the music pavilion. Two rows of aluminium buttresses flew up with nothing to support between them: the crystal for the cathedral walls had gone to build a triumphal arch at the Gunpowder Gate. The lead from the lightning conductor was melted down and beaten into sheets to fill the clerestories of the library. The dome above the Audience Hall shed mica tiles with every gust of loo; the gypsum was wanted to seal the Water Gate. The bowl of a garden fountain was carried to the other side of Sans Souci to serve as a mandap in front of a proposed temple. The dome-dressers of Petersburgh threw up their hands and started for the Khyber Pass; the master-builders of Ellora and Elephanta paced the dockside waiting for a riverboat that was not polluted by Cochin Chinese coffins; the Scottish mason had already gone without waiting to be paid; the Isphahani spirit-levellers vanished without a trace, the Memphis stylites shook the dust off from their sandals, and an entire camp of gipsy lohars disappeared overnight into the desert. The grounds around *Sungum*, the pride of Sans Souci, returned to their former state.

Who remained? Of those who remained was one of the gipsy blacksmiths' number, an enchantress left behind to stamp out the furnace embers which smouldered unaccountably on. Unable to assist her was the ancient Tibetan plinth-master who remained to meditate on the field of cannonballs. More successful was the Macedonian sculptor, Alexander, whose work was not yet done.

Who came late? Of those who arrived late was a Turinian cripple, wounded at Borromini. He had been commissioned to engrave a series of mezzotints showing the progress of Sans Souci, and was now compelled to work from memory. Also there were two Nepali brothers, Munnoo and Nankoo, last surviving members of the caste Floor-Polisher, which had in latter days (they lamented) become a mere trade filled with self-seeking men.

Who came last? Qaiyum-i-najum, astrologer-and-poet, better known as Qaiyum the Tardy, a handsome bloated wineskin of a man, never without a tumbler of palm toddy by his divan. Some called him Qaiyum the Toddy. His loaf of bread was flat, the book of verse slipped sometimes from his grasp, the woman never came, but his cup ran always over with country liquor. A great lover of the Persian poets, he read astrology for its couplets and only rarely falsified a planetary conjunction to suit his own attempts at rhyme. Diligent in his divan, he could spend months together polishing a single line.

The workers gone, these artists stayed behind, each burnishing the chosen mirror of his soul. *And is this not a lofty end?*

Presently, imperceptibly, the scars in the barren plain closed over, thanks to early rains, to the gardeners who made Nakhlau famous among garden cities, and to Sultana's pointing finger. With its failing strength it flickered this way and that, finding a hinge, a nail, a spirit-level, a pair of lost tongs. The larger, immovable objects—a brick kiln, a lime pit—were allowed to remain, but Sultana exacted close descriptions of them from Her Ugliness before she was satisfied. When the palki had moved on, Justin would arrive with a team of gardeners and insist that the feature be worked into the plan, the kiln turned into a Japanese tea-house, the quicklime pit into a lotus pond. These anomalies apart, the gardens were laid out on classical lines which cut across the contours of the land, regardless of salients and dips and showing little concern for texture whether in the grouping of trees or in the shrubbed grading of a bank. "Formality, regularity, uniformity," the French firangi lectured his team of puzzled gardeners, "—only, hurry!" The gardeners dispersed to join his will to their desire, and the plans were subtly changed. The mehndi-hedge maze in the sunken garden lost its severe corners, its right angles softening into whorls until it came to resemble a giant fingerprint in relief; the stiff ranks of hollyhocks were infiltrated by hobson or jasmine creepers; and the toddy-palms around the Tank grew up in clumps instead of forming an impenetrable fence along its banks.

(VERSE)

Who will praise these heart-expanding gardens?
Who match in verse these chest-expanding walks?

Where peacocks glist and custard-apples are dense
And sweetly high the darkling cranny squawks?

(CHRONICLE RESUMED)

One morning the Great Trotter rose in good spirits. Today was the hired gardeners' last day, and it was also his customary day for visiting the East Tower. He had a gift for his wife (who was now on the topmost level of the tower and running out of room) and moreover, he had slept through the jackals and the answering pi-dogs. If that were not enough, word had come to him the previous evening through his young baker-and-prospector that a seemingly endless vein of curry powder had been struck in the saltpetre hill. He meant to verify the claim himself, so after breakfast instead of making his way down to the gardens he stepped out at the Indigo Gate (carefully threading the narrow gate-within-a-gate, although there was still no fence on either side of the massive pillars) and, leaving the old armoury behind on his right, followed the path past the kitchens which led to the mines. The baker-and-curry-favourer proved to have been right, though how he had got his information when the ovens were a considerable way off and the mine superintendent had himself only this morning learnt of the find, was hard to say. The deposit, one of exceptional purity, ran alongside a lode of middling saltpetre and then appeared to widen indefinitely.

On the correct method of mining curry powder (Memb. III Sect. 2 Subs. 2)

The correct method of mining curry powder is this. They first locate a vein. The signs are a whitish yellow flocculation at the surface where the matter has oozed. A shaft is sunk into the living rock and from it subsidiary shafts let in, radiating outwards like the spokes of a wheel but always at an angle just above the horizon. During this process a thin high-pitched wail will be heard, distractive to most workers, attractive to some. It must be ignored, being simply a show of reluctance. For up to a week there will be no result. Then of its own accord the powder will loosen and travel down the secondary shafts borne by its weight under the force of gravity. Gravity is the preponderant element in this operation. (It is much the same with rubber and maple sugar.) Collection tins may be placed at the bottom of the central pit, but some use jars neatly labelled, for example, *Elephant Brand Famous Hot*, or *Col. Trotter's Medium*, or *Major Grey's Mild*. They are drawn to the surface by rope, bullocks being skittish and wasteful, and the tray sent down again.

(CHRONICLE RESUMED)

Congratulating himself on his luck with the hill, the Great Trotter descended towards the music pavilion humming the Rejouissance from Handel's *Fireworks Suite*. "Sans Souci!" he shouted inly, and unable to contain himself he glided into a roulade: "Sans Souci-i-i-i-i, i-i-i-i-i, i-i-i-i-i, i-i-i-i-!" until he was out of breath and sweating aesthetically. It occurred to him as he approached the pagodalike structure that he had not heard a note of music since the last Company bugle call. He made a mental note to scan the Calcutta and Bombay papers for a fiddler or two, a couple of hoboys and perhaps a French horn (or failing that, a *cor anglais*). Climbing the steps of the pavilion, he found nine of its ten sides glassed in; the tenth, by which he entered, faced away from the stone amphitheatre and towards the tableland. "This won't do, this won't do," he muttered, a beam of annoyance playing on his forehead where until now all had been pleasant and cloudy. He had meant to make this the start of a walking tour of his estate, and here was an unpromising beginning.

He crossed the chrysoprase floor, noticing the hush as the noise of the world was shut out. Then he looked out at one of the glassed sides. What he saw almost unhinged him. He darted to the next window, and there was a fresh invitation to madness. He ran from window to window around the pavilion, his brain dizzy from each new assault on reason, until he knocked his forehead on a ladder. From above came a sharp curse in Italian, followed presently by the swearer: it was the cripple, Marazzi. He slid down the ladder, gripping its sides with hands that seemed to grow directly out of his shoulders, while his barrel chest (which made him wider than he was tall) struck a descending scale of notes on the rungs. The scale ended abruptly when his feet slammed into the floor. He had been too absorbed in his work to notice the visitor, but when he saw who it was a high laugh erased the expletive.

"Monsieur Trotter, welcome to the Music!"

"But what is all this?" the Great Trotter cried. He pointed through the pavilion windows at a deranged Sans Souci. "What *is* this, Marazzi!"

The cripple's face went directly from pleasure to melancholy.

"It is what you asked for, Monsieur Trotter—views of your château's progress."

"But my château is reduced to a battered fortress—a ruin—an hotel!" Justin was waving his arms. "What has *happened*, Marazzi?" And he turned, making as if to run out and check.

"It is all still there, Monsieur Trotter," Marazzi said softly, bowing his head so that his fingers reached up to his ears in a gesture of reproof. "And," he continued, dropping his voice still further, "I am faithfully reproducing (or you might say producing) it. Only, since I was not present at the time of building (I lay bleeding at Borromini) I am compelled to rely upon memory. And memory (especially memory of what one has not seen) is a most coquettish thing; wanton, one might almost say (if one might say)."

He hobbled across to the window which looked directly out at the dome and the three finished towers.

"You see," he said without turning, "I was obliged to paint her as she might have been, and this might-have-been (especially when it might yet be) (but probably will not) is a most elusive thing; spectral, one might almost say (if one might say). Let us say (may we?) it might have been a place of experiment, of vision, of breadth, but the people who lived there did not have enough (how to say) faith (?) in themselves." He spoke as one looking back at the future.

"Why, it's *paint*!" exclaimed Justin, going up to the glass and examining it with a fingernail. "But so lifelike! And it moves when you do—behind the glass." He peered around the edge of the frame, and more of the scene appeared, but when he stepped back the picture shrank and the window beside it showed another view altogether. "Do you know," he offered, his good humour returning, "I mean to call my seat Sans Souci."

Marazzi's eyes disappeared in a smile. "Monsieur Trotter is doubtless aware that every house built in Europe since the peace is called Sans Souci. There are six in my district alone. I know a sculptor whose bread and butter is Sans Souci gate plaques. He will make his fortune yet."

Justine broke in. "The amphitheatre!" he accused the painter-and-illusionist, "—it's gone—it should be there." His finger pointed downwards through the window opposite the entrance.

"Stained away, Monsieur. And the Armoury, too. And the West Tower—and the Gunpowder Gate. *Puf!* But they are there in the next window."

"And that one there?"

"That is Sans Souci from the other side. And this is Sans Souci from above, and this," he pointed to a pane almost opaque until one came up close, "—is Sans Souci from below. And these others are possible Sans Soucis, and that is an impossible Sans Souci—but since it is there it is perhaps not impossible but merely improbable; tall, one might say (if one might say)."

"Sans Souci from above! Preposterous, Marazzi," said Justin. He peeled and ate a hand of bananas. "Sacrilegious, one might say," he ventured, catching the painter-and-suppositionist's infection. He looked at the dark window showing Sans Souci from below. It was a ghostly blueprint of his château and the land about it on which there appeared a great deal more than he had planned. Faults, seams, ancient burial pits, vanished foundations, underground streams, and root systems showed through, etched into the smoky glass. Even the mineshafts sunk in the saltpetre hill stood out whitely like the bones of a splayed hand.

"Well, Monsieur Trotter, I must go back up," said the little man, sucking a paintbrush. "There are still some stubborn skylights to do, and who is to say what is visible through them?" He grappled with his ladder and shook it till it stood firm, then, taking the brush between his teeth and pressing his palate between cheek and shoulder, he rammed his way back up, rung by rung, to his perch. "If you wish," he called down, "for something more plausible or (how to say) delectable, I will paint the ceiling of your Audience Hall for you." And with that he returned to his skylights, cursing the glass, which seemed to reject every kind of paint.

Sobered, Justin emerged from his glassed-in music pavilion, bracing himself against the noise of the world. Coming around to the other side, he found the amphitheatre still there. Its steps, which he began to mount, were of sandstone from the quarry, grey, solid, and irrefutable.

The Great Trotter sloped across the open ground that lay before the Indigo Court. July had painted it a soothing green, but he found himself droning the adagio from the Water Music. As he neared the Hava Manzil, a deep low answering note began to buzz in his ear. The Hava Manzil was a square building of milky green marble topped with a clear dome, built with no end in view other than to rhyme with the Begam Kothi, an identical structure on the other side of Sans Souci. The Begam Kothi was his gift to Sultana; unlike her present quarters it was visible from the West Tower. Justin walked around the Hava Manzil looking for a door by which he might enter. He found none. His frown deepening, he saw that the dome that he had taken to be of clear glass was in fact a skeleton frame, open to the sky. No door, no roof—had the same mistake been made with the Begam Kothi on the other side? He hastened across the court, up the apron of steps, and in at the northeast door. He had not gone three paces when he tripped over a crouching figure and fell heavily on the Audience Hall floor. Sitting up, he saw that it was not one but two figures that had brought him down: it was Munnoo and Nankoo, the floor-polishers.

"What in God's name are you two—?" Justin began, but swallowed the rest of a foolish question. Munnoo and Nankoo were polishing the floor. From their point of view, however, the Great Trotter's inquiry was justified, since their posture did not change for any other of life's essential activities; Munnoo even preferred to sleep crouching.

"Our work," he explained gently.

"Our duty," Nankoo refined. His was the subtle mind.

"Yes, yes, I see that now," said Justin, anxious to be on his way. "Very good," he added, picking himself up and noticing that neither man moved to assist him. "They are not of the caste, Helper," he consoled himself, "or the subcaste, Raisers Up. Their duty extends to raising a shine. Besides which, to touch a foreigner would be polluting, even to one of their mean caste." Then he remembered a bill paid. "But hasn't the floor already been polished?" he asked out loud.

"That it has," said Munnoo laconically.

"If you can call it that," said Nankoo, pressing the matter, "when hired labourers have done the job."

"Wage earners," put in Munnoo.

"Now, you see that portion of the floor," Nankoo persevered. "It was done by them. And this portion is our work."

"Our duty," Munnoo reminded him.

Justin looked at the two areas distinguished. They seemed no different, neither superior to the other. If the gloss on the one was a shade brighter, it was because that patch was nearer the door. He explained this to his interlocutors, who were not impressed.

"Well, consider *these* two portions," said Nankoo, shifting crabwise across the floor. He was all legs and arms, a study in contrasts with his elephantine brother.

The Great Trotter followed him and could still see no difference.

"But you've only begun to look," pursued Nankoo, whose life had been spent staring into the heart of stone.

The Great Trotter stooped and looked long and hard. The longer and harder he looked the more certain he was that the division was imaginary. He looked up to say so, and in that instant Munnoo and Nankoo's portion flashed brighter. He looked down again at once, but the glow was gone; as he looked away, it came back.

Nankoo smiled and nodded, recognizing the recognition.

"You must do my tower next," Justin conceded, straightening up.

Munnoo was also smiling. "We ask no wages—simply our keep."

The Great Trotter hopped away. At the Begam Kothi he was relieved to find the dome satisfactorily glassed in and a door where the door should be. He strolled through the rooms finding everything in order, every window, balcony, and threshold in place. "Then why couldn't they get the other one right?" he demanded. "I and symmetry required it; why were we disobeyed?"

Leaving by the back door, he caught sight of the double row of Corinthian columns and was drawn into their avenue. He passed between them, now looking at the sky, now stopping to gaze at the carved foliage on the top of a pillar, now letting his eye run down a fluted column to the base where a man and woman lay locked in a naked embrace.

"Alexander!" he hissed, turning away.

The gipsy-lohar enchantress leapt up and ran off, her elbows glistening darkly like beaten iron. She disappeared into the nearby Gothic roundhouse, from which Alexander had coaxed her into the sunlight. The roundhouse, built as a ruin to suit Justin's melancholic moods, answered the music pavilion on the other side of Sans Souci; its stones deliberately askew, its mortar crumbling from carefully planted weeds, it lay open to the sky except for one corner where the oracle tree overhung it. Here Alexander had found a temporary studio where he wrestled with the problems of his art, covering the floor with chips of stone. The sculptor-and-fornicator darted behind a pillar from where he cried:

"My commander!"

"Shameful Alexander! Shameless Alexander! In broad daylight."

"My commander!"

"Is this what you are paid to do? And today a working day."

"I was working, my commander."

"Indeed?"

"On Diana, my commander. Diana of the Ephesians."

Justin considered this. "And what other progress have you made since we last met?"

"A great deal, my commander. Achilles is done. And Hector, and many heroes. But Diana . . . In a little while she will be complete."

"A little while," Justin warned. There was a note of envy in his voice. "Remember, you have my tombstone to do." He strode off towards the East Tower, determined to see his wife. As for that muscular maid of hers, Her Ugliness could be sent on a long errand.

She met him at the outer door as usual, barring the way.

"Begam Sahiba is very weak," she muttered.

"Yes," replied the Great Trotter, undaunted. "That Greek has discovered an excellent tonic. Go and find him at once. He should be in the kitchens."

Her Ugliness stood undecided a moment. She had heard of the medical skill of the Greeks and she liked the look of this one, but it was the kitchens that moved her. Her new bangles clanking, she stamped downstairs calling for the palki bearers to be ready and reminding herself that she did this for her mistress's sake.

When she was gone, Justin picked his way across the room and slipped into Sultana's bed. She lay there motionless as stone yet fine as silk, dimly conscious of his presence. With great tenderness he began to unravel the strand of her legs, stroking the frail netting at her elbows as his excitement grew. But when he invited her in his tremulous falsetto to come with him on his journey, she made no answer; she had already set out on another journey so far into herself that her body faded away altogether, and when he opened his eyes Justin was left with the stain that would haunt him ever after. Sultana was gone. Hunt as he might, she was gone, invisible as the chikan work at which she excelled. In the extremity of his sorrow Justin was conscious of a pair of eyes fixed on him nevertheless; there was another presence in the room. Turning, he saw the boy. He was sitting upright in his cradle by the bed, his bullet head glowing. He had a toad balanced on one hand, and he was staring fixedly at his father without a smile.

Sultana was laid to rest that night, the chikan-worked bedsheet supposed to contain her body being carefully wound about itself and secreted in a niche in the grave. All night Justin stood beside the tomb, pricked with remorse and salted with self-reproach. The next day, the sun shone down through a skeleton dome whose panes had gone to glass in the music pavilion. There were no doors to the mausoleum, but the wind frisked over the grave and plucked the harp of the roof, releasing the deep low note that gave the Hava Manzil its name.

Before many days had passed, the boy began to speak. His vocabulary was wholly lacking in adjectives and verbs except those that could be formed from nouns: *inky* he would say for *black*, *pudding* for *to eat*, and *breast* for both *love* and *to love*, as well as for the thing in itself. But inside the bullet head a phenomenal memory was stirring. At two he already knew the names of a thousand things, mainly those he had broken, and by six he had mastered the list of his mother's effects, all of which were transferred to the house that was to have been hers. There, in the Begam Kothi, he lived with Her Ugliness, who oiled his khaki body and made a wrestler of him, rubbing his blue foreskin when he cried or when he lost a match with one of the older Sagarpaysan boys. At night he listened intently to Alexander's tales of war and conquest, of how, as the oracle tree foretold, snow and fire rained down on the first Alexander's men after they routed the Indian king, Porus, or so the Great Macedonian told his tutor, Aristotle. Or Alexander might plunder the Old Testament for stories, telling of how Samson slew ten thousand Philistines with the jawbone of an ass and laid waste their corn by releasing into the fields twelve foxes with firebrands tied to their tails. The boy listened round-eyed, ignorant of case and syntax, careless of who killed whom with what and delighting only in the blood. He was not afraid of the ghost of Al-Iskandar, and sometimes stayed up late hoping to catch a glimpse of the bogey, or at least a fiery fox. In the morning, Her Ugliness would find a decapitated sparrow or garden lizard by his cot. The boy slept blissfully on, with sometimes a trace of red about his lips; and every day he grew stronger. Of his small family, only Justin did not rest in peace.

For two years after his wife's death every remedy failed to induce sleep in the Great Trotter. One day he thought of music, and trying out a few bars of the Water Music adagio, found florets of rust on his voice. In the next breath he said: "The boy needs a mother. He's growing up wild." Justin began to ferret among the Calcutta and Bombay papers.

Advertisements

TO BE WED—A girl aged fourteen or fifteen years, country-born but of white complexion. Obedient and useful, of good temper and character. Educated to the age of thirteen years at the Lower Military Orphanage, Calcutta, and presently employed there.

—*Calcutta Herald*

STRAYED—From the service of his generous master and mistress, Mr. and Mrs. Bull [Ball?], a Christian slave boy aged twenty years or thereabouts, pretty dark or colour of musty, of medium height, broad between the cheekbones and marked with the small pox. It is requested that no one after the publication of this will employ him as a writer or in any other capacity, and any person or persons who will apprehend him and give notice thereof to the printer of this paper shall be rewarded for their trouble.

—*Bombay Beacon*

TO BE SOLD—A boy aged twenty years who writes well and can play very well on the French horn dress hair and shave. Of medium height, dark of colour, his face pitted with the small-pox. Sicca Rupees 100/-

—*Bombay Beacon*

(*CHRONICLE RESUMED*)

The following morning, the baker-and-factotum carried to the Nakhlau dispatch office two letters, one for Calcutta and the other for Bombay. Before the summer was out, two journeys to Sans Souci had commenced, one from each city. The girl, aged twelve, was accompanied by Her Ugliness (sent to Calcutta armed with a letter and a boatload of Sans Souci bodyguards). They got no further than Monghyr when their boat miscarried, all aboard going down. The young man, escorted by a baker-and-comprador (sent to Bombay to collect him), arrived in good fettle, having travelled well, and made no attempt to get away. He had already escaped and did not wish to jeopardize his freedom until he suspected a new slavery; besides, he was eager to see the Sans Souci of which he had heard tell.

The day after his arrival Justin examined his teeth and nails, made him copy out a passage from the Old Testament, and had him play two pieces on the horn. The teeth he found good, the writing fair, and the playing execrable. "What have I bought?" he was lamenting to himself at bedtime when he heard a cough. It was the slave-boy Fonseca. "If you please, sir," he begged, "I have heard that great princes burdened with affairs of state employ story-tellers to talk them to sleep. I am no master of the art of kahani, but you have not yet heard of my journey from Bombay." That night the First Trotter slept as he had not slept for many years. And when in the morning his jowls were shaved and his thinning hair dressed with consummate skill by the same lad who had talked him to sleep, it was difficult to say which was the master and which the slave. In his after-dinner story Fonseca had not yet left Mint Street, Bombay.

The very day word arrived from Monghyr of the river disaster, an offer came from a certain Mr Wilkinson of Jamalpur who had heard of the First Trotter's Muslim marriage. The son of a British indigo factor by a similar marriage, and himself a strict Muslim, Salim Wilkinson had a tribe of sons none of whom he could marry off because of their foreign name; no upstanding family in Jamalpur—and there were many—wished its daughter to turn into a Wilkinson. His one daughter, therefore, though a universally acceptable match, Salim Wilkinson wished to give in marriage to a European convert. Justin raised an eyebrow at the word, but he had slept alone too long to scruple.

The wedding, in the heat of June, was not a success. On the second day, the henna dye sent by the bride's party would not take on Justin's hands and feet. Worse, the sweets which custom required him to snap at while blindfold fell one by one to the floor. On the third day, as the bridegroom's horse went past the Hava Manzil, a gust of wind from the dome caused the creature to rear up, throwing Justin in all his finery into the dust. Finally, when the officiating mullah asked the girl whether the wedding was by her consent, she refused to answer. She had heard that Justin was four times her age. Disgraced, Salim Wilkinson turned the girl out, apologized to the Great Trotter for the scandal, and returned to Jamalpur a broken man. Justin, admiring the girl's spirit, sent for her and made her an offer. "If you cannot be my wife," he said, "be my son's mother." And Farida Wilkinson, a girl of fourteen, was installed in the East Tower.

Introduced to his stepmother, Justin's son said *inky* and turned away, demanding *breast*, but agreeing to *pudding* because Her Ugliness was no longer there. That night there was an explosion below the East Tower. The tower itself was not damaged, nor its occupant hurt, but the armoury and most of its contents were destroyed. How such a quantity of gunpowder had been conveyed from the hunting-lodge-cum-magazine to the armoury, and how the perpetrator had come by fire, which was banned in Sans Souci outside of the kitchens, remained a mystery. Also a riddle was how the perpetrator could have passed in the first place through a vent that would barely take a child. Justin, who had his suspicions, discovered while rummaging among the twisted remains of his fowling pieces, the butt of a country cigarette. Bidi in hand, he marched off round the saltpetre hill—

—When horses without number were his for the riding, Narrator?—

—rode off around the saltpetre hill and across the burning plain he had once used for target practice. There, among the weathered cannonballs and crumbling stupas, sat the Tibetan plinth-master, meditating.

"Teach my son wisdom," the Great Trotter begged. "That Alexander is teaching him to smoke." He waved the offending fragment of rolled tobacco leaf as he spoke. "What's more, I've heard he sprinkles salt on leeches."

The master smiled without opening his eyes, stretched out his arm and ran it along the horizon of the Plain of Cannonballs. "This is your handiwork?" he asked.

The Great Trotter hung his head. "It was done in the years of my folly," he mumbled.

"And now you have found wisdom?"

"If my son could find it, I would be happy." The Great Trotter looked around. "I will have these projectiles removed," he promised.

"Oh, no, please. They are aids to meditation, grist to the mind's mill. But you may wish to restore the stupas."

"Certainly—I will build another."

"There is no need," the master smiled and opened his eyes. "Your son wants instruction?"

"Yes. That Pseudo-Alexander fills his head with the rubble of war."

"That is not in itself a disservice," said the master, surveying the Plain of Cannonballs. He shut his eyes once more and added: "But we will see what can be done for him."

Justin returned to his tower and began to send out for books, chiefly Buddhist works to add to his library. As each one arrived he read it, took notes, and sent it below to Qaiyum, his poet-and-librarian. At the same time he purchased all the curious weapons he could find to fill the new armoury. He sent out men to repair the stupas, and he saw that his son went daily to the plinth-master.

His son's education begun, he turned to the boy's stepmother.

From the start Farida was devout, praying at every watch and much of the day besides, and fasting not only at the appointed season but on feast days (*Mistress of Piety, Excess of Paucity*) and Fridays. She saw no one except her maid, and once by chance the barber-and-explorer, Fonseca, with whom she exchanged a searching look. The slave boy, she knew, had come to Sans Souci in circumstances not very different from her own and at much the same time. She lowered her eyes and returned to her prayers with spots on her vision that resolved themselves as the barber-and-man's pock-marks. At the end of the rains, Farida had the East Tower painted blue inside and out, declaring that the colour was most conducive to meditation and thoughts spiritual. Next, finding all other colours a distraction, she removed or had dyed such furnishings as were not between blue and violet; her trousseau was already indigo. Once, when she was ill, the cupper-and-leechwoman let out that it was the first time she had ever seen blue blood. When she recovered, Farida gave thanks by distributing bolts of indigo satin.

One night, after she had regained her strength, Justin brought her a dish of sweet jamuns (*Eugenia jambolana*). She agreed to see him because it was dark, and they ate together, staining their fingers while their mouths grew more and more parched from the desiccative agent in the fruit: each jamun left the mouth drier than the last and in urgent need of the next. The bowl empty, Farida required another, but as there was no moon by which a jamun-picker might see, the Great Trotter took leave of her with a timid kiss. Tasting his lips for the first time, the girl forgot about his age and refused to let him go. After that, whenever Justin visited her (on nights when there was no moon by which she might see the lines on his face) Farida received him on her divan with an ardency that did not escape him and that she could hardly hide from herself. On those nights the air was blue with their love-making, and the toads and crickets round about fell silent; the nightjars at Water Gate grew still, and screech-owls blinked at their mates in wonderment. In the morning, Justin would leave the girl to wash away every trace of sin, but all day there shone in his eye a light that was between blue and violet.

How a fortune is made

I wish to shew how a fortune is made. Good adept, take twelve villages, more if small. Empty the smallest and raze the huts. This is no great matter with huts made of mud. The villagers will complain, but their memories are short and you now have an additional field. When you have land sufficient, explain to the cultivators (or send one to explain) that wheat will not do, nor corn, nor chick-peas. The new crop, the improved crop, the miracle crop, is a cash crop, paid for in money. (Here you, or your agent, will hold up a coin.) The villagers will complain, but there is now a body of landless labourers and division in the ranks. Sow, good adept, the ground in spring with indigo seed (*nil*) 3 spans apart. Indigo seed, rape seed, cotton seed, and a variety of cash crop seeds are to be had from J.c. Solomon & Son in the usual place. Loamy soil is best, so it be moist; next best is black soil; worst is red. In two months you will find grown up to waist height plants with small smooth leaves, the size of almonds. They are oval, the colour of gunmetal (but some call it ploughshare blue) arrayed in pairs along the stem with an odd one at the tip. In a short while blossoms will appear of yellowy madder and then will come pods the length of your little finger perhaps, furry, dark, and filled with tiny seeds of a repellent hue and odour. At this stage it is best to produce another coin (or the same) for display. When enough labourers have gathered, arm each with a sickle, retiring yourself immediately, and let the harvest begin. You need not remain to oversee the business; the workers will not dally in the field, the smell being nauseous. Snakes, too, are shy of the plant; you will lose no labour that way. Loss of potency has been remarked by some planters, but this is a problem for future generations. Children may be born with (say) a blue hand or ear or such, but this can be considered an auspicious mark. The labourer must be instructed to allow a handswidth of stem to remain, for the plant will replenish itself by August and again by November and again by February and so on, praise God. Every fifth year you must uproot. Your labourers have by now forgotten that they ever cropped anything but indigo (*nil*) and are quite happy to be called after the plant *nilchis*, viz. blue-chis or blue ones.

Next you must have, good adept, the works. J.c. will come or send a man to measure your ground and estimate your needs and expenses. He will supply materials and builders and in no time you will have a plant or factory. You are now an indigo factor. Convey the cut indigo to this place, which may be described thusly: a freshwater canal which feeds a series of tanks or baths. The grand canal begins at the headwaters of the Kirani river where it leaves the saltpetre hill; it runs along an embankment (also an aqueduct) to the indigo baths. The baths are a row of waterproofed pools above a second row lower down the slope, and then a third; all are connected by pipes and stopcocks to form a regulated cascade. Plunge, good adept, into the topmost baths the plant, stem, leaf, and pod, first filling the baths with water. The plants are now in the *leaching* baths where they may steep. Let them ferment overnight or up to a night and a day. Do you wish to go for a ride the whilst? Or fly a kite? Or fancy pigeons? Do so. During that time the water will bubble from the inborn heat and because the colour is turning. Still another coin (or the same) is produced and held up this way and that. Nilchis will appear. The cocks on the uppermost tanks are now turned and the water rushes downhill into the second row, the *beating* pools. Meanwhile, the leaching pools are cleared of the rotting matter, the sharp adept holding the nose, the most cunning retiring altogether. At the second level, each nilchi is given a flail or bat or oar and the beating commences. The men stand up to their knees in the water and thrash its surface without stopping. Within the space of a watch, the water turns blue; a little more beating renders it colourless again. The blue salts formed from commerce with the vital essences of the air have settled. Stir once more to rouse them, and turn the second set of cocks. Beneath the third row of pools, which are shallow, fires are roaring. These are the *evaporating* pans (some use a single pan to which all the channels tend) where the solution is evaporated. When all is still, the clear water is drawn off the top while the remainder boils away.

For the last time the coin is held up (just as before). The scrapers and squeezers arrive, the one to scrape and the other to squeeze. The latter press the indigo in presses using cloth. A patter at the end pats the blue dough into a mould and marks it with T. A baker-and-foreman supervises the baking and stacking and cooling and packing. The adept must now in fairness pay out the coin to the nilchis. Some, the base and vulgar, will murmur that this is not enough (there are always these), and others even of the elite will agree. But clear-sighted men, reasoning men, the elite of the elite, will recall that this was all that was promised. Good adept, sweep up the crumbs; waste not. Gathered into little muslin bags, called blue bags, indigo dust is excellent for household washing, turning whites whiter. It is also most soothing when applied to wasp and bee stings. Give, good adept, the baker-and-disciplinarian a portion and return to your tower, smacking your wallet and crying *hrp! hrp!* for your fortune is made. Ships, dyers, drapers, and customers throughout the world wait on you. Better, set up a dyeing concern of your own. Give thanks. Give great thanks. Praise God.

(CHRONICLE RESUMED)

The day after the explosion below the East Tower, Alexander (who had finished all but one of the statues and had begun work on the Great Trotter's tombstone) was banished. Taking up sword and chisel, the Greek crept from the shade of the oracle tree and entered with his wife and a brood of daughters an exile that would not end till the coming of the ice. Together they wandered the desert, the marsh, and the jungle at the three Tank-points, keeping to the fringes of Sans Souci and settling at last in the quarry. There the girls grew up among the rocks, their slender bodies grey as sandstone, their eyes the colour of the Aegean. Not content with slipping like lizards across the smooth rocks and splashing in the quarry pools, they would steal at night through the jungle to paddle in the indigo baths under an ashen moon, giggling all the way home before daybreak.

With Alexander gone, the Next Trotter began his lessons on the Plain of Cannonballs, being carried there every morning in a palki. The palki was the same his mother had used, only its glass bottom was closed in and the palki-bearers numbered six instead of four. For the next six hours the boy learnt of the mass of spheres, the parts of speech, the rudiments of anatomy, the fundament of meditation, the goad of desire, the balance of pain. Then he was carried back to Sans Souci, proceeding directly to the dining hall, where Justin was already seated at the Nakhlau end of the long table. Lifting his eyes from his trencher, the Great Trotter examined the boy who sat at the Old Armoury end staring back at him. As they waited on the baker-and-headwaiter, the father questioned the son about the day's lesson, and the son replied in monosyllables: *eight*, *pain*, *no*, *twelve*, *bliss*, and sometimes, with difficulty, *n-non-violence*. Since levelling the old armoury he had shown no desire for cigarettes, bidis, lucifers, and explosives. He appeared to have softened towards his stepmother, and had even carried to her tower bowls of mulberries, grapes, and purple plums, but not the sweet jamuns with which she liked to stain her teeth a meditative blue. Justin learnt of these gifts with pleasure from his baker-and-informer, because he had forbidden the very same articles of food in his son's diet. He had noticed with alarm that the boy was turning blue.

The cooks were advised to ply the Second Trotter with yellows and greens and reds. Justin himself would extemporize on the virtues of mangoes and honeydew melons and monsoon guavas; on some days he might forgo a dish of carrot halva so that it could be carried to the Old Armoury end. The boy submitted patiently to the imposed regime, but each morning saw him turn a darker shade of blue. At night Justin would shake his head in perplexity and lock the boy into his room on the upper storey of his mother's house. But when all the lights in Sans Souci were extinguished and the jackals and pi-dogs had begun their shadow opera at the horizon, the Second Trotter would vault out of his iron cot, unlatch a window in the Begam Kothi, scale down a gutter-pipe, and march across an as yet unnamed court. Past the new armoury he marched, up the apron-steps, through the Audience Hall, out at the Indigo Door, down the apron-steps, past the devastated Old Armoury, across the Indigo Court and up to the massive Indigo Gate. Ignoring the fenceless stretch on either side of the gateposts, he would push open the gate, close it behind him, and strike out past his mother's tomb, the Hava Manzil with its deep aeolian note, across an open stretch of ground, past the amphitheatre and the dimly phosphorescent music pavilion, past a row of mulberry trees. Then he was over the crest of the embankment, a spring coming into his stride as he rounded the end of the canal. The giggling of a dozen girls carried up the grassed slope from the indigo baths; they were waiting for him. There the boy and the half-Macedonian nymphets would sport, thrashing about from pool to pool until they finished in the bottom row just as dawn began to stain the sky above the jungle with its unwelcome light.

At the end of a year, these revels had turned the Second Trotter completely blue. The rest of his wild strong body now matched the blue spigot with which he had been born, keeping its dye through the daily scrubbings which the Great Trotter instituted in a bid to reclaim his son. Justin talked to the boy, consulted his tutor, thrashed the floor-polishers-and-night-watchmen, and changed the locks on the Begam Kothi. Getting no results, he broke two malacca canes on the boy's rump and talked to him some more. The Next Trotter gazed evenly into his father's eyes and curled his lip. Justin spoke to Farida and she replied: "He is not my son. I will make you one of my own." But she did not, and her stepson continued blue. "His mother is dead, his nurse is dead," thought Justin. "He will listen to no one." He remembered Alexander and sent to the quarry for him. "I will not parley," the Macedonian replied. "Besides, the boy has been tampering with my daughters." "Impossible!" cried Justin, going to the quarry himself. "He is not yet nine." "My daughters are not yet eight," said Alexander, and the gipsy lohar woman held up ten fingers plus two to signify all twelve daughters. The girls laughed huskily at Justin, who returned to the Audience Hall befuddled and irresolute. "What is to be done, Marazzi?" he shouted up into the vault, and Marazzi, without looking down from his ceiling, replied: "Boys will be men, Monsieur Trotter!" and added with a chuckle, "*I* could use a dozen models—*half* a dozen (if one might negotiate!)." "Do something," Justin pleaded with the Tibetan plinth-master, and the plinth-master replied: "Very well, but the remedy will be stern." "Anything!" Justin said. "If he grows any darker he will be invisible." "True," said the Tibetan, and disappeared.

The next day the boy failed to appear at breakfast, but Justin already knew something was amiss. A line of footprints, blue and spaced like a runner's, led from the indigo baths in the northeast through the Audience Hall to the Begam Kothi on the south side, ending at an empty bed. By the bed was the burst chain with which Justin had chained his son the night before; embedded in the iron anklet were two rows of milk teeth.

Munnoo and Nankoo, who had risen early, were vainly scrubbing at the footprints on the Audience Hall floor when the Great Trotter pounced on them. "Which of you kept watch over the indigo last night?" he demanded. It was Nankoo the mosquito, but his brother spoke up. Justin sent for the baker-and-henchman and had him bind Munnoo's hands behind him. The floor-polisher-and-night-watchman was led out of the Indigo Door and along the indelible row of footprints. Just short of the baths was a shed where the indigo cake was stored before being loaded onto the camel-carts. Munnoo was led into this shed. A rope was passed between the hands already bound behind his back, knotted there, and its loose end tossed over a roof beam. When the baker-and-right-hand man pulled on the rope, Munnoo's arms jerked up behind him. With another tug, Munnoo's feet were off the floor and his face was contorted with pain. The Great Trotter took up a cane and began to whack the man's bare legs, starting at the calf and ending at the soles of the feet. "Vigilance, responsibility, method, accuracy, efficiency . . . " he chanted. "A fixed wage for a fixed time. A night-watchman is paid to keep watch at night. Thanks to your slackery I now have a permanent dye without knowing its specific agent. You will now recount to me every detail of your rounds, every step from the moment you come on duty. Begin."

Munnoo gasped with every stroke. "I arrive at nightfall—some days before, some days after—I make a round of the baths—then I go as far as the Music—I sit in the stone pit—I smoke a bidi—I consider the day's work—I clear my throat—I spit across the stage—I get up and walk back along the mulberry trees—I check the stopcocks in each row of baths—I sit by the bottom row—I fart the day's dal—I spread out my sheet—I lie me down and rest—I watch the stars in the heating baths—I keep awake, keep awake—at dawn I get up—I stretch my arms and legs—I—I—"

"You—?"

Justin swung the cane.

"I piss in the tank—I come back to the . . ."

But already the bastinado had ceased. At a sign from the Great Trotter the baker-and-tool slackened the rope and Munnoo's feet were on the ground again. He preferred to kneel; when his hands were unbound he rolled over onto his side and lay there senseless. He had not cried out once, although in another minute both arms would have broken at the shoulder.

The next day Munnoo was allowed to rest, and the Great Trotter sent him a crate of mangoes and a basket of sweetmeats. His pay was increased by a rupee and a bonus tendered him in the pocket of a new suit of clothes. When he could walk he was given the lightest of tasks and allowed to retire before dark. Nankoo grew envious, but remembered his brother's ordeal which should rightly have been his own, and said nothing. Only one duty was required of Munnoo, but it was one he shared with every able-bodied male in Sans Souci. Each morning before the day's work was begun, there would appear along the bottommost row of baths, the evaporating pans, a line of men, motionless as statues in the cold half-light, solemnly adding to the indigo the urinary salts necessary for the production of a permanent dye. Justin tested a bolt of cloth fresh from the dyeing-tub and watched it go from white to blue before his eyes as the oxygen in the air fastened the dye. It kept its colour through successive washes, and when even a concentrated bleach slid off it without effect, Justin darted from the shed crying: "I have found it, I have found it!"

Only then did he remember his lost son. He had not seen him for over a month; nor had the Tibetan plinth-master reappeared. When he started to write out a notice for the local crier and for the Calcutta and Bombay papers, he remembered that the boy had no name. And when he came up with a suitable description it sounded so fantastic that he was ashamed to publish it. Yet reports had already begun to trickle back to Sans Souci of blue revels and god-sightings at cowdusk by girls returning to their villages along the road to Calcutta.

The night of Munnoo's bastinado, Justin sat at his marquetry table and made a jotting in his journal.

Day's-end jotting in the Great Trotter's Blue Book

There is a patience in the native that will endure great suffering without complaint and can spring from one source alone, namely Love. And this virtue of the soul, so generous that it is all-encompassing and denied to none, is like balm to the oppressor, laving his tortured conscience and assuaging his urgent need for forgiveness. The impression of this man's face upon me is one that the Shroud itself could not make, for where the other solicits my compassion, thereby exalting me, this face excites my cruelty, thus increasing my debt. Out of this mysterious bond is born a great love. What is the sweetness in my shriven soul but an assimilation to the All, and what is the exquisite suffering of the floor-polisher but a tingling in the presence of the Eternal? I am drawn out of my this-ness (and so is he) by the ineffable That, that which knows our puny selves to be other than they are, and knows further that they *are* not except as they partake of its roseate substance, the changeless, formless, imponderable One.

(CHRONICLE RESUMED)

The next day Justin (*Backsliding Trotter*) longed to share his thoughts with the Tibetan plinth-master, but the plinth-master was not there. So he rode out to his indigo fields and cursed the nilchis, driving them to cut and bind faster and still faster until the sweat streamed from their backs and his soul went out to them. Then, in a state of fiery exaltation he spurred his favourite horse so hard that the creature flew back to Sans Souci, passing itself going the other way. Both horses reared up in astonishment and Justin was thrown from the first saddle, striking his head on the wet earth. The second horse galloped on, and when Justin arrived home he could not explain the mud on the back of his shirt. Moreover he had no memory of the excursion, although sometimes at the edge of sleep he was haunted by a vision of an indigo field in September, a horse, a lash, and bending labourers. From that time on, the Great Trotter no longer went out into the fields, appointing his baker-and-whip-hand man to see that production was doubled. "The men are unhappy," Yakub reported at the end of the week. "Triple the work," Justin ordered. "Their unhappiness is a necessary illusion. They are unconscious agents of a great Love."

Descending the West Tower stair, Yakub stroked the wick-moustache he had begun to cultivate. He admired his master's dedication to an absolute indigo; he too would have liked to rid the last vat of every fleck of impurity, abolishing all stars from its ambit. He appreciated the need for substantial and regular supplies of cut indigo from the fields and the consequent need for discipline, and he even liked the idea of a single bond uniting his master (on whose side he reckoned himself) and the labourers. But that the bond should be called Love he found first a puzzlement and then a mistake, and no sooner had he passed his first considered judgement on the Great Trotter than he felt a pleasing surge of power. He felt sure it was a transfer which impoverished his master in the same measure as it enriched himself. Stepping out into the as yet nameless court where the smell of horse dung was sharp and intoxicating, the baker-and-foreman decided that the Great Trotter's right hand was to be feared and his left hand, the shameful hand, used. He crossed to the stables and demanded a horse with such peremptoriness that it was given him without question. A senior officer of the horse saddled the best Arab but one and brought it to Yakub himself. Without looking at the man, Yakub led his mount off to the desert. Before the day was over, he had taught himself to ride.

On the muster of horses

Horses are dear to the Great Trotter's heart. He has been known to leap broad streams with a horse under each arm, but the report is likely an *exaggeration*. Horses are God's noblest gift to man, after reason. They are plentiful here, up to ten thousand. They are mustered on Thursdays and curried on Fridays. Grooms are classed by age and quickness and paid on the last Wednesday of each month. They have first rights to the dung, but neither they nor their families may produce glue. They are not to be confused with elephant mahouts, who are easterly and wear red. They are generally short but sometimes untidy, always slight yet uncommonly truthful. Horses are of three kinds: *Arabian*, *crop-tailed*, and *fickle*. The last are kept apart in the farthest stables adjoining the Elephant Wing where tall grooms prefer to gather in ragged knots and gossip. The crop-tailed are charmers and the Arabs spirited, as their names show.

Among the Arabs are:

Salaam whose nostrils are the hospices of thunder

Salim whose war drum is the earth

Suleiman who gargles fire

Saltpetre who burns up the hills

Sarandap the sly princess (she may be crop-tailed)

Scheherazade who will not stop

Among the crop-tailed are:

Chamak whose watered silk coat doth blind

Chikna than whom butter is not more smooth

Chetak with sinews of forged steel (he may be spirited)

Chub or *Khub* whose eyes Hell hath sent for our undoing

China whose name speaks for itself

Charivari the burnished

Chichi the finicky (she may be part fickle)

Chanukkah

Cicisbeo

Illegible

Illegible [of the comely forelock?]

These are simply some of the many. The fickle will not bear naming. All are exercised daily by the grooms. They are fed twice, in the morning and in the evening, their diet being as follows.

In the morning the Arabs receive two measures of bruised pulse for every one of grass fodder, with sugar mixed in on Sundays. In the evening they receive a mash of boiled peas or else grain in which ghi is sometimes mixed. The reverse is the case with the crop-tailed, except on second Fridays, when it is the same. Thus when Arabs eat stale peamash the crop-tails have it fresh, and when crop-tails eat stale peamash the Arabs have it fresh. But when Arabs eat fresh bruised pulse (with fodder), you will never find a crop-tail eating stale peamash, for it is fresh peamash time. By these lights you will know it is morning, for it is then that their cooking is done. One cannot cook farrago twice a day for horses. When grass is not to be had, hay is substituted, but then sugar cannot be mixed in. But if molasses be substituted for sugar the hay will take it, except in winter. Then, of course, the oats must be chopped with a sharp instrument and the lamps lit early. Salt is given freely to the fickle, and little else, but sugar never.

The gelders are stout men, the master-gelder a Turk. Branding is deeply discouraged, saddlery advanced, and horse-doctors paid on time. The Great

Trotter in his wisdom fines the tardy paymaster. Putting his foot in the stirrup of resolution, he charges that delay be put to rout and all men from lowly grooms to poets-and-chroniclers be generously paid.

This is not the place to describe the elephants or the manner of their burial, or the camels and the mode of their oiling.

(CHRONICLE RESUMED)

Each day Yakub rode out effecting his master's will, lashing the nilchis, goading the servants, driving the cooks. And recognizing that the displacement of command from his master to himself would leave a gap in the Great Trotter's day, he introduced the sport of cock-fighting to Sans Souci. The Great Trotter had already started a fowl run in the southwest crescent, at the elbow where the crescent met the Elephant Wing. Although hemmed in between the elephants and the horses, the fowls did so well in the care of an egg-brahmin named Sunya that the entire crescent had come to be known as the Comb. Resenting the name, the baker-and-master-gelder (who would have preferred Mane) began his campaign of harassment by pilfering a pair of cocks and staging a fight for the Great Trotter's amusement. Filled with love for the losing cock, and feeling the strength return to his whip hand, Justin demanded a rematch. Within a week he was committed to regular matches and the purchase of fighting cocks and quails from every part of the world. The hall with a tilt he named the Cock Hall, but on Yakub's prompting it became simply the Spur. Originally built to answer with symmetry the dining hall, it now found a function. Yakub moved out of the suite above the kitchens and took up residence there, occupying the entire upper storey. On the cedar floor of the Spur, the baker-and-cocksman staged ever more elaborate cockfights for his master, who watched from the ringside or from one of the galleries with a taut heart and twitching hand.

The night before a match Justin fed the birds himself, mixing chopped meat into the grain and sliding a saucer of warm blood into the cage. The night after a match, he went to the blue-washed tower brimming with a terrible love. But where his prize birds fought bravely and with success (he had begun to challenge various Nakhlau owners, local Muslims such as Afridi Beg and Amir Ali as well as firangis from White Town such as the Colonels Mordaunt and Martin), he himself could not produce an heir to replace his vanished son, wrestle as he might with his wife till dawn. In despair he turned to shooting, and painted the fields and jungles red with a slaughter that eased only with the killing of a woodcutter-and-beater whom he mistook for a sprung partridge. After that he killed selectively, preferring dark meats, said to be most potent. Still there was no issue. On the egg-brahmin's advice he took to chewing pan and became addicted to the betel-nut in it. But although crimson stains began to appear in the embrasures of the West Tower and the number of Sans Souci spittoons multiplied, Justin could not fashion another child out of his violent love.

Once again he grew sleepless, and Fonseca had to stretch his story-telling skills to the utmost to steal an hour's rest at night. The barber-and-surgeon asked his master if he thought bleeding might help; the Great Trotter lashed out with his crop. Then he drew the young man to himself and kissed the spot, saying meekly: "Yes, let a little. But let it be the leechwoman. I will not learn to live in fear of my barber's razor." The cupper-and-leechwoman let three cups, which bubbled for a week as if on a stove. She had seen all kinds of blood, the old crone muttered, even indigo blood. But this was something new. "It's ice you want," she said as she slouched off.

Justin took her words to heart and sent Nankoo to the bazar for Himalayan ice, but it was sold in such thin sheets that Nankoo brought home an empty gunny sack. When he had finished flogging the floor-polisher-and-odd-jobman (who yelped with every cut) Justin wept for joy and forgot the leechwoman's omen. Under no circumstances would he forgo the hot curries that had become his daily fare, nor could he bring himself to regulate the fire of the dishes by adulterating his curry powder. Instead he drank two surahis of water chilled with saltpetre to flush out the heat generated in his system by those vast and highly spiced meals. He had thermantidotes installed along the length of the dining hall as well as a row of pankhas along the ceiling.

Pankha

PANKHA (also PUNKAH), n. 1. Manually operated fan of any kind; device for circulating air and thereby cooling either oneself (e.g., hand *pankha*) or another (e.g. peacock *pankha*). 2. Ceiling fan contraption said to have been invented by an Anglo-Indian (see KIRANI or WRITER) in the service of the East India Company in Madras who on a hot day hung his desk from the ceiling and attaching a string to the hinged lid commanded his office peon to pull it back and forth (cit. Busteed, *Echoes of Old Madras*). 3. Refinement of above, substituting vane of canvas or duffle for desk; the pull-cord passes through a hole in the wall so that the operating slave (PANKHAWALA or PUNKAH WALLAH) may not see or be seen. 4. (hapax legomenon) Admirer, flatterer ("And all the *punkahs* as they passed/ Cried, 'My how fair you are!' " —E. Lear)

A small invisible army of men was employed to operate the fans, flapping the warm humid air in the dining hall; others stood on ladders at the high windows to pour buckets of water on the khas-khas-tatis. Comforted, Justin ate on, smiling through the heat haze at the cooling devices of India which adorned his Grecian hall. Their vivid red and purple embroidery in which tiny mirrors and peacock's feathers had been worked, contrasted sharply with the severe lines of the stone hall, and Justin shook his head smilingly when he realized that not many years ago he would have found the clash repellent. Yet here he was, revelling in the frisky banter of a Muslim green with a Romish blue, of Hindu reds and ochres swishing garishly to and fro between the chaste Doric pillars. The crush of mobile colours put him in mind of Marazzi's ceiling, which was making rakish progress in the Audience Hall. Might he suggest to the Italian that here, above the flapping pankhas, was another blank space that wanted filling in a new and fit style? But no; Marazzi had fixed notions. He was like that Qaiyum, only at the opposite extreme. Qaiyum would not allow that civilization existed west of Persia; for Marazzi, art east of Venice was a contradiction in terms. No painting in India (not even his own) met with the cripple's approval. Shown a cache of Mughal miniatures that Justin had lately acquired from the Nawab, he screwed up his eyes and sniffed (*Nice Marazzi, Judicious Eye*). The Nawab would agree completely with the Italian, for the price he had put on the miniatures, choice specimens all, including some by Masud the Elder, was trifling. Yet for second-rate European works he paid handsomely, and had offered that bounder Zoffanij an astronomical sum for his portrait (*Careless Sovereign, Profligate*).

An idea came to Justin as he sat there. Now that the dining hall was complete, he might avenge last year's grand breakfast to which his employer-and-friend, the Nawab of Tirnab, had invited him. He sent for paper of his own manufacture and began to jot down a suitable menu, with entertainments to follow, beginning with an elephant match and leading up to a cock-fight. He set the day for Christmas to allow three months of preparation, and sent the invitation along with a musical clock of Lyonnaise manufacture which showed a greyish-green fish of uncertain nationality swallowing up a British marine at noon and spitting him out a minute later to the tune of "London Bridge Is Falling Down."

While preparations were going forward for the Great Day, or Burra Din, as Christmas was coming to be known in India, the Great Trotter turned to settling matters of religion. Leaving Yakub Khan to send away for the Nawab's favourite sweets—macaroons from Cayenne, meringues from Montreal, lamingtons from La Perouse, madeleines from the provinces—Justin sent away for God. How, he asked himself, had he allowed Islam and Buddhism to keep him from the chief religion of Hindustan? Accordingly he purchased all the relevant Sanskrit texts from Mathura and Benares to Madurai and Belur, sacred and secular, for his library and began a study of the language and the religion, using Panini's grammar in the original and working from internal principles. Enchanted with the elegance of an inquiry whose head and fount was not language but divinity, not grammar but God, Justin's soul vibrated in sympathy with this ancient faith. The scales fell from his eyes and he saw the fallibility of the Christian faith into which he had been dipped in infancy, and then the Muslim faith that he had espoused, and then the Buddhist faith that he had capitulated to on the Plain of Cannonballs. But when after a month of study he came to sound the grammar on his palate, he found the first person singular constantly slipping away into a vortex from which escape was impossible. He paused. If I cannot securely say *I believe*, then who is it that believes? If I am simply *known*, then what good are my beliefs since God who knows me has no need of them? Abruptly Justin's Hindu grammar began to pall on him, and once again the beliefs that he thought he had left behind showed signs of vitality. In his impatience to touch on the flowers of every faith, and finding himself growing daily older, he felt obliged to flit to other and still other faiths. One day it was a Shinto pilgrim who had strayed as far as Nakhlau, the next a Confucian merchant, and the third a Polynesian animist travelling in the company of some quiet Dutchmen. But the wider his field, the less able he found himself to choose among the conflicting versions of the hereafter and the heretofore.

To rid himself honourably of a burden of decision which he had voluntarily taken up, the Great Trotter proposed an open faith to be formed of the confraternity of its many adherents. It would have (he promulgated) no temple, and no spatial being as such except at that site where two or more persons happened to gather to dispute. The Din Havai, or Religion of the Winds, would embrace as many faiths as the number of its believers, for certainly no two members of a single faith could interpret that faith in the same way. Nor indeed would this mode of reckoning suffice, for a disputing Jain of Tuesday would not be the same man on Wednesday, and a Tuesday in winter was quite another matter from a Tuesday when there was yellow pollen in the air. If the cherishers of the new faith of faiths insisted on a concrete symbol, they might regard the Hava Manzil as such and worship (which was to say, dispute) or eat their lentils in its shade. But enter it they could not, for here the only proscription of the new religion applied: ladders of any kind were strictly forbidden. Nets, however, were admissible if of a fine mesh. Eructation and the breaking of wind were allowable modes of salutation for initiates; indeed, silence was frowned upon. As for schism and doubt, these were to be the foundation of the Din Havai, zealously promoted at synods to be held every fifth year in the open air during a severe dust storm. Thus the choicest fruits of a man's meditation would be snatched from his lips and whistled away while his ears and mouth (and those of his neighbours) filled with the singing of the sand.

Concerning the Great Trotter's Din Havai

The Great Trotter has an acute sense of reality, chiefly of those impregnable realities that lie beyond the grave. However, if one might be allowed to voice an opinion, his Din Havai is not the light of the age it purports to be. This is not to say that its one convert so far (apart from the Great Trotter himself), namely, the floor-polisher, Nankoo, is a complete idiot. However, such intelligence as he may have has so far been jealously hoarded. This reflects only on the frailty and fallibility of mortals and not on the Great Trotter himself, whose forehead is a beacon to errant men. However, it must be said that the so-called Din Havai is no more than a pale imitation of Akbar the Great's Din Ilahi. This is not to say that the Great Trotter's Faith of the Winds lacks divine afflatus and other qualities to recommend it. However, what has been tried once and proven ill-conceived and fruitless cannot without compounding folly be repeated. This is, of course, a reminder only to those who seek to net the wind, not to the Great Trotter himself. However, it has been said that the Great Men of the present age would do better to emulate the Great Mughal's practice of paying his servants on time, and leave abstraction to specialists. This by no means implies that particular Great Men or particular servants are at issue. However, what is the general but a mode of inference from particulars?

(CHRONICLE RESUMED)

After he had flogged Qaiyum for impertinence,* the Great Trotter wiped his glowing forehead with a cologne-dipped napkin and in a blaze of delicious penitence visited the East Tower in broad daylight. There he turned a hot

---

* Here one senses the beginnings of a rift between the Great Trotter and his chronicler-and-poet. The flogging cannot have been much, Qaiyum being a well-built man, and a man, moreover, of some rank, but in the scuffle either Qaiyum himself or a firkin of toddy appears to have fallen to the floor, or so at any rate one surmises from the tone of an occasional poem written in the heat of the moment:

> The rough hand of injustice lashes
> Where most it hurts—life's vessel dashes
> 'Gainst stone—the vital fluid splashes;
> Sackcloth for him—for me hot ashes.

Ashes were commonly applied to minor cuts in those rough-and-ready days, but might equally have been used to mull a consolatory cup of wine.—E.A.T.

day into a blistering one, following page by page a classical Sanskrit text by the aesthete-and-choreographer Vatsyayana. "Dirty filthy book!" Farida moaned faintly as Justin translated the words for her, but she was held all the same. That night she prayed that the day's sweat might be turned into a son, and for weeks after she walked with a limp, persuaded that she carried in her belly the beginnings of a holy warrior. But with the new moon the tides returned and no child was presaged. Peeved, she shut herself up in her tower and prayed with renewed ferocity, while Justin channelled his heat into a variety of practical experiments, designing the soap-saver, the watering-can, the revolving trencher, the piano stool, and a pallet of mango wood for which he felt sure a use would in time be found.

One October evening, not long after he invented the shower, Justin stepped out of his private bathroom (the public one, the Guzal Khana, where in the style of bygone emperors he sometimes received petitioners, was downstairs by the Water Door) and found himself instantly bathed in sweat again. It had been an unseasonably hot day, one of those sweltering freaks which mean that winter will be longer at the other end, and he called irritably down the air vent to Fonseca. The barber-and-man sat in his room reading, for the twentieth time, the *Letters* of Alexander Pope, and wriggling with new pleasure at every monstrous turgidity. When the call came he put down his book and came running upstairs to dress his master. The dhobi's daily bundle lay in the usual place on the Riesener commode, but when he peeled back the four corners of the cloth Fonseca found instead of the day's shirt, breeches, and stockings, a suit of Nakhlau-style clothes freshly laundered. He withdrew his hand a fraction, slackening the wrist. Justin, who noticed the changeling clothes at the same time, gave a theatrical groan. There was a pause in which both men stood staring at the unfamiliar garments.

"Well, I cannot stand here naked forever," the Great Trotter said, as a puddle of water formed at his small plump feet, "even if that Dhani Das is a muddling nincompoop of a dhobi."

And Fonseca, with an air of shocked but silent demurral, helped him into a pair of Nakhlau pyjamas of the finest cotton and a kurta embroidered white on white at the neck. The effect of the light but sumptuous attire was extraordinary.

"Hurry it on, then," Justin urged his barber-and-man, fancying that he stood naked still, like an emperor deceived.

"It is already on," Fonseca pointed out, with a trace of vindictiveness. He took a deliberate step back, the pontiff who has warned the heretic and now washes his hands of the matter.

Only when he himself moved did Justin notice that he was in fact clothed.

Gone was the constriction at the waist, the tightness at his privates, at the knee, along the calf, the chafing he had known every day of his life and felt with particular irritation ever since his arrival in India. Instead he seemed at once clothed and naked, decently attired and yet deliciously, almost indecently free, at liberty to float away if he wished. The sense of mortal deliverance, of the coil falling away, was gently balanced by the exquisite sensation of the fabric against the skin. Clothing, which he had hitherto seen as a species of armour, a shell protecting one against the world, had now become a second skin which turned its soft caresses inwards, a tender comforting envelope in which one might lose and find oneself. Wafting to the almirah mirror, the Great Trotter saw that his tactile sense had not misled him: there, instead of the hard edges of his customary garments, were clothes whose limits were indefinable, lost in a shimmering flux whose aura threatened to engulf even the disapproving barber-and-man.

Justin's eyelids fluttered and his forehead shone, and he made a series of airy backward leaps like a delirious moth. A single word escaped him. "Music!" he gasped, his eyes glittering. Then, detecting a change in his barber-and-musician's expression, he held up a hand: "No, not the horn, please, Fonseca. Send to the city for the best sitarist, and a tabla master."

The barber-and-French hornist plodded down the West Tower stair, his discomfiture complete. Upstairs, Justin settled down to wait, feeling the heat drain out of his body in one long swooning release. When he opened his eyes, he found himself seated on a mat with his legs crossed, although his favourite chair stood empty beside him. He reached out for a small silver pan-box, opened it, took out a green triangle of betel leaf, popped it into his mouth and began to chew contentedly.

The next day Justin sent for Zuhur Ali, tailor master, and under Fonseca's horrified eyes had himself measured for a new wardrobe. While the tailor busied himself with chalk and string, the barber-and-valet wept softly into his handkerchief. Only when Justin opened the doors of his almirah and made a gift of all his former clothes to Fonseca was the barber-and-dandy comforted. And when the Great Trotter sent him off advising him to practise well on his horn for a public performance soon to be held, Fonseca recovered face and spirits. He threw himself into his finger exercises morning and night and scalded his lips on mulligatawny soup rather than waste musicianly breath. Of an afternoon he tackled the theory of music, making sufficient progress to have a concerto by each of the masters, Rameau, Haydn, and Mozart, ready by December. He contrived to ignore the sitarist and tabalchi who, together with a very tall tanpura expert, had taken up residence in the Comb. Their nasal strains floated down the air vent from Justin's rooms at all hours.

Meantime, the baker-and-bandobast-master had begun to step up preparations for the Christmas breakfast. If the event were a success it could be an administrative coup, placing in his hands an authority he would know better than to let slip. But first he must see that the responsibility was not divided. Of course the day was the Great Trotter's, but when it was over and the Nawab had thanked the Great Trotter, the Great Trotter in turn must have someone to thank. That one must be he, Yakub Khan, once orphan and future Chief Steward. To ensure the result he must establish a chain of command with himself at the top, issuing orders in the Great Trotter's name. Orders once given and (what was more to the point) taken, would set a precedent, establish a hierarchy. The number of those who happily surrendered responsibility was always greater than those willing to take it up. So Yakub went from site to site, shunting underlings, testing their foremen with directions that might be the Great Trotter's or might be his own, trying appointed officers with requests that might be commands. Were the spice carts dawdling? The curry factor had better be on his toes—the Great Trotter was easily angered. Was there sugar enough in the godowns? (*Diligent Yakub*) The food sergeant must know the Great Trotter's rages. And how were the fighting elephants and camels coming along? Some fenugreek in their bran might not be amiss to make them ruttish and aggressive. No? Well, the Great Trotter would not care for a tame show—and if it were simply a matter of saved fenugreek . . . As for the cocks, these Yakub entrusted to no one, locking the cage that kept Heaven's Vengeance against the Great Trotter himself.

The morning of the Great Day was crisp and blue. A column of white smoke stood over Sans Souci, scented and tilting in the sharp December wind. As the sun rose, the cloud went from white to saffron to gold and back to white again. From before dawn there had been a hubbub in the kitchens, with cooks and confectioners bawling for sugar or butter at one and the same time (*Exalted Masters*) and their fetchers-and-carriers doing irate sidestep jigs as they got in each other's way. The heat from the ovens withered the nearest of the Chinese orange trees and attracted a row of Sagarpaysans who sat along the outside of the kitchen wall holding their hands and feet out to the bricks like mute lepers. The nilchis, who were to get half the day off from noon, began work at dawn as usual, but as the indigo baths were downwind from the kitchens and the water in the beating pools was cold, they were torn between basking and hopping on the spot. At intervals the pale gold light was shivered into needles by a trumpet blast from the elephant stables, a call answered from the West Tower by an agitated Fonseca. The cocks crew in relay, strutting with erect blood-red combs and dropping twice their usual quota of dung. Pleased to be in the limelight, Sunya went up and down between Comb and kitchen with baskets of eggs, a job he ordinarily left to an understudy. Gunga the bhisti made his seventy-fifth trip from the Glacerie well, bent beneath his dripping masak, the splay of his webbed toes showing the strain, and still there was need of more water. And through it all Yakub galloped, from the Spur to the indigo baths, from the stables to the kitchens and back, shouting orders, smoothing over quarrels, deftly untying knots of confusion, sending runners to the Gunpowder Gate to see if the Nawab's outriders were in sight. At length a dust cloud on the Trotter Road showed that they were, and Justin, who had been standing watch at his window, called down the air vent to Fonseca to have him help fit on an item of formal dress he had not worn before: the turban of Sans Souci.

Fonseca balanced the cloth-of-gold egg, chattering about the programme of music he had prepared to match the morning-to-noon ragas of the opposing team. He had been rehearsing with a couple of fiddlers, hired for the occasion from White Town, since the first of December. He counted off the titles, reserving for the last a solo piece fresh from Europe (it had been published that same summer) to be performed by himself. When Justin heard the name of the piece, his mouth fell open and his fingertips pressed up against the barber-and-hornist's belly.

"*Eine kleine Nachtmusik*," he croaked. "At breakfast!"

"Well?" said Fonseca, who had been studying music, not German. But then the Nawab's trumpet sounded.

There was little conversation to mar the breakfast. The Great Trotter met the Nawab at the Gunpowder Door and conducted him on a brief tour of the main building, but both men were happy to abandon pretences and proceed directly to the dining hall. Justin showed his guest to the chief seat at the Nakhlau end and made a remark about the weather. The Nawab agreed, his eyes skipping gently from cover to cover on the table before him. Words failing, the host walked the length of the board to the Old Armoury end. A gong was struck and eating commenced (in fact, the Nawab had already taken advantage of Justin's turned back). With the extra leaves inserted in the table, conversation was in any case impracticable; even without the music it would have been necessary to shout if one wished to be heard at the other end. Between settings, while the table was being cleared of its wreckage, the Commander-in-Chief would amble over to his guest-and-employer and exchange a word.

"I'm thinking of calling the chief building *Sungum*, the *Watersmeet*."

"Tiens! *Another* sungum!"

"Pardon?"

"Every firangi—forgive the expression, mon general—every foreigner I know has called his seat *Sungum*. There must be sixty *Sungums* in occupied India. The macaroons are delicious, by the way."

Then the second setting was ready, with a change of flowers to marigolds on the Nawab's side and daffodils on the Great Trotter's. Justin returned to his seat and the musicians at his end struck up a midmorning raga while at the Nakhlau end there began a little night music. The music was loud enough to drown out the nilchis' singing in the distance across the Indigo Court, but now and then a few snatches filtered through. They were singing a familiar song:

> *Heron sits*
> *plunder*
> *Barbed Tengan*   *dart*
> *Dingdong*

When the meal was over, Justin smoked his hookah and the Nawab his Dutch cigars. Out of politeness they exchanged their smoking apparatuses for a minute. The waiters saw to it that neither device was lit for this ceremonial interlude, and the two men simply sat there sucking vacantly for a space before returning to their favoured tobaccos. The smoking concluded, the digestive seed eaten, host and guest were conveyed in palkis to the saltpetre hill, comfits of candy (*qand*) and anise being supplied for the journey. At the top of the hill, which was twelve feet from the bottom, they sat under the same marquee that had been used for the fireworks. The animal fights were staged, beginning with the elephants (a greyish white giant against a small black one) and progressing through camels and stags to the cocks, of which the guest had brought his own in a gilt cage. For the last match the company repaired to the Spur, Myrobalan comfits being provided for the journey. Muscled on saucers of blood in the Room of Gilt Cages and ignorant of politesse, Heaven's Vengeance made short work of the Nawab's prize bird. "I thought I ordered the second-best bird to be used," the Great Trotter whispered to his baker-and-cocksman when he saw how the fight was going. But Yakub had been unable to bring himself to play a losing card.

The Nawab departed smiling and enraged, promising himself that he would outdo the breakfast before the year was out. On the new year's eve he did: Heaven's Vengeance lost. Then he lost again and was destroyed.

Breakfast at Dr Bellows's School, Madras

Sunday	Tire and rice*
Monday	Tire and rice
Tuesday	Tire and rice
Wednesday	Tire and rice
Thursday	Tire and rice
Friday	Tire and rice
Saturday	Tire and rice

Breakfast for nilchis at Sans Souci

Itvar	Chick-peas
Somvar	Chick-peas
Mangalvar	Chick-peas
Budhvar	Chick-peas
Brahspatvar	Chick-peas
Shukrvar	Chick-peas
Shanivar	Chick-peas

(CHRONICLE RESUMED)

That night Justin had trouble sleeping. The double-onion mutton curry and the Goanese masala fish of the fourth setting were doing noisy battle in his stomach, on top of which there were flanking movements by a luscious date halva, itself harassed by an insurgent khir. He tossed and groaned on his bed, now rolling himself into a ball, now lying on his back with his feet straight out, now stretched diagonally across the bed with one knee bent and his arms spread like a trapeze artist. Eventually he called down to Fonseca, and Fonseca, knowing that the sitar troupe had asked and been granted a week's leave, suggested a little music. But he had no sooner begun to play his breakfast Mozart than Justin belched waterbrash and put his fingers in his ears. "Please, Fonseca," he begged, "make it a story." The barber-and-kahani-master obediently packed the horn into its box, cleared his throat, and took a deep breath.

---

* *Tire*, O Wedding Guest, is called *dahi* this side of India. It is soured milk or curds. In the rains, pepper-water was given the boys in place of tire. Rice is much improved with butter. The addition of sugar and milk, together with raisins, coconut, and cinnamon, produces *khir*. When rice flour is used in this dish, the famous result is Nakhlau *firni*. But your Madras will be Madras.

Chick-peas, in the next section, are best ground into flour, mixed with sugar and butter, and formed into *besan laddus*. Or else they may be fed to horses.—E.A.T.

A kahani

Believe me, after that we left Poona, and crossing the hills in the mango season, came to ————

(*CHRONICLE RESUMED*)

"No, no, Fonseca," the Great Trotter cut in. "Please. We've covered the Bombay road."

The barber-and-kahani-master swallowed and without turning his face began again.

Another kahani

Believe me, there was once a boy who would not smile. After his mother and wet-nurse died, he lived on toads and carrot halva and played with matches all day long. What need of more words? One day he blew up an armoury and shook his stepmother's tower. After that he ran wild and played all night with a dozen gipsy girls, frolicking in ponds and lakes and vats until he turned blue. His father gave him into the keeping of a Tibetan monk-and-plinth-master who taught him the five sciences, but one day both master and student disappeared, leaving no trace other than a row of indigo-coloured footprints and a set of milk teeth embedded in iron.

Let me tell you about it. They took the east road. They walked and walked. They slept under the stars, and the old man taught the boy the names of those he knew. There were many others. The boy lay awake listening to the dark nim trees tossing their hundred heads and whispering. He watched the sky reel from a frayed cuff of cloud which half hid the moon. Lulled by cool night breezes he fell asleep and the old man spread a sheet over him. In the morning the koel woke them with its mounting cry. As the sun came up behind the guava topes, they set out once more, starting early to avoid the heat. When they passed a village, the old man took out his begging bowl and went from door to door. They walked a short way past the village and sat down to eat, dividing the chapatis, the dal, the onion. After breakfast they rested, drew water from the outcastes' well, and went on their way. Hear some more. As they walked, the Tibetan kept long silences, sometimes forgetting to adjust his pace to the boy's. When he spoke it was to ask the boy a question: What was the meaning of pain, what was the remedy for desire? Look you, sometimes he would stop a peasant going the other way and ask the name of this tree or that bird. Sometimes a bullock-cart or an ekka going the same way would invite them to climb on. Then they rested their legs and travelled quickly. If the beast was already burdened, the Tibetan would smile and say, no. If the bullock-cart driver goaded his bullock, the Tibetan would ask why he did it. Sometimes the driver put away his goad, sometimes he scowled or shouted abuse and goaded the creature more cruelly than before.

You must know that in the evening the Tibetan chooses an open space and sits down to meditate. The whilst the boy goes in search of the village well and lies in wait for the girls who come there with their pots. If there is a pond he goes looking for cow-girls, and each day he loses some of the blue on his skin. What more shall I say? When the travellers came to a big town sometimes there were curried vegetables with the bread. But usually afterwards they lost their way and had to ask it of several. Why make a long story of it? In this way they passed through Allahabad, Benares, Patna, and Monghyr, watching the countryside change from yellow to drought white. Always, in every direction, it was flat. Then once again the earth grew moist and they came to Bengal. Their shoe-leather was brittle and worn by the time they reached Calcutta.

"You must have a name in this city, little one," the monk-and-plinth-master decided. "I will call you after a foreign friend of mine in the high country: Mikhail. Do you like it?" The boy tried on the name like a new shoe. It pinched at the heel. "Mik is better," he considered. And is it not? "Yes," the Tibetan agreed, "Mik is enough." Above the noise of the grain-carts on every side, he said: "Perhaps we can find you a school here." Mik stood puzzled; he did not know the word. "It is a place where boys are kept in rooms facing a black board on which the teacher writes." Mik was not impressed. "They go out to play sometimes," the monk-and-plinth-master added, and breaking off he went into a Chinese shoemaker's shop to ask about schools. The shoemaker sent him to a bigger shop on a grand street, and the merchant there sent him to Dacre Lane, where they found only a school for girls. The mistress directed the travellers to the Lower Military Orphanage across the river whence they had come. In Howrah, Mik saw scores of crannies and writers-to-be cringing on the playground. The Lower Military Orphanage, impressed by the boy's natural spirit, sent him to the Upper Military Orphanage with a note saying the boy represented himself as the son of a colonel. The Upper Military Orphanage, where the boys stood upright and played manly games, put Mik into short drill pants and sent the plinth-master off.

Understand that the old Tibetan never went far. He kept a constant eye on the boy and communicated with him by signals. Only when his charge was herded with the other officers' sons into one of the classrooms did he go about his business, now straying as far as Fort William, now appearing outside the civil offices. On the first evening the boy signalled: *not good*. The next day he signalled: *much worse*. By the end of the week whenever he caught the

Tibetan's eye he turned over an imaginary begging bowl in the traditional Buddhist manner signifying: *I refuse*. On Sunday he came to the old man bleeding at the nose. What shall I say? He had been fighting, not one but many; two or three he could have managed. The Upper Military Orphans were not nice, he said. They called him Michael and pretended they were sahibs. The schoolmasters beat into him the geography of this country and the history of a country on the other side. The old man considered for a moment and said: "Well, you already know the geography of the north. Let us go south. But first let us make a little history happen here."

This is what happened. The telling is short. He had Mik change into his road clothes. Then he took him by the shoulder as a blind man might, and walked slowly as far as Roberts Road. All around them was the bustle of the city. Food stalls lined the street and hawkers sang their clay toys and mirrors and knives. Women sat behind pyramids of green and yellow fruit and chatted with their neighbours, men pushed or pulled carts of firewood, pumpkins, and grain. The days were cooler now with winter coming on. People stepped carefully amid the trodden filth, dressed in their finery for the Puja festival. For you must know that it is then that light and darkness meet and wealth stands poised on every threshold. Tonight there would be myriads of clay lamps lit to welcome the goddess, and roofs and walls would be lined with soft nuggets of flame. And I can assure you that already in the mid-afternoon children were playing with squibs, cracking them at the feet of passersby and between the legs of horses and bullocks so that the air was pungent with powder. Now hear what they did. "That is the revenue office," the plinth-master pointed. "Go in and say you are looking for your father, who works there. They will send you from one desk to another and in the end they will throw you out. But while you are there you will mark the best window for getting back in tonight."

I assure you that Mik did as he was told and it happened as the old man predicted. Then they went to another group of buildings. "Those are the courts," the plinth-master pointed. "Go and see." Once more Mik obeyed. Then they came to the Writers' Building, then to Fort William. Lastly they went to Bow Bazar and mingled with the crowds buying firecrackers to cel-ebrate the festival of light. That night there were fires and explosions in various Company buildings and offices, including one in a powder magazine at Fort William, but to the merry-makers of Calcutta they were part of the din and dazzle of the celebrations. You may take it for a fact that records and titles and much that was writerly perished in the blaze, and a larger quantity of powder was lost than the holiday warranted. "Let us call this our Little Game, Mikhail," the Tibetan said. "*Mik*," the boy corrected him gravely. "Mik—to be sure!" the old man agreed. "Did you chase off the cat at the law courts—

Mik? We would not wish to hurt anyone." The next morning they left Calcutta by the south road, passing on the way a smoking black hole where the Writers' Building had been. "History will not record it, Mik. That is an illusion," said the old man pointing at their handiwork. "But there are other blacker holes in this city which are real, or so they say."

The truth is, as they recount it, that winter, all along the coastal route to Madras there was a rash of non-violent fires in the public offices of the Company's territories. Since nothing was ever taken and the destruction of records was random, there was talk in Calcutta of foreign saboteurs in the Czarist pay. You may take it from me that these were the first sparks of a rumour that would be fanned into a stubborn flame in fifty years' time. But no one who looked remotely Russian was ever seen or apprehended. Only towards the end did intelligence reports piece together a picture of the criminals' mode of operation: a boy neither dark nor fair would appear in the town's public offices asking if his father worked there. He would pass from one embarrassed firangi to the next and leave or be ejected. That night a fire would break out in the sonless offices, but the office cat would escape barely singed. By the time the intelligence was conveyed back to the territories concerned, Mik and the plinth-master had put away their tinder-box and firecrackers and arrived at Madras.

We are at an end. "You must try harder at this school," the old man said to Mik as they stood at the gate of Dr Bellows's academy. "It is said they favour numbers over history. They make surveyors of the best boys, and since you seem to like rambling, it is the job for you. I have a good friend in the high country—the same—who is a surveyor much of the time. I must go back there now. If you come that way, stop with him. You will tell him by the bearskin and the samovar. As for me, do not expect to find me alive. I am done with the Wheel. However, I will appear in Nakhlau so your father knows you are in good hands." Mik's unsmiling face grew still more solemn, and he shed the first tears of his life. They fell into his hands and sputtered there like water spilt on a hot griddle. He did not know what to make of them, but they vanished quickly in puffs of steam. "And don't play with fire," the old man grinned. Slowly, painfully, Mik smiled into his fists the first smile of his life. When he looked up again, the plinth-master was gone. This was the kahani.

(CHRONICLE RESUMED)

"*Wahh! Ustad!*" Justin exclaimed, his eyes red with impending sleep. "You are one master of a kahani-teller, Fonseca! No one can make make-believe come to life the way you do. The Nawab himself cannot have a better man. It *is* finished—by the way—the story? Is the chronicle resumed?"

"It is," Fonseca bowed. Although his master had begun to yawn noisily, he himself was wide awake, but a distant look in his eye meant his soul was still wandering like a kite on a silver string. Justin fell asleep almost at once and had troubled dreams of his missing son. He awoke the next morning convinced that the boy was in mortal danger somewhere and blamed himself for not having tracked him down or even mounted a search. When he shared his fears with Fonseca, the barber-and-man went on lathering the Trotter chin and said he was certain the boy was in no danger at all—at least not yet. "He is in good hands, count on it," Fonseca averred, but Justin would not be comforted.

"To think," he blurted through the lather, "—to think I've not given him a thought since the day the indigo took." Even in his sorrow he was confident that had he, the Great Trotter, shot one such saving thought his son's way, Mik should have been immune to mischance. "He is about to die," he insisted, cracking his knuckles under the barber's sheet and swallowing flecks of foam.

"He is in good hands, count on it," Fonseca murmured, concentrating on his razor. Through the little window he had opened in the lather on Justin's cheek, he saw an explosive adolescent coupling in progress. It was the Mik of his story, grown a little older and in his last year at Dr Bellows's academy, seducing the angular Poppy Bellows, third daughter of the Head and his Persian wife, and darling of the senior class. Three months later (Fonseca shaved a little more), her belly already beginning to swell, Miss Bellows was hastily engaged to a Welshman pur sang, Captain Llewellyn of the Company's artillery. A mild deaf and aging soldier, the captain had escaped promotion and consoled himself with plans for an easeful retirement. He had been dreaming of the joys of tropical bachelorhood when the news of his engagement reached him. Married on a short fuse, he came to suspect that the daughter born five months after the wedding might not be his, but since he was unable to engender any further issue in his wife he preferred to give himself the benefit of the doubt and let the matter rest. He took no interest in the child's rearing, and returned to his fantasies of a bachelordom filled with plump dusky women.

Mik was saved from expulsion (Fonseca saw) by this lucky arrangement, and Dr Bellows grudgingly retained his second-best pupil. The boy had grown up tough and stringy, with long unsightly muscles in his arms, and legs that refused to fill out. In his last year at Dr Bellows's school his voice had broken and a blackish moss sprouted on his upper lip (both factors had swept along the unfortunate Miss Bellows). He took the prize in trigonometry, but ranked

second in the class to his friend Willy Webbe.* Both boys qualified for places
at the Engineer Institute in Bombay and travelled across the peninsula together
to begin their apprenticeship as surveyors. Arriving in Bombay in winter, Mik
saw in a superior tailor's window a light coat of fashionable cut which he
thought might suit him. Having no money, and expecting none during his
apprenticeship, he was tempted for a moment to turn cranny: there were
clerical openings with the Company, he knew, for young men who could
figure and write. But Willy Webbe prodded him on. They presented themselves at the Institute, where they were taken in at the senior level, where
in addition to geography, draughtsmanship, and mathematics they learnt
furniture-turning and helped to operate a lithographic press. To their great

---

* By a curious coincidence another Mr Webbe of a later generation has left an account of miseries
undergone at a similar school in Madras, Dr Bell's. The reader will note in what follows that rice puddings
were given *only to the sick*!—E.A.T.

To His Excellency Sir John Malcolm, &c.&c.&c. G.C.B.
Sir,
—According to your desire, I beg leave to state the following as the mode of treatment used in Dr
Bell's school, regarding the diet, clothing, and care of the boys whilst I was in it.

The boys had for their meals tire and rice, and in the rains, pepper-water and rice for breakfast, curry
and rice for dinner, and pepper-water and rice or milk and rice for supper. These were served to us in an
earthen dish, with a pewter or china spoon, on a mat and on the floor. The boys, I am sure, as it was often
my case, could eat twice as much more as was given for a meal, but a second supply was never allowed.

Clothes were given three times a week to change; these were a coarse pair of trousers and a shirt; a
jacket and a leather cap were the only additions made to the dress when the boys went to church or elsewhere.
Shoes were not allowed, even if the parents or friends were desirous of supplying them.

We slept on the floor on a country mat, without pillows or covering, except in the rains, when a light
quilt was given to the boys. We felt no bad effects from this, as it was a brick floor. All kinds of exercise
were allowed to the boys, and a playground was enclosed for this purpose. We were indulged with bats
and balls, and all sorts of amusements conducive to health, and to make us hardy and strong.

The boys in hospital were treated with great care; two nurses were attached to attend on them, and
the food was agreeable to what the doctor used to direct, rice puddings, all sorts of broths and conjees, and
a little wine occasionally was given, and the boys were clothed warm, had a bed and a cot to sleep on,
and a quilt for a cover.

The hours for learning were from eight in the morning till twelve at noon, and from two till five in
the afternoon. We sat on benches and had tables to work on.

This mode of treatment to orphan children is, in my opinion, the best that can be adopted in India; it
makes them hardy, and it takes away a good deal of that high and foolish notion which the youth on this
side generally imbibe the moment they leave school. It would make them fit for any employment, and they
would cheerfully be resigned to any state, should circumstances, after filling a higher station, reduce them
hereafter. I respectfully state this from experience; witness the many (some are now on this side) from Dr.
Bell's school, who are now doing well, they would not think it degrading should fortune so change, to eat
their meals again from an earthen dish. We never knew the use of a knife and fork while at school, and I
never handled one until I accompanied your Excellency on the first mission to Persia.

I am, Sir, with respect,
Your most obedient Servant,
(signed) *W. Webbe.*

Poona, 6th August 1829

surprise, they were allowed forty rupees a month, and when in the field on survey duties, a subaltern's tent, four porters for carrying instruments, three bullocks for the carriage of said tent, two ditto for private baggage and expenses for "grain, forage, boy, and shoeing of a poney." The boy was someone else now: Mik had grown up.

By the end of two years (Fonseca saw) the pony had carried Mik to the source of the Narbada river, whose valley he surveyed. The following September, the Deputy Surveyor General's department fitted him out with a heavy overcoat of coarse woollen stuff and sent him with the first expedition across the mountains to Persia.

"Well, are you going to shave me or not?" the Great Trotter grumbled, looking up.

"Sir!" said Fonseca, and began to scrape rapidly, demolishing the window on Persia.

"I must make some sacrifice," Justin continued, "to safeguard my son, or he will expire momently."

"It's past," Fonseca said. "He's no longer in danger, I'm sure of it."

"Ah, Fonseca. You're a good fellow to comfort me. But I tell you I'm of a mind to give up something or my boy will give up the ghost."

"Well, then, give up sweets. Bring forward Lent—Easter is a movable feast."

Justin seized the barber-and-man by the collar and jerked him close. "Do you know what you ask, Fonseca?" he said.

Fonseca made no reply. He disengaged himself and held up the mirror to right and left. Then, untying the barber's sheet, he said: "Very well, with all respect, you could give up your life."

The Great Trotter sank back into his chair and mopped his forehead. "Thank you, Fonseca," he whispered. "Thank you."

"There is royal precedent for it, sir," Fonseca continued, dusting a little talcum on the wig his master had refused to abandon. "Believe me, the first Mughal emperor, Babar the Brave, did precisely that. As his son, Humayun, lay at death's door, the first Mughal went thrice about the sick-bed repeating: *I have taken up the burden, I have taken up the burden*. And the fever left Humayun and came upon him."

Justin sprang to his feet. "Yes!" he said. "Yes, the idea takes me. Splendid, Fonseca, splendid—to sacrifice one's life!" He took out his handkerchief and dabbed his eyes. "Far better," he wept, "far, far better. To die for one's son." He began to dance on tiptoe with his hands clasped in front of him and his elbows out, cooing: "Oh, it will be a glorious end, sung through the ages. The *Great* Trotter! Come, Death!" he said, going up to the tall mirror, "empty this glass—too long have I filled it to overflowing."

After breakfast, Justin had the Audience Bell rung and made a public announcement of his intention. Then he sat down to write his will. Dipping his pen into the inkwell, he smoothed back a sheet of writing paper of his own manufacture and brought the nib to within an inch of the surface. It was only then that the fact of his mortality struck him and shook a black spot onto the page. Never one to waste, Justin pressed a blotter to the spot and smoothed back the sheet again. So, I am to die, he thought. It's one thing simply to be alive and subject to the risk of death; and besides, he added, thinking of the skating escapade in Quebec, and the *Fatty Salaam*'s sinking in the Bay of Bengal, I was young then. It's quite another thing to be alive and court death—and what's more, write letters to it. What am I to say? What is usually said? Do wills have a preamble, a middle, and an end? Do they have a life of their own? Can they reproduce wills in their own image? I have heard that the will of the deceased is kept alive by the will of the deceased's executor so that the deceased's executor and the executor of the deceased's executor are regarded by the law as one person. And if I name three executors they are again one person. Miraculous consubstantiation of the law!

Preamble to the last will and testament of Justin Aloysius Trotter

Know all men by these presents that I, Justin Aloysius Trotter, being of sound mind and meet digestion, of right good spirit and in fine fettle (*is this the way?*), of doughty wind and solvency mercurial (*only the other day I made eighty thousand rupees' commission on the purchase by my eunuch friend, Afridi Beg, of two chandeliers from Bohemia*), in debt to no man or woman or any other sort of person whatever in respect of currency, notes and bullion, coin, specie, ornaments, chandeliers (*put it down, put it down*), jewellery, nor valuables of any description, nor property movable, nor property immovable, being of assets firm and goodwill boundless, never inmate of any lunatic asylum or debtor's prison or penitentiary civil, criminal, or military, charged with no moral turpitude, articled to no concern, bound to no bondsman, indentured to no state (two *states, yes*), in habits sober, in disposition kind, in digestion mild, in character reputable (*why, I have in my vaults diamond-crusted swords and ropes of pearls given me for safe-keeping at thirty percent*), in fortune sufficient, in adversity stout, in rout defiant, in fleeing resolute, in turning about assiduous, in pursuit valiant, in victory merciful, in pacification a dove, in reconstruction a mule, in administration an owl, in business a fish, in credit an elephant, in collecting a crocodile, of integrity unimpeachable, of address insouciant, of manner personable, in habiliments decent, even dashing, in features becoming, in aspect prepossessing, in mien gentle, in fine a gentleman, being nowise deranged, deluded, discommoded, daunted, drugged with charas, bhang, soma, sotweed, poppy, aphim, opium, or any other narcotic substance, nor intoxicated with fermented or spirituous liquors, from cereal or toddy-palm, having no knife at my throat, no scorpion dangled before me, no centipede in my cup, nor any hint of bitter almonds at tiffin, my pulse normal, my heat sufficient (*sufficient!*), my urine limpid, stool firm, semen virile, lungs airy, heart capacious, cuticles present and defined, bunions corrected, sinuses free, ears without wax, eyes without cloud, mouth without lies, do make this last will and testament as witness my hand and seal at the last page.

Fate having cast my lot in three separate lands of Europe, America, and Asia (*four, if the Africa of my getting be counted*) and brought me at last to this place which I have come to consider my very home, and chance having preserved me from death in Quebec and again in the Bay of Bengal, and countless times in the field of battle when the enemy's fire rained down on every side, to what and whom do I owe this life thus begun and preserved, whose conclusion I now contemplate and whose survivors I here address? What concatenation of natural causes formed me, what breath of history blew me hither? When I am gone, what will become of Sans Souci? (*To the point, there's the tack.*) Will it survive the century to come? Two hundred years from this day will one stone stand upon another? Will one of my descendants fly over it in some future flying machine? Will a funicular car convey him up this very tower? Will he stand at this same window and survey his demesne? Let him then praise famous men and his fathers that begat him; let him hark back to this document wherein he and his forefather become *one person* in the will of Justin Aloysius Trotter.

Who was born on the [*illegible*] of humble parents and came to India a common soldier. Who by dint of honest labour built him a château. Who got him a son (*there's the mark*) out of that chaste woman Sultana (*Cup of Grace*) who lies buried in the Hava Manzil in these grounds. Who founded a faith, the Din Havai, or Religion of the Winds, which holds that all men are made equal, being but dust blown hither and away in their lives, and hither and away after. Who therefore strictly forbids the interment of his body in any sealed chamber soever and enjoins that it be buried without winding sheet or aloe, lead sheeting or coffin, *wheresoever it happens to fall*, whether in eating or shitting, sighing or sleeping, making water or making love, walking out or coming home, on a rooftop or at a well, in the East Tower or in the amphitheatre, Tankside or on the saltpetre hill, on the Steps or in the sunken garden, in the maze or in the stables, prone or regnant, standing up or sitting down, with one shoe off or one shoe on, in the jakes or in the orangerie. Who equally forbids the evasion of this clause by any attempt to transport his mortal coil to a suitable place while life be in it, or a like subterfuge. Where the husk falls, there must it lie until the wind catch it up. Upon the spirit matter or the life essence's quitting my body (*when that soul or effluvium or slippery element drains out*), far better that it become commingled with the Wind which is its very substance and which in life batters the body seeking to release what the skin holds in.

If perchance some friend wish to place a stone at the spot where this common soldier fell, I will not quarrel from beyond the grave. Indeed such a stone already exists in the ruin where my sculptor Alexander dwelt. It is of white marble and reads: JUSTIN ALOYSIUS TROTTER, WHO LIVED AND DIED. I desire no addition to the epitaph, and indeed forbid any. As to the repose of my soul, I beg the Almighty God of my baptismal faith to forgive me, though it was surely by his knowledge that so many conflicting versions exist of those verities beyond the grave. What remains to be forgiven? And even if I were contrite, could I hope to elude the pleasurable mirror of remorse? Let sin bury sin. By a trick of the plurality of faiths what is a mortal sin in one faith is a guarantee of the soul's salvation in another, and where paradise is promised by one faith to the faithful after this life, to another it is twenty millions of incarnations distant, while to a third it is already within. That being so, no man of reason can espouse one faith unless he secretly despise the others and those who practise them—men who with equal vigour and justification despise him—of which is born great hatred and sometimes war. For it is with faith as it is with knowledge—men of different parts inhabit esemplastic spheres which they take to be sufficient, lawful, and proven. Yet they will seek to inflate these spheres into universals while at the same time jealously guarding them against rupture from without. One must have lived in this land to take full measure of the cant that men will credit in matters of faith. Far better that they embrace the tenets of the Din Havai, which I have set down in another place, where no man's words are weightier than another's, all meeting in the end the same fate.

As to the matter of property (*good man*) and its bequest, it may be quickly dealt with here. I give and bequeath to the son for whom I will shortly lay down my life, the following:

(CHRONICLE RESUMED)

But Justin did not quickly deal with the division of his property. Where in Sans Souci did one start, when each object led organically into the next like the fabric of a pleasurable dream? At the bottom, with the smallest bequests? Justin turned to certain modest considerations: a hundred rupees to this faithful servant; so much to be placed at interest for the poor of Nakhlau; so much for the poor of Calcutta; so much to be paid for the release annually of an honest debtor, preferably a military man, from prison; so much for a school in the name of his patron saint. He thought again of his nameless son, the nominalist to whom *Sans Souci* would be an unintelligible concept: the boy knew only things and the names of things. For his sake he must list painstakingly each item to be passed on, with a brief description of its properties so as to distinguish it from all other items of its class.

By five o'clock that evening he found he had not exhausted the contents of even the uppermost room of the West Tower. "He is writing his will," Fonseca explained to the Sagarpaysans who had gathered outside in anticipation of the rite of self-sacrifice. "He is writing his will," Yakub repeated in a louder voice to let it be known that announcements were his province. The news had the opposite effect from that which the barber-and-man and the baker-and-Chief Steward intended. Instead of dispersing, the crowd began to press closer, each man jostling the next in the hope that Tartar Sahib might perhaps look out of a window-slit and recognize his loyal face. "I'm afraid this is going to take some time," Justin whispered sheepishly to his councillors. "It is going to take some time," they repeated to the crowd. The Sagarpaysans were ready to camp outside the West Tower, reluctant to miss either the spectacle of their master's self-surrender or a chance of inclusion in his will. But Justin wrote on and on, covering reams of the creamy paper of his own manufacture, breaking dozens of pens and spilling rivers of ink. At length his camp-followers or ocean-peasants began to tire of waiting and drifted off in ones and twos, turning to look back anxiously every few steps and ready to fight for a place if the Great Trotter's face should appear at a window. It did not, and eventually even the most clamorous optimists fell silent. At the week's end the last stragglers could be seen walking backwards along the path to the village on the other side of the saltpetre hill. Life returned to its usual round in the village, at least for the women-folk; the men wrestled and played children's games with sticks and stones until they tired of that and sat about doing nothing. By common consent none of the paid servants (except the bhisti, Gunga Din) reported for work.

For two years Justin wrote, rarely leaving his tower. His meals, cooked by Munnoo and Nankoo under Yakub's supervision, were brought to the West Tower in relays. Fonseca was kept busy in the paper mill across from the new armoury, dissolving inkstone and pressing tablets of the thick creamy paper that bore the watermark of Sans Souci. During these years the temperature rose without ever falling, so that winters were winters only in name and the birds died or migrated to cooler parts. The drought that began in the year of the great breakfast (when famine was so severe that the Nawab had relief works kept open at night so that the genteel poor might earn their bread without being recognized) grew worse. All except the deepest wells dried up, and the fleur-de-lis Tank was reduced to a bog pitted with the swollen hoofprints of cattle that would soon leave their shrunken carcass-marks on the same spot. Vultures blind with meat fought loutish hissing matches over waterholes. The villagers, having stripped the English tamarind trees of their sweet pods and the Indian tamarind trees of their tart pods, began to eat the leaves. Gunga the bhisti abandoned the rose garden and found enough to do straining muddy water out of the kitchen well into his masak to carry up to *Sungum* for Justin's shower. When the heat grew intolerable Justin would go to Farida in the East Tower and steep himself in her indigo. Then he returned to his table with the barley-sugar legs, where by comparison all was newly cool, and resting his hand on a blue kerchief to avoid smudges, filled another page with the names and descriptions of things. "I have become like my son's dead mother," he said, and for the first time in two years left *Sungum* to walk to the Begam Kothi, the house she had not lived to occupy. There he went from room to room fingering the dusty stones and feathers and leaves by which she had sought to reproduce the world. "All this must be catalogued," he sighed, looking at the world in facsimile, and had his writing desk brought down from his tower.

When word got about that the Great Trotter had moved to the Begam Kothi, the Sagarpaysans returned with votive offerings and surrounded the domed building. Justin was moving slowly through an upstairs room tapping each article in it with the end of his pen. Hearing a commotion, he looked out at a window and saw in the gathering crowd a new determination. All of a sudden he found death less attractive than on that glorious morning when Fonseca had first told him of the emperor Babar's self-surrender. Now his barber-and-man came in and announced: "Sir, they are waiting."

"I can see that, Fonseca," the Great Trotter replied touchily, glancing at the ring of camp-followers who squatted outside, patient pilgrims waiting the holy fair to begin. "But I am not yet finished. There is a world of things to record." And he pointed out to Fonseca that this fan of peacock feathers he held in his hand could not be confused (for instance) with the one made from parrot feathers downstairs (or for that matter the one made from peacock feathers downstairs) and must therefore be listed separately.

"With respect, sir," said Fonseca, "you could simply denote all three by *feathers*, or if there are beaks waiting to be catalogued, by *birds* or *hairless winged bipeds*. Better still, make it *all animals and animal products*. That would save you a trip to the elephant stables."

As he listened to Fonseca it seemed to Justin that huge primeval tectonic plates had begun to shift and grate in his head, revealing a familiar but forgotten stratum. His feet had found a shelf of rock after an eternity of walking in sand. "Where on earth have I been?" he wondered, looking around him at his wife's intricate web of things. He strode across to the mountain of paper accumulated over two years' writing and took up the first four sheets, the preamble and the smaller bequests. He gave the rest a little kick. Seating himself on a divan, with the inkpot balanced on his knee, he wrote across the bottom of the last page: *I give Sans Souci and all things in it, with the aforesaid exceptions, to my son by Sultana (Cup of Grace).* And he signed his name.

"Here, Fonseca," he said, giving the barber-and-signatory his pen. "And we will need another witness."

"Here," said Yakub, appearing at the door.

When the ink was dry, Yakub produced from his pocket a candle, a tinderbox, and some sealing wax together with the seal of Sans Souci. "No, no seal," Justin decreed, and the document was sent to Qaiyum to be deposited in the library paper-catch. Meanwhile, the Great Trotter appeared to have lost interest in the will and was sitting on his hands at the edge of the divan humming an air from *Julius Caesar in Egypt.* Suddenly he stood up and said in a loud voice: "I am ready." The baker-and-Chief Steward went to the window and called down: "He has finished," and the Sagarpaysans cracked their knees and cleared their throats approvingly. Some stood up and with glazed eyes began to chant, others clapped finger-bells. The Great Trotter approached his son's bed and meditated a space. The cot was empty except for the burst anklet with the double row of teeth in it; dust had turned the sheets grey. Communing with himself and with his line, he began his walk around the bed. At the window Yakub held up one finger, then two, then three. As the third circuit was completed a cry broke from the First Trotter's lips, and his legs gave way under him. He fell in a heap on the floor whimpering incredulously: *I have taken up the burden, I have taken up the burden.* Lying with one cheek against the smooth marble, he let his eye rove feebly over its surface. At once he sat up. The accusing indigo footsteps leading up to the bed were gone. *Thoo!* he spat. "My dye is still not permanent."

By nightfall he had begun to shiver.

Concerning the generation of heat and its transfer

Sugar, it is well known, generates heat. Other sources are the *sun,* great *anger,* and a surfeit of *love.* To guard against cold, surveyors and mountaineers commonly carry gypsonometers, which will do just as well for hot drinks as for cold (as well as for surveying). However, those going towards *Persia* and those parts, where such inventions are common, tend to leave theirs behind, imagining a great coat of coarse black stuff to be enough. When such persons reach the Khyber Pass and find it is already October, they are greatly *angered* and do not notice the cold. When they come upon a Pathan boy with a bottom like a peach they are fired with *love* and do not notice the snow. When they come upon Mikhail, a Muscovite surveyor-and-agent in distress, they give away their coat, and keeping to south or sunny face do not notice the wind. When the *sun* goes behind a cloud they catch cold. They begin to shiver and hold up the expedition. They have no one to blame but themselves. They long for the flesh-pots of Ind, for pepper-water and rice pudding and cowbells, but there is no going back. There is little going forward either. They are stuck. They volunteer to remain behind, asking the leader of the mission to press on; they are surprised when he agrees. He says the party will leave the next day. That night, just as their comrade Willy Webbe begins to chafe the soles of their feet, a pleasing heat surges through them, from the head down. They stand up and walk. They need no covering, no coat; they can sit cross-legged in the snow like a lama. Willy Webbe's hands have turned blue, but theirs are like fire. It is a miracle. The next day they and the whole party move on. Standing on a peak, they survey *Persia*.

(*CHRONICLE RESUMED*)

While everyone else in Nakhlau sweltered, Justin lay shivering under a pile of blankets. Through the night Fonseca chafed the soles of his feet and Hakim Ahmed stood by the bedside with a specific compounded on the spot from his bag of simples. When he learnt that the Great Trotter's self-surrender was imminent, he had been ready with a potent febrifuge. The moment word reached him of Justin's collapse he hastened to the West Tower (where the sick man had been transported) but was taken off guard by the symptoms. Fonseca, too, had stared disbelievingly at the thermometer before adding a mongoose-down quilt to the pile of blankets. Justin moaned his gratitude. Lying there with his wig on, this great fleshy man presented a pitiful spectacle. Even Hakim Ahmed, a muscular physician accustomed to human suffering, was moved to tears as the Great Trotter blenched and shivered, squealing at times that he was stuck and that there was snow on every side.

It was only the following morning that Fonseca thought of sugar. When he did, it seemed the most obvious of remedies, and he wondered why it had not occurred to him before. But the servants refused: the Great Trotter was still alive and must atone for an incomplete self-sacrifice. At length Yakub decided it was no use reasoning with cooks and ordered that the horses' quota of sugar be doubled, that the camels be given twice as much milk as usual, and that from now on the elephants were to have green mangoes along with their bamboo shoots. Each day, Justin's restorative was brought him by way of the stables, having been mixed in a trough by Munnoo and carried upstairs in Gunga the bhisti's buffalo-hide masak. Thus was invented mango-fool.

The Great Trotter responded well to the treatment. He asked for the mongoose-down tick to be removed and his tremors diminished. He was, however, obliged to be secretive in his consumption of the restorative (which in those days was drunk warm), and here the gypsonometer found its function. With each morning he recovered more of his spirits, if not immediately his form, and one day he remarked how mild the weather was in the plains compared with up in the Khyber Pass. He had, all the same, lost considerable weight from the shivering, and it may have been at this unfortunate stage that an alleged painter, one Zoffanij, came by with his bristles (*Oil Painter, Mythologist*) to leave an entirely erroneous impression for posterity.

> *And now, O Narrator, tell me a true and credible story of how sweetness won the*
> *day at Sans Souci in the generation of legend.*
> *A credible story, Cup-Bearer?*
> *That is what I said, Narrator.*
> *You will not disbelieve me?*
> *I am credulity itself.*
> *Very well, Cup-Bearer. Those were large days. Fetch me a jug of mead from*
> *Germany. Already! Now listen. I have heard from the golden oriole that it*
> *happened in this way.*

(CHRONICLE RESUMED)

The Nawab of Tirnab, hearing of his friend-and-Commander-in-Chief's illness, made his first bid for Sans Souci. The negotiations, he saw, would be a delicate business, not to be trusted to fools. He summoned his Prime Minister to call up the wisest man in his court. Several candidates stepped forward, but the Nawab sent one of them to the palace library to fetch his librarian.

When Munshi Nishan Chand appeared, tetchy and truculent from having been disturbed, it was difficult to say whether his refusal to bow stemmed from self-esteem or from the fact that he was already bent in half. He was an old man. He omitted the sour ducking of the head that with him passed for obeisance, and stood there scowling at a point between the Prime Minister and the Nawab. Tirnab, who had lately begun to tire of his scholar-librarian's arrogance, responded with a few distant words of command: the *Munshi*—he knew the effect of the title on the librarian—the *Munshi* was to go to Sans Souci to ask after the French firangi's health. Tomorrow he would go again, and the next day he might drop a hint about Sans Souci. "And," the Nawab added, when Nishan Chand swung grumpily away, "take that German's daughter along as a gift from me—the Commander-in-Chief is said to be cold." There was a tittering among the nobles. The munshi was widely supposed to be infatuated with his prodigy, the casual daughter of a foreign ink vendor and a local courtesan. The girl's father, an English-speaking burgher from Ceylon who posed as a Dutchman and was taken for a German, had lost favour at court and been poisoned (with his own inks, it was said). His daughter, barely twelve at the time of his death, was brought up in the nawabi harem, where she caused a scandal by dressing as a European and playing chess (albeit from behind a screen) with twelve masters at one time. Within a year of passing under the librarian's tutelage, she was performing in public stupendous mathematical feats. The Nawab would not lightly have lost her, but he wished to wound his librarian and saw with satisfaction that the thrust had gone home. The munshi snarled and tottered away.

It was late evening when the pair arrived at Sans Souci. Nishan Chand had gone directly from the audience to his rooms to gather up his things. If the German's daughter was to leave, he did not intend to remain at court a day longer, certainly not after his public humiliation. "You are to go with me to Sans Souci," he barked at his student. "Pack everything." And the day was spent readying books and trunks and bedding rolls and mosquito-nets to be loaded onto a couple of tongas. The carriage customarily used for state business was otherwise engaged. Whips cracking, the tonga-walas bullied their horses to a trot, and Nishan Chand, scholar-gipsy-and-librarian-at-large, was borne away from his most recent home. Elise, a girl of fifteen, clung to her perch on the sloping back seat and watched the scene of her childhood recede in the dusk. She took careful note of the sights fading on both sides as she lurched backwards towards Sans Souci; emotion did not come readily to her. In twenty minutes they joined the road by which Sultana (*Cup of Grace*) had fled to join her foreign husband, and Farida the child-bride had travelled to the wedding that never was.

Justin was at his window, out of bed for the first time since his rite of self-surrender. He was staring wanly at the evening star when the sound of horse-bells filtered through the warm air to him, growing steadily louder as the tongas came up the drive. He frowned his puzzlement and looked enquiringly over his shoulder at Fonseca. Yakub, whose senses were keener, was already downstairs waiting at the Gunpowder Door. Shortly, there came the crunch of gravel from below, some grating and shuffling, and the clink of coins. Then a silence, broken by an exchange of voices. The tongas drove off and once again Justin looked at his barber-and-man. In a little while Yakub came up to announce an emissary from the Nawab. "At this hour?" Justin grumbled. "And in a tonga?" He sniffed. "Is it terribly urgent?" Yakub was not prepared to run down two hundred and forty steps simply to determine the degree of urgency; it was all very well for the Great Trotter, who was carried up and down by six men. He answered selectively, and with truth, "Yes." "Very well, show him up," said Justin and climbed back into bed.

Three-quarters of an hour later, a breathless and very bad-tempered Nishan Chand hunched in the doorway. Behind him, visible from the waist up, stood Elise.

"But my steward said *an* emissary!" exclaimed Justin, starting up before he remembered his state and then hurriedly pulling the bedclothes up under his chin. Elise turned delicately aside. It was the first time she had seen a man in undress, and the sight was confusing until she assimilated its cognitive value. After that momentary confusion she felt no embarrassment.

"Yes," Nishan Chand declared, his chin dripping sweat. "I am he— though 'refugee' might better describe me. *She*," he added, half turning, "is a gift."

The Great Trotter considered this fresh bolt, as did Yakub and Fonseca. All three men wished to examine the girl more closely and for that reason looked very sternly in every direction but hers. She in turn scrutinized them with a cool curiosity, as if each were a problem to be addressed and solved. In a little while she appeared to have the correct answer on all three heads and became interested in the furniture.

"I am to ask after your health," the librarian continued. "But I ask also for sanctuary."

Justin spread his wasted hands. "By all means," he said. "Welcome."

The librarian grunted.

"As for my health," Justin went on, "you see me as I am." But he remained under the sheets. "My servants intend to make a pir of me, and they are most exacting of their saints." And he laid bare his plight.

That night the librarian was given a desk in the library, since he slept (he said) sitting up. Elise was given a bed in the vacant South Tower. The next morning she was up at dawn and found her way to the kitchens.

The baker-and-Chief Steward, who was having a spartan breakfast before supervising the lighting of the ovens, stood up as she came in; the cooks and underlings became busy with nothing.

"Since the Great Trotter is forbidden sugar," Elise announced, "I have a recipe that will satisfy both you and him. It is a kind of Dutch-German bread."

Two hours later, the baker-and-headwaiter carried a small round wicker basket covered with a green napkin to the West Tower. In it nestled a covey of soft brown loaves. Justin, who was tiring of surprises, lifted a corner of the napkin and peered critically at the offering. He dropped the flap and demanded his breakfast. "This is it," replied Yakub. "The Jarman guest ordered it made." Elise, who wished to be present at the trial, appeared at the door. "It is as he says," she confirmed. "I thought you might like a change." Justin, too taken aback to protest, obediently broke off a piece and put it in his mouth.

It melted on his tongue, spreading its healing sweetness to the very root. When he had emptied the basket, gathered up the crumbs at the bottom with a moistened fingertip, and shaken the napkin carefully into his open mouth, the Great Trotter asked: "From *my* kitchens?" His face was transfigured, his forehead shining. "Yes," Elise answered, and the baker-and-supervisor nodded his corroboration. "But—how—what is it?" Justin asked faintly. Elise's smile was precise and brief. "It's honey-roggen," she said.

That day the beehives were installed. The mock-ruined roundhouse was selected as the most logical site, being near enough to the gardens and the mango tope and yet at a healthy remove from *Sungum* and the stables. It was moreover open to the sky and vacant, Alexander having long since moved out with his family. For the idler bees there was, overhanging the ruin, the oracle tree with its fleshy pink flowers now at their best. Under Elise's strict eye, but also under the forlorn gaze of a dozen half-finished Dianas of the Ephesians, a colony of bees grew up and multiplied and went about their vital business. In gratitude Justin offered to name the as yet nameless court that looked out on the distant apiary (on the opposite side of *Sungum* from the indigo) after his deliverer, but she dismissed the matter with her concise smile and asked only if there were a tailor who could make six white dresses identical to the one she had on.

After the defection of Nishan Chand, relations between the Nawab and his ex-Commander-in-Chief cooled. But the summer continued hot and windy. The drought, which was in its fifth year, showed no sign of abating and the kites wheeled higher and higher above Sans Souci hoping to pierce some damp grey cloud. But there were no clouds in the sky and the sun beat down mercilessly. Peasants lay stunned in their villages or migrated to starve in the city; all the crops and half the cattle were dead. In the Nakhlau markets only the melon sellers wore smiles: they had hereditary rights to the riverbed where a trickle of the Moti Ganga still ran. Besides, the heat was good for the melons. In Sans Souci the cooks worked in an inferno, while the cripple Marazzi, lying on his back squashed against the ceiling of the Audience Hall, introduced some few tortured souls into his otherwise bucolic frescoes. Below him, Munnoo and Nankoo dripped away like candles, their sweat running into the marble and giving it an imperishable gloss. Qaiyum, the poet-and-(since Nishan Chand's arrival, deputy-)librarian, lay in bed all day nursing his liver with a cup of wine and now and then sighing, poor man, as he heaved his moist belly back up to prop a book of verse. If any felt the heat, it was he. In the garden the daffodils were blasted and the lotus pond dry, its basin littered with the skeletons of goldfish. Hot loo winds skipped along the Grand Steps leading up to the Water Court, wearing them down with sand so that they looked as if multitudes had marched up them through the ages. Only

Nankoo the convert to Din Havai was to be found out-of-doors at such times, standing on the perron and braying his faith into the wind. Grit lodged in his teeth; elsewhere it peppered the indigo cake and harried the bees. The hens stopped laying and of an afternoon the air was brazen with the trumpeting of elephants.

With regard to the oiling of camels and the injecting of oil into their nostrils

Camels everywhere get hot and rut in winter. In summer, mostly, they are placid, remembering the past, laying up stores for the future. Their stables are the farthest away, in the Elephant Wing but beyond the elephants, near to the desert which is their element (but not as far as the aerolite). This side of the animal cemetery is their dock, before the humps of the elephant graves but long after the elephants. One may walk a long way and see only elephants. One may walk a mile before the camels appear. But cherished smiles await one and it is worth it in the end, really. They are anointed in the usual way with sesame oil, and the mode of injecting oil into the nostrils is this. Equal portions of brimstone and sesame oil are diluted in seven times their weight of buttermilk and then just *injected* into the nostrils. That is all, for a year. The dromedaries look on indifferently; their smiles are formal only. In very hot weather they, too, begin to chafe.

The dairy cattle

They are in the Crocodile Wing, opposite. Just adjoining the forest. The Great Trotter, whose wisdom extends to all things, put them there. Formerly the Crocodile Wing was called the Dairy, but the Great Trotter changed the name to the Crocodile Wing. This is much better. Following the Great Mughal in all things, the Great Trotter has given much attention to the administration of this vital department. If I may quote the illustrious Abu'l Fazl, author of the *Akbar-Nama* and many excellent works, "Milch-cows and buffaloes have also been divided into sections, and handed over to intelligent servants." The same is done here. Cows are the best of creatures, calves the next best. Buffaloes have a rank low, being called after their gross babble, *Bos babulus*. In summer they yearn for ponds and streams—they are commonly called water-buffaloes, or failing that, mud puddles. There is also a yak, very costly. They are milked morning and evening by intelligent servants, but in the hottest weather they stop. Milk is a delightful drink, it is said.

(CHRONICLE RESUMED)

One afternoon in the midst of the general distress, Justin noticed a dampness under his arms and realized with a joyful start that he was sweating again. He saw that he held in his hand, and had been using all day to mop his face, the blue kerchief which he had last found occasion to produce the day before the self-surrender and the onset of the shivering. He was congratulating himself on his recovery when the thought struck him that, the weather being what it was, a normal body temperature was perhaps a mixed blessing. If during the past few months he had been uncomfortably cold, he had at least not been intolerably hot. Now the second prospect began to open before him and for a moment, looking out at the blaze of ochre lawn in the Gunpowder Court, his spirit quailed and he wished himself back in the Khyber Pass.

In time Justin was sweating as freely as the others and cursing rather more so. He grew prickly and listless. He threatened to dismiss Qaiyum, the flatterer-and-deputy librarian. He was short with Yakub and abusive with Fonseca. He took to spending whole afternoons in the dining room, where the pankhas and thermantidotes were kept in constant motion. Or else he lay naked in the bowl of the feeble central fountain in the Audience Hall among the dolphins and the half-finished mermaids, hating the Creator of the sun. Inevitably his eyes were drawn to an inscription that echoed the one in the Mughal Audience Hall in Delhi: *If there be a paradise on earth, it is this, it is this*, and the mockery of it drove him down another flight of steps to the library, where it was a shade cooler. Why not, he reasoned, as he lay stretched on the floor between Plato's *Timaeus* and Kant's *Critique of Judgment*, burrow still deeper into the earth? He got up and went in search of his baker-and-major-domo. It was fortunate that he did, because no sooner had he gone than Elise, stumbling along in the dark, came down that very aisle to hunt out two books not widely reputed for the advancement of natural science and practical knowledge.

The digging began that night in the West Tower. Working by lamplight, the labourers broke the ground for a shaft to be sunk to the depth of one further storey, or roughly the distance from the floor of the Audience Hall to the floor of the library. Although most of the work was below the packed earth of the man-made plateau, the soil was hard from the drought, and pickaxes were needed all the way. In an ordinary year the ground would already have shown signs of moisture, but the water-table had fallen. When finally the clay was found to sweat, a bend was introduced to bring the cut to the centre of *Sungum*. Here the shaft was widened into a kind of bulb or

cave and an air vent bored upwards to the northwest wall. Gravel was laid
to a depth of two feet, and the walls, floor, and ceiling flagged with stone.
When the paving was complete, it was found that no two sides of the cell
agreed (only stonemasons with squints having been chosen), so that instead
of a regular room there was a kind of irregular many-sided cavern that one
did not so much occupy as infiltrate. In the centre was set a solid near-
rectangular plinth of white marble, a block rising to a man's height above the
floor, its five unequal surfaces polished to a mirror finish by Munnoo and
Nankoo, who were led there blindfolded. The upper face was the length of
an ordinary table with a stepped recess at one end for a seat. There Justin sat
dozing on the hottest days with a book in front of him; only there did he ever
remove his wig. Between his bald head and the sun hung eighty thousand
tons of masonry.

The Great Trotter became addicted to his underground retreat. He spent
so much of his time there that by the end of the day Fonseca's legs were
crippled with tiredness from having run a hundred times up and down the
West Tower with books and dainties. (It was this daily punishment that led
him to invent the dumb-waiter.) Had it not been for the damp chill air of a
night, Justin would have taken to sleeping in his cellar. As it was, he repaired
there directly after disposing of the day's business with Yakub in the Audience
Hall. Shielded from the sun, he grew sleek and etiolate, and sometimes as he
looked at his reflection in the marble plinth, he seemed to see his former self,
a thinner avatar in a long-forgotten uniform, safely shut in. Then he would
thank God that the two hundred pounds which imprisoned that miserable
wraith were added after and not before he went skating on a Quebec pond
in early spring.

> *And now, O Narrator, tell me plainly how ice came to Sans Souci in the days*
> *when all things were possible.*
> *You wish to know, Cup-Bearer?*
> *I wish to know. I have put away all doubt.*
> *Then fetch me some cloudberry liqueur from Quebec. Back already! Now listen.*
> *The Canada goose tells me that it came about like this.*

(CHRONICLE RESUMED)

One day towards the end of May the weather took a turn for the worse.
Justin, who would not have thought it possible, saw the first sign as he hurried
down to the cellar from his rooms: before his very eyes a fire broke out
spontaneously at the half-finished sundial and flashed across the lawn until
the entire oval was ablaze. The gravel drive that ran around the lawn prevented

the fire from spreading to the maze in the sunken garden, and no sooner was the yellow nap consumed than the flames died out, leaving a woolly carpet of white smoke. The whole thing happened so quickly that Justin was inclined to doubt his senses, but he took it as an omen. Downstairs in the Audience Hall, Yakub was waiting with a tale of woe: the dairy cattle had stopped giving milk, the yak was dead, a long crack had appeared in the saltpetre hill, making further mining dangerous. "Nonsense!" said Justin to the last piece of advice. "Have the workers press on, or their wages will be docked. I've found it's cooler the deeper you go." And he would not stay for an answer (*Justin Pilate*), bounding away to his own burrow. "Today," he called, turning in the doorway, "I do not wish to be disturbed in my—ah—my—what is it called?"

"Tahkhana," Yakub suggested.

Justin was crestfallen. "Is that it?" he said. He thought perhaps he had invented something.

"Yes," said Yakub. "For a thousand years my people have been building tahkhanas in this hellish country."

By ten o'clock the dampness in the air of the tahkhana was gone. With the dryness came a new glare; Justin had never known it to be so bright in his cellar. The light from the mirror tube which he was experimenting on, in the hope of one day developing a soft shadowless light, thrust in like splinters of marcasite. It fell on the plinth and scattered across the irregular walls where it hung shimmering in a strange array of geometrical shapes. Below the plinth it ruled a band of black shadow which crept along the floor, shrinking into itself when it found its way barred. The ceiling, except for a white oblong where the upper facet of the plinth was reflected, took on a luminous sheen, a grainy half-light of the kind Justin saw on an ordinary day when, lying prostrate on the plinth, he shut his eyes. Today as he lay there he saw only the blood pounding on his lids and quickly opened his eyes again. Beneath him, the plinth, normally a cool block of marble, took on a vitality of its own: it first answered his body heat, then began to feed it. Justin sat up. The marble was actually hot. He hopped off the plinth and padded around the tahkhana, but the floor was hotter still. Thinking to return to the Audience Hall fountain, he climbed the first few steps of the tower. But the heat grew fiercer as he climbed and he was driven back; it was just as well: the water in the fountain was seething.

The plinth was still the coolest place in Sans Souci and Justin returned there, shedding his clothes as he did. Lying on his back, he was afraid to shut his eyes again, so he let them roam over the irregular walls, examining the curious shapes of light, polygons, parallelograms, and tetrahedrons that hung there like crystal stalactites. He noticed that they moved fractionally with the sun. Selecting one, he watched the light gather at a tremulous tip, break off—and draw the whole shape after it with a glassy shudder. Then all would be still with that shape until the next tremor. On every side the reflections shook themselves along the walls with a halting, barely perceptible advance, changing shape as they slid across the uneven surfaces. He watched spellbound as they began to gather speed, tripping over each other's heels in their dance around the cell. Now they were overtaking and absorbing other shapes, racing along, chasing their own tails, swallowing themselves up at such a rate that Justin could not tell whether it was the room spinning or the plinth. Without closing his eyes, he gave himself up to the frenzy and spun on countless shifting axes until he shot off at a tangent. An eternity of ricocheting brought him to the other side of the planet where, little by little, he made out a pond frozen over and a figure in blue skating on it. The figure was himself.

That evening at dinner he shared his vision with the would-be-German's daughter. She sat at the far end of the table, some of whose leaves had been removed to allow for conversation. As he spoke, Justin recalled solitary dinners past when he longed to look up from his trencher and see at the far end a beloved face. Now that seat was filled in a manner he had least expected, and above it hung a face which suggested an icicle; it could not have looked less like his dear mama. The impudence of the face at first impressed and then irritated Justin. Plainly lacking any special interest in him, the chess-prodigy-and-gift made no attempt to interest him in herself. Yet she took her meals with him in the dining hall while his concubine, Farida, ate in her tower. The combination of neglect and proximity fascinated him: the girl became a challenge, and since she was not without a certain severe charm, he was ready to meet it. It was both a help and a hindrance that in matters of the heart she was either a child or an ignoramus. Justin recognized that the distance between himself and this cut-glass marvel was more than half a century—but so was that between himself and the girl who clung to him so passionately on moonless nights. He resolved to win her after her own fashion, by tactics she would respect: he would impress her with his powers of mind.

"Today," he began, "I visited Quebec."

A thousand miles from the nearest seaport it was an impressive gambit, certainly a better subject than the weather. Coming out of the blue, it might have told on Elise had her brain not been otherwise engaged. When he got no response, Justin peered short-sightedly at her, craning his neck and leaning to one side to see what it was she was doing. She appeared to be scribbling on a sheet of paper. Justin frowned. The table was an altar not to be desecrated with the written word; the last time it was a book, now this. In his agitation he knocked over an empty decanter. The accident had the desired effect. Elise looked up.

"Today," the Great Trotter began again, "I visited Quebec."

Elise lifted her eyes to the flapping pankhas. She said: "You could not have picked a better day. I trust it was cooler there."

Justin refused to be put out. "It was. In fact, I went skating. On a pond," he added loftily, "whose precise latitude—"

"Skating in May!" Elise broke in. She had never left the Gangetic basin but knew about North American winters. "And in your condition?" Her eyes were cold points of light set in an umlaut above the narrow U of her nose.

"No, no—it was not I who was skating," Justin clarified, "but my—my—self, my former self, you see. And what's more, he fell in and barely escaped drowning—by the skin of his teeth—or I should not be here. It was the most extraordinary experience, watching oneself and knowing that one is about to go down but being unable to prevent it. Just as well there were friends with me—with him, I should say, for I went alone—who fished him out. He took back a chunk of ice as a souvenir. Of course, it melted—or else it should be in my pocket still!"

And jestingly the Great Trotter put his hand into his pocket. The smile left his face. His fingers had closed around something colder than a coin or a key. He took it out and laid it on the table. It was a piece of ice.

The Great Trotter almost leapt out of his chair, but, recalling that he had meant to impress the pseudo-German's daughter, he gripped the armrests and rode out the frenzy in his brain. When he could think calmly, he looked up again and saw that the girl had returned to her scribbling. Well, at least she had not noticed. He stared hard at the fragment of ice. Removed from its insulated hiding place, it was melting rapidly. It shifted fractionally as the water rose around it. Presently there was only a puddle on the teak surface, but the cold light which burned in Justin's left eye showed he had had an idea. He blurted it out.

"Next summer," he cried, "—next summer"—he was shivering with excitement now—"you shall have a shipload of foreign ice! No more of this compacted Himalayan snow which they adulterate with talc, which costs the earth and is gone by June. The time has come for genuine ice. New World ice. Sweetwater pond ice. Do you realize the merchant ships that side carry stones in the hold for ballast when they come this way? *Stones*, I ask you! Give me one year—less—one winter, and you shall see. I will buy a ship and fetch me some Quebec ice—from my pond. I will drink again of the waters of my youth—"

Justin bit his tongue: waters of youth was not the way. But the girl was again preoccupied, glancing over her scribbled notes. He sucked in his cheeks and frowned more deeply than before, but as he did she looked up.

"Why not make it here?" she asked.

"Make what here?"

"Ice. Why not make our own ice?"

"Make . . . ice . . . here." Justin stated the proposition slowly in a dry staccato, the corners of his mouth pulled back and his teeth set, as if he were repeating *Water runs uphill*, or *All men are Socrates*. He gave up and smiled. "I'm afraid the top of the saltpetre hill is twelve feet from the bottom— altogether too low for snow. In fact, I hear it's sunk further today. Yakub tells me a shaft collapsed, burying two miners."

"I was thinking of ice, not snow," Elise returned. "I believe the natives have always had ice pits, but it appears these are primitive and inefficient, little more than frost holes with thatching. I have a better idea."

As always now, Elise spoke French with the Great Trotter, but the word *native* was in English. Justin, who could never fasten on the substance of a conversation, being easily distracted by its shape and sonority, noticed the word and saw how curiously it sat on the girl's lips. Although country-born and at least one half Indian, she used a European distinction to set apart the very person he, a European, was doing his best to become. He began to doubt the success of his adaptation, and to reassure himself crammed a wad of unsweetened pan into his mouth. As he chewed, he continued his introspection, nodding at intervals in a pantomime of close attention which convinced not only the girl but himself.

Like some fountain whose ingenious mechanism remains hid from the bemused wayfarer, concealed by water-jets and scrolls of stone, so Elise's words play before Aloysius, observed but unconsidered.

—*Simile, Narrator, simile!*—

The burgher's daughter spoke evenly for the space of an hour. She betrayed no excitement over her discovery and indeed felt none. Occasionally she paused to take a sip of snow-chilled water in which the flecks of talc were all too evident. She had made, she said, a study of ice, beginning with Plato's remarks on the tendency of water to solidify when the air and fire left it (thus forming hail above the earth and ice upon it), and coming down as far as the modern, Immanuel Kant, who in his *Critique of Aesthetic Judgment* had a re- markable passage concerning the crystallization of water through a sudden concursion. The quantum leap away of heat in the final stage of freezing was, Kant noted, a most remarkable phenomenon, the water so far from having gradually gained in viscosity, remaining perfectly fluid whilst its temperature fell to ice coldness. Thus on either side of that moment of simultaneous release and imprisonment that was the formation of ice, the critical character of the water was the same. This being so, Elise reasoned, if the quantum leap or caloric flight could be locally accelerated by some mechanical or other means, vast quantities of stored water (made ice-cold through the agency of, say, saltpetre) could be converted into ice at a moment's notice. And since the water remained fluid though already virtual ice, it could be transported by insulated pipes to any desired location and there accelerated into ice instead of being transported en bloc. Since supplies of saltpetre were abundant at Sans Souci, it remained only to develop an accelerator here, and there would be no need of either Himalayan snow adulterated with talc or North American ice riddled with oakum. The quantity of ice would be limited only by the quantity of water available. In time, supposing mechanical pumps, a cheap driving force, and appropriate gases were introduced to replace tubs of water immersed in cisterns of saltpetre, such an accelerator could be installed in every room. And since doubtless new uses other than the cooling of water, food, and air would be found for quick ice (and the Great Trotter should not think at once and exclusively of warfare), Sans Souci could be turned into an ice palace and the entire country would benefit from the marriage of a natural phenomenon of immense simplicity to a mechanical device of supreme consequence. Such a device was theoretically possible, as the calculations on this sheet of paper plainly showed.

Pushing back her chair with a conclusive squeak, Elise rose, came around to Justin's end of the table, and handed her scribblings to him. Justin, who had just decided that he could never, no matter how hard he tried, turn Indian (any more than he could revert to a European), and that it was best if he were reconciled to the fact and became a third thing, blinked at the girl standing by his side. He was still more confused by the sheet of paper covered in closely written Indian numerals with a few sketchy diagrams.

"Oh—ah, yes. Yes, of course! Quite so. I shall consider it most carefully," he promised the theorist-and-mathematician. Then, dropping his eyes again to the maze of figures, he added: "*Most* carefully."

Elise shot him a cool impudent look and returned the way she had come, leaving by the Old Armoury door.

"Extraordinary child," said the Great Trotter to himself, setting the piece of paper down on the table and trying to remember what it was he had been thinking when she interrupted him. That she was attractive? No, that was not it—besides, she was, well, resistable, her flesh being pale to the point of transparency so that she took on the colour of whatever was behind her. At the other end of the table she was maroon from the dark leather upholstery of her high-backed chair; standing beside him just now and viewed against a window she seemed the colour of late evening. Still, he would have liked to pat her hand in an avuncular way, and a sudden warmth recalled to him the fact that he had not yet touched her. What would it be like to kiss her forehead? Would it burn the lips like Farida's? Would it be as cold as her eyes? And her elbows—what were they like? He decided to overtake her, and pushing back his chair, rolled forward to grip the table, making ready to rise. His head brought down to within an inch of the tabletop, he found himself staring at Elise's sheet of paper. Something strange had happened to it. The pomegranate ink had bled and run into a mottled pink cloud while the paper itself (it was of his own manufacture and bore his watermark) floated greyly on the table, having soaked up a quantity of water. But the decanter was empty! he protested; and then he remembered the fragment of Quebec ice. He snatched up a napkin, spread it over the sheet of paper and pressed gently down, but the paper was wet through and came away in soggy scraps on the cloth. "Now I cannot kiss her forehead," the Great Trotter cursed, and for some days he avoided Elise, coming down either early or late for his meals. When it became impossible to dodge the girl, he told her he was giving the matter the closest scrutiny. Occasionally she reminded him of it, until one day she caught sight of him counting on his fingers. After that she left him alone.

Justin did not give up his ice notion. The tahkhana epiphany was branded on his brain, and although there was never again a day as hot, he spent the month of June writing letters to Calcutta to negotiate the purchase of an ice ship. Before the year was out, the good ship *Mandalay* was registered in his name to ply between Quebec or Halifax or Boston and Bengal, carrying tea and indigo and spices one way, and ice together with apples, pears, strawberries, or any seasonal temperate fruit the other.

Meanwhile, without consulting Justin, Elise had begun a series of ice pits not far from the apiary, on the opposite side of *Sungum* from the indigo baths. The ice accelerator, she decided, was ahead of its time: better to use techniques suited to the country. So the ice pits were dug in the time-honoured Indian manner, being lined with clay and cowdung which hardened to a cementlike finish, and having ladders of bamboo let down into them. The mouth of each pit was covered with a circular wooden lid and above it was built a thatched shelter. But because the winters were now never cold enough to freeze water, the pits lay empty, serving no purpose except to answer symmetrically in the southwest the indigo baths of the northeast.

If the pits were barren of ice, they did have another effect. On learning of their existence, several of the Great Trotter's retainers began to suppose that the post of Ice Manager would be a handsome sinecure and to imagine themselves peculiarly fitted by nature, experience, and destiny to fill it. Even Munshi Nishan Chand, who ordinarily kept to the library and ignored the other members of Sans Souci's staff, was tempted to enter the lists, having read somewhere that the ice monopoly in Mexico was worth fifteen thousand dollars a year to the king, after a five percent deduction by the Comptroller of Ice. "I knew of ice pits before their *fathers* were born," he scoffed. "Besides, I have degrees, including one in glass-making. The basic principles remain the same." The egg-brahmin, Sunya, was not especially interested, but his wife (whom he secretly called the Water-Buffalo) thought he should be. "A *proper* job," she taunted. "Ice Collector, ah! Not collector of eggs—chhi-chhi-chhi! What kind of brahmin are you, wading through dung to collect eggs?" "There is a man I depute to gather them," Sunya answered back, but when his wife tossed her head and lumbered away he took a guarded sniff at himself. "It *would* be better than pulling teeth," thought Hakim Ahmed (*Roadside Dentist, Rotten Sadist*), "or even grinding herbs. But I shall have to consider it thoroughly." And he returned to his mortar. "It would mean the finest of dry wines," smiled Fonseca to himself (*Uncouth Valet, Faulty Palate*), "and Havana cigars. And that emerald-crusted vase which the old Armenian is always trying to flog." He sat back in his battered wicker chair and let the cheap sherry go to work on his day-dream. "The post is mine," said Yakub, and rode off to inspect the indigo cake. Qaiyum-i-najum looked up from his epic-in-progress. "Sixteen pages for one rupee," he grumbled. "A gem of a quatrain: rejected." He gnawed at his melon rind and took a swig from a bottle of toddy. "Even the liquor is warm. Who wouldn't become Ice Manager?" He took up his pen again and started with a clean sheet.

On the correct handling of contradictions in the manufacture of ice

Superficial observers believe that ice is manufactured by the addition of coldness. But men of insight know it is formed by the removal of heat. It is a haphazard observation which leads luckless men into error. It is no simple matter, but Respected and Beloved Trotter mastered its difficulties in a short time. It is said to owe its erroneousness to busybodies who are altogether ignorant of scientific matters. It is most welcome in the months of May and June when the sun is high, but July and August will take it, and September and October. It is very likely the fault of certain trespassing gallows-tree-shaped dotards who think that degrees are everything. It is frozen at 0°. It is probably one of his malicious doctrines. It may be seen to ride most picturesquely on a hot stove (poets will best appreciate it and are best suited to its collection). It is time it were scotched. It is most useful for cooling drinks and in the preservation of all manner of fresh fruit and vegetables, such as melons. It makes no sense at all. It is most epiphanic [*khub*], transfiguringly exquisite when diluted in water in summer in the afternoon in the library in a tumbler. It is crystal-clear, glass-coloured, painful to the touch, but ravishing in the mouth. It will melt away into nothing.

Leaving the ice-fields of the Khyber Pass, Mik came to Isphahan; leaving Isphahan, he came to Turin. The survey of Persia was complete, the embassy a success, and his own health perfectly recovered. The blueness of skin which had returned briefly in the snows had long since left him, so that the soles of his feet were yellow once more and the rest of his person (the monumental member apart) a dark khaki. He wore a plain blue serge coat and white leggings, and in his coat pocket was a letter of introduction from Sir John Malcolm, leader of the Persia expedition. He had landed at Naples, gone directly to a gelateria, and proceeded to Turin to inspect the Holy Shroud. That done, he crossed the Alps and entered France, thinking how pleasant it might be to have an army with him. Having none, he supposed the next best thing would be to join one directly he had concluded a tour of the fatherland. He stopped a week in Lirey, where he inspected the hostelries and found himself a room above a baker's across from the Church of St. Joseph of Arimathea. On the Sunday he went to forenoon mass and afterwards lunched on red sausage, strange crusty bread, and cheese full of holes. Then he twirled his moustachios, of which he had grown a luxuriant pair, and taking with him a flagon of muscat, climbed to the top of a hill overlooking the town. There, tucked in between sloping fields of barley and a belt of ancient pines nestled the forgotten Cimitaire Ste Fatima. Surrounded by crumbling tombstones, the Next Trotter spent a golden afternoon with three gipsy girls whose language was a brew of familiar gutturals and mocking laughter.

Slipping away during the night, Mik came penniless to London. He asked directions of a swarthy gelato vendor and learnt that the pawnshops near the East India docks were already closed for the day. Obliged to sleep under a bridge, he drew on the former stock of surplus heat, causing a momentary chill in a distant tahkhana where the lights were revolving at a considerable speed. The stone ledge between the arch and the black jelly of the river was wide but foul with tell-tale disjecta: bandages from some hospital, a suicide's wig, a single shoe once black, scraps of brown paper, cabbage stalks, and fish heads. The place smelt of spirits and urine and was already tenanted, but Mik's face aroused no curiosity among the earlier comers, perhaps because they were sodden with gin and the evening was dark. The Next Trotter took his place between a dog whose belly was raw from constant scratching and a heap of clothes which cunningly disguised a man. Generating a warmth which drew the grateful sleepers steadily nearer him, Mik weathered his first night in the English capital.

He awoke in the blue light of an autumn morning to the sound of horse-carts clattering by above. Wraiths of mist wandered down the river, and

beyond the embankment smoke trickled from hundreds of chimney-pots. Just
beyond the shelter of the bridge a basket of snowy cauliflowers stood unattended; on top sat a blackbird singing a strange foreign song. Although it
was still early, man and dog were gone; with them had vanished Mik's coat.
Mik rubbed his eyes, crawled to the edge of the embankment, and looked
down at his reflection in the black river. His long solemn face rippled a foot
below, mud-coloured and flanked with dark green moss. Lying flat on his
belly, he scooped up a handful of water and patted his face. He took some
in his mouth and spat it out at once. There was now nothing to pawn except
the locket about his neck, and Mik did so directly the shops opened.
☞ *The locket is pawned.*

It brought him enough for a suit of clothes and a fortnight's lodgings:
during that time he must locate Sir John once more and ask for another letter.
Even for a trained surveyor the task was not a simple one, leading down
lanes bristling with dogs, across ancient stone bridges, past ruined abbeys,
along busy roads, past houses full of Englishmen doing English things. At
length, he came to the house. The leader of the embassy to Persia had arrived
some six weeks earlier, not having tarried in Italy and France. The afternoon
Mik knocked at the door, an old colonel from the Royal Military Academy at
Woolwich was visiting. Struck by something in the young man, he agreed to
recommend him for a career which would suit his aptitude for survey as well
as his inclination to gunnery. Mik was, the colonel pointed out, already above
the usual age, but he and Sir John would see if this and certain other irreg-
ularities could be overlooked. He had himself long suspected that the secret
of efficacious gunnery lay in military survey.

Armed with two letters of introduction, the Next Trotter sat in the hall
of the Military Academy flicking the crumbs of a muffin off his coatsleeves
as he waited his interview. When his turn came, he found his mouth hopelessly
dry and his scalp tingling. The interview was not, in its early stages, a success:
no sooner was the Next Trotter in the chair than he found himself afflicted
with his childhood speechlessness. Finally, one of the questioners, a jocular
major with full fat cheeks, intervened. He had noticed Mik's eyes wandering
freely over the furnishings and returning regularly to the window. Did he
propose breaking in there that night? the major asked with a wink. Mik replied,
finding his tongue at last, that he simply wished to satisfy an early-formed
habit of producing in his mind the exact replica of every room he happened
to enter. "To the last elephant?" chuckled the major, picking up a pin. Mik
answered, *yes*, and was put to the test. Blindfold, and with his head turned to
the right, he gave aloud the name of every object along the wall to his left,
including the titles of books visible in a bookcase and descriptions of the
pictures hanging there. Next he turned his head the other way and called the

names of things on the right wall, passing from there to the wall facing and thence to the floor and lastly to the objects on the desk before him. When that was concluded, he offered to recite the catalogue backwards, but his interviewers had already agreed by an exchange of glances, some astonished, some annoyed, to have him. He was given a uniform, a number (which he promptly forgot), and a sword which he delighted in waving over his head when alone. For two years he was trained in every department of military science, not excluding the gathering of intelligence. At the end of this period the cadet was given the rank of Fireworker and assigned to an artillery regiment. In addition, he had a brief for covert activities. "He will make us a capital spy," beamed the major with the rubicund cheeks, for he had found his swarthy protégé to be formidably sharp and resolutely foolish.

In April, when the fields of England and those parts are green, Fireworker Trotter was about to embark for India when he received a summons from the Court of Directors of the Honourable East India Company. Making his way along Leadenhall Street, he wondered what honour awaited him on a day when the river was a garter jewelled with the sun. Above, the sky was as blue as the robin's egg in his mother's collection. Dung flew up from carriage wheels and spattered a barefoot boy who dodged in and out of the traffic balancing an enormous silver tea urn. The street widened a little. "That be it," said a weasel-seller, nodding at the yellowish stone portals behind him and staring with frank curiosity at Mik's khaki face. Mik raced up the steps, but was required to wait in an antechamber whose contents he memorized in case a fresh trial of intelligence awaited him. An hour slipped by, then two. Finally a door opened and he was ushered into a chamber dismal with oak and red leather. A phlegmy whispering greeted his entry; the respondent was even darker than had been reported. The old men on three sides of a broad black table leaned towards each other, while the oldest, who sat in the middle, stroked his chin with the plume of his pen and cleared his throat noisily in a long rattling swell during which the rest of his body remained perfectly still. A few pertinent questions were put to the Next Trotter, who answered each without hesitation. Where was he born? Why was the Asia mynah? Who was his mother? *Was* there a laughing hyena? Was Nakhlau nice? And what was the melting point of ice? Then he was allowed to leave. Mik, who had been hoping for an opportunity to display his remarkable mnemonic gift, was disappointed. He bought a piece of weasel from the curious vendor (who took no money from him) and, munching distractedly, returned to Woolwich on the free ferry.

A resolution

> Mr T—— was called and having withdrawn—
> Resolved unanimously that no person the son of a
> Native Indian shall henceforth be appointed by this
> Court in employment in the Civil, Military or Marine
> services of the Company. Standing Order.

COURT OF DIRECTORS
Honourable East India Company
Minutes for April 19, 1791

(*CHRONICLE RESUMED*)

The order was conveyed to the authorities of the Military Academy, where preparations were already afoot for officers to join an East Indiaman sailing for Calcutta. The jocular major, who had had plans for Mik, was displeased and made representations concerning the irrefrangible necessity of a khaki skin for British military espionage in India. He also pointed out that considerable expense had been incurred on the training of Fireworker Michael Trotter, and that the Court of Directors' ruling could very easily be enforced on all *further* sons of Native Indians. The financial consideration moved the Directors to relent. Mik was allowed to proceed to India on sufferance. Word of the order had, however, already reached his fellow officers, and although most preserved their customary camaraderie, others, put out by some past surliness in Mik or by his habitual aloofness, responded with sneers and taunts. The fights which resulted were seen as proof of the Directors' foresight, and Mik lost those friends who had stood by him. Once the Next Trotter found himself in ship's custody staring gloomily at a nooselike strap which hung from the ceiling, keeping the perpendicular as the cabin rocked from side to side and the *Bellerophon*, pitching rakishly, ploughed northwards through the shifting meadows of the Indian Ocean.

On arrival in Calcutta, the Next Trotter was censured for misconduct and joined his regiment in bad odour. His commandant stared hard at him and put him on night duty, a charge that immediately came to be known as the Black Watch. Mik took to smoking again, and to lighten the tedium of the long pacific nights invented the cigarette-holder-cum-fusee. He was not promoted to lieutenant as quickly as he would have liked, but that may have been because, while sharing his father's zest for gunpowder, he lacked the Great Trotter's genius for ballistics. The expected intelligence assignments did not come or were intercepted, but Mik had his baptism of fire fighting under the British flag. With his men he was popular; among his peers he was generally disliked; by his senior officers he was treated with reserve. In 1795 he was summarily discharged from the army.

A command

> *No person the son of an European by a Native mother*
> *shall serve in the Company's army as an officer. Such*
> *persons may be admitted as fifers, drummers or farriers.*

THE GOVERNOR-GENERAL IN COUNCIL
Calcutta, at *Fort William*
April the 21st, 1795

(*CHRONICLE RESUMED*)

Unable to drum or fife, and with only a foggy notion of the farrier's art, Mik submitted to the latest whim of fate with a curl of the lip. He saluted the commandant, turned in his uniform, and took a tonga to the city. The horse clopped and jingled along the cantonment road with its rows of alternating red and white bricks on either side. Mik sat at the back and watched the fort recede like a waking dream, his head altogether empty, his body glad of the lurching. The saw-toothed row of bricks became a blur of chasing figures. "*Lieutenant* Trotter!" they called, mocking the man who had dreamt of being a general, till they fell behind and Mik found himself at the edge of the city. He turned in his seat to remind the tonga-wala of the address, a street which ran between White Town and the black city. Then he returned to his reverie as they bowled along past smart carriages parked in front of cream-and-white mansions.

"Sahib!"

Mik found his luggage deposited on the pavement; they had reached Cimmerii Street. The houses there were grey and peeling and streaked with moss from many monsoons; built fifty years ago by Europeans, they had lapsed to shabby genteel Anglo-Indians and been divided up into tenements. As the Next Trotter paid his fare, another tonga arrived, rattling and jingling, and then another and another and still others. From each one stepped a newly discharged Anglo-Indian officer, a Skinner, a Powell, a Hearsey, a Gardner, a Gray. Mik was puzzled: he had imagined himself the only one. So, apparently, had the others, who were standing erect in their civilian clothes and wondering what to make of it all. In the steely twilight neither they nor their destination seemed convincing, but as the clip-clop of the horses died away they approached one another and introduced themselves. By common consent they made for the house of a merry widow whose mulligatawny soup was creditable and whose dessert was an open secret. Tonight, however, they exhausted Mrs Farryner's candles, arguing till dawn in tones that were edged with menace. The next day the tongas were back and reloaded, bound for the horse market beyond the bridge. There, the ex-officers bought horseflesh and wagons which would carry them across the country through jungles, over hills, and across white-pebbled fords into the service of one or another of the independent Indian princes. Made welcome, they trained troops, taught the use and making of the newest weapons, and fought alongside men whose quick manoeuvres over rugged terrain had won them a name given half in fear: *mountain rats*. The discharged Anglo-Indians were officers again, only the flags were different.

A proverb

The ice is not to the swift.

(CHRONICLE RESUMED)

The ice ship *Mandalay* (Captain Daud Dickason of Rangoon) docked in Hughli, the port that served Calcutta, a week early. Fonseca, who had been sent down the Ganges to await it, found it awaiting him, so that he was obliged to hunt up a boat and boatmaster at once and give up his plans of touring the fabled city. The barge on which he had travelled from Nakhlau had capsized in the process of unloading its indigo and spices; in any case it might not have managed the ice. The barber-and-agent went from wharf to wharf looking for a boatmaster willing to undertake the voyage upriver. Presently a mettlesome, perfectly pear-shaped entrepreneur was found agreeable, and the goods were transferred to his boat. A bill of lading in the name of Justin Aloysius Trotter changed hands, and immediately the homeward journey was begun.

At home the Great Trotter, unwilling to trust his neck to any other razor than Fonseca's, shocked Sans Souci by growing a beard (*Unlovely Trotter, Rebarbative Frank*). He did not care for the white growth himself (its chalky white underlined his advancing age) and would never have let Fonseca go had Yakub not been injured in a fall from a spirited Arab. The baker-and-Master of the Horse lay on his back in the Spur, seething from something other than the summer heat, and every now and then crying out from a pain that did not arise in his spindly right leg, swathed to the hip in bandages. Spurred to an impossible jump, Chetak had reared up and fallen sideways on him. Hakim Ahmed, just returned from a pilgrimage to Mecca and like the Great Trotter sporting a beard (though his was dyed red with henna), visited Yakub from time to time. He shook his head disbelievingly as he slid his bamboo stethoscope shut: never had he heard a heart race so. Whenever he climbed the steps of the Spur, he fully expected to find the baker-and-Chief Steward dead from heartburst. "That would mean the highest office in Sans Souci—" He did not finish the thought, preferring to mull it over while grinding his herbs. He gave Yakub a potion whose recipe he had learnt in his recent travels, and returned next morning to see its effect. Yakub was not stricken. "You're *sure* you feel better?" Ahmed asked professionally, but Yakub ignored him. He had thrown away the potion. As always, he drew strength from disappointment. Ice Manager: the post would be his yet, he swore, limping across to the stables to stare down the guilty Chetak. At the end of three weeks he removed the splint himself. By the time Fonseca returned with the ice, the leg was mended.

"No, you ring it," Fonseca insisted when the boatmaster bashfully refused the mallet.

The two men faced the gong which Justin had placed outside the dining hall in preparation for the first consignment of Quebec ice. Hari Om took the carved wooden hammer, stepped delicately to one side, and tapped the Ice Bell once. The bell vibrated like a glass sounding bowl, and trembling, rubbed up against Hari Om's reluctant mallet with a nasal twang.

"Harder, go on."

Hari Om pulled up his sleeve, a new light in his eye. In what was over the years to become a ritual motion, he found a comfortable grip on the mallet, limbered up his shoulders with a rolling motion, and then very slowly rocked a long way back on his feet until for one perilous moment it seemed he would topple over. He released all his weight at once and hurtled forward like an avalanche, falling upon the Ice Bell with such passion and energy that in no time at all all Sans Souci had come running.

Justin, slower than the rest, elbowed his way through the crowd and embraced Fonseca.

"Thank God!" he whispered. "This beard has been driving me mad!"

The barber-and-slave, not a little put out by the public display of emotion, was even more aghast at the Great Trotter's beard.

"Come," urged Justin, "you must shave it off at once."

"But—the *ice*," Fonseca hissed.

"Ice?" repeated Justin, glancing from face to face in the throng which had turned expectantly towards him. His eyes came to rest on the bullock-cart train with its mysterious megalithic crates.

"Ah—the *Mandalay*!" he sang. "Well, what are you all standing there for? Open up those crates. Let's take a look at our ice. And next year"—he turned reprovingly to Yakub—"you must fetch it from the dock with horse-carts. Bullocks! Why, it must have melted quite away!"

It had not. When the crates were opened, eleven giant icebergs glittered in the dusk, breathing a cool vapour on the awed faces of the crowd. It was the first chill in Sans Souci for seven years, and every man stood still. From where the Great Trotter stood, it seemed as if the aluminium flying buttresses on the distant plain enclosed and supported this soaring frozen mass of white stones from the other side of the world.

Ice! he intoned, holding his arms out like some white-bearded Byzantine patriarch.

Ice! came the antiphon from every lip. Even Nishan Chand had left his cubicle in the library; bending reverentially beyond his habitual right angle, he croaked: *Ice.* Qaiyum, who would gladly have seized the opportunity to dash to the deputy librarian's office and sit there groaning at his desk, found himself drawn from his Persian poets as if to a magnetic pole. *Ice*, he murmured, and thought of his cup. Munnoo repeated the word over and over as though he were a Tibetan telling his beads: *Ice, ice, ice* . . . Nankoo, who had only that afternoon stood on the perron in the Water Court praying to the hot wind, frowned when the syllable escaped him: *Ice.* Marazzi, suddenly nostalgic for the Alps, muttered: *Ice*, and broke into a sweat. Gunga the water-carrier went up close to a block and very slowly put out a finger; he drew it back sharply and sucked the burning tip like a child. He began to weep softly, ashamed of his disbelief, sobbing: *Ice, ice.* Sunya removed his turban, baring a speckled dome, while Hakim Ahmed at his side rolled his eyes up piously. *Ice!* they chanted in unison, and exchanged a charitable smile. Farida, watching from the East Tower, felt the word settle on her tongue like sin: *Ice*, she shuddered and wrenched herself from the window. Yakub was gazing scorn-fully at the rest when the word sounded between his ears: *Ice.* Surprised to hear his own voice, he added quickly: "—Manager Sahib." Only one person in Sans Souci did not join the solemn celebration: she sat in her tower reading, oblivious of the congregation on the other side of *Sungum*. Elise had heard the strange glassy chiming and put it down to some frivolous entertainment of the Great Trotter's.

"Right—get on with it, then!"

Justin snapped the assembly out of its trance. Men ran off for ropes and pulleys, sackcloth, ramps, and tubs of sawdust. The boatmaster was introduced to Justin, the oarsmen paid and fed and given a suit of clothes and a towel each. The Sagarpaysans' awe having evaporated, the ice was summarily har-pooned, wound around with hemp cables, and hauled across the terrace outside the dining hall, running freely on the still hot flagstones. Yusuf the carpenter sawed it into huge books while his son-and-understudy hopped from foot to foot on top of each block, driving wedges into the cut to prevent its healing. The books were slid one by one down a ramp into the cavernous godown beneath the dining hall. There they were cased in jute and shelved in orderly rows, twelve to a shelf. When the last one was in, Yusuf collapsed from exhaustion and was dosed with cold mango-fool while his son was wrapped in blankets and given tea. They too were awarded a suit of clothes each and a towel.

"I will declare tomorrow a feast day," said Justin to himself.

Before he could give the order, Yakub was crying from the parapets: "Tomorrow is a holiday!" (*Unfeasting Satan, Famine-gripped Soul.*) "Amnesty," he continued, "is proclaimed for all rebels. And from this day forth, be it known by the Great Trotter's decree, the dining hall is to be called the Glacerie."

Justin shook his head in amazement. Why, that man reads one's mind. The very name! And to think he speaks no French. He will make an excellent Ice Manager. He turned to Fonseca and said aloud: "Now, sir. The shave."

Fonseca dragged along behind his master to the West Tower. He was tired and sweaty from the journey and would have liked to go directly to his own bathroom and stand under the watering can. But already, it seemed, duty called. He had got no thanks for his part in the affair, aside from that bruising embrace, and he guessed the meaning of the Great Trotter's admiring shake of the head when Yakub announced the new name for the dining hall and its ice godown. At the Old Armoury end of the Glacerie the barber-and-man paused by the voice flue to call across to the kitchens for a basin of hot water; that done, he damned ice and all its works and started after his master, who was whistling vulgarly through his moustache as he mounted the Indigo Steps.

At dinner the Great Trotter, clean-shaven and smug, boasted happily of his success to Elise. He found a hundred occasions to remark on the purity of the water and had many witty things to say concerning ice. The Ceylonese burgher's daughter agreed politely that the *Mandalay* was an improvement on talcum-flavoured water, but thought the whole operation could be simplified (and the ocean voyage shortened) by harnessing icebergs from the Antarctic and towing them up across the Indian Ocean. The Great Trotter scoffed and took a sip from his Quebec pond. Elise made no defence, saying simply: "It will be done some day." She cordially proposed a toast to the future of the North American enterprise, and when it was drunk set down her water glass and prepared to leave. But Justin would not hear of her going: there were a thousand toasts and as many choice maxims which he had memorized and wished to float. So the dinner stretched far into the night, becoming an intolerably liquid affair, even by Elise's standards, with a ceaseless babbling from the Nakhlau end and a purling of yawns and sighs, at first suppressed, from the Old Armoury end.

In the West Tower, Fonseca, whose job it was to serve the Great Trotter's nightly mango-fool, found himself unable to face the two hundred and forty steps up to his master's rooms. The river journey wanted sleeping off, and he found himself looking meaningly at the dumb-waiter which had hitherto been used only for books and correspondence. He packed the gypsonometer with ice, placed it in the wire cage, and at the supper hour ran it up the vent. The cage struck a trip bell at the top, and as was his custom, Fonseca allowed it to hang there for a few minutes to give the Great Trotter time to come over to the hatch, slide open the door and take the delivery. Having waited the usual space, Fonseca let the cage down again. The gypsonometer was still there, untouched. After a little while he ran the cage up again and waited the same interval before letting it down. Once more the gypsonometer stood there, a cold sweat forming on its enamelled skin. Irritably, he repeated the process over and over until the dumb-waiter was racing up and down the air vent like the mechanism of a demented clock.

It was going on three when the Great Trotter staggered into his room, drunk on Quebec water. Hearing the hatch bell, he slid back the door and saw not a book but the gypsonometer. He barely had time to retrieve it when the cage shot down again. "*Cretin!*" he shouted down the vent, startled, and promised to give the barber-and-experimenter a piece of his mind when he came up for the bedtime kahani. Not too severely, of course, because Justin was overwrought from the *Mandalay*'s success and knew he would want an especially skilful story if he was to get any sleep. Glancing around guiltily from habit, he went to pour himself a cup of mango-fool. Nothing came out of the spout, not even the water that usually filled the outer vessel. "The bastinado for him," he muttered, and Yakub appeared in the doorway with a length of rope and a selection of Malacca canes.

Just then, Justin recalled that the gypsonometer had felt unusually stable in the hand; usually the liquid in it shook or sloshed about. He took off the lid and peered inside. There, instead of water, was ice. He removed the lid of the inner vessel. The mango-fool had congealed. "Shall I heat it?" Yakub offered. Justin shook his head, then without looking up added: "But if you have a spoon on your person?" Yakub produced a silver spoon from the pocket of his tunic. The Great Trotter dipped it into the gypsonometer and scooped up a spoonful of what looked like pale green snow. When he tasted it, he took up the gypsonometer without a word and made for the South Tower.

Justin needed no story that night. In any case, his barber-and-kahani-master had fallen asleep himself as soon as he found the dumb-waiter empty. He did not hear the insult which the Great Trotter shouted down the shaft at him, and he slept through the morning shave hour, well into the afternoon. Nor, for that matter, was Justin interested in the shave, because morning found him in Elise's bed dallying with her long translucent fingers: they did not seem so cold now, and they appeared to be dallying in return. Only once did the Great Trotter rise from what was now his couch—to give orders for more of the new congealed delight to be made and distributed among his courtiers. Wakened, Fonseca mumbled the instructions to Gunga and fell asleep again. The ice confabulation came out as before and was shared out. Yakub, who was careful of his teeth, refused his portion. Qaiyum, who would have preferred a base of toddy, made an exception and soon found himself eating the baker-and-Chief Steward's share. Hari Om belched and declared Fonseca a genius; then he excused himself, saying he must hurry home. When they had finished their servings Munnoo and Nankoo looked for more, though Nankoo felt obliged to add: "Arre, this is no discovery. It's simply newfangled kulfi without the falooda." Alexander, who had accepted the amnesty, agreed. His ancestor, the first Alexander, he said, had long ago made a confection of honey, fruit, and packed snow, and kept a special chain of runners in the Caucasus mountains to deliver it every day through the summer. Marazzi, too, was unimpressed with the novelty of it but ate his share with a distant look in his eye.

Only Fonseca was missing from the gathering of the celebrants. He slept through the feast day, revisiting the stages of the river journey, touring the Calcutta he had so narrowly missed. He awoke at sunset to find Justin shaking him gently by the shoulder and repeating: "Time to rise, time to rise, *Mr Ice Manager Sahib!*"

Journal entry in the Great Trotter's White Book

Can it be that I am out of love already? After the unutterable bliss of that night and the next day? How quickly she warmed to me and how quickly has my heart turned cold! I must have loved her longer than I knew, for since the day she entered my sick-room with her misshapen tutor I have not once gone to the East Tower with a dish of dark moon jamuns (*Eugenia jambolana*). Love her I did, though I did not show the early signs of my passion, whether to her or to myself, because she was careless of me and froward as a child. But the seeds were sown *by her*. Love me she must have done—my nature is not unlovable nor my person unattractive. Or why did she devise that other recipe to sweeten my age? That being so, could I help but love her in return? Love begets love unfailingly. And having penetrated my defences she delivered her masterstroke, which was, consummately—*nothing*. She did nothing at all. Compelling *me* to act, to crawl to her tower.

No, I was not to blame for first loving her; nor am I then culpable for relinquishing that love. I release it now, here—*go*!

But what intoxication in the smell of a new creature! It is on me still—there—there. Like green mangoes—no, the early blossom white on the branch.

Still no hint of rain, not even mango showers.

Will I now return to the other one when the moon is dark again?

And the dead one [*Cup of Grace*], like watered silk, where is she? Is one destined to pass from caress to caress like some feckless libertine? I shall ask Fonseca for his thoughts. No, best not—the poor man lives alone. Perhaps by way of a story that might involve a German inkvendor's daughter by a concubine—how would he complete it? Do affairs of the heart have a pattern as do crystals in nature, or is it always the chance collision of bodies which will sometimes produce an issue—such as this delightful new concoction of Fonseca's—and sometimes not?

The *elbows* on her, par Dieu! Like darling hailstones.

(*CHRONICLE RESUMED*)

Having thus excused himself for his rapid retreat, Justin felt at ease. Two days had passed since the coming of the ice.

But Elise was not to be so lightly set aside. The glow inside her, both while Justin had lain in her bed and after, was new and delicious and distracting, so that she had trouble applying herself to her books when he had gone. At length the emotion subsided, leaving in its place a memory; she was relieved, being more comfortable with ideas and better able to examine her response through their glass. Whatever the cause of the change in herself, she must look to the effects. Her former state as house guest, she saw, had been exceedingly precarious; her new position would expose her to the black queen. Farida, though not married, had certainly a prior claim and possibly a formidable ally in that Master of the Horse. There would before long grow up the tangle of intrigues which she had known as an outsider at the Nawab's court. She must disguise her love without losing her lover, remain bookishly cloistered while ensuring that Justin remained an avid reader.

The next move decided, she surrendered herself to the glow. So this was love! For the first time in her life she began to feel secure.

And come to her Justin did, without knowing why and in spite of his formed intentions; what was more, he seemed to enjoy each visit. But he did not need her genius to see at once that his own movements as king were restricted. If the Great Trotter wished to visit Farida's tower, it had to be by way of Elise's: there was no crossing the central dome, and the North Tower stood unfinished on the far side. There was a sense in which Justin was the architect of his own limitations: in *Sungum*, no direct route existed from the West Tower to the East. The realization did nothing to improve the Great Trotter's morale.

To flaunt his power would have offended Justin's niceness, but decorum demanded that his worth be at least tacitly recognized. Of all the residents of Sans Souci, only Elise failed completely to give him the homage he was always modestly deprecating. Others were slack or jealous or toadying; she was at first indifferent and then, as the old glassy pallor gave way to a luminous quality, familiar. Why, the Great Trotter asked himself, am I not content with intimacy? He would not believe the answer when it came: what you desire is not love but devotion. And this one calls you simply, *Trot*.

As a result nobody, least of all Justin, was quite sure when or how Elise went from Jarman Bibi, or the German mistress, to Jarman Begam, or the German wife. It might have been their breakfasts together in the Rain Room on the Glacerie roof.

The second morning after the ice, Fonseca arrived at the Glacerie punctually at ten to find scrawled across the door of the ice godown the word: UNFAIR. He had just passed Yakub going the other way with the *Essays* of Francis Bacon in his grip. Yakub was teaching himself English. Reading the word as a punning slur on his dark skin, Fonseca (a devotee of Alexander Pope) returned to his room and shut himself up. If that was the way they took it, he would show them: the ice could look after itself. He spent the afternoon blaring out his scales on the horn, to the disgust of Nishan Chand, who was busy making revisions to his history of Mexico. From that day on, the ice department was neglected, though whether or not it suffered from Fonseca's neglect (or stood to profit from his vigilance) was a moot question. The barber-and-Ice Manager found his new job very pleasant indeed. He did not keep away altogether, but if while there he wished to leave early, he returned to the door, studied the chalk graffito (which he refused to allow to be washed away), and repeating that he would show them, turned the key. Not that there was very much to do on the inside except on those days when a consignment of ice was sent by horse-cart to the city for sale at twice the local rate, being foreign. Of course, later, when the demand for Sans Souci ice grew in Nakhlau and the ice pits were activated, the volume of traffic increased considerably. But that was after the storm.

A note on winds

Air in motion is called wind. It is not known in itself but in its effects. Glass will stop it but not reveal it. A net will fail to catch it and tremble, but a cranny will make it howl. A fingertip moistened will tell its direction; so will elephant grass. Bamboo will bend before it and groan, reeds snake and rushes rattle. Ice will shrink from it. Chaff is driven before it; also paper, carpets, prayers, and leaves. Water goglets are cooled by it and melons made sweet. When it is mild birds ride upon it; when it is strong, huts. Clouds are its welcome passengers but sometimes they get carried away. In summer dust is its bosom friend, vexation their common cause, hindrance their running conversation, sores their mischief, and a vale of tears their paradise. Winds are of three types: *breezes* (or zephyrs), *winds* (or, in summer, loo), and *yellow storms* (andhi or toofan). A breeze is a wind without the dust and speed; a wind is a yellow storm without the colour and conviction. The first kind is best for picnics (these are a European device for making eating uncomfortable). In the second, crime increases and poesy languisheth. Before the third, horses prick up their ears and elephants lie low. But the camels they are smiling spiritually. Banyan trees withstand it best from their spreading roots; palms are cruelly maimed. Half an hour before, the sky will turn yellow. It is best to shut all doors and windows securely and bring in the washing. Bring in the donkey too, or set him free, cutting the hobble. Put out all fires whether of dung or wood or tobacco. Dismantle the fireplace, unhook the hookah. Uproot choice carrots, leave the trees, cover the well, put a doily on the indigo vat. Pray for your husband if he be not home, pray for your wife if she be, but light no candles (it is too late). Fie! do not creep under the bed: the craven pi-dog is already there, his tail between his legs. When it is howling and the very walls vibrate, a shot of toddy will improve your spirits. Let it rage. Quaff and sing wildly at its peak. After it is gone, count to ten ten times. The silence will be palpable. Then unlatch your door and peep outside.

(*CHRONICLE RESUMED*)

Walking out after the storm, Justin realized for the first time the incompleteness of Sans Souci. The damage was certainly impressive, but it occurred in the context of a prior imperfection that the storm's ravages merely served to heighten with touches of the spectacular. To start with, the wind, which had come out of the southeast, had ransacked one corner of the library, the corner where the Great Trotter's personal manuscripts were stored. It had invaded Qaiyum's office and rifled the paper-catch, carrying off all but four sheets of paper; the rest it scattered across the Tank, over the marsh, and as far as the Kirani river. "The *Cranny* River," he mused. "I should have changed the name long ago." Among the papers lost were the Great Trotter's prolegomena and early chapters of an abecedary on the new religion provisionally entitled *Elements of Din Havai* and to have been followed in due course by the *Rudiments*. To Justin, whose faith was ever restless, the loss merely pointed a structural weakness in the southeast wall of *Sungum*, part of which had altogether collapsed. It was through this gaping hole that the papers had flown, and through it now the deputy librarian-and-poet (who had taken cover under his divan) crept, his mouth hanging open with disbelief. Catching sight of the Great Trotter, he instinctively assumed a look of anguished concentration and began to mumble, supposing pain to be an integral part of work and mumbling a compulsory function of poets.

Qaiyum's display was lost on Justin, who was kneeling to examine a new piece of destruction: two of the Indo-Greek statues that had stood on the ramparts of *Sungum* lay smashed on the stone porch outside the Water Door. (It was impossible to tell from the rubble, but getting up again to check those missing from their pedestals, Justin saw that Achilles was one.) It's just as well he's back, thought the Great Trotter, meaning Alexander. He dusted off his knee and walked on, glancing at the bent water-clock whose innards still hummed and tinkled. Past the Old Armoury he went, across the Water Court and down the Steps where a few stray sheets of Trotter paper flapped forlornly. He picked up one and read: *teeth, with alert mind and judging your powers, face the flying sand* . . . He cast the sheet aside and continued down the Steps, hips rolling and nostrils flared. Above, the sky's yellow was retreating before a front of grey. The cattle were lowing, whether from relief or from a remnant of fear, he could not say, but the noise was a comfort in the enfolding silence. Along the Crocodile Wing, three enormous English tamarind trees lay uprooted, and the east-facing windows were all smashed. A week ago Justin might have blamed the damage on sabotage; the windows were after all within raiding distance from the quarry. But now Alexander was an ally, and from the dusky faces of a dozen girls peeping from behind the broken glass, it appeared the family had taken up residence on the floor above the dairy. Rounding the end of the wing, Justin saw for the first time that it had never been completed. It petered out a stone's throw from the jungle, the roof and the second storey vanishing first, then the doors, then the walls. At the very end, beyond the last melancholy cairns, there was only a tongue of red-and-black mosaic floor stuck out at the encroaching vegetation and jutting a few inches above the ground. The wear on the tiles showed that their exposure was not the work of today's storm. Where the road ended in a smudge of uncertainty (Justin had never been that way before) was a gatehouse, unfinished but evidently occupied, its roof not the work of the original builders; there was no gate.

The Great Trotter turned back towards *Sungum*, following a path beaten over the years by woodcutters and cowherds. He made his way across the arid plain which a later generation would call the Sea of Rains and before long found himself bogged down in a squelching wine-coloured morass. Bending, he saw that the earth was covered with mulberries. But the mulberry trees were a good furlong over to the right, by the indigo baths! The wind must have shaken off all the fruit in one swoop, borne it off in a red cloud, and deposited it here. The same freak, Justin saw, would account for the dari of white mango blossoms further on. A solitary aluminium buttress remained of the host that had been erected in anticipation of a cathedral; the rest were missing, whisked away. Climbing towards the canal, Justin saw that the indigo crop in the fields beyond was ruined; the baths were choked with sand. On the slope lay a glass treble clef, undamaged. The mulberry trees, stripped of fruit and leaves, were nevertheless draped in strong colours; coming up close, Justin saw that they were hung with carpets that had sailed out of the West Tower where the shutters must have blown away. At the foot of the nearest tree a china tea-set lay smashed, except for four Willow-pattern saucers. Tangled in a babul tree near the indigo shed was a flying fox, its wings in shreds. Justin released it tenderly and it fell with the sound of a plucked harpstring and crawled mewing under a bedstead. Just past the amphitheatre a single jakfruit, green and spiky and the size of a sugarsack, had been twisted off its stem, carried thirty yards, and impaled on the fleur-de-lis–topped fence around the music pavilion. In the pavilion itself only two of Marazzi's trompe l'oeil windows had been spared; as for the conical green roof, it was sitting two miles off in the middle of the Plain of Cannonballs, an exotic stupa. From beyond the saltpetre hill came a collective wailing; the storm had destroyed the Sagarpaysans' huts and scattered their possessions. The wailing was punctuated with the high-pitched shrieks of a child looter who was being made an example of.

Abruptly, the Great Trotter entered a zone which appeared to have been unmolested by any wind whatsoever. In a belt which stretched from the Hava Manzil westwards he found the vegetable garden intact, the orangerie untouched, and the very cotton on the silk-cotton trees trembling innocently on its mooring filaments. On the path which led to the Sagarpaysans' hutments, a dhobi's bundle sat unruffled, with six bleached handkerchiefs folded in a shining pile on top. The Hava Manzil stood glowing self-consciously, its marble polished to an unfathomable depth and its skeleton dome humming long after the passage of the wind. Justin stopped before it a moment, sneezed, and passed by on the other side towards the Glacerie. Minor damage there: a corbel dropped, some few slate tiles dislodged; nothing to compare with the central dome of *Sungum*, which had lost all its mica to the south and east. As for the North Tower, it was not derelict at all, simply incomplete. Unfinished too was the sundial, and the Spur beyond. The mehndi-hedge maze had had holes blown into it, and all but one of the Corinthian columns had fallen down, the capitals lying in a jumbled heap of white marble this side of the ruined roundhouse. The minaret beyond was leaning like a drunken toddy-palm; its mosque had never got built. Unwilling to go further, the Great Trotter returned to his tower and sat in silence. He knew without looking that the stone umbrella outside the projected Hindu temple was carried away and he did not care to discover how many horses had gone mad. Yakub would soon be by with his report, and the others would follow.

All that evening and the next day Justin sat listening as the staff filed by. So many chandeliers fallen, so many eggs smashed, so many store-rooms pillaged. The ice evaporated to half its weight, the mango crop nipped in the bud, the sugar-cane flattened while still knee-high. Sans Souci's entire stock of paper, except for four sheets, dispersed, the paper factory ransacked, the press overturned. Justin was for sending the Sagarpaysans on a paper-chase, but his energy failed him; on top of it all, he had a toothache. He ordained limply that in future all paper was, as an economy measure, to be used on both sides. In the library, Qaiyum was inconsolable. True, he had saved his epic-in-progress, clutching it to his bosom under the divan, but the toddy-palms that stood around the Tank were denuded of both frond and fruit: it would be two years before the next crop of tiny potent orange-coloured dates, and a further six months before the liquor was ready. He would have liked to start work at once on an elegy, but the Great Trotter required another poem.

(VERSE)

On the late destruction by storm of the sugar-cane crop

> Cut down in the green of youth
> By yellow storm amok, uncouth,
> Purple denied the cane, the tooth,
> Black-veiled we cry alack forsooth!

> *O cane yet unjuicy*
> *O bitterest pain an'*

Grief in Sans Souci
Lamentation in Canaan!

(*CHRONICLE RESUMED*)

There had been other losses too. Farida had lost her indigo trousseau, Jarman Begam a piece of transparent tissue no wider than a thumbnail, Fonseca a wig of corn-silk, Nishan Chand a crystal paperweight. Yakub had lost nothing; he had few belongings and they were never out of place, but six horses in his charge had lost their wits and a young elephant, Cumulo Nimbus, turned rogue. Nor was the trouble at an end. Two days after the storm the oracle tree, whose roots had been loosened, gave up the ghost and fell on the roundhouse. Brought down in its prime, it lay across the splintered masonry, the fleshy pink and yellow lips of its flowers drooping at the corners. The roundhouse was now crumbling in earnest and to Justin's administrative problems was added the aesthetic one of whether to repair a mock ruin. Well, he thought to himself, at least there was no fire. Then he remembered there had been no rain either, just wind.

The Great Trotter's trials were only beginning. If he accepted them without complaint, it was because secretly he found in them the excuse he needed to stay away from the South Tower. Not that his absences discouraged Elise, who simply assumed he had work to do and got on with her own. Fonseca, who sometimes brought a book up to her from Nishan Chand, found her a new person; she even arranged for him to curl her hair. Justin noticed her quiescence with relief. Bills had begun to arrive from ordinarily patient Nakhlau tradesmen, some of them ruined by the storm, while others came from foreign parts, one from a mason in the Outer Hebrides. Servants were clamouring for back pay, and a cartel of oilmen was threatening to double the price of oil. At the depot where the good-natured Munnoo was nightwatchman, crates of indigotin were being regularly filched by somebody. Efforts to resume mining in the saltpetre hill were dogged with mechanical malfunctions, and the endless vein of curry powder appeared to have petered out at a depth of twelve feet. When he turned to look for his baker-and-troubleshooter, Justin found him gone on an urgent errand to some distant quarter of Sans Souci. He knew the man well enough to recognize that the task in question was probably a crucial one and that without Yakub's constant attention matters might well be worse. But the Great Trotter found himself compelled to rely upon his barber-and-man in little things or else turn steward in his own house. Scores of books and antique weapons arrived each week from his agents abroad, invaluable manuscripts bought for the price of a dinner, and someone had to collect them, if only to consign them unsorted to the catacombs below. Nishan Chand, put out at having been overlooked as Ice Manager, left the cataloguing to his deputy, and Qaiyum was polishing a couplet. Meanwhile Yakub, riding out conscientiously to correct this ill or repair that flaw, kept the larger machinery of state running, but a fraction less smoothly than it might. And in case the Great Trotter should grow complacent, he fomented rivalries and brought them swiftly to his master's notice.

The grooms' dung-gatherers wish to ventilate a grievance

Excellency,

The poulterers have of late been much encouraged by the performance of their so-called golden goose and have begun to infringe on the proper and just rights of the grooms, who in turn are much depressed by the unfair judging at February's contest in Dilkhusha, not to speak of that case of madness. I beg to inform your Greatness that this is a most delicate affair fraught with the sternest possible consequences. A groom's farrier has threatened that if his wife is defrauded of another week's dung by those thieving poulterers, he will shoe [*qil, nail*] any fowls that come his way. He is an irascible man, but a man of his word. I mention this only in passing; myself I would choux their eggs. Would your Excellency take a moment to issue an edict on the matter? The poulterers have their own source of dung, the grooms theirs. The elephant mahouts likewise have first rights to theirs (God is just). The coops and the stables are divided by a broad bean trellis which it should be an offence for poulterers (or their clients) to cross going one way or the other except on the most pressing business. The grooms are sullen, and this mood has not escaped the horses. The dung is theirs by tradition, and this fact must be publicly acknowledged if the thieving poulterers (or their clients) are to be checked. Only last night a thieving poltroon was chased as far as the aerolite, but showed a clean pair of heels. The bastinado is clearly called for. I take no sides in this sordid business, but a stalwart groom assured me this morning that if things are not made straight from now forwards the ice-train could slow to a walk. We must think of April and May, even if certain insouciant Ice Managers do not. Your Greatness should make it plain: if the dung is the grooms' (or their clients'), very well; if not, not.

With due respect,
Yakub Khan
(Master of the Horse)

(*CHRONICLE RESUMED*)

It was in that year that the Great Trotter invented the filing cabinet. Ashamed at having to send out replies beginning: *Your letter will receive the closest . . .* he recognized the surcharge of conviction carried by a reply beginning: *Your letter is on file and will receive the closest . . .* He set about the task with due humility for a man who had once invented the spiral-action cannonball, and within a week of taking up tools had a tall grey chest of multiple narrow drawers, each with a brass half moon on the outside and slotted partitions within. Fonseca, who stood watching with a mixture of envy and scorn (he was inwardly comparing his dumb-waiter with this glorified bread bin), shook his head sceptically. But when Yakub's letter fitted exactly into one of the slots, he gave his grudging approval. "You may have something there," he allowed, and then thinking that perhaps he had gone too far, added: "*Colonel.*" He liked the sound of this word, feeling some of its military polish rub off on him; he himself was sure he would rather be considered a batman or orderly than a barber-and-man, and he thought it only natural that the Great Trotter should prefer *colonel* to *sir*. Lately he had begun to use on all occasions the honorary rank that the East India Company had given the Great Trotter while continuing to send him a captain's pay.

At that moment the hatch bell sounded again and Fonseca frowned. These days it seemed any and everybody found an excuse to use his invention. He crossed the room and slid back the door. Another letter lay on the cage floor. The barber-and-inventor fished it out and stood for a minute gazing in admiration at the dumb-waiter until he remembered the letter. It was another bill, this time from a Sans Souci resident.

Monies outstanding to Qaiyum Beg, master poet

For,

1 panegyric-in-progress	27 rupees	(thus far)
1 epic-in-progress	383 rupees	(until now, God is merciful)
2 occasional poems	5 rupees	
couplets without number	—	(no charge)
3 or 4 throwaway lines	4 rupees	(or 3)
TOTAL	420 RUPEES	(say).

(*CHRONICLE RESUMED*)

"Say!" screeched Justin, snatching the bill out of Fonseca's hands. "*Say!*"

He was about to tear it up when a new use occurred to him for his latest invention, and he knew at once that inventors are slaves not masters of their own device. The vertical cabinet with its air of upright interim efficiency, if viewed from a fresh angle (horizontally, say) and in a certain light, had a look of morbid finality. Not to put too fine a point on it, it looked like a coffin and could make an excellent dead letter office. Justin peered into the open drawer: Yakub's memorial looked exceedingly forlorn.

"File, Fonseca," the Great Trotter sighed, handing the bill back.

And Fonseca filed.

"For this I left France!" Justin rolled his eyes up to heaven. "Forgive me, France. For this I left my dear mama! Sweet mama. *Throwaway lines* indeed! As if it's not been a decade since my last grand breakfast . . ."

The Great Trotter stopped and looked at Fonseca with a gleam of intent, but as he did the hatch bell rang yet again. Fonseca stamped across the tower room once more. "For this I left Bombay!" he muttered angrily to himself as he threw back the hatch door. There lay still another envelope.

Justin saw that the paper was of a buff military colour and opened the letter himself. He read the salutation with a sense of boding, then leaned on the nearest window ledge for support. His eye had run on to the next line but was refusing to travel beyond the first full stop.

"Look at me, Fonseca," he moaned. He removed his wig and spread his hands. "Is this septuagenarian fit for battle?"

Fonseca wobbled his head. He had not quite caught his master's tone, and the occipital rocking could be construed equally as *yes* or *no*. Although he shaved the Great Trotter daily, he noticed now for the first time the silken fineness of the few remaining hairs at the temple and the white bristles that sprouted from each ear. The barber-and-counsellor took the letter from his master and glanced at it.

"—*a military adviser*," he read out loud, raising his eyebrows.

Justin snatched the letter back and read it through for the first time. "My coat," he barked. "The military one."

The coat was produced. It had faded altogether and was besides too small.

"No matter," the Great Trotter commanded. "Have it dyed." Out of the remote past he seemed to remember an earlier Governor-General's advice at a dinner party.

The coat came back shrunk still further, its fabric turned to lint; in the undignified tussle that followed, the barber-and-valet was left with two tarnished buttons in his hands. At the Water Gate, Justin gave orders for the gun, *Urban*, to be readied for transportation. Then he selected a rose-coloured horse, Raksh, and took a boat downriver to Calcutta. On the twenty-fourth of May he sailed for Madras.

The order

Dear Colonel,

Be so good as to report to HQ for a spot of military service this month, will you? We're in a bit of a pickle down there in the Carnatic. A ship sails for Madras on the 23rd or so. Trust all's well with the beebees. Not to worry—you'll be serving in the capacity of a military adviser. Must run. Damn Maratha rats.

Yours,

the Gov.-Genl.
Fort Will.
Cal.

P.S.   Could you bring along a twist of Nakhlau arrowroot for the Mrs?

(*CHRONICLE RESUMED*)

When Mik arrived at the Maratha court, he had been given a provisional welcome and put to the test. The discharged lieutenant's knowledge of ordnance, though not as great as his father's, was sufficient to impress on his new masters that he was not an impostor, and he was given command of a handful of guns together with a supporting force whose junior officers were country-borns like himself. The unit was in constant training under Mik, learning about the newest European techniques though many of its field pieces were upward of a hundred years old, having been captured from the Mughal army in bygone skirmishes. Ignorant of the mysteries of metal fatigue which were shortly to occupy the Great Trotter, Mik cast new guns from older cannon (some of which were themselves made from other cannons melted down) and with his combined artillery razed mock fortresses and sackcloth bastions, and blasted holes in ranks of straw infantry. He knew every one of his men by name, and the men, gunners and cavalrymen alike, responded with a loyalty rarely accorded northerners.

During the first year of his service in the Hindu army, Mik's duties ran chiefly to the collection of taxes. This was a simple affair, needing no big guns. He would appear at dawn in a village at the head of a troop of armed horsemen, one of whom carried a firebrand. The villagers, warned by approaching hoofbeats, would already have sent their women and children to hide in the fields and themselves gathered in a silent group by the village shrine. There, under the pipal tree they would pray to the vermilion-daubed elephant god for protection. But the soldiers, who also worshipped Ganesh, always arrived unhurt. There would be some preliminary rattling of sabres and the man with the firebrand would ride up close to the thatched roofs of the huts. The villagers' coins and ornaments would then be handed over and thrust into saddlebags. Mik would turn and ask the name of the village and promise not to return till the next harvest. As the soldiers rode off to the next village, a long reedy wailing rose up out of the millet fields. Later, the regular tax-collector came to exact his raja's share (and his own); the rajas too paid tribute to the Marathas. In this way gold and silver were amassed in the Maratha treasury and daily turned into iron.

In time, the uneasy truce that prevailed between the Marathas and their neighbour to the east, the Nizam of Hyderabad—technically a vassal of the Mughal emperor in Delhi—broke down. The Marathas, driven by imperial ambitions, were not distressed: their ever mobile army of mountain rats wheeled about and roundly defeated the Nizam. Mik lost a quarter of his men, including six Anglo-Indian officers killed at their guns, and was himself wounded in the calf, but it was his artillery that won the day, its cannon glowing white-hot into the night long after the enemy had fled. Years later, his men would tell of their commander who marched up and down the line of guns, smoking like a gun himself and now and then, as a reproach to a tardy gunner, bringing his cheroot to the touch-hole. Hyderabad taken, the Nizam's dominions became a launching ground for sporadic Maratha attacks on the East India Company's Madras hinterland. Their own army in a state verging on mutiny, the British permitted the incursions to go unchecked while sending for reinforcements from Bengal. It was as part of the relieving force that the Great Trotter and his horse and cannon sailed to Madras.

The battle of giants in the south (after Firdausi)

Men go to battle for four reasons: to escape their wives (or concubines), to escape themselves (or the wheel of life), to earn their bread (or loaf), and as military advisers. These reasons are not mutually exclusive (for example, the loafer element may combine with the escapist, and even military advisers can find wives), and one man may be actuated by two or more of them. Of course, none of these considerations motivate the truly Great, who are impelled by elemental drives even as are the sun and the moon. The Great Trotter, whose fiery rages are like the Euphrates in flood and whose ocean-evaporating glances rain confusion on his staff, hears with eager heart the call from the south. Forthwith he seizes a cannon longer than the toddy-palm is tall and searches for a beast that can bear him. He looks this way and that but only in Trans-Oxiana, which is the seed-bed and eyrie of all capable horses, does he find one. Raksh, who is the colour of the Persian rose, whose thunderous hooves flash lightning, whose speed gives pause, whose heaven-whisking mane is the terror of gazelles—Raksh is his choice. Southwards he rides to lands where the men are narrow and vegetarian and the women bare-faced. He laughs a laugh with lips like Yemen corals, this elephant-bodied warrior. Up he draws his troops with pachydermal cunning, advising them. On the other side the enemy are massing, the dust of their horses obscuring the sun, their horses wearying the earth with their tread, their cannons glowing white-hot at noon.

But who is this leading the foe with celestial eyes and a heavenly body? Is it not the moon, the Great Trotter's son, this boy whose thrice-forged head-reaping steel is rather alarming? Was he not born of that same Sultana (*Cup of Grace*), conceived in a night without tedium? Though the milk is not dry on his unsmiling lips, he is a commander of men. He launches at the large man opposite some unspeakable insult and attacks before the other is ready. The Great Man simply laughs and cries: "O delicate! Look well upon this body: mark its elephantine sweep, its awesome bulges." Then he in turn hurls steel upward into the sky which spirals down upon the enemy causing worry. This continues until the raven of night has tucked the beak of wrath under the wing of rest. Long before the koel of morning has filled the breast of reposing man with the fever of waking, the combatants return, the Great Man having yielded not an inch. "Your mother's milk is wet upon your lips," he taunts the other (not knowing him), "better far had you licked it up [fattened yourself on it], moon-sliver." To this the son of Sultana returns another unmentionable jibe. (All the world's sorrows stem from envy; let us have done with it; other notable sins being covetousness, pride, anger, and lechery.) "O last thread of the moon," sings the Great Trotter, "before this night comes your eclipse." And saying so, he fires one last ball into the sky. As when some comet, once in seventy-five years, bursts into the welkin, outstarring other stars and outshining the very orb of night, so flew this noontide harbinger of grief, soaring ever upward until it started to come down, flaring jeopardy upon the host of men till tail-turning they fled, all but one. He stood his ground, the son of Sultana, till struck down from above he lay upon it, clay his pillow. Faint of breath, he cried: "Father!" and at once the Great Trotter's brow was ploughed with the field-furrows of consternation, for he knew that voice. "What have I done?" he asked the daysky spread with stars. Then looking down he saw no indigo upon the boy's skin, but only khaki, nor any locket of the Careless Place [Sans Souci] and he saw he was deceived. Triumphant, he returned to the Southern Capital [Madras] to press the vine-wreathed head upon the cushions of delectation.

(*CHRONICLE RESUMED*)

Returning to Madras, the Great Trotter toured the city, taking in the sights and waving from time to time at the evening crowds. And yet, although his military advice had won the day, an unnamed anxiety gnawed at his heart. It was as if he had lost some part of himself in the battle (though his limbs were all present and accounted for). He sought comfort in a dancing school at the edge of White Town run by a retired old soldier, a Welshman *pur sang*. His young wife many years dead, Captain Llewellyn lived by teaching dancing to the officers of John Company's army; only, since he was too old for demonstrations, the steps were shown by a putative daughter he had been saddled with late in life. Gazing at this young creature as he danced, Justin found himself stricken with love. A new prospect began to open before him as his white eyebrows tickled her downcast eyes. Now, in the evening of his life, when he could expect only gathering gloom and final enclosing darkness, the sun appeared to halt its relentless round and tremble forever just above the line of the horizon.

—*Figure, Narrator, figure!*—

Dispensing with ceremony, he asked the old captain for his daughter's hand, hinting that there might be some money in it for him if he agreed. Captain Llewellyn found the offer handsome, but his livelihood was being taken away. He demanded twice the stated figure (he had always suspected that the girl was not his). "Done!" said Justin, and having settled on the pensioner-and-dancing-master, he carried his young prize back to Sans Souci. He was rattling up the drive through the Gunpowder Gate when a thought struck him, and he leaned over to the child to ask her name. She looked sleepily at him with timid red eyes and answered: "Rose."

A warning

> TO ALL ANGLO-INDIAN OFFICERS OF THE MARATHA CONFEDERACY!
> *It has come to our notice that certain Anglo-Indian officers*
> *formerly of our army are in the military employ of certain*
> *refractory native princes. Such officers are to understand*
> *that the present state of war between the Company's Army*

*and these same princes renders the continuation of their
services to the said princes, in whatsoever capacity, treason-
ous, and the officer in question a traitor.*

THE GOVERNOR-GENERAL IN COUNCIL
Calcutta at *Fort William*

(*CHRONICLE RESUMED*)

Shortly after sunset, Mik found himself being picked up out of the dust
by two of his men. He opened his eyes to that fleeting smoky passage of
light called cowdusk, his favourite time of day, when he was given to sporting
with milkmaids who carried the sharp scent of dung fires in their hair. This
evening his limbs felt uncommonly heavy, which was extraordinary because
one of them had been blown away. A ball coming down from above had torn
off the right arm at the shoulder. Mik was left senseless for the space of six
hours, during which the battle raged around him. By a freak of chance the
extreme heat of the ball had annealed the wound, stopping the blood vessels
and leaving a grotesque cicatrix where the arm had been. It was the odour
of singed cotton at the upper edge of his vest that had confused the Next
Trotter on his first waking in the twilight. In place of the nubile village girls
he saw two men, moustachioed like himself, who seemed intent on causing
him the greatest possible discomfort.

When next he awoke, it was night and he was lying on a charpai in a
hut. One of the two moustachioed men, whom he recognized as an alert junior
officer of the horse, Badal by name, fed him a sop of millet bread in milk
sweetened with jaggery and told him how the battle had gone. It had been a
furious inconclusive affair, with both sides claiming victory and neither remaining to verify the claim. In the mutual retreat Mik had been left for dead,
and not until several hours later had a party returned for the wounded. The
Maratha Commander-in-Chief, enraged to learn at the end of the day that six
cannons had exploded in the firing, blamed the inconclusiveness of the victory
on that accident and the accident on Mik. Besides, certain spies in the pay of
the British had circulated a printed proclamation from the enemy calling on
all former officers of the East India Company to reconsider their loyalties.
The Commander-in-Chief had had a copy of the handbill deciphered by a
vakil and was threatening to use it against the careless (or was it, he hinted,
careful?) half-European artillery expert. But then word had reached him of
Mik's supposed death.

Badal produced a copy of the British proclamation and held up the oil
lamp. The words swam before Mik's eyes and he went to fold up the paper

and put it away for some other time. It was then that he noticed his missing arm and fainted from the shock. When he opened his eyes again, it was morning and the two Marathas were gone. They had with threats and inducements prevailed on the owner of the hut to shelter Mik until he was fully recovered. After that they fetched a withered old herb doctress, left their artillery commander in her charge, and returned to their camp. Over the next two weeks Mik learnt to smoke and eat and wash with his left hand. Lying on the charpai and gazing moodily at the thatched roof, he had sufficient leisure to ponder Badal's unspoken advice and reflect on the Company's latest announcement. The division in himself hurt more than his shoulder, tormented as he was with doubts. Madras or the Marathas: which way, Mik? The question plagued his days and dogged him in his dreams. One morning he swung out of his bed, his mind made up. He paid the villager and rewarded the old doctress, mounted his horse, and turned towards Madras, leaning to one side as he rode.

At Madras, the day Mik arrived a French bible-ship was detained and two hundred missionaries-and-marines were taken into custody. Napoleon-phobia had been rampant ever since the French occupation of Egypt, and here was confirmation. When Mik presented himself, handbill in hand, he was arrested; there were too many gentlemen about with dubious French connections. However, his father's services to the Company were considered, and the turncoat son of the turncoat Frenchman was released.

"When will I step out of his shadow?" Mik growled, and the answer sounded between his ears like a mortar: "When you cast a shadow of your own." He decided to get himself a son. For that he wanted a wife, and since Madras could produce nothing to compare with the angular Miss Bellows of his schooldays, he thought of the Upper Military Orphanage of Calcutta; the girls of that institution had always provided the Company's officers with wives. He set out for Calcutta and arrived late for the annual ball: the last orphan of age was already promised. In any case, when he paused before the hall mirror in the light of a chandelier, Mik was forcibly reminded of his incompleteness as a dancing partner: the right sleeve of his jacket hung limp and unpinned at his side. "I will take a wife at Sans Souci," he said, remembering all at once the Alexander sisters. He made his way to the boat docks upriver from the sailing ships. An ice boat had left that morning, he was told; perhaps he could catch up with it. He did not; instead he travelled the first stage in an aromatic vapour of rice, having found a berth in a grain barge going as far as Krishnanagar. There, at cowdusk, he was detained by a company of milkmaids. And it was the same all the way upriver as the seasons came and went.

Some remarks on the monsoon of Hindoostan

The rains of Hindoostan come after the summer and before the winter (just in between). In the south they come in winter too, but that is another matter. The main rains come in between and that is the point. To us of the north they are brought by winds from the southeast, but geographers call it the southwest monsoon. It is most perplexing, but even in new bottles a little old wine is worth all the tea in China. *Monsoon* means simply, season; thus is the confusion confounded. The rainy monsoon, then, is my theme; blame the Arabs: it is their word. Gentle breezes come skipping over the Arabian Sea, gathering moisture, the little poppets. Arabs in dhows sigh and set their faces homeward. Dolphins grin and flying fish frolic, but the clam he will scruple. Clouds are massing, the southwest wind blows and the curtains go up. Now the Malabar rice paddies are glinting bosom-jewels. On the Konkani coast a shapely mother tumbles into the church of St Francis Xavier, warm fat drops falling around her. Goans are clapping, Bombay is buoyant, but here in the northern plain is still no rain. From the Arabian Sea the cloud messenger mounts the Western Ghats; Mandakranta (slow-stepping) is his pace. Lovers' hearts quicken, breaths hasten, lips fasten, and pulses are firm. But that is the south and it is all very well. Here the ground is still cracked and wineskins are crazed. The monsoon advances to the Vindhya range, weeps over Ujjain, darkens Bengal. But here in the north mouths are dry, throats parched, and beaks kept open. Assam is awash, Cherra Punji afloat, Darjeeling soaking: but Nakhlau is a desert, Sans Souci an empty cup.

When, up stand the Himalayas, beside which the Western Ghats are footling stools, and the clouds are deflected up the Gangetic plain. Kites, circling at two thousand feet, spy them first. Next a joyous peal sounds from the elephant stables. The Turcoman master-gelder's nostrils flare. In the library a sheaf of paper stirs, stroked by a thumb of wind, but the bard is not alarmed, for the monsoon is a second-order wind. It is not like the yellow storm, which upsets wine jugs onto precious manuscripts and keeps the epic poet up till shoot of dawn drying folios under towels and blankets. Lightning flickers, thunder growls—fie, pi-dog: do not crouch under the desk!—and the skies are a delicious grey. The first patter comes, of pearls, then a drumming of diamonds. Earth's cracks heal, wineskins mend, and lovers put tiffs away. All is made green and lovely. The chambermaid looks with longing eyes at the poet, but he will not. Pearls ground up with wine are said to help; he stands his cup outside the Water Door. The lotus pond is filling up, the water hyacinth blushes, the water chestnut pales. The Tank swells, the Kirani babbles, toads tattle, urchins ululate; but the camels are smiling formally. Green are the fields, the lawn, the maze; purple the jamun, rose the eyes of my beloved. We are all in love with her: is she not as pretty as a boy? Has she not brought the rain from the south after long drouth?

Rain, rain, when will it stop? Now the poet fetches in his cup, but there are only diamonds. The gargoyles spout and wink; it is all very well for them. But what of the sundial? And the ice pits? The well water is muddy; another mineshaft has collapsed in the saltpetre hill. Mosquitoes multiply, snakes take succour, crickets insist. There is a mire outside the elephant stables that will not bear speaking of. The poulterers' clients have my sympathy; the grooms' are welcome. The indigo baths have run over and a blue pond formed in the pit of the amphitheatre. The music pavilion is an island—Trotter's Folly, a guest was heard to remark, while another asked which he meant: the pavilion or the rest? Enough is enough, I say. The powder is wet, the wine adulterous, melons sodden. Mildew blights shoeleather, earthworms grow brave. And still it rains. Peasants despair and city-dwellers have their doubts. And still there is no end (the beginning, too, is hazy). In the sunken garden only the chimney of the Japanese tea-house is visible; the rest of the old brick kiln has taken water. The humps that way are camels' graves; the livestock are on the second floor. The archipelagoes to either side of the Trotter Road are the tops of silk cotton trees; the other way those are tamarinds. And who is going to swim for the mangoes? The dear toddy-palms reach up with supplicating arms: alas, they will not fruit for yet another year.

(VERSE)

The beautiful boy

His slender arms beckon but O it is late—
Or early for plucking th' intoxicant date!

(CHRONICLE RESUMED)

The rains, which were late, broke on the first of August and continued without stopping until people lost count of the days.

—*Narrator*—
Cup-Bearer?
I sense troubles mounting, Narrator. Tell me, are the large days done?
*Almost, my sweet Cup, but the rain brings its own largesse. There is time enough
   for the narrowness your heart basely craves.*

Go! Fetch me some water-white maraschino from Dalmatia—the southern Slavs
make it best. Good. Now listen. This is what the kite says.

On every side lay an endless sheet of muddy water, covering even the aerolite.
Sungum was reduced to an island whose inhabitants went about their business,
thanks to Justin's foresight, on high ground. Then the rain stopped.

On the first dry day, people used their Solomon umbrellas out of habit
and swore the usual oaths. It was Qaiyum who noticed. When he brought in
his calabash for his daily draught of rain-water (a tonic prescribed by Hakim
Ahmed for his flaccidity) he found it empty. He went back out and looked
long and deeply at the sky. It seemed to him that he had never before seen
anything so ravishing as its blue. A little later, Nishan Chand, who had also
noticed a beguiling brightness from the mirror tube, came outside and gazed
likewise at the sky. Sky-gazing was a particular feat with him, since he had
to sit with his legs stretched out in front of him and throw his head back as
far as it would go. In a little while Munnoo and Nankoo came by and squatted
familiarly beside him, looking upward, and before long a small group had
assembled on the porch of the Water Court with their faces turned to the sky.
Their numbers increased steadily as passersby furled their umbrellas, stopped
in their sloping high-stepping tracks and came to see what the fuss was about.

They sat spellbound. As the clouds rolled away to the west, a ray from
the setting sun shook loose and encircled the island with a pristine radiance
that grew clearer and clearer until it seemed the world was made of light.
The smallest pebble, each blade of grass, every leaf and stem, rainfed and
washed continuously for months, stood out in clean relief, glutted with colour.
Then the sun went down and the colours cooled in a brief twilight as every
man made his way home touched to the heart. During the night the halt in
the incessant drumming freed lesser, unfamiliar sounds, of frogs, of crickets,
of water first dripping then running off down any declivity that offered itself.
Through the small hours the whisper of departing water mounted till by dawn
the roamings of numberless impromptu streams sounded like a groan. By
sunrise the flats were drained and only in the marsh beyond the Tank did
veins of sluggish silver show, barred with reeds.

On the second morning, Justin, who had not been present at the previous
evening's spectacle but in bed, asleep, woke to a glaring light at his window.
Imagining it an extension of his nightmare, of which he had had many of late
(waking in a sweat, though the nights were now cool, full of dread that all
had been taken from him and that he was once more a common soldier), he
rubbed his glaucous eyes and sat up. The light at the window refused to melt
away. God help me, I'm blind! was his next response, and rushing to the
window he squinted at the harsh sky. Its dome, which might have been no

more than the curve of his retina, was speckled with stars. Then it's true! he whispered, aghast. I am struck blind—punished for some sin. He cast his mind back to the eerie sense of loss he had known on the battlefield, to the delirium of Madras, and lastly to the little dancing-mistress. She had not stopped crying since she arrived at Sans Souci. And now I can never see her again, he lamented.

Just then Fonseca rushed in. He, too, had missed the previous evening's show and now came up to his master, gibbering.

"Colonel! Colonel! Have you *seen*?"

Justin, who had expected a voice without a shape, was so relieved to see his barber-and-man clearly and in colour that he first gazed speechless at him and then hugged him.

"The stars! Yes!" he replied warmly, not taking his eyes off Fonseca.

Fonseca stiffened. "Stars?" he scoffed. "I mean the sun, the sky. It's stopped raining." He recovered his good cheer and made for the door, looking back by way of invitation. "Shall we climb to the top of the tower?"

Justin followed meekly. At the top he emerged under the cope of the sky and looked down at the earth spread out below in broad daylight. He did not dare look up again because he knew the stars would still be there. Instead he gaped around him with a dazed expression, waiting for the moment when his eyes would adjust themselves to the new brilliance. Little by little objects began to acquire shape and definition: those were the ice pits, that would be the aerolite, there was the marsh, that was the jungle—He stopped. Where was the river? A frown creased his forehead. The river that marked the limits of his land—the Moti Ganga—where *was* it? He turned to Fonseca, but Fonseca, too, he saw, was staring blankly in the same direction.

"The telescope, Fonseca. Quick!"

Fonseca ran down and returned with an old Dutch spyglass.

"An entire river—disappeared!" Justin murmured as he focussed on the space above the jungle. In the circle of light there appeared, where the river had been, dazzling curves of water, detached and strewn along the former bed like the broken links of some bright chain. Lifting the glass a fraction, the Great Trotter saw his river. It flowed just below the horizon, winding as before—but perhaps twenty miles east of its old course. The scattered links below were ox-bow lakes left behind. Trembling, he lowered the glass, returned it without a word to his barber-and-man, and went downstairs to his suite. The Nawab's decree was plain: all lands to the east of the canal *as far as the Moti Ganga* to belong in perpetuity to Trotters of the blood. All that new territory was now his, Justin Trotter's. It was absolution, vindication. But when he went to the window to test it, the stars were still there. And when he stepped out that night under a clear sky, they were gone.

Relations with the Nawab were never very good after that. It was not that the Great Trotter's gain was the Nawab's loss, for the land in question represented no great proportion of Tirnab. Besides, the Nawab was ailing from a liver disorder and quite content to leave territorial wrangles to his successor; he wished only to spend the remainder of his life keeping up appearances as the Sun King of the East. It was just that after the dramatic increase in his lands, the Great Trotter began to assume plenipotentiary airs, and on the next occasion of their meeting had a cloth-of-gold umbrella carried over him although the rains of his advancement had long since stopped. He seemed to know that the Moti Ganga river would with each good monsoon run ever farther eastward (which it did) and to think that the increase of Sans Souci was sanctioned by nature and welcomed by all men. Could he have heard the scuff of doubt and the scratch of fear in the hearts of later Trotters when each year the thunderheads gathered and a cool earthy wind spiced with rain began to blow out of the east? As for the common people, they were awestruck: who but a pir or saint could move rivers?

The Great Trotter did nothing to discourage the groundswell of veneration, and in time gave it his solemn assent. He gave up honey-roggen and refused (with the exception of his gypsonometer, which he allowed to be kept half filled, or as he put it, half empty) sweetness of any kind. And he allowed himself the luxury of saintly irritation. "Men do not love a saint," he complained to his journal. "On the contrary, they hate him for showing up their imperfections. He is the hostage of their forsaken ideals; their devotion is his closely guarded prison."

Justin also stopped pestering the girl, Rose, but that may have been because whenever he went near her she began to wail louder than ever. Her tears had dried up, but she could still shriek and throw herself against the wall. If he abandoned his amorous intentions and tried to comfort her, she would shake her head and withdraw into a corner, hugging herself tightly with a pair of damask arms. If he lost his temper, she spread her fingers wide and turned her hands inward, threatening to scratch out her own eyes with fingernails that had not been clipped since Madras. At such moments Justin would turn and flee the room, and at length he stopped going to see her altogether. The only visitors to the North Tower were Farida, who lived down the corridor and took a big-sisterly interest in the girl, and the masons and labourers who were set to complete the unfinished structure around her. Sometimes the poet-and-romantic, Qaiyum, could be found skulking in the damp shadows beneath her window (though the deputy librarian's office was at the opposite corner of *Sungum*), but eventually he would sigh and return to his bottle, resigned to the thought that in no time she would grow up and be spoilt with breasts and hips. The girl had a kind of revenge on her captor.

Although Justin kept away from her, she visited him nightly in his dreams, and to the grisly paraphernalia of his nightmares was added a pair of uplifted hands, small and savage, with ten uncut fingernails the colour of mercury.

Frustrated in his desire, the Great Trotter channelled his restlessness into a breathtaking variety of enterprises. Upon waking, he first breakfasted and then repaired to the oratory in the Audience Hall where he sang for forty minutes, his high soprano flooding the vaulted roof and winding about the barley-sugar pillars of the arcade. His mind purified, he turned to matters of intellect. He had become convinced that with diligence and correct thinking a man could chemically synthesize sugar, and to this end set up a laboratory in the remains of the Old Armoury, where he spent an instructive portion of each day. Next, deciding that it was time he turned to account the affliction of seeing stars by day, he constructed an elaborate observatory along the entire length of the northern crescent or Rib. A miniature city of hemispheres and globes, prisms, turrets, dials, gnomons, and pyramids proper, stepped and truncated, sprang up on the broad curving sweep of the Rib's roof. Here he would come after each morning's alchemical research and wander under the noontide stars, taking an alignment off one, measuring the azimuth of another, and recording all in his Rose Book. After that he would spend an hour copying out and collating figures, assigning to each group an arbitrary letter from a Prakrit script, and juggling the ancient alphabet by means of random pickings from a deck of Korean cards. If the result contained two sequential letters from his name, he would sit justified before the universe; if not, he would seize all his papers together with the pack of cards and with both hands throw them up into the air as if releasing a dove. Then he would make his divination from the way they came down.

Following lunch, which to save time he now had brought to him in a five-tier brass tiffin-carrier of his own invention (*Inglorious Aloysius, Sorry Pass*), he descended from the roof to a gymnasium on the second floor where he swung his Indian clubs for ten minutes together (*Reckless Aloysius*) before climbing into a bath of unheated water (*Joyless Aloysius*). Then he descended yet another floor to his invention hall where there waited, in various stages of completion, a goglet that would never run dry, a cup that filled itself, a frictionless mercury-borne chair, the perfect mordant, an eternal dye, a kaleidoscope that showed the future by means of splintered china cameos of the past, a coil of wire that trapped sounds, a mirror tube that caused light to turn corners, a battery for storing sunshine, a net or sock that would catch the wind, an engine that would be of itself in perpetual motion, a miniature game of Aztec tennis played on a table, another game resembling poona, an inkpen to be carried safely in the vest-pocket, a device for loading twelve guns at one time, anti-gravity shoes, a bent pin with its own sheath, a mechanical loom instructed by means of punched cards, a small hot-air balloon that could carry two Pekinese dogs into the air, and one or two functionless or as yet unrecognizable inventions. Finally, so that he might have still more scope for work, he experimented with a machine that would make time stand still. With a pair of hemispherical vacuum cups, two teams of donkeys, half an hourglass and a cone of white sand, he succeeded. It was never known whether the last year of his life was indeed a year or much more, but during that time (if time it could be called) Justin wrote interminable codicils to his will in his head, now giving everything to Farida, now to Elise, now back to Mik, now to any clean-shaven cellist named Raffles; though there were days when he could not for the life of him see why all the property should not go to all of them simultaneously or none of it to all of them at different times.

As befitted a saint, Justin gave up violent sports such as animal fights (or at least the public celebration of them, since in private he still delighted in frog and sparrow and water-spider fights, reciting with the emperor Akbar: *I am in the power of love, and if I have thousands of wishes it is no crime*, and with Akbar's historian, Abu'l Fazl: *hence it is better to go to another subject*). No longer did the Spur resound with the pandemonium of cock-fights; instead the Great Trotter crouched in silence over a hatching machine which he proposed to link up with an egg-multiplier operated on sound biochemical principles. He melted down one of his short cannon and turned it into a ploughshare. He studied long into the night, suppressing his yawns with soldierly discipline, on the subject of metal fatigue. At other times he could be found in the Old Armoury experimenting with the preservation of meat by means of saltpetre, a line he cut short when he found the meat to turn first pink and then a deep rose. Nor did he neglect his indigo, enlisting the services of the dhobi, Dhani Das, for the purpose. He detained the man with all manner of dyeing tests while the laundry baskets of Sans Souci overflowed with dirty linen. And as for his work on refrigeration, he took Fonseca into his confidence, showing him a short cut to the Glacerie and having him spend hours in the sunlight charging a battery which he was certain would, when suddenly discharged close to a cruse of water (but facing away), leave a cruse of ice.

Perceiving a change in his master, Yakub at first lapsed into dudgeon and then began to look about him for ways of getting back at those who appeared to be the beneficiaries of the new regime. While he could not bring himself to adulterate the indigo, he indulged slackness in the nilchis, turning a blind eye when certain filtration processes were skipped so that Dhani Das would have to work with an impure cake. And although he never went so far as to deliberately melt the stored ice, there were days when a window might be found open in the Glacerie godown with the loo blowing through. But what rankled most was the knowledge that cock-fighting, the sport he himself had sponsored at Sans Souci, was now spurned. The baker-and-cocksman turned his wrath on Sunya, the poulterer. When one morning the prize goose escaped from its coop and was found pecking at the runner beans on the wrong side of the trellis that divided the coops from the stables, Yakub's chance came: he gathered witnesses and pounced on the bird. Since Sunya chose to contest the claim (there had been bad blood between them from long before the dung affair), the Great Trotter decided that in all fairness the issue could not be settled by either Muslim or Hindu law. Yakub at once made for the library where he dug up a Talmudic clause relating to young pigeons found on the ground. Said Baba Bratha: *if a bird is found within fifty cubits of its cote it belongs to the owner; if beyond fifty cubits, to the finder. If it is exactly midway, it must be shared.* There were some discrepancies, but it would do. It did; the poulterer-and-egg brahmin was obliged to watch his favourite bird divided. Who, Justin wondered, got the heart—or was that also divided? And the heart of the heart?

The next morning he went directly to his laboratory and dissected a leaf, cutting it down the middle and examining its parts under a glass. And all that day he spent poring over the inner membranes of the leaf, and the inner tissues of those membranes, and the inmost essence of those tissues, and the ghost of that essence, and the shadow of that ghost, and the vacuum in the shadow, and the silence in the vacuum, and the heart of that silence, and the pulse of that heart, and the thing that sits in repose between pulses, and the companion of that thing. And always, no matter how deep he penetrated, there remained a companion of the last thing. If there is always another thing, he asked, then surely it is as vital as the thing itself or the space surrounding it? Was not yesterday's case solved by a third code? And adducing several such cases as he made his way back to the West Tower, the Great Trotter began to devise for himself and for Sans Souci a crest with a motto: TERTIUM QUID.

Nor did he forget the world outside. He drew up a grand scheme for eternal peace between France and England, with India as a mediator, and wrote to the Governor-General (a new man) offering his services as chief negotiator. The offer was rejected, but Justin was not to be easily put off, and only after a similar reply had been extracted from the government of Pitt did he desist. To acquit himself of his duty, however, he sent both gentlemen a further memorandum concerning the Swedish East India Company, which he declared would shortly (if his plans were not implemented) overtop and destroy its British counterpart. He did not communicate with the French government; there he had grander schemes, confessed to no one and hardly clear to himself.

With the energy of the rejected righteous, he returned to building his château. Not that he wished to complete it; it was simply that certain tedious regularities in it now offended the tastes of a man who, out walking in his orangerie, was delighted to find that one row had an extra tree, a custard apple. He put down a bosquet of acacias and plantains to obscure the only view a flat land presented, that of the saltpetre hill. In the middle of a narrow walk he had erected bronze statues of sparrows and grasshoppers. He found stucco artisans to mould fainéant cornices and pilasters inside and out, to graft trumpery fruit over doorways, to hollow out in some expanse of wall an ornamental niche that corresponded with nothing else. For the North Tower he decided a pentagonal shape would be best, and accordingly, the unfinished octagonal fabric lost three sides as it rose. As to his own tower, he ordered that its height be increased by one cubit a day, with horseshoe windows introduced, like those at Ajanta, instead of slits. He topped the four towers with an aerial companionway called the Crown, and hung from it a massive bell of his own casting, the Audience Bell. Again, he sent for trees and shrubs from the mouth of the Amazon and the horn of Africa and had them planted in the sunken garden, in the desert, and on the plain adjoining the jungle. He had all the roses dug up and transplanted downwind from the Sagarpaysans' village to alleviate a sanitary problem; there was not enough money left to widen the one drain, but he imported marigolds from the Lake District to fill the empty rose-beds. The mehndi-hedge maze was allowed to grow wild, with a peacock or two clipped out of it. The drive to the Gunpowder Gate was lined with diagonally laid bricks painted alternately red and white to give his missing son a military welcome. The ice pits were given pagoda roofs, and the Old Armoury, whose top the young Mik had blown off, was given a pointed Rhine castle roof which looked from a distance a little like a dunce's cap. Strolling about the grounds in the last year of the eighteenth century, Justin saw with satisfaction that instead of a spiritless Provencal château replicated on Indian soil, or a humdrum Nakhlau mansion after the traditional manner, there had grown up in Sans Souci something altogether new.

Having triumphed over the endless repetition of the past, Justin was visited by an intense nostalgia for the future. Often, in the midst of an experiment or while out for a walk, this melancholy brooding on the world to come would bring him to a standstill. And there, like Lao-tzu or Scipio the African, he would stand a whole night unmoving, communing with Trotters yet unborn until the sun came up on the other side and he started from his reverie, brushing off the dew. In such a mood one day, he walked to the amphitheatre, climbed unsteadily into a boat, and rowed across the indigo pool, which alone of all the new ponds had not run off. When he reached the steps of the music pavilion he looped the mooring rope around a rail and climbed, supporting himself, to the top. Ever since the storm he had been anxious to examine the last two of Marazzi's stained-glass windows in order that he might through their frames reduce the infinite options of the future to a manageable set of alternatives. But already, as he stood on the top step, he felt his intentions would be thwarted.

A smell like that of Bombay duck, salt vinegarish pinched and putrid, yet strangely tantalizing, hung in the air. The ladder that Marazzi used had fallen through the last of the windows, knocking out the glass: it lay slantwise across the floor, its uprights jutting out over the window ledge and its topmost rung caught in the jagged glass. The window, as far as one could tell from the few remaining peaks of glass, had been predominantly brown. The only unbroken pane was in a skylight set above the entrance, and it was a clear blue, the blue of the sky. Some attempt had evidently been made to stain the glass, but although a sparkling web of scratches showed on the surface, the paint had not taken—except at the base, where what looked like a range of craggy mountains was silhouetted against the sky. As his eyes grew accustomed to the dark, Justin saw that the mountains were not on the glass but in front of it: the blue was broken by the outline of a bulging chest and the profile of a man, his mouth open. In a kind of hammock just below the skylight lay a frightful thing with a brush held tightly in its lifeless hand. How long it had been since the ladder had fallen, kicked away perhaps in one of Marazzi's paroxysms of frustration and rage, Justin could only guess at from the stench, so dense it was visible as a buzzing green iridescent haze. It had been weeks since he last gave the cripple a thought.

Justin did not tarry. He sent for Father Angelico from the Catholic mission, and the two men walked up and down in the Audience Hall admiring the Turinian's ceiling as the afternoon sun streamed through the windows opening onto the Gunpowder Court. After the requiem, Marazzi was buried in a child-sized casket in the music pavilion, which was sealed up around him; the steps leading up to the pavilion were demolished, and the last boatload of workers rowed back to the amphitheatre gallery across the indigo pool. The artist's paints and brushes were fetched down from the nests he had built at various points in the central dome, and stored in the attic of the newly finished North Tower. "I killed him with neglect," the Great Trotter wrote in his journal. He rose, crossed to the mirror, and looked long and reproachfully at himself. "A cherub of man," he whispered, "God rest his soul." A tear trickled down his cheek. He was impressed by its silent dignity. "Perhaps a grave face will win her," he wondered, his eyebrow going up. But the warmth that usually stirred in his loins at the thought of her was not there. "In time," he comforted himself. "She will succumb in time. It's not as if you were deformed. God rest his soul."

Reminded of the soul, Justin realized that Marazzi's husk did not rest exactly where it had fallen, though it was true the painter had not numbered himself among the adherents of the Religion of the Winds. Where would his own husk come to rest? It could not be far away—the event or the place. Tonight, perhaps: here? Justin began to hum nervously. He took out a box of candles and lit them all; the blaze of light cheered him a little. He stared in turn at each of the eleven flames (a Solomon dozen). So steady and yet so vulnerable they were, a breath of wind could set them trembling, a gust put them out. All-powerful Wind! But the questioner within would not be put off. What lay beyond, beside, inside the wind? Was there a stillness at its heart which was not wind? Marazzi knew. When would he, Justin Aloysius Trotter, know?

He pushed back his chair and went down to the invention hall, whistling. So much to do before he surrendered himself to the Wind! But the seed of doubt was sown, and try as he might to fiddle with bolts and wires and scurry from table to table pulling the wraps off ever more impressive machines, the time came when he had to stop and endure its twisting (*Godless Aloysius, Stony Heart*). He stepped out into the night under a sky that was cloudless but bereft of stars, and went towards the Hava Manzil. For the first time its deep resonant note did not greet him; the wind seemed to have forsaken the harp of the skeleton dome beneath which his wife lay. He stood before the monument scarcely able to breathe, the terror mounting in his soul. With an immense effort he broke away and stumbled towards the music pavilion. It was late and the night was dark; Munnoo's snores had died down in the indigo shed and the village pi-dogs were asleep. Justin ran down the first few steps of the amphitheatre, his heels echoing on the stone until he stepped into the water. Making a megaphone of his hands, he shouted across the indigo pool: "Which *is* it, Marazzi?" But there was no answer from the pavilion except for the quick stony spank of an echo and the sound of the ripples lapping up against the gallery. The cry did awaken one person: Munnoo, floor-polisher-and-night-watchman, sprang up in the indigo shed and involuntarily bellowed the age-old refrain of chowkidars calling to one another across sleeping India: *Jagte raho!* he hollowed mournfully, *Keep awake!*

Justin turned sorrowfully away. From behind him there came the rhythmical thump-thump-thump of a bamboo staff being knocked every three paces on the hard earth: Munnoo was striding watchfully along his beat, guarding the indigo shed from thieves and marauders. No indigo was stolen that night, though it was Justin's tortured cry that scared off Dhani Das, dhobi-and-(lately)-dyer, who had been lurking in the shadows. In the space of another watch Munnoo lay snoring peacefully, his lathi laid across his belly, but for the Great Trotter there was no sleeping. He tossed and squirmed, trying to ease the bubble inside him; he knew that there was more wind where it came from, but where the wind came from he could not say. By the last watch he lay empty and defeated, his Din Havai a thing of the past. Through the window there crept a cool grey wash of light that soothed his anguished soul, flooding the chambers of his heart with penitence. Inclining his head on the pillow, he fell asleep with the resolve to write a new will in vindication of his reawakened faith (*Eleventh-Hour Trotter, Rescued Soul*).

(COMMENTARY)

A lacuna: Problems relating to the text of an earlier version

In all surviving accounts of the Great Trotter's life, including that by Mr Montagu (*Putative Trotter, Atheist*) there is a gap at this point in the narrative. The gap is more serious than earlier mutilations because it spans the crucial last year of the great man's earthly life. Nor is the Rose Book of any assistance; the bulk of that journal is a mass of runic folly, and there are in any case no further entries following the oblique record of Marazzi's death. One is obliged to rely on the fitful and regrettably self-absorbed (at least latterly) diary kept by the Great Trotter's second bibi, Jarman Begam. Or else one may rudely conjecture, the course apparently chosen by Mr Montagu, who makes no mention of the events of that harrowing night. He records, it is true, in language that one shudders to transcribe, that "the vaunting escalation of the West Tower was summarily halted," and that the Great Trotter "retreated into himself" (how are we to interpret this cryptic phrase?), but from these precarious footholds he leaps recklessly into a void of guesswork and pusillanimous speculation. "There exists," we are informed, "a family tradition of deathbed repentance, but it is apocryphal." Unquote (*Uncouth Heathen, Unhouseled Wretch*).

Let us in calmness suppose that the garden of the Great Trotter's faith was hedged about with doubts. Let us allow that the beams of his belief were thatched with reservations. Are these the grounds of eternal despair, the fabric of impenitence? Surely not. Are not all thinking men subject to the passing chill of disbelief? And do they not, once the bout is past, warm themselves gratefully at the old hearth, drawing closer to the fire of the true faith? This was the Great Trotter's experience, and we may reasonably assume that his last year was spent in mild penance for the pride of the old self as manifest in the old will. How else are we to construe Jarman Begam's remark: "Trot bends to his labours with a new will," and other instances too numerous for mention? No, there is only one conclusion to be drawn from all this: the Great Trotter gave up his old ways and spent his remaining months in preparation for the writing of a new last will and testament which but for an unfortunate accident might have come down to us and resolved all doubts. It was not

Marazzi's death alone that was the agent of the change; as early as the great storm by which a hidden hand dispersed his wicked abecedary of Din Havai, the wise man began to see the error of his ways. Of course, none of these proofs could have been visible to Mr Montagu (*Self-styled Trotter*) for the scales on his eyes (*Malicious Serpent, Arch Worm*).

(CHRONICLE RESUMED)

The next day the vaunting escalation of the West Tower was halted. Justin rose late, gave the order, and having breakfasted at noon went outdoors as usual, but it seemed to those who saw him that he had retreated into himself. He looked straight through Jarman Begam (who was on her way back from the apiary) and even the substantial Qaiyum (who was slinking back from a Nakhlau carousel with the junior Solomon) passed unnoticed before his eyes. He sent Fonseca off to the paper factory in the Rib to see how badly the press had been damaged, and when the barber-and-peon returned to say, *very* badly, sent him back with orders to produce four sheets by hand. Habit took him to his laboratory, where he spent a few idle moments before summarily checking himself. With one sweep of the arm he sent his alembics, jars, and burners crashing to the floor. Out of the corner of his eye he saw a rare flinty earth expire in a shower of sparks which, falling, ignited his papers. In a little while a coil of green flame began to stir among the crumpled receipts. Justin did not stay to watch the Old Armoury go up in smoke for the second time. He went directly to the invention hall and replaced the covers that he had torn off the unfinished inventions the night before. Those devices which were complete and which he deemed useful to mankind (such as the mirror tubes for conducting light, and the apparatus that caused water to run uphill) he had transported and installed all over Sans Souci; the others he left unfinished. Before shutting the door forever on his playroom, he paused to cast his blue eye over the tented tables. They stood in ranks that followed the curve of the Rib, their white covers spread over a variety of objects, some the size of a church organ, one no bigger than a mouse; several had long fingers of hidden machinery upraised; one had a giant saucer into which the cloth sagged. In a dark corner stood a dozen flasks of Burma mercury, their mouths sealed with leather; over each hung a halo of tender light. Crossing quickly to them, Justin leaned over the vapour and breathed deeply. Then he returned to the door and let himself out.

The following day he interrupted Yakub who was supervising the installation of the mirror tube in the library. "Let Nishan Chand see to that," he said. "I have another task for you. Two tasks, really. First I would like you to order the following meteorological instruments from Europe by the next ship—earlier, if possible. And also, if you don't mind writing it down, the following book, in large print." And he dictated a London publisher's address for a hefty black Bible. After that he led the baker-and-Chief Steward to the back of the Rib where he pointed out the site and rough dimensions of a vaulted room he wished to build; it need have no particular shape, he said, and its function would in time become clear. Waiting only to see the ground broken (there was no need for plans, he assured the carpenter and the mason: let the stones go one on top of the other and the builder surrender his will to a greater Design), he proceeded to the library where he began to gather all the works he could find on the subject of balloons. Each day after the morning shave and breakfast, which he no longer took in the Rain Room, he would hang a sign outside his door saying that he did not wish to be disturbed. The weather having cooled since the rains came, he no longer went to his tahkhana, and he stayed away altogether from the other three towers.

Farida no longer expected the Great Trotter; Rose was relieved when he stopped coming. Elise bore his absences with resignation, but could not entirely forget the erotic lessons taught her. When her husband (as she now thought him) locked himself away, her desire was subtilized into a kind of floating force which moved with her and threatened, without her knowing it, to transform the first person to come her way. That person happened to be Fonseca. The hairdresser-and-man took to dressing her hair and telling her by day the stories his master no longer required at night. He touched only her hair, but his presence within the charged field around her took on an electric quality. Her love reserved for Justin, Elise could offer Fonseca only her admiration: the beautician-and-kahani-master was a paragon, clever, charming, and that oddly exciting thing, a man. In Fonseca the regard had started earlier, almost the first time he brought up a book for her from the librarian, and although after the first few times he had considered building a dumb-waiter for the South Tower, the climb now bothered him so little that he was constantly seeking excuses for repeating it. There were books that travelled up the stair which the old man had certainly not sent; and then there were the gifts, bought from the old Armenian pedlar.

The Great Trotter saw nothing in a process hardly visible to the principals themselves. But rumours began to travel down the South Tower stair and out into the thin air of Sans Souci. It was true that when Elise went to inspect the bees, Fonseca could be found in the vicinity of the ruined roundhouse, but the barber-and-man was too much of a romantic to declare himself; he would simply watch from behind a telamon and return to his room full of unspent desire. Elise returned to hers and read two books at a time, one of pure mathematics and the other of profane love. Yakub, busy in the shapeless balloon room, smiled to himself: rumours, he knew, were not to be trusted but used. In the East Tower, Farida sat alternately listening to gossip and praying. In the North Tower, Rose knelt alternately wailing and digging her grave with a teaspoon. In the West Tower, behind a door that warned all comers against disturbance, sat the Great Trotter reading alternately from a great black Bible with a gold fore-edge and forty modern books on the wholly secular subject of hot air.

How the hot-air balloon is made

I wish to shew how the hot-air balloon is made. It is quite simple, really. The constituents are three, not all of which appear in the name: *hot-air balloon*. It is not enough to get you a balloon and put hot air in it. You must have a *gondola*, and here is where J.c. Solomon & Son enter in. The best gondolas in the world are found in Venice, but as is well known, they are wet, cumbersome, and musical. If the adept wants a canal ride, let him go there; if not, let him go to the elder Solomon. The one with the dog-ear and the pencil stuck behind it is the father; the one without the pencil is the son. Another way of telling is *age*. Go to the one with the white hair. He will ask you about meteorological instruments. Say you already have them. He will ask you about chandling and victualling. Say you have made provision and all you need is a gondola. He will ask you about wills. Say you are making one and will he kindly shew you the gondolas? He will shew you the gondolas.

Pick, good adept, one which is neither too large nor too small (but just medium). It should hold forty chickens (or so). Having emptied and garnished it, test the bottom. If it does not give, it is what you want. Buy also some whalebones and a fishing net. The muscatel is on special this month. Back home you will find waiting in the balloon room a *balloon* which the tailor has made of cadmium yellow close-silk stuff in the cut of a papaya or an upside-down pear. Attach your purchases to it, first the whalebones, then the balloon, then the net; that is the way. Do, good adept, not forget the mooring rope. A crest on the balloon will look fine. All that remains, victualling and chandling apart, is the *hot air*. The front bench of the House, the Chair of Economics, the soap box: shun these, stout adept; do not overfurnish. A simple brazier, such as country liquor is boiled on, will do. Stoke it well with coals from J.c.'s depot and chain it cunningly to a hoop. In the gondola place a rug and some particoloured cushions of blue-and-green silk, your one hundred and forty meteorological instruments, a spyglass, an astrolabe, an horologe, an horoscope, a barometer, a gypsonometer, four sheets of writing paper such as wills are written on, an inkhorn, three pens, two curried doves, and a partridge in a covered dish. A skin of ice-water will not go amiss.

On the twenty-first of June, 1799, swing the balloon up and over and let the hot air go to work. You are, as the base and vulgar put it, off. Do, sharp adept, not rock the gondola. This is what I wished to shew. So do that. Praise God.

(*CHRONICLE RESUMED*)

On the twenty-first of June, 1799, from ten minutes past ten in the morning until the stroke of noon, a man not much above four feet tall, portly, handsome, eighty, alive and well, floated in the sky above Sans Souci, looking down in unspeakable wonder upon the dwarfed features of his château and the lands about it.

The rest is legend, as I have told it.

Great Trotter &c. &c. &c.

Great Trotter, Beloved of God, Cynosure of Mankind, Builder of Sans Souci, Feeder of One Lakh, Who Sweetens the Melon, Who Will Shortly Walk in the Sky, Whose Tower Scrapes the Heavens, Valiant One, Who Plucks the Liver of Crocodiles, Namer of Stars by Day, River-Course Changer, Holy One, Sleek Master, Herald of the Ice Age, Causer of Lakes to Appear, Causer of Water to Run Uphill, Virile One, Beloved of Many, Who Fathered a Fat Son, Who Is Himself Fat, Who Eats Jakfruit Whole, Shapely One, Who Cannot Be Outeaten, Who Ate the Nawab to a Standstill, Who Is Sweetness and Weight, Whose Very Glance Is Fattening, Plump Wineskin, Full Vessel, Nectar of Sans Souci, Soul of Generosity, Wealth-Dripper, Father to His Subjects, Especially Poets, Open Hand, Open Heart, Whose Praise the Cranny Bird Will Sing in the Branch, Whose Praise the Imperfect Poet Lisps, Whose Cock's Spurs are Legendary, Whose Indigo Fadeth Never, Whose Bounty Is Unending, To Whom the Graceful Palm Bows, Before Whom Elephant Grass Bends, For Whom the Elephants Trumpet, For Whom Camels Reserve Their Choicest Smiles, Whose Very Voice Is Ear-Enchaining Music, Who Taught the Black Partridge to Sing, World-Renowned Marksman, Who Spotted the Leopard and Let It Go, Bookman Extraordinaire, With Aesthetic Fingers, Armourer Without Peer, Who Leaps Broad Streams Without Crutches, Who Leaps Heart-Stopping Streams with a Horse under Each Arm, Inventor of the Spiral-Action Cannonball, Inventor of the Filing Cabinet, Inventor of the Gypsonometer, Inventor of the Mirror Tube, Of the Five-Tier Tiffin Carrier, Of the Ice Cube, Sponsor of the Dumb-Waiter, Founder of the Gun called *Urban*, Founder of a Certain Religion, Whose Rages Are More to Be Feared than the Yellow Storm, Who Pays His Writers Handsomely, As He Himself Is Handsome, Master of Modesty, Never Lustful, Slow to Anger, Free-Spending, Eye-Enchanting, Never-Stinting, Ample One, Whose Vaults Hold Boundless Treasure, Who Pays His Poets Handsomely, Who Draws Not in His Purse-Strings, Victorious Battlefield Treader, Spoil-Taker, Largesse-Giver, Ideal Paymaster, Whose Gunpowder Is Not to Be Sniffed At, Who Will Not Let His Epic Poet Starve, Who Sweetens the Melon, Feeder of One Lakh, Who Could Walk on Water if He Wished, Who Could Walk on His Poet if He So Desired, River-Course Changer, Who is the S and the Q, Beginning and End, Philanthropist, Shining Forehead, Sweet Rain Cloud, Munificent One.*

> *Disposed of at last, Narrator! Is the decline begun?*
> *Less gloating, my gannet. What is in the cup?*
> *Lichi cordial, Narrator—only dying is sweeter.*
> *Ah! Now listen. Here is the phoenix speaking.*

(CHRONICLE RESUMED)

The balloon came down empty, this much is plain. Had the Great Trotter returned to earth in his *Salamandre*, the day would have been sufficiently momentous, for here was the first recorded human flight in the history of India since Vedic times when chariots and saucers filled the skies. But an empty gondola took Friday the twenty-first of June outside and beyond history.

A little after two, the Sagarpaysans scrambled up the glacis of the saltpetre hill and stood gawping at the empty vessel. Yakub Khan, baker-and-chandler, leapt into the basket and began tossing aside the blue-and-green cushions as if expecting to find the body of his master shrunken but whole in one of the wicker crannies. The Great Trotter was not there. A space of dusty silence followed in which each man eyed his neighbour with suspicion until the wandering eyes began to settle on Yakub. Before they had time to ripen into mischief the baker-and-Chief Steward barked out his orders and the search began. The remainder of the day was spent in comings and goings, and those who slept that night dreamt busy dreams. The two fattest men in Tirnab had an unquiet night: the poet-and-deputy librarian at Sans Souci dreamt that he starved to death, while the Nawab-and-Sun King dreamt that he was cheated

---

* There is a melancholy footnote to this, Qaiyum's commendable late bid. The panegyrist-and-deputy-librarian is said by his contemporaries to have "wasted away." One source close to him said he "starved to death," though Mr Montagu (*False Trotter*) dismisses the claim as an exaggeration, implying that the toddy-palm trees were there for all to climb. His own history has: "grew thin and died," which is typical of his insensitivity.—E.A.T.

of his summer palace by a chess queen who lay motionless upon a marble tomb, her alabaster fingers steepled on her flat white breast.

The morning after, the Nawab sent to Sans Souci and learnt that Justin Aloysius Trotter, who lived and died, was already buried deep within its vaults. Just how deep only two persons, Jarman Begam and Fonseca, knew. The Nawab lost interest—he had no wish to inhabit a tomb—but the same morning the British Resident in Nakhlau sent an officer to examine the balloon for any evidence of foul play in the death of a man who had, after all, been a colonel in the East India Company's army, even if he drew a captain's pay. The balloon, impounded once more on the hill within the same simple cordon of rope, was examined in the cool of the morning. At length the officer declared himself satisfied that the death was accidental, and the huge slack bag of yellow close-silk stuff was rolled up and locked away in the balloon room. The contents of the gondola, its horologe stopped at noon, an horoscope in which birth and death days now coincided, one hundred and forty meteorological instruments never touched, and four blank sheets of paper (on which the Great Trotter was to have begun a new will), were deposited in the West Tower in a sealed trunk. It was not, however, the end of the affair.

When she had finished breakfasting as usual in the Rain Room on the roof of the Glacerie, Jarman Begam returned to the Audience Hall. There, at the door to her tower Nishan Chand, librarian-and-probate, awaited her empty-handed. The will he was supposed to bring with him had disappeared. He had looked in the usual place, then in some unusual ones, and finally had ransacked the library for the document without success. The length and fruitlessness of the search—it had kept him up all night, except for one dreaming stretch—had done nothing to sweeten his temper. The fact that for the first time his student had sent for him did not help. He growled his message and swung away, salivating vindictively, though he realized that the loss did his own cause no good. The Great Trotter, he now accepted, had probably never come to write that last addition to his will that would shower gifts on his biographer. Unpardonable omission, base ingratitude! Who—*who* had trained this slip of a girl who would save Sans Souci from the Nawab? Who had taught her that the line must be preserved at all costs? None other than he, the forgotten, the slighted, the neglected Pandit Nishan Chand. Still, he wanted to be sure, so he went down to have another look.

Wilfred Ignatius Albuquerque Fonseca, who had been one of the witnesses, frowned when he learnt of the loss of the will, but in the distracted way of one materially untouched by its contents. He was, besides, exhausted after his night of grave-robbery and his early morning errand by the river and could not work up an interest in anything short of his pillow. The night's activity had numbed him to surprise, so that he barely twitched when, on entering by the Water Door, he thought he heard a familiar voice whisper his name. Strangely, it was his old nickname—Will—that echoed in the Audience Hall, and here in Sans Souci he was never anything but Fonseca. In the next moment he was undeceived: the voice had not been directed at him. Glancing to the left down the arcade he saw that he had overheard the tail end of an exchange between Elise and her mentor. The two were already going their separate ways, but the keynote of their discussion, lofted in astonishment, revolved around the vaulted ceiling: *Lost? The will!* But Fonseca had had his share of intrigue. He crossed the hall to his room and threw himself on his bed.

As the barber-and-undertaker was disappearing through the door to the West Tower, Yakub Khan and the Resident's officer, returning from their inspection of the balloon, entered *Sungum* by the Indigo Door. The baker-and-poulterer had risen punctually at five and brushed his long white teeth with a bitter nim twig. He was breakfasting on fresh eggs from his run when the Resident's officer arrived. Yakub met him at the Gunpowder Door, enquired his business, and conducted him to the Glacerie for a Sans Souci breakfast. Delighted at such a reception, Captain Blake, a fine-looking country-born soldier with wide hips and a heavy military tread, unbuckled his belt a notch while Yakub sent a runner to the top of the saltpetre hill to tidy up the gondola and restore the cordon around it. The inspection an hour later was a cursory affair, and Yakub led a contented officer back to *Sungum* before the sun had cleared the toddy-palm trees. On the way back it occurred to him that his instinct to cover up had misled him: perhaps he should be uncovering instead. When he entered the hall, the suspicion was strengthened. From this same door Jarman Begam had scared him last night with a ghostly whisper; now she had left another echo, one which did not frighten him at all. The will lost! Yakub had learnt to modulate his surprise. When he saw the barber-and-Ice Manager disappearing through the far door, he sensed a complication and hooded his eyes: complications generally worked to his advantage. As the second witness to the will, he knew that all Sans Souci was bequeathed to the missing son; as Steward of Sans Souci he would be quite happy to serve an absent master. The will must be found or reconstructed. Turning gravely to Captain Blake, he explained the echo and its significance and declared that an inquest was now certainly warranted.

The message was carried to the Resident. It might have come to nothing, but there happened to be in town a celebrated peer who heard of the affair and expressed interest in it. The Viscount Lentavia, traveller, member of the British House of Lords, and a man of some legal experience, was passing through Nakhlau when the Great Trotter's eclipse occurred. He had meant to visit Sans Souci, and here was added reason. The Resident, happy to devolve his duties, begged his lordship to preside over the inquest, and Lentavia, eager for exotica, agreed.

He arrived late, the Resident's carriage having broken an axle on the Trotter Road. In the event it did not matter, since the witnesses and spectators, who lived by another clock, were later still—all except Yakub, who was early. Yakub had the advantage of living upstairs in the Spur, where the inquest was to be held, but he would have been early all the same. He ushered the officials to the dais where in former times the Great Trotter had sat to watch the bloody progress of some cock-fight whose outcome in the days of Heaven's Vengeance was never in doubt. The Viscount took the chief seat while the Resident sat beside him, frowning deferentially. Below the dais stood a row of Louis XIV witness chairs, comfortable, smartly upholstered in green velvet, and satisfactory in every way except that they held no witnesses. To fill in time, Yakub apologized that ice was not available this year owing to mismanagement in certain quarters, but if their excellencies wished, some mangofool could be prepared with saltpetre-chilled water. The Resident waved aside the offer while Lentavia, who did not know of the cooling properties of mangofool, simply tested the gavel on his palm and gazed charitably at the motley audience in the gallery. Presently Yakub gave orders for the windows to be shut against the sun and wind and dust; that done, he had the witness chairs dusted and rearranged. Behind the upholstered chairs were others of bare wood, and behind those, benches. In front of the first row, below the dais, stood a low lectern of dull brass worked in the shape of three monkeys who (in turn) saw, spoke, and heard no evil. This was to serve as a witness box. Beside it was a desk and chair at which sat Captain Blake, the recorder. Upstairs the Sagarpaysans were still drifting in, the women in bright colours, the children cracking monkeynuts between their teeth.

At length the witnesses began to appear. Nishan Chand tottered in, swivelled and fell onto the first chair, with a curse for the carpenter and Louis XIV. Farida and Rose entered by the main door and took their places demurely, the elder with her face veiled. Yakub nodded slowly at the two remaining seats, and as he did, Fonseca arrived making a great show of winding and shaking his watch. He sat himself down at the other end from Yakub and drew his chair fractionally away from Nishan Chand. One seat remained empty, the lack plain as a missing tooth. At last Jarman Begam came in, dressed in mourning black. Before sitting down she faced left and right and apologized for her lateness with an announcement which stunned the gathering. She was unable to hurry, she declared, being with child to the deceased.

There was an immediate buzz in the hall, and conscious of the aim of every eye, Elise spread across the belly that now teemed with public interest a protective hand. The fingers were like icicles upon the black bombazine.

The buzzing increased. That she was the Great Trotter's begam was generally acknowledged, even, with reluctance, by Yakub Khan, but nobody was prepared for this extension of her marital claim. To compound the confusion, her claim proved infectious: she had barely sat down when Farida, styling herself Farida Begam, stood up and announced that she too was with child to the Great Trotter. The buzzing became a clamour in the midst of which Rose, who in all things imitated Farida, got up to declare that *she*, Rose Begam, was likewise with child to the Great Trotter. At that, the assembly suddenly remembering the original purpose of the Cock Hall, erupted in howls of protest, abuse, and innuendo. In the gallery the Sagarpaysans began to cast bets. Yakub, who saw the estate being whittled away before his eyes, stood up to protest that the will, even if missing, was sacrosanct. He, Yakub Khan, had been a witness to it, and he could swear that the property was left entirely to one person—the absent heir. *"One,"* he bellowed above the chaos, "one alone!" The Viscount applied his gavel vigorously through the din, but it was some time before the Sagarpaysans realized that the firangi was not playing with some kind of foreign rattle.

Proceedings of the inquest into the death and bequest of Col. Justin Aloysius Trotter held at Nakhlau, 23 June 1799

> Presiding: Viscount Lentavia
> Assisting: W. L. Marchant, Resident
> Recorder: Capt. J. V. Blake
> Witnesses: from Sans Souci, as hereunder

Viscount Lentavia: Order! (*restored*) The will will please wait. I need hardly remind so distinguished a gathering that the purpose of this inquest is first to determine the circumstances of the deceased's death, and only then to address the apportioning of his property. Let the first witness be called. (*First witness stands forth*) Am I to understand that the deceased was your husband?

Jarman Begam: He was.

2. And that he met his death by falling out of a balloon?—Yes.
3. How is that fact known to you?—It happened above my tower.
4. You saw him fall?—He fell into the tower.
5. He fell out of the sky into your tower?—That is so.
6. Do you not find that strange?—I do.
7. Do you not find it passing strange?—I do indeed. But it is written that a camel may pass through the eye of a needle.

8. The eye, certainly, madam, but the tip?—Sir, if you prefer, he fell just outside, past my window. I allow for the marvellous.

9. Indeed you must. And what did you do next?—I conveyed the body to the vault where he lies buried.

10. Were you assisted in the enterprise?—I was.

11. By whom?—By my husband's valet.

12. In what condition did you find the body of the deceased?—It was greatly bruised.

13. Did you in any way attempt to conceal the bruises?—I prepared the body for the grave.

14. You attempted to conceal the bruises?—I dressed him in his grave-clothes.

15. You did not conceal the bruises?—I did not.

16. Thank you. When was the burial conducted?—As soon as a priest and an imam could be found.

17. An imam?—He is a Mussulmaun priest.

18. The burial service was both Christian and Moorish?—It was.

19. Who were present at the ceremony?—The priest, the imam, the two bibis (*objections, overruled*), the steward, the valet, and myself.

20. The bibis?—Mistresses.

21. Was there a public viewing?—There was, while the priest was awaited.

22. Who availed of the opportunity?—Some few of the Sagarpaysans.

23. The sugar-peasants?—The ocean-peasants, which is to say, the camp-followers, members of the Great Trotter's retinue. You see them here in the gallery.

24. Was the burial service short or long?—I would say in between.

25. What was the mode of interment, Moorish or Christian?—I would say in between.

26. Where is the grave?—It is in a vault beneath *Sungum*.

27. What is *Sungum*?—It is the central building of Sans Souci.

28. What followed the burial rites?—The tomb was sealed in my presence.

29. Is there a stone to commemorate the man, or any inscription?—There is a stone designed by my husband himself.

30. What is the inscription thereon?—JUSTIN ALOYSIUS TROTTER, WHO . . .

31. Who . . . ?—That is all. It was not completed.

32. Most extraordinary. Have you anything else to add?—No.

33. We will call the next witness. (*Second witness*, Farida Begam, *refuses public interrogation*) We will call the next witness. (*Third witness*, Rose

Begam, *refuses public examination*) We will call the next witness. (*Fourth witness stands forth*) You were valet to the deceased?

Yakub Khan (*through interpreter*): Indeed, no. I am Steward of Sans Souci, Government.

34. You know no English?—I know it well enough, Government, though I do not speak it with the facility of a hairdresser. I read Tartar Sahib's will, of which I was a witness and signatory. I am an educated man, though left an orphan at birth.

35. You have done well to reach so high.—A man must make his way, Government.

36. We are not the government of the land.—Not yet, Government.

37. Intriguing, but you may leave off the honorific in question. You were with the deceased on the morning of the twenty-first of June?— I was the last person to touch him alive. He leaned on me as he climbed into the gondola. He leaned on me in much else. I was responsible for victualling and chandling the craft and firing the balloon. I govern the kitchens; the tandoors are my province. I hold the key to the balloon room. I keep the seal of Sans Souci which was used to seal the will.

38. At what time would you say the balloon rose into the air?—I would say at ten or eleven minutes past ten by the Europe clock.

39. At what time did the balloon come down?—I did not see the clock then, but I would say at two.

40. When it came down, the balloon was empty?—The gondola was empty of Tartar Sahib.

41. Did you see the deceased fall?—No. I was at some distance from the tower into which he is alleged to have fallen.

42. When next did you see the deceased?—In the evening, in the tah-khana.

43. The tahkhana?—It is a cool underground retreat used in the hot season. The body was laid out there, though the will specified—

44. Did you notice any bruises upon the body?—There was but one candle to see by, and perhaps another on the stair.

45. The entire body was covered in bruises?—It is dark in the vault even by day.

46. You saw no bruises upon the body?—I did.

47. Thank you. Were you present at the sealing of the tomb?—It was done under my supervision. I have the key to the cement room. I hold all keys in trust for the heir appointed in the will.

48. Have you anything else to add?—I will say that if the ice had been

managed with care—with even a modicum of competence—there should have been no need for unseemly haste with the burial. Tartar Sahib was a saint and deserved a fitting funeral. His will bears ample testimony to his virtue; it is an epoch-making document. I find its disappearance beyond belief.

49. We will call the next witness. (*Fifth witness stands forth*) You were valet to the deceased?

Wilfred Fonseca: Believe me, I was the Colonel's batman and kahani-master.

50. What is a kahani-master?—I assure you he is a weaver of tales. At night it was my practice—

51. We will begin with the morning, Mr Kahani-master.—You may take it for a fact that the morning was not begun until I bore a steaming basin—

52. You shaved the deceased?—Every morning, that is the truth of it, and at night—

53. We will confine our attention to the morning of the twenty-first of June. (Do your countrymen frequently wear European dress, as you do?)—It is the custom of Anglo-Indians. These garments were given me, please understand, by the Colonel himself when he took to wearing the garb of the country.

54. You are what is called a cranny?—I am, but I assure you I am a hairdresser by profession.

55. By trade a barber. Charming. What followed the morning shave on the twenty-first of June?—The Colonel did not call for me that morning. Directly after his ablutions he called for his breakfast. The mess was run up to him from the kitchens, of whose odours the less said the better, and he took it well enough. He was a brave man.

56. At what hour was breakfast customarily served?—Breakfast, my lord, is an offence committed daily at seven, but on that day the Colonel rose late. You may take it for unvarnished truth that the steam had altogether died on my basin—

57. At what time did he finish breakfast on that day?—At perhaps a quarter to ten.

58. What did he do then?—He went directly to the balloon. The meal can barely have been digested—such of it as he ate, and such as might allow of digestion.

59. You think it might have been something he ate, something that might cause dizziness at a great altitude?—Indeed, the kitchen fare here will cause dizziness at any altitude. But now that I think on

it, it could not have been anything he ate—nothing that would warrant exhumation and opening up of the belly. He ate, I now recall, nothing that morning. He left the breakfast tray untouched, as well he might.

60. Were you present at the launching?—No. I remained behind to attend to my duties. I am Ice Manager of Sans Souci. The management of ice, unlike the management of bread—

61. When next did you see the deceased?—Believe me, when I helped the German Begam carry him to the tahkhana.

62. Was the body much bruised?—It had fallen from a great height, that is the truth.

63. The body was not much bruised?—The Colonel was an old man, but stout.

64. Did you attempt to conceal the bruises?—I fetched a suit of clothes for the Colonel.

65. The body was covered in bruises?—I did not help dress him.

66. The body was not bruised in the least?—It was.

67. Thank you. Have you anything else to add?—It is the turmeric one finds hard to forgive.

68. I meant of an official nature, Mr . . . von Scissors?—Fon-*seca*, my lord. As in: to Fonseca, or, to have Fonsecaed. Concerning the Colonel, I will say that he was a soldier, not a saint, but I agree that the will, to which I was chief witness and signatory, is—or was—a remarkable document, worthy of the most diligent inspection. Believe me—

(*CHRONICLE RESUMED*)

Here the meeting was called off for the day because the intense heat had considerably slowed the examination, questioner and questioned, translator and recorder alike lapsing into a kind of thermic torpor. The Viscount had turned crimson from his exertions, not least from several oblique sorties directed with great cunning and verve at the state of the deceased's body. It was decided that the visitors would stay the night, continue the inquest early next morning, and be done before noon.

Lentavia retired to the Purple Suite overlooking the Water Court, and did not emerge until the sun was low, when, in the cool of the evening, he and a sort of low artist companion made a tour of the estate. At the far side of the Tank, where a general view of the chief buildings was to be had, they stopped. A double *Sungum* faced them, the real and the reflection in the water. The kept artist set up his camera obscura, in which the illusion was doubly

inverted, and allowed himself a short derisive laugh as he copied out a version
of the château. A light breeze sprang up and corrugated the reflection. His
Lordship, released from uncertainty, echoed the laugh and added: "Faith! But
what a provoking patchwork seat!" Promiscuous, vulgar, clamorous, its boldness without vigour, its whimsy without grace, a veritable hodgepodge (he
was writing now, in a marbled notebook that had been from Port-au-Prince
to Potsdam) . . . of styles . . . in which . . . the best of each . . . is stu . . . diously
ignored . . . and the worst . . . avidly cultivated. He read the sentence over again,
and the sound of the jingle pleased him. Then he snapped the book shut and
inspected Henry Salt's progress.

(INTERPOLATION)

Concerning Henry Salt (1780–1827) and others

One Nakhlau picture by this academician survives, and it's not of *Sungum*
(that's lost, or destroyed). It's his *View at Nakhlau*. But for an accurate notion
of his powers, take a look at his engraving, *The Pyramids at Cairo*. Palm trees,
camels, dunes, and the rest, Arabs going on Orientally, a kind of stork in the
water, Egyptian reeds. All very well. Hopelessly misshapen bulrushes, of
course, but then not everyone's at home with those from infancy. So. Stage
props all present and accounted for. But where are the bloody pyramids? Pore
as long as you like over the picture, but not a trace of a pyramid will you
find—at least not in the print at the Victoria Memorial in Calcutta. Did the
wandering dunes of the Sahara creep up on them while Salt looked down to
mend his pencil or concoct some foul linseed concoction? (An oil painter.)
Did the eye of the Great Pyramid open just as Salt was thumbing his brush
at it and blind the poor bugger with its mythic refulgence? Had an excess of
sodium chloride in the Henry Saline system hardened the sclerotic and clouded
the lens?

Be that as it may. Cairo is, after all, merely Cairo. The point is illustrative.
When Salt comes to Nakhlau (*City of Cities, Dulcet Name*), spilling his seed
into the bargain (*Cellar of Lust, Pillar of Infamy*), he is not only blind to the
most palpable objects, he has begun to see what is not there. His *View at
Nakhlau*, literal enough in the title, shows gates where bridges should be, and
a river winding through monuments that belong in Mandalay. Habit and short
sight, no doubt, but apparently the fashion of the age—judging by his con-
temporary, beastly William Hodges, whose *View of the Mosque at Mounheer
from the South-East* shows the northwest minaret. Or that lousy coach-painter
Samuel Davis, whose *Ruins at Rajmahal* shows the ruins at Bithor. Or that
wretched etcher, macerated Daniell's *View of the Fakeer's Rock in the River Ganges*,

near Sultaungunge, which shows the rock of the Fakir of Jangira. Or that colourist-by-numbers, James Wales, or that cave-dauber, Tilly Kettle—but you get the picture. Small talents buried deep. Not artists. And least of all Henry Salt, lean pinched monsoon-damp Salt. A *View of Sungum* by scurvy Salt! God forbid. Let me make amends. The Wedding Guest-and-gentle reader will permit an artistic passage?

An artistic passage

The border is purple dusted with mica or fool's gold. There may be fish and fleurs-de-lis in water blue and lily green.

An alluvial plain, cake-board flat, and of like colour, except to the northeast where it is pink at the edges and tinged with indigo, and to the southwest where an almond tan shades into icing sugar. In the evening the colours to the southwest are constantly shifting as veils of light fall from the sky. The plain is brindled with fruit groves, topes, and spreading trees such as the jamun (*Eugenia jambolana*), which in summer stains the earth with its delicious purple shade. In the foreground is the Tank, whose moods change with the hour, the position of the viewer, and the seasons. In winter it is a green julep, in summer a saucer of clear honey; in the monsoon its bosom clouds over, is ruffled and pitted with the glissade of rain. Afterwards it prepares a mirror to catch the short complicated sunsets which the season brings.

A Water Gate with carved dolphins leads to the Grand Steps, a perron set in a man-made plateau. The steps, the Water Court, the porch are concessions to the prevailing horizontal mode, the clef bass.

In the heart of the plateau, underground, is an area of nothing. Lesser artists cannot capture it. Its cold black gelid lumps, once friable, are now past crumbling. It rests on four covered wells of brackish water inhabited by snapping turtles which would be grey-green were there light to see them by. A tahkhana is at the centre of this space, a small chamber with irregular walls which looks like a cold hearth. It is lit by a mirror tube which slants down a gentle gradient along an air vent. Its walls are no more than membranes, fine and complex as the gills of a fish; they connive in the surrounding emptiness. The floor round about is honeycombed with blind wells. At a height impossible to determine is the next floor, also underground, the library, where shelves radiate from an empty centre. The library is also lit, imperfectly, with soft blue light from mirror tubes. Bitterness, as of dried nim leaves, impregnates the ancient books, warping their boards. A light combustible pollen creeps from shelf to shelf, and the general moan is tenor, almost inaudible. The ground level is reached.

Four towers soar out of the earth, of mixed grey stone and stucco.

Between them they support a dome tiled with mica and glittering like a single gilded breast, whose display among males was once in courtly vogue in Nakhlau. Under the dome is the Audience Hall with its vast echoing frescoed ceiling and its yellow barley-sugar pillars that support a whispering gallery above and form an arcade below. In the centre is a fountain which froths tepid water. An inscription around the base reads: *If there be a paradise on earth, it is this, it is this.* The water bubbles an alto note, clear but faintly acid. The towers are thronged with terraces and parapets on three sides, Indigo, Ice, and Water. On the fourth is a sheer face down to the Gunpowder Court. The descent to the Water Court opposite is gradual, tier upon tier of cheesecake masonry rising and falling to the air of a lost canon sung by grave sweet counter-tenors.

The whole edifice is cemented with a mixture of sand, lime, and jaggery, which hardens to rock strength.

The terraces and parapets: one a stone pasture with moss-blackened Indo-Greek statues of named and nameless heroes with clay feet and blank white eyes: in the monsoon, clouds drift among them like tattered dreams; another with chest-high marbles of milky glass, hail being the local name when one of them rolls off and smashes on the basalt court far below; another is bare, but the air skips with dragonflies; another a mammoth slab of grey sandstone with a white pipal tree growing out of its heart; another a hanging garden with red-beaked parrots and red-bottomed monkeys. Another with stone elephants, demons, shepherds, mandarins. Many others.

The rooms: a Purple Suite overlooking the Water Court; a chapel; a room entirely filled with a gigantic humming top; a room horrent with machines on which name-callers are corrected; another with a curved roof by which the names one is called come back painless; another with concave mirrors in place of windows; a bridal suite; a concealed hall which might be turned into a military museum; many others.

The walls: are of mixed stone and stucco with butterscotch pilasters and fenestrations from casements to hexagons of fretted marble fine as mosquito netting. They are coated with a distemper made of limewash and milk. The ceilings are moulded and painted in three kinds of blue. Outside, the walls and ledges are piped and beaded, but there are no glazed half-cherries or silvered cannonballs set in crockets of marzipan.

The towers: are the principal apartments, served by spiral stairs and, in the West Tower, a hatch. They are topped, except for the South Tower, with bulbous domes of beetroot red, viridian, and turquoise. Their note is female soprano. They communicate with one another by means of dizzying aerial balconies, scalloped and guava pink, but there are no doors above a certain height where winds make crossing impossible. Lesser turrets have crenellations like ruined teeth.

The crown: a sugary gavotte, crystallized motion, unites the towers at the top. From it hangs a bell, fourteen tons in weight, silver in certain lights, for all the world, O Wedding Guest, a favour. When the wind frets the crown it releases an angelic note high and sweet and unmatched by any falsetto. The note is male soprano.

The pinnacle is connected with the base by magnetic threads, capillaries of stone up which are drawn and constantly transmuted secretions from the wells below. The process, by night a trickle, by day a surge, distinguishes this Sans Souci from the fossil near Potsdam. Forever transcending itself, *Sungum* escapes the pluperfect fate of the Prussian palace. From one vantage it is Anglo-Saracen, from another Sino-Byzantine, from another Hindu-Gingerbread, from another Gothic-Ecumenical. From all it is a miracle. Pigeons throng the ramparts cooing, *ro-co-co, ro-co-co.* Charges of frivolity are daily seen flying wide of the mark.

This was the artistic passage. There will be no more. Praise God.

(CHRONICLE RESUMED)

As Lentavia and Salt made their way back to *Sungum* in the failing light, an urgent conference was taking place in the South Tower. Jarman Begam had sent for the baker-and-Chief Steward. The next day Yakub made no mention of the will and spoke no more of the appointed heir. Not that it was his turn: Nishan Chand, Qaiyum, Alexander, Gunga the bhisti, Munnoo and Nankoo, and various others remained to be questioned. The interrogations took longer than was expected because Nankoo insisted that he had seen not a balloon but a Roc in the sky, while Munnoo contended that the object, while certainly a bird, had a yellow beak and purple wings that quite plainly marked it out as Vishnu's chariot, Garuda. Engrossed in the details of tropical folklore, Lentavia did not notice that the day had slipped away, and the party were obliged to spend yet another night at Sans Souci to allow for a decision.

One thing was clear: the will was gone. Even Fonseca, looking hard at Jarman Begam, had to admit its disappearance. Intestacy. The word was more and more frequently used as the second day of the inquest wore on. Primogeniture counted for nothing: the son-and-supposed heir was a country-born and as such had no rights. An entire class of persons like Mik, sprung equally from Europeans and Indians, was altogether destitute of law.

There was another telling point against the so-called heir. He was still nowhere in evidence.

*Tell me, Narrator, what happened at the turn of the century of legend when the
generation of chivalry was rising.*

*You wish to know, Cup-Bearer? Then why do you neglect me? Why does the cup
run over no more?*

It is as you said, Narrator. The days of plenty are done.

*Then go to the desert. Fetch me a cactus liqueur from Palestine. None? Then go
to the Sagarpaysans for a shot of toddy. Now hear what the brain-fever bird
told me.*

(CHRONICLE RESUMED)

On the third day the company assembled early. The brisk fall of the
gavel spoke decision: the Viscount had made up his mind. Just then a tonga
was heard to rattle up the drive, the handle of the driver's whip stuck a short
way into the spokes of the wheel. A man neither short nor tall but powerfully
built sprang out of the driver's seat, ran up the steps of the Spur, and entered
by the main door. He seemed to know his way, walking confidently but with
a slight tilt. A sword slapping against his thigh as he walked seemed to be
his only encumbrance. Dust had floured his uniform a neutral beige. He had
an unsmiling face and a heavy military moustache. With his left hand he
tossed aside a cheroot butt as he crossed the floor that was once a cockpit.
He had not bothered to pin up the right sleeve of his jacket, which flapped
at his side. He found an empty space on one of the benches behind the row
of chief seats, and sat down.

Lentavia spoke for everybody. "You will do us the courtesy of introducing yourself?"

Mik did. The effect could not have been more devastating if his cigarette
had fallen in a keg of gunpowder. At once there was a scraping of chairs from
the front row (Rose Begam's fell back), while the Sagarpaysans in the gallery
began to roar and slap one another on the shoulder. At the end of ten minutes
it became clear that not all the noise was approving. Mixed in with the cheers
was a certain amount of hooting, while one or two voices raised a cry which
developed into a kind of partisan chant. "Proof! Proof! Proof!" chorussed the
begams, loudest among them little Rose Llewellyn, whose belly had ballooned
alarmingly over the past two days. Yakub, who was looking sideways at
Jarman Begam, joined in the chant at politic intervals, while Farida looked
narrowly at the stranger and sat with her lips compressed. The Viscount and
the Resident appeared to be of the doubting party, the hall being roughly
divided between the doubters below and the believers in the gallery above.
Lentavia recovered his legal balance and began another cunning series of

probes. What tokens did the newcomer have of his identity? A strawberry-coloured birthmark? A violin note sweetly held? A flourish of trumpets? A locket?

☞ *The locket is missed.*

Mik answered *no* to each question.

"Then will you explain to us the nature of your claim?"

"I am the Next Trotter," Mik stated evenly, as though that were proof enough. The title still caused him pain; very soon he would step out of the shadow.

"And what eleemosynary principles do you suppose should move us to take your word on the matter?"

"I am the first-born son, born out of my father's first wife." For all Mik knew, there might be others.

"Is that lady present?" Lentavia looked idly over the row of chairs.

"She died when I was a boy."

"And where have you been this . . . quarter of a century?"

"I have travelled and fought battles." Mik shook his empty sleeve with a soldier's bland arrogance.

"Under which flag?"

"Under more than one flag. Both my masters chose to disown me, the foreign and the native."

Lentavia considered this. "Even allowing you are an inveterate soldier and an incorrigible wanderer, neither of these qualities marks you a Trotter."

Mik clenched his fist. "This is my home, sir. I slept nine years in the Begam Kothi." He went to point with his right hand, but the gesture became a lunge with the shoulder. "Everything in the world was there. My mother was a great collector." At that an idea came to him, always a gratifying event. He smiled inwardly, savouring the tickle of thought before making an offer: he would recite from memory the contents of the entire Begam Kothi.

Lentavia chuckled. "To the last elephant?" The joke had reached India.

"Yes," replied Mik, and offered to be blindfolded.

The company adjourned to the Begam Kothi, Munnoo leading Mik by the arm. The Next Trotter had not finished cataloguing the effects of a single room when Lentavia cried a halt. It was all there as Mik said, the world in replica. But who could endure the replica of a replica? The company reassembled in the Spur. It was then that Nankoo the mosquito raised an objection.

"The boy who went missing," he droned, "was blue."

"The dye," shouted Dhani Das, dhobi-and-dryer, "is still not permanent."

"The sun," agreed Hakim Ahmed, "is a bleaching agent. But there *was* one part of the child—" And he broke off out of delicacy because there were ladies present. It was the part that long ago led him to predict that the boy would be a great lover. As the boy's first physician he offered to verify the matter and settle all doubts.

Mik and his physician retired, with Alexander as a witness, to the Room of Gilt Cages behind the dais, and were closeted there for a short while. When they returned, Ahmed and Alexander were plainly awestruck, but nodded and smiled at the crowd. Mik remained unsmiling. The foreskin was indeed blue, and fresh jubilation greeted the disclosure. But although Mik's identity was established, it did not follow that Sans Souci was his. The fact of intestacy remained and there his birth dogged him: he had no rights because as a country-born he had no law.

The Viscount, who did not wish to spend another night at Sans Souci (there had been some trouble the night before when Salt was accused of deflowering a young girl from the village and packed off to the Resident's house), made his decision. Mik, he ruled, had an uterine nine months in which to seek out the will that declared him sole heir, or else the estate would be divided. And having settled the order and proportions in which the surviving relatives would benefit, Lentavia and the Resident departed.

The race was on. Mik, to whom nine months was an eternity, was the last off the mark. His interest in the business varied from day to day depending on which side of his bed he got up from, and since it was usually easier to roll to the right, he forgot about the will and concentrated on training his new sword arm. Dawn would find him flourishing his Maratha sabre and roaring obscenities under the jakfruit tree in the Gunpowder Court. Sometimes his brow creased and he paused to recall the Viscount's ruling, but it was far too complicated and he turned with relief to hacking at the huge spiky fruit and yelling Romany curses every time he missed and swung all the way round.

If Mik had trouble remembering the will, Farida Begam was hard put to think of anything else. It needed only a child in her belly for all the neglect and powerlessness of the past to be wiped out. A male child, especially, would redeem her: she would give anything for one. In the South Tower, Jarman Begam, who was already ahead and drawing away (though not as swiftly as her smock suggested) merely smiled distractedly as she leafed through the last pages of Ibn-i-qasim's *Cup of State*: there was nothing new there. Quickest of all had been Rose Llewellyn Begam, but the ballooning of her frocks was put down to, and (in an unfortunate brush with a rose-bush) conclusively proved, air.

In three months Mik had mastered the sword and turned to the lance. For that he wanted horses and found a good supply (though not as many as in the Great Trotter's day) in the stables. The baker-and-master-gelder, whose features had not changed in twenty years and more (*Unregenerate Yakub*), was always at hand with a fickle horse. Mik took what he was offered and managed creditably, though sometimes the harness would break or the saddle come away or the horse would rear up as if ginger had been mixed in with its feed. The jakfruit no longer bore sabre cuts: they were run right through and carried half-way up the shaft of Mik's spear. By the time the monsoon guavas were ripe, Mik was picking them off the tree at a gallop; before long no fruit tree in Sans Souci was safe from the Next Trotter's spear. Even when he was not lancing, Mik lived in the saddle, ranging about the estate from the jujube groves to the Plain of Cannonballs. But for the fact that the rains had broken he might have slept on horseback. To keep his only suit of clothes dry he slept indoors in the West Tower, covering with a saddle blanket on chill nights, his boots sticking out at the bottom of the bed. From these habits, as well from stray hints of his travels he let fall when drunk, he came to be called Gipsy Trotter. He did not disapprove of the title (it was better than the Next Trotter) but would not allow it used to his face. Yakub, who disapproved of drink, thought Tipsy Trotter was a better title, but kept it to himself. Without meaning to advance his case, Mik had taken up residence in his father's tower. He could not have cared less for precedence: it simply happened that the other towers were occupied by the begams. Nor was it his fault that Rose Begam, who had the North Tower just along the corridor, walked in her sleep.

One night, kept awake by the mosquitoes (it was their whine, not the bites that bothered him), Mik went out onto the connecting balcony for a cheroot. He leaned there, gulping draughts of darkness while staring down into the chasm of the Gunpowder Court and slapping his ears from time to time. Finding no reason to go to Jarman Begam, the mosquitoes were twice as active in his tower. He was on the point of inventing the mosquito net when something—a kind of netting—brushed past behind him. The effect, barely perceptible, was of the lightest gauze drawn across the small of his back. Out of the corner of his eye he saw a pale figure glide past. He gripped the balustrade, his heart thudding, and turned to look fully at the apparition. The figure was too frail to be his father, and it was not, on consideration, a ghost. It was that chit of a girl, barely pubescent, whom he had first seen in the Spur the day he arrived, her belly improbably swollen and one tiny finger stabbing at him as she shrieked: "Proof! Proof! Proof!" Now her arms were folded tenderly in front of her and held a short way out from her budding breasts as if she was cradling a parcel of some sort. But she held nothing, and smelt of sleep. It was the sleeve of her night-dress, bunched in frills at the shoulder, that had brushed against him: she could not have reached higher than Gipsy Trotter's midriff.

Mik started after her, meaning to strike up a conversation. He could commiserate with her early disappointment, which Yakub had informed him of with a snigger. And yet, if she wished to talk, why would she have slipped past so noiselessly? Perhaps she wished to snub him—but why at this hour? Only then did it dawn on him: the girl was asleep! She walked calmly to the West Tower and then turned away to the south. Mik followed, frowning. At the South Tower the girl turned away to the east: so, she was simply doing a circuit of the towers before going back to bed. A single firefly alighted on her hair and pulsed there a space before flying off across the Water Court. On this side of *Sungum* the prattle of monsoon frogs was always loudest, with the ceaseless chirruping of crickets pitched many tones above. Now there was another noise. The girl had begun to mumble something, a deep burbling altogether at variance with her childish features. Mik came up close behind and leaned toward her, but could make out little more than a dry popping of the lips followed by a thin rush of air. At the East Tower, Rose turned left again and walked along the last balcony to the North Tower, completing the square. Well then, it was only a night walk.

Just short of her own door Rose stopped, turned around, and looked directly at Mik. The Next Trotter emerged from the shadows and came forward, fumbling for words to excuse his conduct. But Rose turned from him, her breath still light and even, and going to the precise spot where earlier he had stood smoking, hopped nimbly up and seated herself on the balustrade. Mik froze. Below the balcony was a sheer drop to the Gunpowder Court where the flagstones looked like miniature tiles glazed with the light of a broad dim newly risen moon. Two hundred and forty steps above the gulf sat Rose, kicking the balusters with her soft heels and sleeping a dreamless sleep. Mik approached cautiously; one did not startle a sleepwalker, he knew: one either followed or gently led. Very slowly he put out his hand to her, but as his fingers closed around hers, her hand seemed to glide away. Alarmed, Mik tried again, fearing that at any moment she might lean backwards and plummet to the Gunpowder Court. He went around to the other side, looking into her face as he did, and, encircling her waist with his arm, tried again. Again his hand slid away. It was not as if it closed on nothing—the creature before him was real enough—the hand was simply refused contact. He could trace the outline of the body to within a fraction of an inch, but he was denied the privilege of touch. Wherever he attempted a handhold, putting aside gentleness in his frustration, the two surfaces skimmed over one another, offering the delicious resistance of a pair of magnets wrongly matched. Mik was marvelling at the phenomenon when Rose hopped down from her perch and returned softly to her room.

There was no rest for the Next Trotter that night. His boots were on, his jacket buttoned, but sleep refused to come. His ghost arm ached and his thoughts kept straying back to the balcony overlooking the Gunpowder Court. The next night he waited for the girl, but she did not come; the night after that she again failed to appear. When he had begun to give up hope, she came. There was no pattern to her appearances, except that she seemed to prefer moonlit nights. On overcast nights Mik watched as anxiously as ever, but in vain, for only if a moon, however slender, hung in the sky did the North Tower door swing open and release a pale staring girl cradling an invisible bundle and burbling a moronic refrain. At last Mik deciphered the words, disappointedly, as: "Proof! Proof! Proof!" but the former demand had become a kind of plea. Sometimes the girl chose a new spot for her perch, smiling unseeingly into Mik's face, and always there followed the strange dance of resisting handholds with Mik's arm repelled but unrejected around her tiny waist. Mik's movements, by day as well as by night, became restricted. The rover who disdained to look more than once upon the same woman would wait at the oddest hours for a glimpse of one face alone. It was not even an especially striking face, but then Gipsy Trotter was in love.

Nobody would have recognized Mik. To start with, those who knew him as a boy were confronted with a man fully grown, while those who knew him as a man were now left behind. But even the man who returned to Sans Souci a few months ago was changed beyond recognition. The missing arm, the luxuriant moustaches were as before, but there was a new deformity of the face, for ever since the night of the first moonlit dance on the balcony overlooking the Gunpowder Court, Mik had worn, shamelessly and without apology, a smile. On him it was more like a grimace, and like all men with a new toy, he did not know when to put it away, offering it freely to passersby with a liberality bound to offend those who still regarded him as a kind of interloper. Farida, one of his first victims, began to retch on the spot; Jarman Begam turned aside at once to protect the child she carried. Only Rose seemed immune and even throve on the Next Trotter's smile.

Gone was the miserable red-eyed child of last year. Her crying fits had ceased with Justin's death, and she put away her grave-digging teaspoon. She submitted to having her nails cut, washed her hair with camomile and zafaran, and sang sultry monsoon love songs from her window. If she saw Mik come onto the balcony by day her heart did a queer jib and she flushed a deep red, lowered her lashes, took three steps backward, and fell onto her bed, where she lay trembling. She reproached herself for her treatment of him on that first day when she had petted her balloon of a belly and howled at him like a little fury. But he had forgiven her, surely, or why would he stare at her window? If only he would come up to her some evening when the moon was full and ask her to dance! Maybe he had never learnt—with that arm. She would teach him, she who had taught so many officers; she would learn the secret of his torment, smooth away that anguished grimace, make him give up those horrible cheroots, be his solace, his friend, his— Here she usually turned over and buried her face in the counterpane.

Mik rarely went out of sight of the North Tower. On the stickiest days if he wished to create a little breeze around him, he sent for a horse and clattered up and down the Indigo Court playing a solitary game of polo. By mid-September it was dry enough to allow for a nocturnal variation of the game dreamed up in his youth. On moonless nights he set alight a camphor ball and chased it around the court, his horse's hooves drumming a crisp tattoo on the flagstones. When the flame was about to die out, he cantered across the field and fired a long shot through the Indigo Gate that lacked a fence on either side. The ball went through the little gate within the gate, and Mik turned and saluted a certain window and trotted back for a fresh ball.

He was not the only one playing with fire. When winter came around, anybody who looked closely might have seen a trickle of smoke issue on some nights from the Spur. Yakub was burning paper. He was not cold, but all the same he combed Sans Souci by day for every scrap he could find and burnt it in his room. It did not matter that a sheet was blank: for all he knew the ink of the will might have been designed to fade and show up only under a special violet lamp. He moved methodically through rooms the Great Trotter himself had not seen, using keys untouched since the locks first went on— which was before this tipsy soldier-boy was born. He worked his way diligently from south to north and back. It was surprising how many people broke the rule about not keeping paper out of the library—especially those who couldn't write—though it was rarely more than a page and sometimes a piece no bigger than an insole. In Gunga's room there was a piece the size of a monkey's paw, worn smooth and yellow from constant stroking. When Mik was out playing his desultory game of polo, Yakub searched the West Tower from top to bottom, but it was as barren of Trotter paper as the library. So it was small satisfaction to learn (just when he decided that he had looked everywhere and that the will was safely and irrevocably lost) that the Next Trotter had in a moment of idle curiosity slid back the hatch door in his apartment, hauled up by main force the dumb-waiter that was stuck between floors—not having been used since his father's death—and found in it an envelope addressed to *Colonel Trotter*.

The rank fitted. Mik called down for Fonseca and agreed to accept his painfully worded resignation. Fonseca, who was by now quite happily (though secretly) engaged to be married, begged the Next Trotter to disregard the old letter and offered to tear it up himself. He was on the point of doing so when he saw that the handwriting was not his—or at least not on the underside of each page. And then he recognized the fat round hand with the bellying *b*'s. It was the Great Trotter's.

A rejoinder on coincidence (so-called)

It is not every day that the poet-and-chronicler (not to speak of deputy librarian-and-astrologer) is called upon to answer for coincidence. We are a busy tribe, not to be detained by nigglers and naysayers, certainly not over trifles. Weighty matters, yes: tragedy, moral uplift, character—these are our daily cup. Let symposia multiply on these subjects. But *coincidence*—what is it to the great mind? True, there has of late been some heated discussion of it and a clique formed to discredit those who use it to excess. But what is excess? One man's excess—no, really. I suspect a certain gallows-tree-shaped dotard who cannot bear to see people get on is behind it all. The *cup of state*! One's blood curdles at the thought. History! Let the will be proved (I hear it has been found) and we shall see how the historian fares. Courage—the library will be yours again. History books! We shall know what to do with them then. Now a *chronicle*—there's something. A record of the past set down with genius and sang-froid, not to speak of afflatus and Nakhlavi brio. And if a soupçon of coincidence (so-called) enliven the brew, what of it? Is it not plain FATE that these asses are now exercised over? Why not call it by its proper name? Why the newfangled jargon—a bit of English thrown in to impress? The other day a youngster let fall *progress* and glanced across at me. Puppy! A bit of progress under the belt might have done him good. Progress, coincidence: *thoo!* What was it that struck off the handsome heir's right arm? Fate, fate alone. Coincidence! Baqwas, bulldust! Fate by any other name would smell as feet.

(CHRONICLE RESUMED)

The will left everything to Mik. All Sans Souci was his except for the minor bequests. Having little use for money, he settled with the begams as Lentavia had suggested and saw to it that the various retainers got their due. His worst fears confirmed, Nishan Chand resigned in disgust, bundled his books and baggage into a tonga, and returned to Tirnab, where there was a new Nawab. The old one had died of his liver affliction (*Earthly Sovereign, Girthly Lord*) compounded by disappointment. Elise was in no condition to accompany the librarian, for the uterine race had been close and exhausting, if in the end a labour in vain. Not many days after Farida gave birth to a black son, she brought forth a white one. Both were premature, but then the will was found and that was that. As for the other bequests, Yakub got a silver spur (it was one he had left in a spirited Arab), Fonseca a stringless lute, Hakim Ahmed a mortar whose pestle had gone astray, and Alexander a scabbard encrusted with semi-precious stones. Gunga Din got a good word, Munnoo got a mango grove by the Cranny river, while Nankoo, the convert, got a wind instrument. One name was missing from the list: Qaiyum-i-najum, poet-and-flatterer. Not a single toddy-palm tree was his for the tapping, not even a melon patch by the marsh. He hung on in the library, of which he was once again sole librarian, hoping to be noticed by the new master, but of course Mik had no time for books. Next he tried the ice pits, where Mik was dutifully ice-making. It seemed to have become the family trade, but Gipsy Trotter's heart was not in it. Fonseca occasionally stopped by the chief librarian's office in the afternoon on his way to work to share what each time he took to be a valedictory cup. Qaiyum, he saw, would be lucky to last out the summer.

How Trotter ice is made, these days

I wish to shew how Trotter ice is made. Forget the past: the past is so much water running off. Ice exists in the present, and the future too is precarious, these days. In the old days ice was imported from America and those parts, though the thin cold begam had a recipe for making it here by magic. These days it is made like this. The new Trotter, Second Trotter, who is quite handsome (let us see) has revamped the entire system and activated the ice pits. He shows *much* promise.

In winter as soon as high feathery clouds appear and a hoar-frost is expected, they fill thousands of shallow unglazed earthen bowls with water and cover them with straw. Left in an open field under the bitter cope of January a thin crust of ice forms on the surface and fattens through the night. At four o'clock in the morning or five (some such hour) the ice master (not the Ice Manager) sounds a drum and cries: *Ice rising, ice rising*. The labourers come running in the dark. By torchlight they work, brushing off the straw, scooping up three or four rounds of ice. These they carry in their bare hands as far as the ice pits, which lie open, waiting. The pits are perhaps twelve feet deep and lined with clay and brick. (J.c. or some other will supply the needful. Does it matter?) Howling like demons, they cast the ice in. It is a freezing job at the best of times and they are ill clad. Their state is one of the deepest pathos. Ah, Poverty is a dreadful thing! Before first light the lids must be on. The pit mouth is made secure, insulated against the sun and wind and sealed against rogues and thieves. A rogue can do much damage if it fall in. Four months later, when the cruel dart of summer has pierced the bosom of contentment and the heel of the sun crushes the plumpest of heart-joys, the ice ration commences. That is May. If April be hot, the pits are opened then, but it is finished sooner—and June is when the cup most needs it. This very cup that in former days was full to overflowing. But all that is water under the bridge running swiftly off a duck's back onto the knee of suffering. Do it as I have shewn, or don't—as you please. I say: handsome is as handsome does. Perhaps I will publish my collection of recipes and have done. How long is one to go on slaving? God is—well, God.

(CHRONICLE RESUMED)

There were few guests at the wedding of Elise and Yakub Khan. Yakub wished to economize—he was against celebrations of any sort—and Elise herself was only half there. Fonseca came out of politeness (though he had another wedding to attend) and there were one or two others. The ceremony was performed by Hakim Ahmed, and a cool green drink was served afterwards which Fonseca refused. Elise wore her fifth white gown because the day was a Thursday, but afterwards put on a black tent which covered her from head to foot, leaving two netted holes for the eyes. This she wore to her dying day; it was especially useful when she went once a week to tend the bees. She moved out of the South Tower and joined Yakub in the Spur above the Room of Gilt Cages. There she lapsed into a moody silence and took little interest in the rearing of the boy, who was named after his father, Yakub. Nicknamed Cricket because he had bandy legs and chirruped constantly, he might have grown up illiterate from the absence of books in his mother's boudoir. But he had a mind of his own and besides there was Yakub *père*, whom age and marriage seemed to mellow. The Chief Steward-and-husbandman's whip hand remained as steady as before (he taught the boy to read, using political tracts in Persian, Urdu, and English, and a switch cut from a bamboo clump in the tea-garden), but there were times when he sensed that the world was a larger place than he had imagined.

The other wedding Fonseca had to attend was far more extravagant. It was his own. The ring alone, purchased from the ancient Armenian, was worth several years' salary, and the sweet rice had raisins in it as big as Iraqi dates. The sweets, from Mansoor & Boy, the halvai across the Ganda Nala, went as far as the new Sans Souci villages. On her own the bride offered to be christened, a matter that caused Father Angelico no heartburn since she was pious and eager. She brought with her an indigo trousseau from an earlier attempt at marriage, but chose to wear a white European-style gown tailored in Calcutta by Blanchard Bros. It was said she was too beautiful for the groom, but lucky to find a husband, considering. Fonseca was naturally the father, everyone agreed: between the two of them they had produced a child so black it was almost blue. The barber-and-man could never understand why, if Farida was such a poor sleeper, she had not felt the need of a kahani-master long ago. As it was, she had developed insomnia the first night of the inquest and needed a story every night for a month thereafter, though it was usually Fonseca who ended up falling asleep. After the will was found, and it became clear that the child born of that hectic story-telling would not inherit Sans Souci, the boy still needed a father. An Ice Manager, Farida decided, was a respectable man if a story-teller was not. Looking out of her window she saw the indigo works in disrepair, while on the other side the ice pits were doing well enough to lend their name to the court which looked out on them. The future seemed to lie that way. Besides, Christianity was monotheistic, a religion of the Book, and it allowed, even encouraged, the severest penances. So Farida chose, and Fonseca was led to the altar—quite happily, because Jarman Begam had given him a fright and his shaken love found a welcome refuge in Farida's certainties. He also liked the zeal with which she put him to bed at night. Their son was called Henry and a number of other names ending with Fonseca-Trotter. It was to be the same with all children born in Sans Souci: whatever their surname, Fonseca, Khan (later Kahn), or Alexander, the Trotter followed them like a floating decimal, only its sign was a hyphen.

When the rice had been gathered up from the chapel floor and given to the nilchis to supplement their chickpeas, Rose Begam remained to meditate on her future. Latterly, Gipsy Trotter had been missing from the balcony, and when he did appear he seemed to avoid her eye. The look of love he had worn for a year had modulated first to mute accusation, then to despondency, and slipped at last into a forbearance that she found most appealing of all. Of late, though, a new resolution was written across the face. Gipsy Trotter was in a state. His moonlit dances got him nowhere; the girl seemed a coquette. He could not remain forever at Sans Souci sighing and weeping: there were battles to be fought, a name to be made. To remain behind, to watch and wait, was *her* duty. He would have liked to win her, produce an heir, and ride off, but if he couldn't even touch the girl, well.

Gipsy Trotter began to roam once more. He did not have far to go. The twelve Alexander girls were still at Sans Souci, in their new quarters above the dairy cattle. They were less frolicsome than before (they had taken to milking the cows) but they welcomed the Second Trotter with the same smoky laughter he remembered from his boyhood when his skin turned blue. The old gipsy blacksmith mother, with an eye to the ground floor of the Rib, which was drier than their present quarters, covertly encouraged the match. Alexander, whose hair had turned snowy white, simply marched up and down under the tamarind trees rattling his sword, which did not quite fit the new scabbard. When Mik came up he growled *Io, io*; he was a little afraid of the boy who had come home, though Mik revered him as his first military instructor. At night, Gipsy Trotter, who was still smitten by Rose, would return from the dairy and wait shamefacedly on the balcony, but even when she did come, Rose was unreachable. Mik might lean right over her and breathe her perfume, but he could not touch. The Alexander girls, though they smelt of mown grass and dung cakes, had skin like buttermilk and would always yield to an embrace. By springtime they produced among them a child, and the triumphant grandmother brought the little bundle to Mik.

Mik acknowledged his own and pronounced the boy his heir. The infant, a plump hairless wonder who glistened like suet (*False Promise, Counterfeit Delight*), was suckled in the dairy by his mothers, but he slept in the New Armoury because his father wished to accustom him to the smell of gunpowder and the shock of cold metal. His cradle was filled with rusty arrowheads and instead of a swaddling sheet he was given a saddle blanket. At first the Alexander sisters took turns at watching over him, but Mik sent them home saying the boy must learn to sleep alone. He had not reckoned on Rose's suddenly altering course one night and finding her way down the North stair, across the Audience Hall, through the Ice Door, down the apron-steps and over the cool basalt flags to the New Armoury. Before he could prevent her she had scooped up the bundle and turned back the way she came, muttering the old refrain with a new assurance: "*Proof! Proof! Proof!*"

Rose took over the rearing of the boy and had him christened with a name of her choosing. He was dipped in the Audience Hall fountain, roaring all the while like one of Marazzi's lusty cherubs, and Father Angelico pronounced him Charles Augustine Pote Trotter. Mik, who would have preferred Hercules or at least Horatio, bit his lip and said nothing. What was done was done and he did not want to jeopardize the boy's claim by adding or changing names. That would mean a repetition of his own trial, and he wanted to make all plain before he left. He drew up a will in quadruplicate, checking both sides of the paper (it was a single sentence on a single sheet) and lodging the copies with responsible persons in Nakhlau. Then he commended Sans Souci into Yakub's keeping and the ice pits into Fonseca's, and vaulted onto his horse. Half-way down the Trotter Road he turned in his saddle and looked back to where she was watching from her window, a frail pink petal. He drew his sword and flashed it at her. Then, smacking it down on his horse's flank, he rode off at a gallop.

Extract from Gipsy General: The Life and Adventures of Michael Trotter, Irregular Soldier, *by Maj.-Genl Victor Cholmondley, VC London, John Eames, 1911*

Men mature quickly in the East. Michael Trotter was not yet nine when he lit his first charge of gunpowder. It is a battle-scarred soldier who leaves Sans Souci for the second time.

That year Trotter served under the French adventurer Marcel Petard. Petard!—nicknamed Padshah from his regal bearing—there was a name to conjure with in those piping days! No less renowned was his adversary, Patrick Kilpatrick, Rajah of Paddipore, whose standard drew men of valour from the farthest corners of Hindoostan. In the midsummer of the year Petard was sent by his Mahratta masters to humble the self-styled Irish Rajah. He came north by forced marches and appeared before the fortress of Killar-ni-qillah on the twenty-second of June. Foreigners both, the two men faced each other battle-proud in a strange and colourful land. Such was the romance of old India!

Petard had mustered a battalion each of Afghan shock troops and Mussulmaun riflemen, eight battalions of Telenga foot and eight rissalahs of horse drilled to English cavalry evolutions. One of these rissalahs was led by Michael Trotter. Of armour the Frenchman had forty-five field pieces, 300 artillerists, and a European or country-born (i.e. Anglo-Indian) officer for every gun. For his part, the Irishman could present a score of cannon officered by Europeans or country-borns and a motley but loyal force of Arabs, Rajputs, Jats, Turks, Pathans, and hill aborigines. On the face of it the advantage was with Petard, but war is a fickle mistress. Kilpatrick, moreover, had the high ground, and his guns were cunningly emplaced in old earthworks in the qillah's lee, a wide circumflex curtin below the southern wall and six skewed half-ravelins on the eastern slope. Beyond these last stretched a grassy plain at whose farther edge streaks of blue and grey showed the vanguard of Petard's force.

The sun stood low when Petard drew up. He did not arrive late by chance. He had camped some twenty miles away the night before and could have covered the ground to Paddipore before noon. Instead he struck camp after breakfast and brought his force up at a snail's pace along the river till they were past the town. Then he wheeled sharply so as to come out of the west, with the sun behind him. Kilpatrick, expecting some such manoeuvre, was already prepared on the western glacis but shifted a battalion of foot to that side. Petard in turn swung left again and led his train off at an oblique angle. From the battlements Kilpatrick watched bemusedly the Frenchman's display of irresolution. He sent an aide to the eastern ramparts to look for signs of a pincer movement and shook his head in amazement when he learnt there was none. At that moment Petard halted his van north of a line between the fortress and the declining sun, and turning, galloped down the line with his aides, repeating the same order to each unit he passed. Quicker than a lit fuse, battalion after battalion turned right and the Irishman found an entire army already drawn up at his doorstep, poised to strike. In the new disposition the van was the left flank while the rearguard, coming from *behind* the commissariat—a crisp line of blue breaking through the black mass of grain carts—presented the most immediate threat. But Kilpatrick was a seasoned campaigner. He withdrew the battalion he had just shifted, and advanced six more guns to the earthworks half-way down the slope. Petard, no fool, suspected a feint and attacked at once. The Irishman commenced bombardment.

Michael Trotter, who was first on the field, charged the guns cheering wildly. His company were shot down around him in large numbers but broke through as far as the irregular foot whom they harried briefly before turning back. He records the exploit with modesty: "I found myself deeper in than was intended," he declares; but valour is ever bashful. The first thrust made, the cavalry withdrew in good order. The Mahratta guns, needing no more than a ninety-degree turn where they halted, were by now primed and returned fire. Kilpatrick, canny of old, replied with a charge at the enemy's left flank, drawing away some of the rifle fire while he softened the blue-and-grey with the sabre. At the same time his own guns raked the Frenchman's centre. Expecting some such ruse, Petard bade his men stand firm, and the infantry withstood a murderous cannonade for full twenty minutes without flinching. Then, upon a ringing word of command, they advanced, coolly holding their fire until fifty yards from the enemy. Kilpatrick, no mean defensive strategist, poured down fire from above, taking a heavy toll of Petard's second Telenga battalion, which had pushed as far as the glacis but was now forced to scramble back. Only then did the attack come from the expected direction. At 6:15 P.M. the Frenchman's left flank bared its steel. It fanned out of the sun and fell upon the Jat musketmen cut off from their fold by a company of Afghans. The Jats fought like lions but the riders swept over them, giving no quarter. Alarmed by this late development, the Irishman redoubled his fire along the entire length of guns, causing the attackers to waver and fall back. Thereupon he released three of five cavalry rissalahs held in reserve behind a mango bosquet. The eager squadrons swooped down the slope but met an energetic countercharge from Petard's Seventh Horse, which checked their career. During the countercharge Trotter's horse was shot from under him and he continued to fight on foot. Those were hardy days! Meanwhile the Afghans had taken over the enemy's northward slope and made a bold rush for the outermost guns, spiking three before being vigorously repulsed with the bayonet. Petard's heavy guns now gave back a determined fire. During the half-hour before sunset no fresh moves were made, the artillery on either side keeping up a barrage such as would have opened a more conventional engagement.

That night, under cover of darkness, Kilpatrick withdrew his force into the fortress by the north gate while keeping up a sporadic fire to the west. Petard, who had long experience of warfare, cried *"C'est accompli!"* and gave himself up to a victory carousal. Expensive wines flowed in the general's tent while on all sides his men abandoned themselves to country liquor. In the midst of this singular piece of French folly there came at 9:45 P.M. a sudden shower of rain, heralding with unusual abruptness the arrival of the monsoon over Hindustan. A good half of Petard's powder was wet before the tarpaulins could be found, while by an extraordinary freak of chance one of the powder carts that remained dry was struck by a rocket fired from the enemy's battlements. The resulting explosion flung Petard several feet into the air, but he was miraculously unhurt. Although the rain eased in half an hour and had stopped by 10:30 P.M., the damage was done, and might have proved irreparable but for the intervention of Michael Trotter.

(CHRONICLE RESUMED)

Appointed to the cavalry instead of the artillery, Mik made no objection, for the past year had made him an expert horseman, as dextrous

—Dextrous, *Narrator?*—

as sinister with the lance and sabre as with a fuse. His fellow country-borns were given charge of field pieces, but Mik was warned off: word had apparently reached Petard of the affair of the exploding guns. In electing to fight under Petard, Mik avoided taking up arms against his former masters, the Marathas, who as far as he could tell had done him no wrong. He trained his rissalah on the march, modifying its movements to suit the local conditions of weather and terrain and enjoining strict silence on his men when it came to a charge. Within a week he knew the name and roll number of every man in his command.

Petard (nicknamed Padshah from his prodigious talents at *crepitus ventris*) marched north with reluctance. He had no particular quarrel with Kilpatrick and was for the moment quite happy to stay where he was, notwithstanding his hero Napoleon's dictum that one could do anything with bayonets except sit on them. Only after repeated orders from his Maratha chief did he move. When he arrived in the Irishman's territory his scouts misjudged the distance to Paddipore and the army camped a mere fifteen miles from the fortress. The following day, the twenty-first of June, he was proceeding along the river when he found he had overshot his mark. Kilpatrick might have come up behind him and pushed the entire army into the river, but his own spies were dilatory and he himself was in the arms of his favourite mistress, Tibti Bibi. Hearing of Petard's arrival quite by chance (one of the Afghan shock troopers by the river decided to empty his musket into a Brahminy duck) he hastily assembled his forces on the western slope outside his fortress. Petard, discovering his error, struck away from the river, but a marsh lay in the way and prompted a further detour, by which time the sun had already begun its decline. On the spur of the moment Petard decided it was too late in the day for a decisive engagement: the marsh would provide excellent protection during the night, and the battle could be fought at first light when his men were fresh. He halted and sent an aide down the line with the command. By the time the message reached the rearguard it had translated itself into an order to attack.

Gipsy Trotter, whose regiment brought up the rear, did not ask twice. He led his horse through a line of grain carts that stood in the way, urging his men on across their first barricade. When the regiment had re-formed on the other side, cursing the bullock-cart drivers in many languages, he gave the order to proceed at a canter. Their progress was casual enough for the enemy to suppose it a feint. At the very last minute Mik gave the sign to charge, and with no more than a whisper his men lowered their lances. The effect of a silent charge above the thunder of the horses' hooves was uncanny enough to paralyse the enemy. The last fifty yards were covered in a flash: before the Irishman's officers could give the order to fire, the cavalry were upon them, spearing and hacking with silent abandon. Only then did Kilpatrick's musketmen kneel and fire, but in the cloud of dust and fright they shot down many of their own gunners. The charge having spent itself, the cavalry withdrew in haste, but not before those at the back were picked off by a second, more accurate round of musket fire. One quarter of the rissalah was lost in this way. At last the Irishman's guns found their voice, and the next rissalah had a tougher time of it. Mik's second charge was more uncomfortable than the first. At the very moment he saw a lieutenant friend's head blown off, his own horse was shot from under him. In the confusion he ran the wrong way and spent several minutes weeping with frustration as he wandered among men whose coats, even in the dense smoke, bore no resemblance to his own. He had just been spotted by a mighty Pathan when he saw a riderless horse go by and sprang into the saddle.

Petard, hysterical with rage, sent for the officer who had led the first charge, but it was impossible for the aide to cross the line of battle. Already his infantry had rushed pell-mell into the fray and discharged their muskets at a hundred yards. Next they charged with bayonets, but on reaching the slope began to fall back. One of the Irishman's cannon, loosed by successive recoils, rolled down among the attackers, crushing a foot-soldier and causing a momentary panic among his fellows. A gunner, fusee in hand, gave chase. He was joined by his comrades, who rushed downhill after the runaway gun oblivious of the battle around them. The action sparked off a local sortie that turned into a collective charge. The defending troops, still reeling from Petard's cavalry thrust, took courage and began to fire wildly down the slope despite their officers who ran up and down screaming orders to the contrary. Where the charge ended, coming up against a wall of Telenga infantry, there was now serious fighting, although the opposing troops were so tightly packed that to work a hand loose or free a weapon was an operation in itself. As more of Kilpatrick's men poured down the glacis, propelled by those behind them, those in front were pinned against Petard's infantry, themselves unable to move. A few who collapsed of exhaustion slipped directly down—it was impossible to fall forward or back—and were trampled while many died of suffocation on their feet. The short stabbing motions of those in front began to find their mark: dark red stains showed and spread down the coats of men who appeared to be doing nothing at all. Now and then a shell would fall into the straining pack and blow a hole in the mass, putting an end to many a steamy private struggle. Those left alive stared wearily at each other across the bloody clearing, brought to their senses for a moment.

So the battle went, entrenchments falling into the hands of the enemy and being won back each time with a new mound of dead. Maggots blossomed under the sun on corrupting flesh, and there was the sour stench of half-digested food. Near the centre of the field stood a single nim tree, blasted and blackened: it had lost all its leaves but when Mik looked up at it it wore a panic of butterflies. Without a wind to carry off the smoke of the cannon fire a thick black-and-yellow cloud hung over the field. The dust raised by cavalry charges and countercharges and falling shells mixed with it, and as a result scores of wounded men choked to death in the strange clamorous twilight. A long-haired giant lay motionless on his back with no trace of a wound while a squirrel buttoned under his jacket ran up and down under the cloth. A cavalryman burned across his chest and hands in a fall across the barrel of a cannon ran howling toward the river and threw himself in. From the mango grove came a fresh cavalry charge, contrary to Kilpatrick's orders, which broke up the thick wad of infantry, slamming into one side and carrying it along intact for fifty yards before it fell apart. No sooner did the riders extricate themselves than their own guns hindered their regrouping: horseflesh was now added to the piles of twitching half-dead as the cavalrymen shook their fists up the hill and shrilled curses at the artillery. As if in reply, the guns on both sides redoubled their activity, thundering with such devilish energy that the noise drove a tiny grey drummer boy mad. Six country-born officers were killed at their guns in the dusk exchange. Through the twilight the cannonade was kept up while the infantry limped back to their respective sides. The cavalry had already withdrawn.

After dark the Irishman ordered his battalions to return to the protection of the fortress, while twelve guns remained outside with orders to keep up a sporadic fire up and down the line, withdrawing one by one from the centre. When Petard observed the pattern, he said: "Good," and drank a glass of port. He was satisfied with the day's fighting in spite of its unpremeditated start. Tomorrow he would deliver the masterstroke for which he was famed throughout India: the hoist. Once again, he had not reckoned with Mik. Kilpatrick too had his plans: already his spies were mingling with the Frenchman's cooks and batmen and watercarriers to learn from them the location of the main powder magazine.

Mik sat by himself a short way from the battlefield. He had slipped out of the officers' tent and walked till he came to a hillock away from the groaning of the wounded. The field was black except for the dotted campfires. The stars were faint and there was no moon. Somewhere down below, two rissalahs of Kilpatrick's cavalry, fearing the battle was lost, were walking their horses over to the enemy, while a company of Telenga foot, with its own interpretation of events, defected the other way. The Irishman, who was bracing for a siege, turned the Telengas away and they were obliged to defect back to Petard. There were men who defected four times that night. In a little while the sky was crossed by what looked like a low bright shooting star. The star was followed by another and another, until the blackness was criss-crossed with hissing orange streaks: the Hossain fireworkers were firing rockets from the battlements. Each rocket traced a parabola with its glowing head and trailed a hairy tail of sparks. Some burst in the air and shook out a spray of light, others corkscrewed downwards and exploded on the earth. Once a misfired rocket whizzed vertically up and ended in a flare which faintly illuminated the entire field.

Marvelling at the transient beauty of the display, Mik lit a cheroot and lay back to get a better view. "Samson's foxes," he thought, recalling one of Alexander's stories, "with their tails on fire." As he lay there, there were two brilliant flashes of light from opposite directions, each followed by an explosion. The second, out of the east, was thunder; the first sounded like a powder accident. In no time at all a fat drop of rain found its mark on Mik's outstretched body. He got up at once, but before he was half-way to his tent he was soaked to the skin: the monsoon had broken. He fell onto his cot and slept deeply for an hour, while the rockets etched their tracks across his eyelids. It was still dark when he awoke, his brain on fire. He had had an idea. Saddling his horse, he rode across the field towards Petard's tent. Halfway there he changed his mind and, turning, spurred his horse through the busy tribe of corpse-raiders to his own rissalah. There was no time for arguments and permission.

Extract from The Military Memoirs of General Mik. Trotter (*translated from the Persian*)

That night I and three chosen by me rode behind the enemy lines. The jackals were retreating into the fortress. We took a few prisoner, among them a captain of artillery, a [*illegible*] coward.

We assured him that our powder was enough to carry on the battle for many days (in truth it was wet from the sudden rain). That we would invest and batter down the fortress (when in truth our guns were stuck in the mud). Better that he lead us to their magazine and save much time and many lives. He protested loyalty to the Irishman.

We then offered to stuff his orifices with powder and rockets and set him alight. He led us at once to the south wall and showed us the place. Beyond, he said, was the magazine. We found a sluice-hole in the wall at a man's height. We then returned to camp and sought out men of the rat-trapper caste (whom I have described in my *Races of Hindoostan*). They had no trouble, the field being covered with dead. Fuses were attached to the creatures' tails and the cage placed at the sluice mouth. Then the fuses were lit and the cage door opened. In this way after many tries we blew up the magazine. Those of us nearest were thrown several feet back, but this saved our lives, for the wall collapsed where we had stood.

The Irishman fled before dawn with his lieutenants. He lived to fight another day. His men melted away, some coming over to us, some joining him at Topgarh.

We took the fort but quitted it on the second day, marching to Sandila. There we ate a confection. I was made commander of a regiment. Heaven-Kindler was added to the titles. The palm of applause was mine.

(*CHRONICLE RESUMED*)

Three months later Kilpatrick's luck ran out. Defeated twice in succession, he gave himself up. Mik was for dispatching his soul to hell, but a number of other Anglo-Indian officers, among them a James Skinner, spoke up for clemency. The Irishman should be allowed, they said, to gather up the remains of his dream and leave with dignity. Petard, to whom all Britons were Englishmen, listened with impatience to the country-borns.

Plain English

> —*and at last he called out, in his broken English, "Well,*
> *gentleman, you do as you like—I give power; he be one*
> *damn Englishman, your country-man, that treat their chil-*
> *dren very ill." He meant that the country-borns were very*
> *ill-used in not being admitted into the Company's service.*

—J. BAILLIE FRASER, *Military Memoir of*
Lieut.-Col. James Skinner, CB, 2 vols.
London: Smith, Elder and Co, 1851

(*CHRONICLE RESUMED*)

Had he not been busy preparing for a larger campaign against the British, Petard might have formed a cordial dislike for the upstart Trotter. The campaign, which involved the entire Maratha confederacy, was two years in the planning. On the day before the army was to march against the British, an Anglo-Indian officer approached Petard and declared that he would not bear arms against his father's people. He was joined by two other country-borns, and another was said to be undecided. Petard retaliated by dismissing all his Anglo-Indian officers outright. He would in any case have preferred an entirely French officer corps. Mik's father, he knew, had been a Frenchman, but had he not changed his name and gone over to the British? In familiar moments before the affair of the rats, Petard had called his young cavalry officer Trot-toire. Now, when Mik marched in to protest against his dismissal, the Frenchman addressed him carefully: "Goodbye, Mr Trotter. Not trust. Not trust."

Mik and the discharged country-borns rode across to the British lines, where they were coolly received but met with courtesy from the general, Lord Lacre. They were fortunate; elsewhere in the Maratha army, country-borns had their heads cut off whether they were willing to serve or not.

During the campaign against the Marathas, Mik remained inactive. He was called upon to drill sections of irregular horse, and in the process impressed the British general with his tactical instinct and his phenomenal memory. Lacre made him an aide and asked (but did not take) his advice on the silent cavalry charge. After the war, which saw Petard defeated and Delhi captured, Anglo-Indians were publicly warned that they must never again serve Indian princes without the Company's permission. They agreed. As soon as they did, the irregular units they commanded were disbanded. In view, however, of the useful services rendered by the irregular corps it was thought that one such body of horse should be maintained on a permanent footing. Lacre turned without hesitation to Mik. The two men rode out to inspect the regiments of Petard's cavalry that had come over to the British after the Frenchman's defeat. "*Gispy, Gispy,*" a sibilance ran up and down the ranks: Mik had been recognized. Lacre announced to the assembled force that the British were pleased to accept their offer, but they themselves must choose a commander. Whom did they wish?

The men's teeth shone under their moustaches as a roar burst from a thousand throats: "*Tartar Sahib! Tartar Sahib!*" Lances were rattled and pennants waved as the cry came over and over: "Tartar Sahib! Tartar Sahib!" When the shouting and rattling died down, Lacre turned to his aide.

"Well, they appear to have chosen."

Mik remained silent. He was overcome.

"Now *you* must choose," Lacre went on, "a name for the brigade."

For the third time in his life Mik tried his smile. When he spoke he stumbled, abashed.

"I suppose it must be—*Trotter's Horse?*"

> *And now O Narrator, change the tune. Tell me a gentle tale full of sweetness and scented love.*
> *How when the cup is empty, Cup-Bearer?*
> *The grape lies untrodden, Narrator. That is not my work.*
> *O Indo-Anglian, fetch me then a cup of warm sweet milk. Good. Now listen.*

The uniform for Trotter's Horse was as follows. The *ranks* wore tunics of dark red, with green cummerbunds shot through with purple. Across the chest in white appliqué was a bold device in the shape of stylized sepals. On their backs the horsemen carried rosewood shields with brass knobs, and on their heads they wore helmets edged with verdigris. On parade the lance was carried upright and muskets were shouldered.

The *officers* wore damask jackets with red appliqué sepals, serrated chokers, and sterling silver facings. Their breeches were of green, their boots brown with tusk-shaped spurs; their swords were damascened, with tips like needlepoints, their scabbards of black velvet.

The *commander* alone wore a seersucker jacket of radiant white—

> *Forgive me, Narrator, but what is there of sweetness and scented love in this tale?*
> *Cavalier Cup! Have you neither wit nor patience? Attend!*

—a seersucker jacket, I say, of radiant white, and in place of the appliqué work across the heart, a single blood-red rose.

Seersucker

SEERSUCKER, n. Soft white fabric with a surface like boiled milk; sheen worn by the smitten; measure of sugar (compare SHAKRAK or JAGGERY); f. Pers. *sir o sakar*, milk and sugar.

(CHRONICLE RESUMED)

All the time that Charles Augustine Pote Trotter was growing up, his father was away at war. While the boy went from pap to solid foods, his father's reputation went from strength to strength across India. Who else, people asked, would scorn marksmen by leading a cavalry charge in a white seersucker jacket with a rose at his heart? Who could lance a boil at a gallop? Who trim moustaches with two strokes of his sabre? One man: Tartar Sahib! He was known by the rose as *Gulabi Trotter*, and in time the fearsome men of Trotter's Horse came to be called, from their tunics, the Rose Boys.

At Sans Souci, Rose Llewellyn Begam bathed the Third Trotter herself, singing monsoon love songs and strewing white petals on the soapy water. If young Charles broke wind in the bathtub and snapped dreamily at the bubbles, she smiled indulgently as if he were her own. She never chided him for drenching her in play: sons had every right to drench their mothers. After all, who gave him suck when those shameless dairy girls were chased off? She, Rose Begam, whose breasts had filled with milk the morning she woke to find him in her arms.

When he was three she taught him to form his letters with a brush from her rouge-pot. He turned to drawing pictures instead, preferring red ink to black, but quickly adding yellow, green, and blue to his palate. Unlike Farida's son (the barber's boy) who had a dozen playmates from the village in his thrall, or Jarman Begam's son (the steward's boy) who moved constantly with adults, Charles sat for hours alone, covering expensive paper with his sketches. If she entered a room unannounced he would cover his work or come up to her and lead her away by the hand as if she were the child; he was evidently sensitive. At nine, he covered the walls of the New Armoury with cartoons for a fresco to be entitled *Astronomy Consorting with Peace and Progress*, a work which so enraged his father on one of his visits home that he struck the boy with the flat of his sword and locked him up in the Japanese tea-house on a diet of stiff chapatis and water (*Fatal Misprision, Root of Woe*). The boy grew thin, and but for Rose's intercession might have met Qaiyum's fate: that poor man had perished at the foot of a toddy-palm tree. Charles emerged gaunt and unrepentant. Had Mik stayed long enough he would have found on the walls of his son's prison cartoons for *Pilgrims Travelling to the Shrine of Sachiko at Ise* drawn with a lead of pyrite.

By the time he reached adolescence the would-be artist's cheeks were sunken, his nose peaked, and the fetching convexity under the chin was gone. His voice broke and settled deep in his throat, the largest fragment sticking out in the front of the neck. It gave him an improbably guttural pitch and jibbed when he was nervous, set off by a moth striking a windowpane, a scorpion in his shoe, the memory of his foster-mother's breasts. His appetite never returned. He picked fruit for its shape and colour, sitting interminably over a luscious jamun (*Eugenia jambolana*) and then going off to paint an allegory in purple. He had fitted out a studio at the top of the North Tower where he attacked huge unruly canvases, deaf to tiffin bells, tea bells, dinner bells, while at other times there might spring half-formed from his undisciplined head frescoes, etchings, woodcuts, watercolours, and even (*Crime de résistance*) a series of miniatures.

(INTERPOLATION)

Concerning the art of the miniature

Miniature painting is the art of smallness. We miniaturists are a fussy stingy despotic lot when it comes to painting. None of your brawling canvases for us—your blanket-tossed witches, roistering peasants and derring-do soldiers, your flapping Olympian rapist swans, your foreshortened money-changers' toes peeping from behind the overturned tables, your sprawling Guernican acres, you frisky life-sized Avignon naturists. No. Smallness, please. And stillness, and silence. The miniature that speaks is an uninspired fraud— and there *are* inspired ones. The miniature that moves is a bad copy, and there are some very good ones around. A loud bustling miniature is a contradiction in terms (like a big miniature). The choice miniature is caught in amber or perspex or some kind of diamantine crystal—a sort of bank teller's window with no hole in the glass for gibberings and everybody inside, all assets, frozen. Suspended animation, that's it: everything stopped, caught, trapped, reduced, immobile, mute. It's a locked genre, no getting away from it. And quiet as the grave. Not a peep out of the infant in the Granada missal, mother on an ass, father stepping along smartly in the dew—off to Egypt—the ass's hooves chamois-bound, the stars cold, the rustle gone out of the moon-yellow corn. The very soldiers—one step behind—half-pay Judean conscripts looking the wrong way among the sheaves, are charmed. Or take this Mughal builder working with his mates on a palace of red sandstone. His arm has shot up with its hatchet—and there it stops, frozen. Good man! Grunt, grumble, breathe, bring it down, or even pretend to bring it down, and you're doomed. The breath of ordinary life has come into you and corruption closed with your artist.

I'm not done, I'm getting somewhere.

Smallness, stillness, silence: you get the picture. But *in* the picture, only there. Outside it, just above it, behind it, as it were, is another matter altogether. Tell me, who do you suppose painted those bulky rapist swans? You can bet it was a fidgeting spunkless bony-fingered stringbean of a painter. Those roistering peasants? Some pale gormless tuberculotic metempsychotic neur-aesthetic pipsqueak who never left his studio. But the Granada missal? Count on it a bloated belching bully-boy of a monk, the same who when asked what fun a monk has, roared: *nun.* And the Mughal hatchet man? A hell-raising, cock-fighting, ten-wenching bludgeon of a man, wider than he was tall, big-bummed, incontinent, the same who swore it takes a big hammer to drive a long nail.

I'm not done, I'm getting there. You've made the connection already. No? A hundred knee-bends!

Smallness, stillness—who does it best?

Thank you. The big and the peripatetic. Bigness, motion: essential in-gredients, *not* simply preconditions. Each (I'm there at last) is *itself* an art. Art begetting art—and what a begetting! The skill in other words is not in the execution but in the preparation; the pleasure in the anticipation, not the act. There is an art to fatness, an art to moving. Constant mass, constant motion—how often they go unpraised. Because we spin endlessly through space on a solid sphere whose flattest horizon is a curve, the world takes weight and wanderlust for granted. Unpardonable error! Discipline, skill, concentration, genius, have contributed to the rounding off of sharp corners, the V-bend beautifully taken at ninety miles an hour. And this ritual, gift and penance, yields art. Or as Ivor Brydges would say, the work itself. Once *you*, the artist, are prepared—primed full fat and fit—the job itself is nothing. Why do you think some of the earliest Indian miniatures are to be found in a cookbook, the *Ni'mat-Nama*? The cryptic link between gastronomy and the art of the miniature awaits its exegete—but that's for the critics.

Look. With big canvases you're trying to match the world. With min-iatures you're past imitation. You don't parley, talk terms, size up the world, stand back—you simply sit on it. And after a day or two (usually a little longer) there it is, everything, flattened, shrunk to perfection, your epic min-iaturized. All there in a few square inches, nothing hidden, no detail tucked away in some remote corner. Did you ever see anyone stand back from a miniature? From my *Keyhole* series in the Prado, for instance (circa 1690)? Never. They creep up, peep, salivate, and grovel. While you, the artist, loll

on the other side behind your tiny perfect world, looking out of the one-way
mirror like a god, gorging truffles and playing with your toes.

> *And now O Narrator, tell me a colourful tale, full of brilliant pigments: vertiginous
> greens, lofty blues, ruby reds.*
> *Show me first a ruby in the cup. And never speak to me of pigments: they are
> hues or tints.*
> *O you are a stern taskmaster, Narrator.*
> *Well filled. Now listen. I have heard from the bird of paradise that it happened
> in this way.*

(CHRONICLE RESUMED)

Very early on, Rose knew she was mothering a dreamer. The boy was
tender and secretive as a fern. A hider, he learnt the value of deception and
could change colour like a garden lizard. He might stand motionless against
a mural and Rose could swear there was no one in the room. When she left,
a green shadow peeled away from the wall and went about its furtive business.
When he was old enough to know shame, the Third Trotter put fig leaves
on most of Marazzi's cavorting figures. And he was slow. A single painting
of the early period, a bowl of fruit, took him months of labour with those
slender fingers miscalled artistic. It was said of this painting, by the Armenian
pedlar, hardly a disinterested judge, that the birds pecked holes in it (*Vulgar
Realism*). Another painting, of Sans Souci, was said to have sacrificed all fidelity
to nature and left the viewer with nothing but a taste of grey (*Effete Abstrac-
tionism*). The next time Mik returned to Sans Souci on a lightning visit, he
discovered this latest piece and stared gloomily at it, feeling a cloud settle on
his tongue. He strapped his son to the mouth of a cannon and threatened him
with a fusee. "An ar*tiller*ist, not an artist!" he thundered. From him it was a
harangue.

The words were lost on Charles. He waited for his foster-mother to untie
him and primped the old-fashioned ruff he had begun to affect. With his neck
well hidden, his features were softly feminine. He had distant liquid eyes with
sweeping lashes and a lower lip that trembled like a ripe gooseberry. His skin
was olive from his mothers' father and silken from his father's mother, but
to the Trotter line he seemed to owe nothing (*A-Trotter, Misfit*). He continued
to paint, and out of her boundless love Rose tramped, sometimes twice a day,
to the village to buy colours for him: greenstone, orpiment, cadmium, sulphur,
henna, and red gold.

One day he came upon a work by the late Qaiyum-i-najum, a chronicle
of sorts, and decided to illustrate it. His front panel was a general view of

Sans Souci, this time in colour, with a balloon in the sky and his grandfather in the attached gondola. The painting was well spoken of (or puffed, by the pedlar Soravian). It showed the various buildings of Sans Souci as the Great Trotter had left them, with such otiose additions as a studio-loft in the North Tower and a small interim ice shed built beside the ice pits to correspond with the indigo shed on the other side. It showed the amphitheatre filled with dye from the indigo works to form a pond, and a reflecting pool where the rain-water had gathered on the roof of the Glacerie around a marooned Rain Room. In the distance the Sagarpaysans' encampment had grown into a village with muddy lanes and a few brick houses; nearby, on the saltpetre hill the Great Trotter's marquee still flapped forlornly, stained yellow toward the curry mine, indigo the other way, and a cowardly green in the middle where the two overlapped. Along the Cranny river white-scented rat-ki-rani bushes had come up, while the hanging canal that fed the indigo baths was choked in parts with reeds. The painting showed a leaning West Tower overtopping the rest with its late additions but left incomplete when work on it was called off by Justin himself. And it showed Justin himself, suitably penitent, if needlessly thin. The balloon, however, was destined to be green, apparently the neurasthenic's favourite colour.

Four years Charles worked on the folio (*Tortoise Trotter*), doing no more than a dozen illuminations and saving the frontispiece for the end. When he came to the balloon it was spring, on the day of Holi. In earlier years he had often watched the frolic from his loft as the Sagarpaysans pelted one another with dyes. The colours shone far below like gemstones in the mud, and he was spellbound, even envious, but too timid to venture out. At Holi the world became a studio; and just on this day he had run out of papaya yellow for the *Salamandre*. He crept from window to window wondering what to do. To send Rose to the village was madness: on other days she was Gulabi Begam, but today there were no titles. Down below in the Indigo Court he saw Nankoo pounced on by six whooping youths and sprayed red. Yakub, set upon by a band of grinning nilchis as he returned from an early breakfast, was blue from head to foot. Munnoo, already dressed in yellow (from last year's Holi), ran to save his brother and turned orange. Emboldened, Charles crept downstairs to hail the stout floor-polisher-and-night-watchman, but he had barely emerged from the Indigo Door when he was soaked in nil. Halfway across the court he met with rough treatment from the mauves and yellows until Munnoo came to his rescue.

The shops would not be open, Munnoo warned, especially not the dye-seller's, but he knew the man and would take the young master in the back way. He led Charles along the path to the Sagarpaysans' hutments, shielding him from the groups of revellers they met along the way beating drums and shouting lewd songs. Beyond the saltpetre hill the path became a muddy road that ran through the settlement, now a village called Trotterpurwa. "Your grandfather (peace be His) would not recognize the place if he were to come back," Munnoo said. "I can hardly keep up with it myself—and I live here. Not that He came this way often. Once or twice to inspect the mine. And then . . . the last time . . . to go up . . ." He stopped and stared at the top of the tableland with glazed eyes, obviously one of those who rejected the balloon theory.

Trotterpurwa had grown. At first there had been only cooks and bottle-washers, their houses distinguishable by the differing width of the doors. Then some of the builders had stayed, too tired to trek back across mountains and seas to their families. They found new wives, made new children; theirs were the first brick houses. Next came the nilchis. Displaced from other villages, and carrying ancestral memories of a still earlier displacement from their tribal forests, they proved the most prolific, their numbers growing every ninth month because the women companionably chose to give birth together in the spring. Their street, loud just now with new-born babes, was distinctive for its yellow and blue wall motifs: the impress of a hand dipped in nil repeated over and over in rows around a doorway or window, with yellow eyes of flame painted above the fingers. In the course of time a good half of Trotterpurwa's population came to have an arm or hand of sympathetic indigo tipped with yellow nails. In the year of the drought a caravan of blacksmiths arrived with their fretted iron carts and conch-shaped bellows, and already they spoke of moving with the air of men uttering empty threats. The women lolled on cots by the roadside and suckled infant blacksmiths while old men squatted thoughtfully over rattling hookahs and scratched themselves the long way around. Near the Muslim well a family of cottonbeaters had thrown up a grass hut with a permanent look; for the young ones travel was already a memory. With business slack in spring, the father sat plucking deep resonant melodies on his gutstring. A troupe of jugglers whose tricks had gone stale refused to budge from the yard beyond the milkmen, deciding they would rather plait reeds and splice bamboo than move; it was they who dismantled the launching towers on the saltpetre hill. Beneath the yellow acacia in the middle of the village a birdcatcher who had caught no birds since the summer of the great heat, sat unmoving. At noon, when the sun was cruellest, there was added to his torments the rising moan of a brain-fever bird, just out of reach. Out of nowhere came a bird-doctor and his wife, bringing with them basketfuls of sparrows and mynahs, a dozen empty cages, a quiver of feathers, a pottle of glue, and innumerable canisters of dye. Within a week they were hanging out cages of red-bibbed flowerpeckers, golden orioles, and gorgeous parrots. Then there were ousted kite-makers from Nakhlau who flocked to the north side of the saltpetre hill where gum had begun to ooze from a rock; the next week a kitestring-maker discovered a vein of powdered glass. A dhobi squeezed out of the city by his brother came to dip his hands in the Cranny stream and stayed. The morning after he arrived, the skeleton of a hut appeared around him; by noon it was thatched and by the evening he was taking in washing. The next day he began to feud with Durga Das, son of Dhani Das, the resident dhobi-and-dyer, with all the assurance of an indigene. At the far end of the village, weavers and fishermen, both newly arrived, were disputing ancestral territory. At the end of the road a tattooist took up residence in a natural cave and announced that he would beautify all single women free of charge. One morning he realised he had been there sixteen years and had still not tattooed a single woman.

"Here we are," said Munnoo, snapping Charles out of the trance into which so much novelty had drawn him. "We must enter from behind. Not that way—that's the bird-doctor's. Here." He led the young master to his friend, the dye-seller, who opened with the greatest reluctance, fearing a raid. The man knew of Charles: Rose Begam was a regular customer.

The A-Trotter asked for cadmium, but there was none. Nor was there any turmeric or sulphur. Yellow had sold briskly all day yesterday and was gone by noon; all that remained in the shop was a little greenstone, which was expensive. At that Charles realized he had brought no money. The dye-seller began to complain about credit buyers and the cost of living, but Munnoo offered to pay. When the price was stated his eyes bulged, but he swallowed hard and unknotted his money. Charles took his packet of green and thanked Munnoo. As they were going around to the front, a bird of paradise flew over the neighbour's fence and settled on his shoulder. It had a snowy white body and long trailing feathers of orange and yellow in its lyre-shaped tail. A yellow head leaned down and looked him in the face; the feet that gripped his shoulder were pink, the beak and eyes scarlet.

Charles stood still, his breath taken away. The slightest movement would rob him of a dream—and yet the claws that dug into his shoulder were real enough. Could anything be more lovely than this bird? The creature shook its head disdainfully and flew off, its plumes streaming light.

It was then that he saw the girl.

Later on, when he was in his room, Charles relived that visionary moment when his heart turned over and grew light as a feather. Again and again in the days that followed he sought to recapture that instant of stunned submission, of utter helplessness, confusion, and joyful despair. And years later, after they were married and the use of time had taken the edge off their mutual delight, there were moments when, all unannounced, the vision would pierce him to the heart and leave him gasping. The girl who stood there was tall and clear-skinned, with enterprising eyes and cheeks that were a study in mischief. She stared mockingly at him, aware of his nervousness and finding pleasure, even encouragement, in it. When his hand went to his ruff and found it damp and stained, she smiled at his discomfiture: a chameleon moulting, she thought, and showed her perfect teeth. Her own clothes were spattered with colour, but at least they were not strange foreign-looking things. Charles hurried off, but after that he never troubled Rose for paints; he made his purchases himself at the shop next door to the bird-doctor.

Bulbul was a year older than Charles. Conceived on the same night as Yakub's son, she was born on the same day as Fonseca's, but her birthday went unnoticed because she entered the world on the wrong side of the saltpetre hill. Her mother, who had barely reached womanhood, died in the delivery and the girl was taken over by a childless couple who had just arrived in the village. The wife did nothing for a living and was the envy of Trotterpurwa. Sometimes she made a pretence of selling radishes, but on the second day she would warn people off. "Not worth the money," she advised. "Just look at them." The husband, who doted on her, agreed: "Go to Sukkhun. His radishes are much better." And for the rest of the week they ate their own wares. When the spirit moved him, the old man would dip a mynah into a dye pot or a bucket of bleach and paste an assortment of bright feathers on it. The bird, which he gave a long name and placed in a cage with a mirror and a punnet of pumpkin seed, fetched a good price in the city, and for some days there were lentils to set off the radish curry. After they took the infant in, they sold a cageful of birds and bought a goat for milk.

The girl had no education to speak of, since neither foster-parent could read or write. She ran wild with the buffalo girls and the kite-makers' tribe of sons and ruled over them with the authority of the beautiful. Her playmates called her dongli, or two-in-one, because her real father had been a foreigner. Her new father, the bird-doctor, called her Bulbul because she had a widow's peak and twittered with her head at a tilt. From an early age she began to help with the making of the cages; if a cage came out well, she was allowed to help with the making of a bird. Occasionally she grew attached to a particular bird, perhaps a new species of rainbow dove that she had taught to speak, and refused to let it be sold. The old man would shrug and lift his hand with an irresolute twist, and the bird stayed, weaned from its cage or simply too encumbered with wings to fly. Once a month she accompanied the bird-doctor to the city where he went to sell his creations and to buy small mirrors and swings, so she had seen something of the world. Once she saw an English lady and her husbands out for a ride, so Charles's clothes did not come as a complete surprise.

Charles was not aware of it, but the second time he came to Trotterpurwa she followed him back to *Sungum*. After that she spent as much time at Sans Souci as he wasted buying paints in the village. Since he could not bring himself to address her, she spoke first, and it was she who first took his limp wet hand in hers because his courage failed him. It was a source of endless wonder to him that someone so beautiful should notice, let alone follow, a humble insignificant worm such as himself (*Artless Trotter, Critic Just*). He was undeserving, unworthy, unfit. The first gift was also hers, a pastework ring that she slipped on his finger and that he wore turned downwards so it hid in his fist and shone for him alone, its stone flashing now red, now yellow, but mostly in between. After that they walked regularly in the orangerie, and once when she asked to see his work he led her past the crooked custard apple tree to the Japanese tea-house, his former prison, where he showed her the cartoons for *Pilgrims Travelling to the Shrine of Sachiko at Ise*. She ran an eye over the dismal scratchings and asked where the colours were. It was only a preliminary sketch, he said, his throat gone very dry; next would come a base of tempera and ground eggshell. Ground eggshell, she repeated and taking his hand slipped it under her blouse. She gave so agonized a moan when he touched her breast that the A-Trotter at once withdrew his hand, wrung it, and to make amends, sat on it. "No, no!" she whispered, pulling him up against her and replacing his hand. "It was good." And Charles found that it was. The breast was plump and satiny with an orange drupe in the middle that was quite unlike anything in the paintings he bought from Soravian the Armenian, and far more exciting. He could not remember a single work of the old masters which brought on such a fainting fit of pleasure, for no sooner had Bulbul's own hands begun to explore under his clothes than he expired with a shudder that left her puzzled at the brevity of passion. But after that they returned regularly to the tea-house where the vapour of oranges hung in an intoxicating cloud. And in after years, when habit had taken its toll and custom exacted its forfeits, if Bulbul wished to remind her neurasthenic husband of a neglected duty, she placed on the breakfast table in the Rain Room a bowl heaped with tiny, unendurably tart Chinese oranges.

The Harp of India

> *Why hang'st thou lonely on yon withered bough?*
> *Unstrung for ever, must thou there remain;*
> *Thy music once was sweet—who hears it now?*
> *Why doth the breeze sigh over thee in vain?*
> *Silence hath bound thee with her fatal chain;*
> *Neglected, mute, and desolate art thou,*
> *Like ruined monument on desert plain:*

O! many a hand more worthy far than mine
  Once thy harmonious chords to sweetness gave,
And many a wreath for them did Fame entwine
  Of flowers still blooming on the minstrel's grave:
Those hands are cold—but if thy notes divine
  May be by mortal wakened once again,
Harp of my country, let me strike the strain!

—HENRY LOUIS VIVIAN DEROZIO

(*CHRONICLE RESUMED*)

Henry Luis Vivian Fonseca-Trotter was a prodigy. He suspected so himself, and had confirmed his own suspicions before he was six. When his father discovered that the boy spoke naturally in couplets, he sold a vase to Soravian and sent him as a boarder to the famous David Drummond's Academy in Calcutta. Fonseca was still enamoured of the city he had not seen. Luis shone at school and spent his holidays with an uncle on his mother's side who was an indigo planter in Bihar. Then Fonseca ran out of vases. His finances had always been shaky since he returned the forty thousand rupees that somehow or other trickled out of the ice account and into his pocket, and now there was another child, a sister for Luis named Luisa. Luis was brought back to Sans Souci where he taught himself much in the library and others much more, outside. He had, however, picked up a vice in the big city which he could not shake off, namely, poetry.

His first poem was published in the *India Gazette*. Fonseca read it out to his wife, pausing between lines to gaze at his son. Of course, it was not as good as Pope—it was a little wilder—but that one could draw the comparison . . . Farida declared the poem impious, the mark of a rebellious spirit and altogether contrary to the Christian principles she had espoused. (She now fasted on Sundays instead of Fridays and prayed in the chapel conveniently located at the foot of her tower.) The boy, she said, was becoming puffed up and vainglorious; instead of sending his vauntings to the Calcutta press, they should send him into the keeping of the Jesuits before the sin took root. Fonseca felt compelled to take his son's part. The boy did no harm. It had even come to his ears that Luis had rounded up the young cowherds and begun to teach them the Roman alphabet. He kept to himself another rumour, that there was a mound near the oracle tree where Luis sat and discoursed with the tongue of an ancient sage. The Sagarpaysans said the mound concealed the lost throne of the philosopher-king Vikramaditya, and anybody who sat on it gained wisdom. But when they learnt of the use to which Luis put it—a witchcraft called education—they arrived with spears and lathis to rescue their young. It was said the boy (a barber's son) outstared them till they dropped their staves and sat down meekly behind their children, but a blind weaver, who was immune to those glittering eyes, broke the spell. What about that gold said to be buried hereabouts? he asked, and immediately the mound was dug up to reveal a few imperfect Dianas buried when the wall of the mock ruin had collapsed in earnest. Luis was given a hiding, but returned undaunted the next day. "As I was saying," he began, meaning to work up to a rousing sermon on humility, but there was only one listener and she was there because she had never before heard anyone speak in rhyme.

It came to threats on Luis's life. Farida, although pregnant again, decided to take the children downriver to the indigo planter, while Fonseca stayed on at Sans Souci because he feared for the ice office. In Jamalpur, Luis was given a bookkeeping job at the indigo factory but found it irksome within a week of starting. He spent much of his time wandering by the riverside near Jangira, listening to the villagers' stories about an ascetic who had a cave on an island in the Ganges. When he told his mother, she upbraided him with idolatry. "Is it a *Hindu* you want to be?" she wept, because she loved her first-born. Unmoved, he sent his work, a long narrative poem in the romantic manner on the hermit, to the *India Gazette*, enclosing with it a few other efforts. The editor, Dr Garston, not only ran the poems but offered to publish a volume of Luis's verse. That was enough. The boy refused to continue at the factory: ink, not indigo, he declared loftily, was his medium, and proposed to leave for Calcutta by the next boat. Alarmed at the thought of her son, now grown up, in the city of vice (which her husband still talked about with a gleam in his eye), Farida went along. She look Luisa and the new baby, christened Ferdinand, and found lodgings in the Grey Quarter where years ago Mik and the discharged country-borns had spent a night.

The street was quieter now, and more run down. The local Anglo-Indians had forsaken their various trades of carpentry, printing, shoemaking and iron-work, and swarmed to the Writers' Building as clerks (though one of them had gone on to become the port city's most famous shipbuilder, giving his name to the misspelled Kidderpore docks). Well, Farida thought, looking across the little rented room at her poet-son, at least he's not *that* sort of writer; there were limits to Christian humility.

Luis was appointed assistant editor of the *India Gazette* and his first volume of poems appeared the following month. The book was an immediate success. Rival coteries and various Calcutta papers courted the poet, who made po-lemical contributions to all impartially. The clever young men of the local college came to hear him speak and looked out for his articles in the received magazines. And when the post of assistant master of history and literature at the Hindu College fell vacant, there was by universal consent one person alone who could fill it. At eighteen Luis became the youngest lecturer the college had seen. The students flocked to hear his sparkling but closely reasoned lectures, which ranged from speculative philosophy to poetic justice, and afterwards they gathered around him, won over by his charm and springy hair, to broach the issues of the day: the condition of India, the mastery of Europe, the unacknowledged legislators of the world. As the night wore on, lit with beer and fellowship, their voices ran up and opinions became certainties. A mild young man stood up to recite Shelley's *Declaration of Rights*, another offered to die for his friends. But Farida need not have feared for her son's religion; although his college and his students were Hindus, the young men had discovered the West and were eager to discredit old loyalties. They drank wine and ate beef together regardless of caste, declaring themselves free of the past. After one especially convivial dinner they tossed the bones of their feast into the house of a friend to taunt his orthodox father. The man was not amused. He led a deputation of concerned fathers to the principal with a petition to the trustees naming "a certain teacher" as "the root of all the evils" and demanding his dismissal.

At a meeting of the board Luis was called upon to explain his actions. He replied with a poem in which he apostrophised the budding young minds in his charge and spoke of sunlight and fresh air. The board was unimpressed: sunlight was all very well in England, and as for fresh air there was a Maidan for that. The College principal, though a friend and admirer, wrote him a plain letter and asked for a plain answer. Had he, as was alleged, materially injured the morals of his charges? Was the public alarm justified? Did he deny the existence of God? Should brothers and sisters really be allowed to marry? And what was this about beef? Luis replied, in prose, *Lies, lies, lies, lies—half-truth*. But the managers of the college, seven Hindus and two Christians, had already come to their decision. Was it expedient to dismiss Mr Fonseca-Trotter? The two Christians—David Hare, the famous educationist, and the principal, Mr Wilson—declined to vote on a matter touching Hindu sentiments; for the rest, said the report:

Four Baboos declared it was necessary
Two that it was expedient
One that it was unnecessary.

Luis was dismissed. So were the students who had been of the dining party. A scavenger was called to dispose of the bones, a wide corridor being cordoned off so that he could enter and leave without compounding the pollution. Afterwards the house was purified by pujas and priests, and the old order restored. For some time students continued to come to Luis's home for private lessons and meetings, but their fathers sent servants after them, and Farida too would come into the room in the middle of a debate on the existence of God and light candles where the picture of the Sacred Heart hung. Luis was obliged to fall back on journalism. Farida took to doing faces for ladies who couldn't afford Andretti's salon, while the girl Luisa embroidered pillowcases; Ferdinand was almost old enough to go to school. The family grew closer. Luis wrote affectionate poems to his sister excusing himself from marriage. Fonseca's letters from Sans Souci were read over and over till his promise to wind up affairs in the Glacerie and join them shortly began to sound believable. But ice was a tricky business, and besides, the money he sent was useful. Luis's articles for the *East Indian*, the *India Magazine*, the *Calcutta Charivari*, the *Bengal Examiner*, and *Free Thought* grew increasingly mordant. At a public meeting of Anglo-Indians gathered to ratify a petition to Parliament, he spoke in such vinegarish tones that those at the back thought he was an old man. In fact he was twenty-three. At the close of the speech, which he delivered extempore with one hand in his vest after the manner of Fox, he drank a glass of cloudy yellow water. The next day the shivering began and the doctor told Farida it was cholera.

Petition of the Anglo-Indians at Calcutta

To the Honourable the Commons of the United Kingdom of Great Britain and Ireland in Parliament assembled, the petition of the undersigned Christian inhabitants of Calcutta, and the provinces comprised within the presidency of Fort William,

HUMBLY SHEWETH,—

1. That your petitioners are members of a numerous increasing and widely dispersed class of subjects of the Crown of Great Britain, living within the territories at present governed by the United Company of merchants trading to the East Indies, in the province of Bengal, and in the town of Calcutta.
2. That the body of which they compose a part, forms a distinct class of society in British India, which dates its existence more remotely from the time when the East India Company first formed permanent establishments on the continent of India, but chiefly from the more recent period, when the acquisition of immense territories required the presence of an increased number of Europeans to maintain and govern them.
3. That they are descended, in most instances, on the father's side, from European subjects of the Crown of Great Britain, and on the mother's side, from the natives of India; and that in other instances they are the children of

intermarriages between the offspring of such connexions; but that, although thus closely allied to the European and Native races, they are excluded from almost all those advantages which each respectively enjoys, and are subject to peculiar grievances from which both are exempt.

4. The first grievance which your petitioners beg leave to bring to the notice of your Honourable House is, that a very large majority of the class to which they belong are entirely destitute of any rule of civil law . . . whether British, Hindu, or Muhamedan . . . that there is no law which regulates their marriages and makes them lawful,—there is no law which shows the rule that is to define the legitimacy or illegitimacy of their issue, there is no law which prescribes the succession to their property,—there is no law which points out whether they possess the right of bequeathing by will, and, if so, to what extent,—there is no law which declares which of their children, or whether one or all, shall succeed in case of intestacy. . . .

(CHRONICLE RESUMED)

There were six other grievances: that the petitioners, though Christian, were amenable in the interior to Muslim criminal law; that they were excluded from jobs in the Company's covenanted service to which Europeans were admitted, although they were treated as Europeans in not being allowed to own land; that they were excluded from subordinate jobs in the same service to which Indians were admitted; that they were debarred from employment with Indian powers; that their efforts to obtain redress were scorned while those of other sections of the populace were favourably considered.

The petition had been drawn up by several community notables, but the prime mover was, like Luis, a relative newcomer. He was tall, sallow, and spare, with an expressionless face and an impressive jaw. He spoke fluently and well, though he said *exiguous* for small, and *amplitudinous* for big. His manner suggested a childhood begun in imitation of adults and ended without regret. To imagine him younger was to see him smaller, in a series of diminishing replicas always in a black frock coat with roomy (or as he would have it, *capacious*) pockets. His legs, rickety and stiffened with hose, were a set of parentheses enclosing nothing. He was, of course, Jarman Begam's son by Yakub.

As a boy he ate paper, usually newspaper, and developed a stutter which he overcame through elocution. The family breakfasts, at which an abandoned apiary, a decimated fowl run, and cooling ovens (built for grander days) were represented, were strained affairs, and the boy took refuge in newsprint. He asked difficult questions to which he often knew the answers, but he was soft-hearted, earnest, and always willing to help. His altruism was baffled by the fact that Jarman Begam wanted nothing while Yakub the father needed nothing, and it might have dried up at the source but for a strange accident. As it was, one day Fonseca was out walking near the mound where his son had held forth, when he made a find which changed everything. Among the imperfect Dianas of the Ephesians which had been dug up and lay broken and scattered, he saw another figure lying there covered in a kind of blackish yellow moss—which was odd, because the other statues were of exposed white marble. On closer examination the figure proved not to be of stone at all, while the moss appeared to seethe, clearing briefly at the face. Only then did Fonseca recognize Yakub, covered in bees. He was dead, though the barber-and-mortician did not wait to take his pulse. He ran at once to report to Jarman Begam, as he had done years ago when he discovered the poulterer's corpse at the foot of the South Tower. Elise had moved to the Spur, but she was not in. In a little while he learnt why. From the bakery came word of a long narrow puddle of water that went from the ovens to the door and refused to evaporate, and along it on the floor lay Jarman Begam's black burqa-and-tent, wet from top to bottom.

Yakub *fils* took it well. He wept the large clear tears of a child, but already he was embarrassed by grief and consoled himself with the thought that he was now an adult in earnest. Parents generally died before their children, and besides, once his schooling was out of the way a lifetime of useful work stretched before him. Hard-pressed by declining sales in the Glacerie, Fonseca sold his shears to the pedlar Soravian and sent the orphan to the nearby mission school, St Aloysius's, founded with Justin's bequest. He could answer none of the lad's questions and was sure the Catholic fathers would. Young Yakub thought so too. He changed his name to Jacob Kahn-Trotter and was already asking the warden, as he waved to Fonseca, what were the powers of the Chamber of Deputies in the new Constitutional Charter of France? At the end of his studies he arrived in Calcutta a little disappointed in the fathers and in search of a calling in the world. The Anglo-Indian petition supplied a need, and brought him to Luis's door. Luis was sceptical, but signed and attended the public meeting. When he stood up to read the itemized grievances to the assembly, Jacob was conscious of a pair of dark eyes mocking his labour, and he avoided looking at the poet, but by the time he reached the end he had regained his composure. "*And your petitioners will ever pray,*" he concluded, moved by the hallowed form to a vision of all grievances redressed. Humbly he asked the assemblage to name the man whom it thought best fitted to carry the petition to London. The crowd roared *Jacob Kahn-Trotter!* and *Hear, hear!* and a subscription was raised for the passage to England and for expenses suited to an emissary.

So it was Jacob who stood on the deck of the *Cranganore* as it ploughed through the Indian Ocean, rising and falling towards the Cape of Good Hope. There had been the delays Luis acidly predicted, disputes as to the wording of the petition, monies to come in. It was easy to look on and scoff, Jacob thought, but he refused to condemn. There had also been his marriage to the poet's sister, Luisa, a girl with dark Fonseca eyes and Farida's satiny elbows, who brought him twins, Philip and Philippa. Jacob was sorry (he said he was loth) to leave them, but duty impelled him. And yet, as he stood on deck it was not the wife and children left behind that haunted him; it was Luis. He saw a sick-room where a bedside candle burned while it was still light outside. A dark head lay on the pillow, its black curls damp and wilted, the forehead beaded with sweat. From time to time it shook violently from the fever. Jacob was pleading with the stricken poet: would he not recognize the life beyond the grave and repent (*Upright Jacob, Soul's Ladder*)? The candle guttered with a peppery crackle and sent up a last flare as the dying man's eyes opened wide and looked directly at him. It was not fever that shook Luis's head for the last time, but his was a Christian burial all the same: he was laid to rest in the Park St Cemetery with a marble slab placed, at Jacob's expense, on his grave (*Supine Luis, Spirit Level*). All the way to the equator the deathbed tableau plagued the emissary. He had eaten little since the ship left Calcutta, having been troubled by seasickness. Then, as they crossed the line, the sea calmed and his innards settled. A gentle breeze relieved the sun's growing heat and Jacob took a turn upon the deck, mumbling snatches from the petition. Before long he was able to lean against the gunwale of the *Cranganore* and gaze with perfect equanimity at a miracle of flying fish.

A further extract from The Military Memoirs of General Mik. Trotter (*translated from the Persian*)

That year I was in the Sawalakh (One Hundred and Twenty-Five Thousand) Hills. Horse are of little use in that terrain, but we drummed up some infantry. Our irregulars formed a fifth column against the Gurkhas and killed many of them near the Mohand Pass. A lakh of difficulties beset us, but please God! it went well. The name Trotter stood high. My sword-sharpener's hand was struck off in a skirmish with one of the short razor-sharp swords those Gurkhas use to sacrifice bullocks with. My own horse was shot under me and I was wounded. Verghese the bugler was carried off, poor man. His was a fearless heart! We lost forty men thanks to Marston's folly—Loneyackerty could not control him. While I was there I killed a tiger. It had been causing the villagers some worry, so I killed it. The skin was spoilt. When victory was ours we marched back through Saharanpur. There we ate a confection. At Nakur it rained hailstones the size of mongoose eggs. The horses were much distressed and several pigeons were killed. The men's shields were dented as in war! Such as had sacking covered with it. Afterwards I had the men gather up the largest stones and we made a sharbat of crushed ice, milk, green mangoes, and a scantling of sugar. Then I released the foot-soldiers. We rode as far as the Jamuna and ate watermelons on the sands. They cool them with wet sand. That was near the village of Sarsawa. A cool breeze blew. Chater, the Armenian Tree-Feller, sang a song in the moonlight. For that I gave him the village.

The next year we rode against the Pindaris. Those low cruel brigands were a thorn in the side of travellers and a stone of stumbling to commerce. We rode south in a body, stopping at Ajmer to buy grain. There were many heart-expanding buildings, pleasaunces, and gardens. The women are fair. We ate a cloying confection. In the market we were joined by a spahi of the Company's army, Sita Ram by name. He travelled with us fifteen days as far as Nagpur, a great liar but an entertaining man. I saved his life at Hazir the next year and he brazenly pretended to have saved mine! Thankless mannikin. At Nagpur we ate oranges (*naranj*) but they were too sweet.* In November, after we had sent the Pindaris to their death doom, we invested the fortress of Hazir with some few British companies' support. The governor of the fort was Jaswant Rao, a very fat man but [*and?*] brave. I cast a great mortar and three battering guns under his very nose. One of my guns exploded but we laid the walls low with British help. Does the metal lose its suppleness, growing tired? Afterwards I saw Sita Ram running with a handful of gold coins and two of his own officers from that side in pursuit. I rode in between them but they cut at me and the creature shied. I fell onto Sita Ram, knocking the poor man to the ground. The coins slipped from his grasp and were lost to his pursuers. I sprang up but they had fled. This came from forgetting the rule that one must ride over an enemy, not beside him. Thus I deserved it. But the day was ours. The name of Trotter's Horse stood high. The wreath of acclaim was mine. Earth-Shaker was added to the titles.

That summer I rested my troops. To tell the truth I was sick for home, for the Rose-Bodied (*Gulbadan*), for melons and cool water. So after a hundred disgusts and repulsions in this charmless and disorderly Hind, I came home in six marches. In those days I devised the Romany mirror script and kept a diary. I now copy from it.

15 March   I come home with the ides of March. At the Gunpowder Gate was no steward to greet me with the customary slice of melon. God took him! The Glacerie was shut and no Ice Manager stood there with a tumbler

---

* Surely a figurative or Platonic concept. Compare *a scantling of sugar* and *cloying* above. —E.A.T.

of ice-water. God took him! The West Tower was no more, collapsed. They say it fell in and buried him the day before he was to have gone to Calcutta where his son lay dying. The Rose-Bodied was at her window to greet me and I saluted her. Tonight I sleep in the dairy, called the Crocodile Wing by my father (peace be His).

16 March   Today I visited the South Tower and found the Fragrant One despondent and not so fresh as before. I am sure it is the doing of my effeminate son. He does nothing but paint, locking himself in the North Tower with his rancid oils. I was tortured with doubts and moved to write a verse:

> Not poppy, phlox or oleander
> Can touch the silk hem of the Rose,
> But fly the oily canker and a
> Blot will blight, the bloom she blows.
> > Is it to spite her
> > (The sybarite blighter)
> > Or at me to thumb his nose?
> Away, away!
> Alack a day!
> > For the scion's a pansy
> > Not even azalea.
> And the pater Gulabi
> A lily-heart failure.

My clerk thought it was not bad. The form is a Solomon sonnet. I was so much incensed when it was written, I flogged the boy.

17 March   This morning at shoot of day he returned incorrigible to his tower and shut himself in. A girl, well-favoured, from the village came to ask after him, but showed no interest in weaponry so I sent her away.

18 March   I am setting up a military museum of my father's guns and swords. God's blessings upon it! It is to be in the gallery overlooking the Audience Hall on the other side from the chapel. There will be a room for his bust and uniforms. The approach is hidden.

19 March   Today I killed a panther. It was taking cows from the dairy so I took a spear to it. On the way back I saw first a munshi bird, sometimes called a cranny, its plumage greyish and not bad. Then I saw near the tea-house a bird surely of paradise, snowy white with elongate plumes of orange and yellow.

20 March   He is lacking in discipline. I will take him back with me as an aide. But first he must be taught to ride and fire a musket.

21 March   Today my son was married. A great many doves and some strange birds were set free. He told me of it at the last minute, bringing me a portrait of myself as a gift. It is a striking resemblance, bold and not unlike Babar the Brave. He has captured the nobility of the forehead and nose, though the moustaches be somewhat lacking. I will hang it in the museum. He may make a painter yet. He is better than Bih-zad, who used to botch hairy faces.

(*CHRONICLE RESUMED*)

When the wedding was over, Rose gathered up the rice and pink dal from the tea-house floor and sent it to the nilchis to supplement their chickpeas. (Charles had declared himself a Free-thinker and refused to have a chapel ceremony.) Then she packed her things and moved to the Balloon Room to make way for the newly-weds: Charles's studio was at the top of the North Tower, and besides, he had a right. She might have gone to the East Tower, but there was no telling when Farida would return from Calcutta; and as for the South Tower which had once been Jarman Begam's, she shivered at the thought of living there. The West Tower was a heap of stones: when it fell (from a horn blast, some said) the rubble formed a fan which spread across the drive and, on the inside, blocked off the library entrance to the tahkhana, thus entombing the tomb. The outer tomb was not empty, for somewhere in that heap of stones lay all that remained of a barber-and-man. Rose could hardly live there.

In the absence of his father's tower, Mik had also to find some other accommodation. He took up residence with the Alexander-Trotters in the Rib, having first cleared away a host of useless inventions. From the Alexander-Trotters' point of view, the Rib was an improvement on the crumbling Crocodile Wing; from Mik's, it was an expedient compromise since it overlooked the Balloon Room to which Rose had moved. The morning after his son's wedding he stirred himself from his toddy-sodden pile of straw (the twelve sisters were already downstairs milking the buffaloes), lit a cheroot, and decided to ride around Sans Souci on an inspection tour. The firewater might have had something to do with it, but the ride proved a nightmare.

Wherever he rode white ants and dry rot had wrought their havoc, while damp and rust and creeping vines gave the decay a tumbledown picturesque look. A few melancholy mounds were all that was left of the Crocodile Wing; goats and cattle had trodden tracks around them through the thickets and tall grass. He reined his horse about and rode the other way. In the Comb, the stables were bare of horses. With the death of Yakub Khan, steward-and-Master of the Horse, the grooms had ridden off on horses of their choice; the remainder, spirited, crop-tailed, and fickle alike, had bolted or been snatched by wishful beggars and poulterers' clients. In the elephant stables a still more dismal spectacle awaited Mik. The mahouts had decamped with the strongest elephants, while the creatures they left behind had either burst their bonds and run off into the jungle or else perished in chains. Now that he saw them, Mik remembered the shrill trumpeting that had penetrated his toddy fog as he lay in the arms of the Alexander women. He detonated a charge that brought down a portion of the Elephant Wing and buried the creatures. In the dry dock beyond, one camel remained, an emaciated creature which stood erect, smiling histrionically. Mik let it loose and it wandered off into the desert, across the salt flats and past the aerolite. He watched it go, not knowing that years later he would harness it to a short-lived experiment, the cane-press. A few feathers showed signs of a struggle in the fowl run, but the chickens were all gone, and there was no trace of dung. Only the cows and buffaloes in the Rib remained sleek, plump-teated, and content, with silken dewlaps and a seersucker sheen, being fed and watered regularly by the greying Alexander sisters.

Mik returned blear-eyed to his pallet and took comfort in the arms of his Indo-Greek gopis, making sons and daughters for twelve nights in a row. By day he prepared a small rose garden at the foot of the North Tower where his child-love had once dug her grave with a teaspoon. There he lingered at dusk, patting the earth around the seedlings and watering the new moss with the avidity of the confirmed wanderer. Then he saddled his horse once more, rode around to the Balloon Room to salute his untouchable lady, and clattered off down the Gunpowder Drive to his campaigns, leaving the keys to Sans Souci on a nail in the Spur.

It was Farida who found them. Nobody had written to her of Fonseca's death—her little friend Rose couldn't write—but when he failed to arrive for Luisa's wedding she knew. Two months after Jacob Kahn-Trotter sailed for England on the *Cranganore*, Luisa died and was buried next to Luis. Left with Ferdinand and her daughter's twins, Farida wrote to Jacob in London on black-edged paper and brought the young ones back to Nakhlau. From a long way up the Trotter Road she saw that there was no West Tower and her misgivings were confirmed, but she had no tears left. Without a glance at the heap of grey stones that had been a tower she took the children directly to her old apartments where the indigo was peeling off the walls. She looked in the old mirror and saw that she had lost none of her good looks: all the features that once marked her as a beauty were sharpened by grief and heightened by the onset of middle age. Besides, some of her sorrow lifted when she heard that Jarman Begam and Yakub Khan were also dead. She blackened her hair with collyrium and walked with her back held straight. She spent little time among the cushions where she and Rose had once sung a foolish song about a sweet rain cloud; instead, she took off a large silver ear-ring and slipped onto it the keys to the Glacerie, the indigo shed, and the ice pits along with several others that were gathering rust on the baker-and-Chief Steward's chain in the Spur. She dismissed Hakim Ahmed, who on his return from a pilgrimage to Kashmir made a bid for Yakub's office, and poured away the silver tumblers of mango-fool that he sent up the East Tower to appease her. And it was on her orders that the displaced miners were put to work making ice, and the Ice Bell was brought across to the Ice Court from the Glacerie. By the following summer Sans Souci ice was once more on its way to Nakhlau and within a year the pits were being extended.

She was less successful with the children, who deserted her for the Balloon Room where they preferred to live with their Aunt Rose. And there was also the problem of the indigo. The crop was cut and steeped and pressed as usual, but there was nothing to show for it. Each summer the indigo cake was sunned and stored away under lock and key, but when it came to packing for shipment there was rarely more than half a bullock-cartload. Nankoo the floor-polisher-and-night-watchman was dead, while his brother Munnoo was rendered unfit for active chowkidari by elephantiasis. Never vigilant, the brothers had at least been incorruptible; until his brother was carried off in a dust storm, Munnoo slept in the doorway of the indigo shed, but after that he did his duty on the floor of the Audience Hall and would not be moved. The new breed of night-watchman was diligent right up to the time the cake was dry; then he fell asleep by arrangement with certain elements in the village, with the result that Sans Souci indigo was a going proposition only in a very limited sense: it went, unpaid for, around the saltpetre hill to where the firm of Durga Das & Son, Dhobis & Dyers of Distinction, was doing brisk business.

Meanwhile in the North Tower, Bulbul and Charles made continuous and rapturous love, seldom caring to look down on the workaday world around them. The fickle painter abandoned his canvases to explore at first hand the marvel of the female form, leaving his brushes standing in turpentine so that the bristles developed a permanent curl while he discovered with a pained shock that a woman hid her modesty under a bush. (Once again he felt the old masters had done him a disservice; he had expected drapery, not a beard, where the legs met.) Sometimes he did a rapid sketch of his wife as she lay dozing with one arm hanging down, her eyes rolled up under the lids, her breath vibrating the slightly parted lips, but he never finished, because he could only draw what he had learnt to see, not what he really saw. Dropping the sketch he crawled back into bed beside his sleeping mate and gently followed with his finger the outlines which his pencil could not form. Bulbul, waking, smiled tenderly at her love with half-opened eyes, and the two ex-changed a look of unshakeable security, lying very still in each other's arms until the blood began to pound again. Only the slow modulation of those uncapturable forms marked the passage of ten years, as the anaesthete watched his wife's body mature, the breasts begin to sway a little, the buttocks to sag, as if presaging a time when she would be taken away from him altogether. The thought of a hollow beside him in the bed, fresh and speaking yet never again to be filled, would drive him to the verge of insanity, and yet to produce a living likeness of her was beyond him (*Sterile Cuckoo, Flaccid Brush*).

They had given up expecting a child when the Fourth Trotter was announced. It was whispered that old Alexander's intervention was crucial and that the white-haired sculptor-and-soldier had finally lost patience and done his duty to the line, but Bulbul was a faithful wife. The boy was named Thomas Henry and swaddled in gaudy bands stuck with feathers which Bulbul's ancient foster-parents brought from Trotterpurwa. He hardly ever cried (*Dammed Tears, Damned Cheek*) but whenever his mother came near the crib he threw his head back and opened his mouth to an alarming extent until Bulbul lowered one of her long orange nipples into it.

The nursing allowed Charles to rediscover his studio. He unbolted the four casement windows to air the place and found in the process numerous unfinished works that had gathered a rich (*and richly deserved*) harvest of dust. His last completed work, the portrait of his father, was ten years old. It hung in the military museum under the portrait of the Father of the East India Company's Army, Stringer Lawrence, a well-proportioned, full-faced happy man, and once a week Bulbul took a feather duster to the study in contrasts. But Charles returned to painting with a bad conscience. His childhood nervousness, lulled on Bulbul's breast, returned to plague him, so that every morning as he climbed the steps to the loft, his diffidence mounted with him. To steady his hand he started the day with a nip of dry sherry which, in the beginning, worked till noon. Then he found he needed a second glass at ten. True, his painting improved (*it could not have got worse*) and with it his speed: the allegorical canvas *L'Allegro* took a month of Sundays, and its companion piece, *Il Penseroso*, hardly longer. He worked constantly, neglecting husbandly duties and sacrificing his sight from a misguided sense of guilt over lost time. He was so unsure of himself that he never put his name to his work, and attempted only one self-portrait, which he could not bring himself to complete.

Reflections on self-portraiture

All men wish to see themselves multiplied. Some use mirrors for the purpose, others use wives. Both methods are fraught with peril, since mirrors will lie and wives will sometimes not. The most fortunate of men (I mean artists) are not so bound. They may produce at short notice, and as often as they please, *self-portraits*. The true artist (let us be frank) is always painting self-portraits. The false artist (let us mention no names) cannot bring himself to complete even one. Such as he does, such as it is, it is a contemptible thing, bearing an unfortunate resemblance to the European miniature called *Martin Lefranc Writing*, from the series *Les champions des dames*, circa 1640. There is the identical sharp chin and peaked nose, the monstrous eyes that will one day find matching teacups, the wizened arm, the long clerkly fingers miscalled artistic. Such portraits are best destroyed, and since in this case there is but one, the task is made light. Never again will the world be afflicted with his portrait, nor is the world the poorer for its loss. Instead it is the richer for a set of sixteen self-portraits released on the market by another artist, quite different to look at, whose signature appears boldly and without false modesty at the bottom left-hand corner of each panel.

Let us philosophize a little.

The desire to see oneself endlessly reproduced is a natural, even primal urge. The fool fights it, the coward denies it. The true artist redeems it, enables it, ennobles it, frames it as self-portraiture. Self-portraits are of three kinds: the *excellent*, the *mediocre*, and the *Third Trotter's*. (Why keep back names?) Indeed all art will profit from this distinction. Good self-portraiture is the work of passion, not dispassion; it is unafraid of ideals, romance, the aura of perfection. The second kind is drudgery, the third uninspired, bony-fingered dabbling. In the third kind the self is divided, not multiplied; the portrait is not a joyous procreation but a mutilation. It is thus neither *self* nor *portrait*, and perhaps cannot be considered under the rubric *self-portraiture*. It is best forgotten.

Let us pass to another subject.

> *Tell, me Narrator, how it happened toward the end of the generation of carnal romance.*
>
> *Not much carne on those romantic bones, Cup-Bearer.*
>
> *Tell me, all the same. Are there no incredible feats left, doings that might stretch a man's belief?*
>
> *There are, but fetch me first some mulberry wine. Now listen. I have heard from the blue jay that it happened in this way.*

(CHRONICLE RESUMED)

After ten years of fighting, Gipsy Trotter came home again. The British, outnumbered a hundred to one, were making good progress and did not need Trotter's Horse just then. A little put out at the neglect, Mik was not in the best of tempers when he returned. When he looked again at his portrait in the military museum, the moustaches were disappointing and he was once more inclined to see his son as a frilly wastrel. That Charles was thirty-three and married made no difference. Nor did it matter that Mik now had, by the Alexander sisters, eleven other children dutifully named after his instructions. (Agrippa was the eldest; then came, in order, Attila, Caligula, Gengiz, Grendel, Hektor, Nero, Ravana, and Timur, while two others, whose blood was not as hot and rich, came later and were called Alina and Cyril.) Charles was the eldest and that was that: something must be done about him.

Arriving the day before Christmas, Gulabi Trotter saluted his love and went hunting. He brought home a blue bull, two wild boar, four barking deer, six Siberian geese, twelve Brahminy ducks, twenty-four partridges, forty-eight fig-pigeons, ninety-six ring-necked doves, and sparrows without number. The creatures were skinned, gutted, and roasted over a bonfire. The next morning they were spread on the breakfast cloth in the Glacerie. Charles was summoned on the morning itself and appeared half asleep at the Old Armoury end. The sight of so much meat at that hour made his stomach heave; ordinarily he breakfasted late with Bulbul in the Rain Room, limiting himself to a single piece of fruit while glancing nervously at the bowl of Chinese oranges. Today he took his seat opposite Mik, wondering whether the Rain Room was not after all a more congenial place.

" 'Christmas, Father," he offered, addressing a haze at the far end of the table. The fact was he was going blind from his work because he now painted only miniatures.

Mik, who had not waited, ignored the pleasantry. He carved a steak with his sword-arm and stared malevolently at the boy, his jaws working. When he had finished with the blue bull, he spoke.

"I believe you have a son."

"Yes, Father."

"He is yours, I suppose?"

"Yes, Father."

There was another silence in which Mik started on a boar. When he reached the hock he looked up.

"You are not eating?"

"I-I have already breakfasted, Father."

"Then perhaps you would like to drink." Mik clapped his hands

—*One hand clapping, Narrator?*—

clapped his hand on the table, and a bearer appeared with an array of bottles. He followed the pointing sword and came over to the Old Armoury end. Charles flashed his deliverer a grateful smile and seized three bottles. In a little while the liquor in all three bottles stood very low. Nodding his approval from the Nakhlau end, Mik began to relent. Charles signalled the bearer and helped himself to three more bottles; then, with the security of the half-blind, he took one more. The next time Gipsy Trotter began to feel his position threatened (*Tipsy Trotter, Best Bibber*). He cleared his throat of a sparrow.

"Well, now. Shall we get down to business? What do you propose to do with yourself?"

"To do, Father?"

Mik's scorn returned. "To *be*. What do you wish to be, now that you are a man?"

Charles dipped his finger in the empty glass before him and brought it to the tip of his tongue. His Adam's apple was bucking wantonly. Mik went on.

"There is an aide's position vacant in Trotter's Horse. The last man was blown up. The pay is good and you get a uniform. We leave at seven to-morrow."

"Tomorrow!"

But it was then that the men burst in. They advanced in a body towards the Nakhlau end, shouting an old song about a heron and a barbed fish. They were the nilchis. They halted a few yards from Mik and fell silent, staring at the wreckage on the table. Spars of white bone floated on the bunched tablecloth; the hull of a rib-cage lay shattered among haunches of charred red meat. It was an awesome sight for men who ate chickpeas every day of the year, but they turned from it to address Gipsy Trotter. Mik wiped first his lips and then the edge of his sword carefully on the tablecloth. There was a trace of menace in the act, but the nilchis were not cowed. They were tribals, not truckling peasants. Payment was all they wanted: they had not been paid for a year.

Mik could well believe it. The state of the indigo works since Yakub's death was lamentable. True, it had come to his ears that Farida had taken over the keys to Sans Souci, including the indigo shed, but Farida was not Yakub Khan. She was said to have righted the ice, but the indigo was in a shambles. Mik asked the nilchis for a week and they agreed. They were about to leave when he called them back. Would they eat broken meats? The men shook their heads sideways to signify *yes*. Thanks to their intrusion many of the dishes were in fact untouched, but they had no caste scruples. Then fall to, commanded Gulabi Trotter, and the nilchis sprang at the board. A tall one with curly hair stood apart and watched both men and master with a dark smile. In a little while the wreckage was complete, but before the men left, Charles took advantage of the confusion and slipped out at the Old Armoury door.

Next morning Mik did not wait for his malingering son. When the nilchis had gone back to their jobs, beating and straining and squeezing and pressing the indigo, he rode off by the Gunpowder Gate. He returned within the promised week at the head of a troop of Rose Boys. The rissalah performed a series of complicated cavalry evolutions on the plain called the Sea of Rains in full view of the indigo works. They swept across the plain ululating viciously and riddling the crisp air with their lances. When they swung around there was no sound but the drumming of hooves as they speared tent-pegs at the gallop. On the last lap they fired from the saddle at green gin bottles. Then they formed a single rose line and wheeled with precision, splitting up at the half-revolution and weaving in and out until the line was re-formed and faced the original way. Finally the company began to trot, its pennants fluttering, towards the indigo works.

The nilchis were awed and said no more about payment. But that night they met to discuss remedies. The Rose Boys were posted around the indigo works to prevent sabotage, and there were bound to be informers in the village, so they met on the Plain of Cannonballs. Two or three nilchis who had not been there for the meat were for knuckling under in the hope of a settlement. They stated their views but were shouted down. The majority favoured retaliation. "Against armed men?" the pacifists asked. "Against armed men," answered a soft-spoken man. It was the tall curly-haired nilchi who had stood apart at the feast. He spoke with quiet conviction, but the others agreed loudly. "Against armed men!" they shouted, surprised at the courage they found in helplessness. And plans were laid on that field which would have distressed the old Tibetan plinth-master, because they meant hurting somebody. That night a hard bluish grinding sound came from the nilchis' lane in Trotterpurwa, provoking the screech-owls and setting off a morbid howling among the village pi-dogs. The indigo harvest was three months away, but the nilchis were sharpening their sickles.

The next day they stayed away from work. There was no response from Sans Souci, and an atmosphere of strained hilarity held sway in the lanes with the blue-hand motif. On the second day two soldiers on horseback rode up the muddy main road and gave notice that the nilchis were to report for work the following morning or face the consequences. In Trotterpurwa, shop-keepers and artisans began to secure their shutters and batten their doors. The nilchis cooked a last meal on their home fires and took up their tools and chattels, the wives digging up the clay floors for coin hoards, which they tied up along with their dried red chilles into little cloth bundles. Those of their young who had no blue markings were left in the village with families that would have them; the rest were carried or made to carry something of value. Under cover of darkness they trekked around the blind side of the saltpetre hill, crossed the Cranny river and made for the forest. As they crossed the Sea of Rains, they could see in the distance over their shoulders the dark hump of the slope where the stepped baths brimmed, open to the sky and idle. Below the bottommost row, by the evaporating pans, the soldiers were camped, warming themselves and cooking their food. A whiff of rotting indigo carried to them on a wayward gust and for a moment the men felt a collective twinge of regret for a familiar world forsaken. The following morning they watched from the edge of the jungle as the Rose Boys mounted and went through their equestrian paces. Then Mik appeared on the top of the slope by the settling tanks. The rissalah presented arms and heard his address; he never kept them long. Immediately after, they rode off around the saltpetre hill towards the village.

"We too must have a leader," one of the nilchis said, and they all looked at Dori, the tall quiet nilchi with close deep-set eyes in which there shone a mild distracted light. He had a mat of woolly hair and was called Habshi by the rest of the village, but his foreign ancestor might just as well have come from Malaya or Yemen as from Africa. He had never been a beater, having gone directly (this in itself won him respect) to the press. His skin was not black but gum-coloured, except for the left hand, which was blue; also blue were the veins of his right arm which bulged from the strain of holding down the press. It was on his advice that the nilchis had left Trotterpurwa, and as if by way of sanction smoke was now spotted above the village: their huts had been fired. Some of the women began to wail as the blue pall spread, but Dori checked them before the lamentation could become general.

"Enough! What do you expect from their kind? You see now what we're up against. Never mind the huts—huts can be rebuilt. We must hit back. But first the women must find shelter. We can't spend another night exposed. There's a quarry hereabouts but it's too near the edge of the jungle. A little further in and we can cook at night without being spotted. *One* fire, and all food to be shared. When we find a place the women will build shelters. The men will come with me."

A place was found near a shelf of grey rock, and the women set to work. "Today *they* will need the sickles," Dori laughed. His eyes had a bashful fidgeting way and the sides of his mouth twitched irrelevantly as he spoke. He turned and led the way back to the jungle's edge where he found a suitable tree and climbed up it. All afternoon he sat there and watched the Rose Boys' movements. The other nilchis, nervous from doing nothing, began to glance at one another doubtfully, but Dori ignored them, speaking to no one. When he had seen enough, he came down and returned with the men to the camp for the evening meal. Over the next two days they remained in the jungle wrestling and wielding staves. On the third night the men prayed to the Snake and at Dori's bidding each man made a nick in his neighbour's forehead and pressed chilli powder into the wound. "It sharpens the mind," Dori explained, and even the most timid found that it was true: one's concentration was marvellously improved.

The men split up into groups and fanned out across the Sea of Rains. One group gathered up the broken gin bottles, another came behind and dug a wide belt of potholes and trenches which left the plain looking like the surface of the moon until a third group came behind them and covered the hollows with twigs and grass, howling like jackals as they worked. Others went as far as the kitchens and returned with clay pots of cooking oil. Dori took the sentry quietly with a sickle, the first casualty. The oil was poured down the sides of the soldiers' tents and around the makeshift stables where the horses were pawing restlessly at the approach of strangers. When all was ready Dori took an ember from under the evaporating pans, and dropping it into one of the clay pots, blew gently on it. A flame sprang up with a soft hollow sound, feeding on the film of remaining oil; in this way all the pots were lit. At a signal the nilchis smashed the pots and scattered the burning fragments around the tents and at the foot of a haystack near the makeshift stables. At that the horses began to whinny and there were the muffled sounds of men suddenly woken. In another moment the camp was in an uproar. Twelve separate fires had broken out. The horses burst out of their pen, snorting and neighing wildly, and raced across the plain, where many of them were lamed in the lately dug craters. Cavalrymen rushed madly about, their arms searching for jacket sleeves, their boots half on. They fired at random into the darkness or flailed with lances at the burning tents. To the pungent smell of smoking mustard oil was added the reek of burnt serge. The tent fires did not last, the canvas being dew-damp, but the tents were damaged beyond repair. Only the burning haystack lit the confused scene, and it too shrank quickly into an ashen heap, leaving the camp in darkness. The nilchis watched with satisfaction from the forest's edge. It was some time before the erratic thunder of the horses' hooves died down.

"This is only the beginning," Dori cautioned. "They'll have their revenge."

There were no cavalry manoeuvres the next day. The boys of Trotter's Horse were split up into patrols with orders to hunt down and stick any nilchi they saw. An old blue-foot who had remained behind in the village was caught and despatched, but the patrols kept clear of the jungle, even though it was known that the nilchis had taken refuge there. One group which ventured in as far as the quarry was ambushed with ropes and nets and set upon with sickles, but carefully because Dori did not want the uniforms spoilt; like the weapons, they would be useful for raids. The horses were skinned because the nilchis had developed an atavistic taste for meat. Mik sent for reinforcements and threatened to flay any Sagarpaysan caught supplying the rebels.

"Who is with us is against them," he announced in Trotterpurwa. But at night the nilchis arrived and threatened to geld any trader who did not supply them. "Who is against us is for them," Dori said, and the nilchis tasted beans as smooth as butter and lentils they had not dreamed existed. The Rose Boys patrolled the plain and the fringes of the jungle by day; the nilchis attacked at night, striking at random, picking off one or two soldiers and running away. Sometimes a nilchi was caught and tortured without mercy, but the cavalry never once faced a drawn-up foe. The enemy would harry the horses, steal a pile of blankets, or burn down a rebuilt shelter and melt away into the darkness. The soldiers, accustomed to pitched battles, grew dispirited in the face of an invisible enemy and the campaign wore on, wasting from week to week.

"Come out and fight, you rats!" Mik yelled, baring his white seersucker jacket at the forest and brandishing his sabre. The rose at his heart was fresh, but Gulabi Trotter was already getting old.

"You see," Dori explained to his fellow nilchis as they sat camouflaged in a banyan tree and watched the Second Trotter ride up and down below. (Mik could have reached them with his lance, they were so close, but their dark faces were dappled with milk from the banyan leaf.) "You see, our kind win when we don't lose," Dori went on. "Their kind lose when they don't win."

Watching from her tower, Farida had an idea. The ice pits were full now that the harvest was over: why not simply draft the pit men to work the indigo plant? Mik agreed, and to ensure that the new workers were not harassed he decided that the Rose Boys should build a defensive wall.

For a week Dori and his men watched the wall go up as their jobs were taken over by inexpert workers. They retaliated by destroying the young indigo crop in the fields, but there was enough of the last crop already cut and stored to be processed by the miners-and-icemen now drafted for the second time, wading clumsily in the beating with legs that had once known the heat of the mines, and patting hot indigo cake with hands that had grown accustomed to carrying roundels of ice. The job was poorly done, but the factory was running again.

There was only one remedy for the nilchis. Their jobs were in any case gone, and the approach to the works was cut off. Late one evening, Dori took two men and crept back along the Cranny river under cover of the sweet-smelling rat-ki-rani bushes until they reached the canal-head a short distance from where the river itself emerged from the saltpetre hill. From there to the distant indigo works the canal ran straight and wide along an embankment (at points an aqueduct, to allow passage underneath), supplying the baths with clear fresh water. At either end was a lock. Silently the nilchis opened the chief lock and let the river water swirl into the canal, wrinkling its low placid surface. Then they returned to the forest. The canal would take a day to fill, its level rising inconspicuously at the works end; the following day a diversionary attack from the east would allow a couple of nilchis to tackle the second lock.

The nilchis struck just before dawn, while Dori and an assistant, dressed in their captured rose-coloured uniforms, unlocked the brimming canal at the works end. The water leapt from its hold like an animal and instantly filled the catchment tank from which the baths were fed. It skimmed over the conduits and rushed down the slope in a wall that collapsed into the settling tanks, churning up dense stinking masses of fermented indigo stem. Within moments the topmost tanks were full and the wall of water grew up again until the tanks gave way. The whole row collapsed, tank after tank, stem, brick, and water, onto the beating tanks. The beating tanks, already half full, were flooded in a matter of seconds, and the wall of water, now a vivid blue, flashed across the evaporating pans and swept through the tents of the Rose Boys pitched just beyond the ovens. For one brittle moment the defensive wall checked the flood which beat up against it and sent a spray twenty feet into the air; then it buckled at its weakest point and let the water out onto the plain, where at last the torrent spent its force. Two Rose Boys were drowned in their tents and several were wounded by pieces of masonry. The indigo works, products of the Great Trotter's science, were completely destroyed, and the canal was breached at more than one point.

That same day the reinforcements arrived, their fresh uniforms a mocking contrast with those of the first batch of Rose Boys whose tunics when dried in the pale winter sun were found to have turned a deep mauve. Mik met them, trembling from his humiliation. Beside him on horseback was Charles in a damask jacket with a lance and musket thrust into his hands. Gulabi Trotter told the newcomers how things stood and commanded them to carry the battle into the forest. He pushed Charles forward. "Here is my firstborn," he barked. "Cover him with glory!"

The troops rode off towards the jungle, Charles hanging on to his horse's mane and making ineffectual little prodding motions with the lance, which he tried to carry like a paintbrush. At the best of times he could see perhaps three yards ahead of him and that in a kind of multicoloured haze; on horseback his vision was further blurred by the speed and the jolting so that he seemed to sit suspended in a bright diaphanous cocoon until a sudden gloom told him he had entered the forest. His musket was the first to go off, and he dropped it gratefully, its purpose served, and rode on crooning to himself. Then the going got rougher as his face was whipped by overhanging branches, one of which knocked off his helmet. A little further on, his lance dug into something soft which gave a cry so heart-rending that he dropped it at once and shouted over his shoulder that he was sorry but he couldn't stop the horse. Then something crashed down on his head, and he fell to the ground. The departing hoofbeats of the Rose Boys told him that they had not noticed his fall, but evidently someone else had. He saw several pairs of dark legs come right up to where he lay and he marvelled briefly at the beauty of their indigo hue. The tone of the voices around him told him he had been recognized, and he was going to explain that he was new to the killing business when the cocoon shrank to nothing and went black.

Next morning there appeared outside the Indigo Door, on the apron-steps, a sickle and a brass thali. Bulbul, who had waited all night for news of her husband, saw it from her window and ran downstairs. On the thali lay a row of fingers, once thought artistic, with an orange pastework ring worn loosely on the second one from the left.

Bulbul returned to her room and shut herself in. She knew her husband well enough to guess that he would not survive the shock. When her aged parents came up from the village to console her, she sent them back to fetch the carpenter and one of the blacksmiths and had every window in the North Tower barred except for the loft. She sat on the marriage bed and stared at the rumpled sheets where Charles had slept with her a night ago. The pillow still bore the impression of his head. Slowly she felt the world begin to dissolve, the days, the years, the seconds running together, the furniture sliding away under the pressure of her gaze. She tilted her head sharply and clarity returned, but then the insidious slipping away of objects resumed and she began to weep. She reached across to stroke the pillow: the action took a hundred years, the pillow was at the other end of the earth. She shook her head again and again, but each time the clarity was shorter. By the time Rose came by to commiserate with her over their common loss, the madness was complete; the girl who sat on the swing twittering and tilting her head one way and then the other no longer recognized her. Rose crossed to the cot where the Fourth Trotter sat watching his mother with childish awe. She picked him up and cradled him in her arms, tentatively, as if testing his weight. Then she took him downstairs, shut the door behind her, and carried him back with her to the Balloon Room.

For Mik the severed hand was a fresh humiliation. He put himself at the head of the combined troops and led a final assault on the guerrillas, having warned his boys that they were not to emerge from the jungle until every nilchi had been flushed out. The rissalah presented arms, saluted the Balloon Room, and trotted off across the Sea of Rains. By the evening Dori had been taken prisoner and only a handful of nilchis had got away by jumping into the Moti Ganga. There was blood on the leaves, on the rocks, in the grass, at the roots of trees, and the river ran red. The nilchis were never seen again at Sans Souci, but it was believed that those who escaped the crocodiles commandeered a barge and floated off downriver to spread their message to all the indigo works of Bihar and Bengal. Dori's death was quick and painless, the hot plate, a brass thali, not being applied until after the head was taken off. It was a spectacle in the infamous frontier manner, but the prisoner's bashful eyes were spared the last capering indignity. Only then was the indigo chapter considered closed, but Gulabi Trotter never forgot those mauve uniforms and the fact that the only reverse his Rose Boys ever suffered was at his home.

> *Enough, Narrator. A plain tale now, I beg you, without alarms and*
>   *excursions, lances and derring-do, for to tell the truth I am sick of it all.*
> *It will cost you dear, Cup-Bearer, running even to a cup of warm cocoa.*
> Anything, *Narrator, so the tale be bland. Here.*
> *Very well, Cup-Bearer. The sugar is lacking, but let it go. I have*
>   *heard from the house sparrow that it happened in this way.*

(CHRONICLE RESUMED)

Jacob Kahn-Trotter stood in the British House of Lords before the Select Committee on Indian Affairs. Among the assembled peers was the Duke of Wellington, but it was the Earl of Carlisle, on whom Jacob had first waited with the Anglo-Indian petition, who began the questioning.

Two days earlier the Earl had presented the petition to the House and met with opposition from Lord Ellenborough. Ellenborough declared that although he felt, as every person of the slightest humanity must feel, the greatest compassion for the unfortunate class to which the petitioners belonged, and although nobody could be more favourably disposed to their case than he, or was more fully conscious of the need to redress the evils under which they laboured, or felt more keenly the lash of injustice, or rejoiced more readily in the prospect of their speedy. Here Ellenborough and some of his audience fell asleep. Well? asked the Earl of Carlisle, after a pause. Ah—well, said Ellenborough, the Board of Control and the Directors of the East India Company, whom he knew well, had already given the petition the closest scrutiny and found many flaws in it.

Today, with the Anglo-Indian representative himself present before the Select Committee, Ellenborough resumed his *ex officio* mode and plied Jacob with questions designed to exonerate the Company by discrediting the complainants. Whenever a member came close to the mark he intervened to deflect and palliate. Did he mean, Wellington asked Jacob, that as a Christian he was subject to the Muhammadan criminal code and might have his hand struck off for theft?

—*Narrator!*—

Jacob answered peaceably, yes, he was, when in the interior. But, Ellenborough interjected, how many were there of his kind in the interior? Not a few, answered Jacob. Another member addressed the witness: In Calcutta you are entitled to British law, but in Nakhlau you are a Native? Yes, answered Jacob. We are sometimes Europeans and sometimes Natives, as it suits the purposes of the Government. Thus, Anglo-Indian officers employed by the Marathas were warned that they would be dealt with as traitors if they did not return to the Company's territories—yet as officers they were debarred from the Company's army. Ellenborough snorted: did they not run back to the British as fast as their legs, such as they were, could carry them? Jacob hung his head; legs were not his forte (*Rickety Trotter, Parenthetic Blank*). Ellenborough sat back with evident satisfaction and pinched his calves animatedly.

More than twenty years later, when Jacob was back in Calcutta, where he founded an excellent college, his Lordship sat on another Select Committee which cross-examined an Englishman home on furlough from India. He had forgotten nothing; his wits were as sharp as ever, his calves robust, and his ideas wonderfully preserved.

Extract from minutes of evidence taken before the Select Committee on the government of Indian territories

6700. [Earl of *Ellenborough*.] Are not the ladies of that class physically much better than the gentlemen?

[*Sir C. E. Trevelyan, K.C.B.*] I think not. That is not the result of my observation.

6701. Are not the generality of Indo-Britons a class of poor weakly-looking persons; very sallow and unhealthy in their appearance, and very small in stature?

They must not be compared altogether with us.

6702. Are they not inferior to the Natives in physical qualities?

I think not. They are inferior to some races of Natives in physical qualities; but I think they hold a very fair average position in point of physical qualities.

6703. Colonel Skinner was the son of a Rajpoot lady, was not he? He was.

6704. You would not say that the persons called Crannies were a fair sample of the human race, should you?

I think they are. They are superior in physical qualities to the Bengalees. They are inferior to the up-country peasantry; but many of our own people are inferior to the up-country peasantry. The Jat peasantry of the country between Agra and Lahore are a better grown, more developed and much handsomer race than our southern peasantry in England.

6705. Are you talking of their bodies or of their legs?

You look sceptical, Cup-Bearer. Very well, go to the British Parliamentary Papers on India for 23 June 1853, handsomely published by the Irish University Press, and see if I have changed a single word. Volume 16 at page 187. And while there fetch me a cup of Irish coffee, potent and sweet and creamy. Splendid! Are not the Irish an admirable race?

They must not be compared altogether with us, Narrator. But they have brought gold to the tongue.

(CHRONICLE RESUMED)

For a month after his cross-examination Jacob had little to do but enjoy the pleasures of London. With Giddy Abandon

—A tart, Narrator?—

he spent his nights crumbling water biscuits, not wishing to fritter away the subscribers' funds. Once he found himself in a confectioner's and hurried out, whistling. On Sundays he allowed himself a cup of cocoa. When suddenly the Easter recess was over and it was time to attend the House of Commons, where on the evening of the fourth of May the Anglo-Indian petition was presented by the Hon. Mr Wynn.

"I truly enjoyed a rich mental feast," Jacob wrote (*truly, Cup-Bearer*), "afforded by the warm debate arising from the subject,—one which was now, for the first time, fairly and tangibly brought before the Legislature. Without exception, it was decidedly the best thing in the way of a debate in the House that evening as was also acknowledged by others."

Mr Wynn spoke at length with a lively and liberal intelligence and with such generosity and feeling that Jacob, who had a seat in the House below the gallery, was profoundly moved. The petition, Mr Wynn said, was very numerously, and he might add very respectably, signed by persons called Indo-Britons (or Anglo-Indians) whose grievances might be grouped under two heads: they had no law and they were excluded from certain offices by virtue of their birth. As Christians they were, when in the interior, answerable to Muhammadan criminal law; as country-borns they were denied civil and military employ in the East India Company, except as clerks. He knew that there were those who talked of the inherent unfitness of persons of Indian descent to fill offices of trust and importance in India. He should be ashamed to argue with those who upheld such doctrines. He knew, moreover, that such permission as he now sought to obtain as a right for persons of this class would never be too extensively granted to them in practice, for certainly under any European administration, nothing but decided merit would place an Asiatic on the same level as an European. But in a House of Commons that had removed the exclusion of its Catholic fellow-subjects and taken the first steps to emancipate the Jews from their degraded position in the law of the country, he did not expect to find any opposition to so reasonable a prayer as that of the petitioners. He moved that the petition be brought up.

There was opposition. It came from Mr Stuart Wortley, Secretary to the Company's Board of Control, who thought it an unfit opportunity for discussion of the matter especially when the whole subject of the government of India was being considered by a committee above stairs. He then proceeded to show that the state of the petitioners was not as lamentable as it was declared to be by reducing the population of Calcutta's Anglo-Indian population from twenty thousand to two thousand, of whom one thousand were employed. The removal of a cipher thus worked a miracle of employment.

Next Sir James Mackintosh rose to say he had had an opportunity of observing the persons and characters of the men whose petition this was. He would not condescend, he said, to urge anything against the pretended inferiority of national character, or against the notion of there being one class created to rule and another merely to obey. He had ever accounted such doctrines as the common phrases of the advocates of oppression, nor was there a shadow of foundation for them in any part of the character of the natives of India. He had made a minute enquiry in the places of education, in counting houses, and in the offices of Government—where, it was true, some of these unfortunate beings were admitted to inferior offices. His main reason for rising had been his impulse of conscience which obliged him to declare that there was no class of individuals not in actual slavery throughout the dominion of the Crown in these realms that was used with so much needless harshness and oppression as this race.

Jacob's eyes, moist from the contemplation of Sir James, dissolved completely when Sir Charles Forbes rose to declare: "After an experience of twenty-two years in India and seventeen here, the more I see of my own countrymen, the more I like the natives of India." The shimmer of his tears invested Sir Charles with an antique robe: here was the Member for Gaul in the senate heaping scorn on his fellow countrymen. And what was the response of his listeners, secure in the expanding power of Rome? They nodded sagely, stroked beardless chins, or else, stirred by a deeper emotion murmured with a rustle of togas, *Hear, hear!* Even the sceptics, men who deplored phrase-making, contented themselves with a wry smile or a glance at the Member for Alexandria.

In a little while the ritual became clearer. "I congratulate," said Mr Wolryche, rising, "both the House and the natives of India on this discussion—the House, because we perform a sacred duty in showing that we extend our care and our protection over every part of the dominions under the British Crown; and not only that, but that we are ever ready to do our duty. I congratulate the natives of India, and especially the class to which the petitioners belong, on the effect of this Petition, because I am sure that it is only necessary for their interests to have the subject publicly discussed in order to ensure their progress and advancement."

Congratulations, duty, faith in the word: what remained? Only Mr John Stewart, who as everyone could see was wondering whether to rise, and who, as everyone knew, would. He agreed, did Mr Stewart, with all that had gone before (though he disagreed emphatically with the Honourable Secretary to the Board of Control who had thought it an unfit opportunity for discussion). He fully agreed, he said, with the Right Honourable and Learned Gentleman opposite that the oftener the House discussed the affairs of India the better prepared it would be to legislate for the natives of that country.

The petition was then read and tabled.

The Honourable Secretary to the Board of Control begged to observe that he had no objection to discussion, but confessed he was still of the opinion that the petition would, if fully gone into, occupy the attention of the House for a long period.

The petition was then ordered to be printed.

Jacob arrived at his lodgings in Cloudsley Terrace without any recollection of whether he had walked home from the dinner at Mr Wynn's or been dropped by the Honourable Member's coach. He made himself a cup of cocoa, though it was midweek, and surrendered himself to the exalting blaze in his head. It was gratifying that men of position, intelligence, and substance should have discussed with energy and in earnest the cause of a harmless people half-way around the globe. Even those of the Company's persuasion had studied the petition and spoken with an exactness which, Jacob had to admit, sometimes came nearer the mark than the sympathisers.

The next day Jacob was down with a cold from having fallen asleep uncovered in his chair. The chill lingered through the summer with the result that on the second day of his cross-examination before the Commons Select Committee he was advised to go home. He declined, despite a violent irruption of fever. Once again many of the questions put to him sprang from what he described as "certain antiquated notions of an illiberal stamp hatched in a particular quarter connected with India House." His testimony, much the same as that given before the Lords Committee, was again printed and referred to the East India Committee. Then, while he was still in Britain, Parliament was dissolved on the twenty-fourth of July. He sailed for India a month later, carrying a silver plate subscribed by sympathisers. In Madras and again in Calcutta, he was feted by the local Anglo-Indians; in Madras a newspaper described either the occasion or the petition (it was not clear which) as belonging with "the imperishable records of time." A few months after Jacob's return the new Parliament was also dissolved.

> *Cup-Bearer? Asleep!*
> *Forgive me, Narrator, but the house sparrow, Common or Lordly, is a great bore.*
> *It was what you asked for, Cup-Bearer.*
> *True, but who would have thought so much dreariness could stiffen one tale? Go on, but I beg you—no more house sparrows. Where is the cuckoo, the nightjar, the guttersnipe?*
> *Prurient Cup! Fetch me some* Halb und Halb *and hear what the secretary bird told me of the generation of prose.*

(*CHRONICLE RESUMED*)

For the rest of the winter after the indigo rebellion the nearer shores of the Sea of Rains remained caked with blue. When summer came, the dyed clay cracked into a million hexagons that curled up at the edges and looked from a distance like a petrified oasis. In the monsoon, weeds sprang up among the ruined baths and choked the canal, forming isolated pools along its length. The distemper in the East Tower began to peel and curl in the same way as the dye on the plain, but nobody lived there anymore. Farida, who had turned grey in the five weeks of the rebellion, went to live in the South Tower, overlooking the Ice Court. She shut the east-facing windows and spent hours in front of the mirror combing her cobwebby hair and rueing the tiny hexagonal wrinkles that had appeared on her face. The furniture in the room was in poor repair: one of the books which Jarman Begam left behind had gone to prop up the almirah with the mirror. Farida kept the gold fore-edge of the book facing out; on the tooled leather spine which faced inwards a passing rat might have read (had it not been too dark for reading):

Mirror of State and *Cup of State*. The writing desk had become a dressing table. When she was not sitting at it, her elbows shrivelled corks in a wilderness of lotions, Farida spent her time in bed waiting for death to come up and ravish her. Once a week, out of duty to her dead husband, she went down to look over the ice pits.

The children lived with Rose, whose new foster-son, Thomas Henry, showed signs of moderate growth. The Fourth Trotter's real mother remained locked up in her cage, having spoken to no one since her husband failed to return from his ride into the forest. No one disturbed her except Rose, who came daily to tell her that her son was well. Bulbul tilted her head and looked attentively at her visitor with bright uncomprehending eyes; sometimes she broke into a mournful distracted song of two or three notes which went on and on until Rose pushed a saucer of pumpkin seeds under the door and changed the water.

The body of Charles Augustine Pote Trotter was never found. "Our artist," a later biographer wrote (*Milquetoast Historian*), "sleeps in a nameless and forgotten grave." Chameleonlike, he vanished among the rocks and leaves, although Mik had the forest combed by the entire Sagarpaysan population along with two detachments of Rose Boys. In a ceremony of public atonement, Mik scourged himself with a bull's pizzle at the Water Gate and forswore wine to the end of his days. *Silence, Cup-Bearer!* Before the wounds had time to heal, he put his seersucker jacket back on and rode out at the head of his troops. It was a lacklustre salute he offered Rose from the Gunpowder Gate, and though he sat erect enough in the saddle, it was plain that his soldiering days were numbered. His last familial act had been to chuck Charles's son under the chin. Little Thomas Henry gripped his grandfather's finger and gave it a lusty wrench. "No, no," Mik growled, undoing the little fingers and patting them straight so they stuck out like quills, "you must think of becoming an accountant or something." And with that he got onto his horse and gave the reins a weary flick.

Not many months after Charles's death a story began to circulate about a ghost on horseback that roamed the forest by day. You heard the hoofbeats pass right by you and if you were lucky (a woodcutter-and-charcoal-burner had been) you caught a glimpse of the rider. He rode with one arm upraised to ward off the branches, plucking with invisible fingers at the harp of the forest while crooning a deep tuneless air of two or three notes. Sitting on her swing in the North Tower, Bulbul would tilt her head sharply and reply with her own distracted refrain; neither, it seemed, was a songster of any distinction. Their son, Thomas Henry, sometimes came along with Rose to the North Tower, but he always thought he was accompanying his mother to visit an unfortunate lady. He grew up in the belief that Ferdinand and Philip were his brothers and Philippa his sister. Rose did not disillusion him, believing that the time for that would come, and yet an occasion never seemed to present itself. Meanwhile the boy shot up like a papaya tree—and still the time seemed not right to Rose. If it had pleased God to send her another son, who was she to protest? He came to her half-fledged, it was true, unlike Charles who had come naked and tiny as babes should, but then Farida's brood had come fully clothed. She took out the yellow silk balloon and cut pieces out of it for his baby clothes, and since there was still a lot left of the *Salamandre*, Thomas Henry was still wearing yellow when he was past his eighth year. It was then that Philippa, in a moment of anger, said that only cowards wore yellow silk, cowards and cissies whose real mothers were mad and lived behind bars in the North Tower. The Fourth Trotter refused to believe the story about Bulbul's being his mother, but after that Rose had to fit him out from a batch of discarded mauve cavalry uniforms cut down to size.

On his own the boy began to write. To start with, nobody could make out a word of what he wrote, and he himself was just as mystified because he had simply been copying from the middle of a black book which lay open in the chapel. He did not cover his page with the usual aimless curly lines of childhood, and he drew no pictures. Charles, Rose remembered, had shown an early fondness for colours; with Thomas Henry it was never anything but ink, and only black ink. At St Aloysius's School he filled notebooks with transcriptions from any source that came to hand, starting anywhere and ending anywhere. He did not seem to care what he copied (once he copied his own work without knowing it), so long as it was prose and continued evenly and regularly to the end of the page. If he could have written a single continuous line on a ribbon which stretched to infinity he would have done so, for such was the nature of prose. As it was, he was constrained by the nature of the book, and in revenge filled an infinity of notebooks with his patient copying. Nobody denied that he had a well-formed hand (-writing, Cup-Bearer), and he himself took it for granted. Nature, chance, and circumstance connived to make of Thomas Henry a clerk.

It was a moderate childhood. His boyhood was not unpleasant and his approach to manhood not markedly traumatic. He was of medium height, neither deep-chested nor shallow-witted, and he sat in the middle of the class. His teacher noted that while his books were tidy his bootlaces were left undone. The dates of battles came readily to him but he had trouble remembering the names, and although he could mark the major plateaux of the world he could not for the life of him recall a single peak. Kind to insects, he was cruel to birds; he could climb up a tree but had trouble coming down. He ate impartially at meals, preferring nothing in particular to anything else, and even when Rose excelled herself with the gulab jamuns, he ate no more than two: not one, not three, but two (*Middle Trotter, Dark Horse*).

While the Middle Trotter was growing up, his foster-mother, now a matron past middle age, devoted herself to making sweets. For the noonday meal she made, in addition to mulligatawny soup and a curry and rice, Indian sweets; at night she made, to follow the mince cutlets and French beans, European desserts. She cooked in the nearest of the old kitchens and the Trotters still ate in the Glacerie at one end of the long table: the traditions, Rose said, must be kept up. The older children made no objection to a hall whose aqua pillars and dusty pankhas made eating an adventure, and as for Thomas Henry, who found the must and gloom disturbing, there was the comforting proximity of his foster-mother's splendid breasts. Rose nibbled constantly as she cooked, with the result that her bosom, which had expanded enormously in nursing two foster-sons, now grew to magnificent proportions. Her arms filled out too, and shook like jellies while her skin grew daily more soft and creamy though there was still no one in her life to stroke it. Through it all, her wrists and ankles remained delicate, even fragile-looking, and her feet were as tiny as a little girl's. She no longer walked in her sleep and she belched and yawned with a cheerfulness she would not have thought possible in the days when she dug her grave with a teaspoon. Kulfi, almond barfi, malai pan; flan au miel, St Clement's Charlotte: the milk and honey of two continents flowed in her veins. She followed no recipe book: the recipes were in her head, and, more arcanely, in those inspired transactions which occurred in the space between her hands. So it happened that one afternoon in 1844, Rose, called Gulbadan (*Rose-Bodied One, Matchless Bloom*), approached the kitchen in humility and openness, and taking cream and sugar in her scented hands, invented the gulab jamun.

Theses on the gulab jamun (1844)

1 The rose is the queen of flowers.
2 Every queen must have a king.
3 The rose is sweet-scented.
4 The sweet queen must have a sweet king.
5 The king of sweets must combine rosiness with sweetness.
6 He must attain perfection not only in essence [*attar*] but in form.
7 The perfect form is a sphere.
8 All shapes and conditions strive blindly towards this ideal.
9 The blind striving can be harnessed.
10 It should be.

11 Confectioners have hitherto only talked about the perfect sweet; the point, however, is to invent it.

12 It has been invented.

An axiom: If it did not exist, the gulab jamun would have to be invented.

(*CHRONICLE RESUMED*)

The king of sweets, jamun-shaped (*Eugenia jambolana*), anointed with pure ghi, pooped with heavy syrup, and sprinkled with rosewater, appeared regularly at the Old Armoury end of the dining table. But the Middle Trotter ate no more than two.

He did at least partake. Farida, who sometimes came to lunch, began and ended with the pepper-water, her sole contribution to the meal being a sigh at the end. Sometimes she cast a reproachful glance at the children who had gone over to Rose; already they were taller than her eldest, Luis, had been. As for herself, her looks were gone, she knew. The brief rejuvenation that came when she first returned to Sans Souci and took up the keys seemed a cruel trick of fate because it left her more hapless than if age had crept up on her with its familiar glacial advance. As it was, the indigo affair wreaked a sudden ferocious havoc on her face. A newcomer to Sans Souci might have been forgiven for supposing that in the old days it was Rose and not Farida who had looked at herself sideways in the mirror and smiled and hugged her friend because she knew who was prettier.

Farida's youngest son, Ferdinand Fonseca-Trotter, was not for staying. As soon as he was old enough he went back to Calcutta, the city of his father's dreams, with a vision of his own: an establishment on Park St where one might buy every conceivable kind of delicacy, from an oyster to a cream cake. He surprised himself, doing so well that within a few years he had fine food shops in Madras and Bombay as well. In time his tribe of sons spread to towns all across the country, one of them returning to Nakhlau to open a branch (called, predictably, Ferdinand Fonseca's Fine Foods) which would give J.c. Solomon & Son sleepless nights. Philip and Philippa lived on with Rose, companions for young Thomas Henry. They were joined at playtime by Alina Violet Alexander-Trotter and her brother Cyril Brendish, but not by the only other survivor among Mik's twelve children, Attila, whose idea of play was to sweep across the Steps ululating like a heathen. (Heatstroke, rich blood, and brain fever had carried off the rest of his sibs.) Cyril, ginger-haired and dull-eyed, played with string and cigarette tins and talked of the day he would join the telegraphs. Alina, whose muscles showed under her pale butter-coloured skin, spent her time planting jakfruit seeds and could not pass under a low branch without swinging from it and pulling herself up with an awesome display of biceps. Philip, a small lisping boy with a sleepy look, had made himself a railway engine out of bits and pieces from the rubble of the Old Armoury and even managed to lay a length of track for it. He had heard that England was criss-crossed with steel roads and that trains were coming to India before long: his profession was already decided. Small and sooty like her brother, Philippa grew up a wordless uncomplaining girl lost in uneasy admiration of others. Even Thomas Henry, who was her junior by several years, caught up with and outstripped her, so that she looked up to him with abject imploring eyes. Her reward was a string of demeaning tasks which he imposed with quiet satisfaction. She might have been protected by a watchful mother or grandmother, but Farida had eyes only for her own decrepitude and Rose was too full of creamy sweetness to see wrong.

Farida was not the only bitter one. Evidently someone else in Nakhlau had drained his cup to the lees, because one day, fifty years after the death of Justin Aloysius Trotter (peace be His) there appeared on the bookshelves of J.c. Solomon & Son a privately printed pamphlet—it was hardly a book— in villainous yellow covers which appeared to harbour a grudge. The pamphlet sold briskly on the first day, though some said that that was because people came to gawk at the author, a man reputed to be upwards of a hundred and fifty years old, as he signed copies of his work. He stood—or rather bent— there, with his small square wizened face thrust at the world and a dripping quill held in his hand. His cap was shinier than ever and the few wisps of hair that had once stuck out from underneath were gone. Nor was there any trace of a button on his person. On the second day no one came to J.c. Solomon & Son's book bargain, and the few bins of wine that had been carelessly placed between the shelves had to be returned to the godown. Apart from a single order for 150 copies to be delivered to the Fish Palace Library, the rest of the edition went to heat the Nawab's bath-water. The public, it seemed, were tired of controversial books and captious authors. All the same, a copy of the pamphlet did find its way, unordered, to the Gunpowder Door at Sans Souci (nobody knew when) and was duly deposited (nobody knew how) in the history section of the library, under C.

Who Says the Great Trotter was Great?

WHO SAYS THE GREAT TROTTER WAS GREAT?
by
P.U.N.D.I.T.

(author of *The Marvel that was Mexico*, *Where is Guatemala?*, *Crystals and Your Health*, *Glass-Blowing and Related Sciences*, *An Uzbek-Urdu*

Dictionary, The Philosophy of Zero, The Indian Numerals, Ice Exposed, More Zero, The Taj Mahal: A Hindu Mausoleum, Levantine Loiterings, Arakanese Nights, Javanese Mornings, Thibet on One Rupee a Day, Lion of Lhasa, &c, &c.)

Back Cover:

Fifty years ago this day, a man believed by some to have been great fell to his death out of an aerial balloon. Much (some would say too much) has been written about this man, but many questions remain to tease the questioning mind. Of these perhaps the most tormenting has certainly been the one which no historian to date has had the courage to fearlessly ask. Now one such has raised his head and dared to lift up his voice in the prevailing conspiracy of silence. Was, he asks, the Great Trotter really great? For his astonishing conclusions, go at once to page one. When you have reached the end, swept along by his gripping exposé, we feel certain you will also join the ranks and files of those who are already verbally crying from the rooftops of Nakhlau: *Who Says the Great Trotter was Great?*

Some Advance Reviews:

"Peppery stuff"—*Nakhlau Nuntio*

"The chapter on the will, perhaps the nub of the book, is
a model of plain speaking"—*Hazratganj Tribune*

"Fire is the author's forte, to which he has now added
brimstone"—*Tirnab Hazard*

"A *tour de force* of a *cri de coeur*"—*Fish Palace Quarterly*

Work in Progress:
*How to Use Britain to Oust the Old Enemy**
(**And Then Get Rid of Britain*)—expected out in 1858

(*CHRONICLE RESUMED*)

About that time Gipsy Trotter returned, with the monsoon guavas, having finally made his peace with himself. He took off his seersucker jacket for the last time and had a batman prise off his boots. These, together with his sword and guns, he deposited in the military museum, and slipped his calloused stinking feet into a pair of slippers that hurt for months and gave him ingrowing toenails. He sent his salaams to Rose, and asked for his grandson to come up. A young man neither short nor tall and of middling complexion appeared before him.

"Good day, Thomas Henry. Do you know me?"

"An equable day, Grandfather."

"Eh? Yes. Well, true enough. Well, then. And how does the writing go? Prosing along, what?"

"Passably, sir. Sometimes it goes well and—"

"Sometimes it does not?"

"Exactly, sir!" said Thomas Henry, surprised.

"Well, there it is, I suppose." Mik had turned oddly garrulous. "And you?" he went on. "No martial inclinations, I hope. Let me take your pulse. Heavens! Did you run upstairs? And so mild to look at. The world is done with war, you know. Sick to death of it. I assure you. A century of peace we're looking at. Not that I. But you, now. Goodwill towards men. Lion and lamb. Doves. Ploughshares. Any day now. The British will put a pen in the Nawab's hand. Prosperity. Peace. I tell you I feel it in my bones. Well, now. That being so, we must think of finding you a position, heh? A writer in one of the government offices. Would you like that?"

"Yes and no, Grandfather."

The Middle Trotter was put into an office. Mik used his influence to get him a clerkship in the uncovenanted civil service, since as an Anglo-Indian the boy could not apply for a covenanted post. And on the first of the following month, Thomas Henry, who secretly felt that he deserved better, took his place at a desk heaped with medium beige government paper. With a fluid movement he reached for the topmost chit and began to copy it out into a register in his well-formed, regular, medium-sized script that sloped neither to the left nor to the right. But under the moderate exterior an erratic pulse had already begun to beat. Thomas Henry was himself unaware of it, and registered only the minutest tic at his eye. "The *un*covenanted civil service," he said to himself, looking around the office. He did not know what the covenant was, only that he was outside it. The other clerks were too busy to notice the twitching, for each man sat up to his eyes in a bunker of beige paper and scratched away with a pen. Presently the Middle Trotter too became absorbed in his paperwork. When he looked down he found his pen had copied a whole page without his assistance.

Come home for the last time, Mik installed himself in the flaking East Tower. He had lost the art of sleeping in the saddle and no longer cared for straw and rough blankets. The sisters Alexander were now past cavorting in the hay, and Gipsy Trotter himself preferred to let his mind frolic while he sat with his legs up on a platform of mango wood that had once served (though he did not know it) as a drawing board for his son. Slippers, rose-coloured pyjamas, and a dark red smoking jacket piped with black silk made up his daily dress, the jacket because although he kept his vow about drink, he smoked more furiously than ever. He was spared the necessity of inventing the mosquito net: no insect could have survived his noxious smudge fires. His carefully waxed and twisted moustaches were occasional casualties of the vice, usually on the left because he had to hold the matchbox under his chin while striking the match with his only hand. Sometimes he dreamed ruefully of inventing the safety match, but he knew it was too late for small things. He had read somewhere of a man who met his death by spontaneous combustion, and secretly approved of a fiery end, but all the same he used as an ashtray an old mortar that he made sure was completely dead. Polo, of course, whether fiery or not, he had long given up on account of a game knee. Also because of the knee he took the lowest of the rooms in the East Tower. Even so he was high enough to look out across the Indigo Court through one window; through the one next to it he could see, just above the Rib and the derelict Crocodile Wing, the forest. Where his son had been unable to see beyond the tip of his nose, Mik was blessed with long sight, so long in fact that he often saw what was not there anymore. So, of an evening he would sit at his window with a little case of potent country cigarettes and a box of lucifers on his lap and gaze out at the flourishing indigo works, watching the nilchis torch the foul gases. Every now and then a lambent blue flame would whip across the fermentation vats with a lash that sounded at a distance like a gasp, and Gipsy Trotter, who had seen so many marvels in his day, would shake his head in wonder.

And he would talk. The man who in his youth had been morbidly uncommunicative seemed to find his tongue the moment he hung up his sword. During the first months his listener was the ancient Alexander, who invariably fell asleep at the crucial part of the story (he liked the blood) and obliged Mik to start over. The old Greek listened with roaming milky eyes until his lids rolled down again and his chin fell with a clatter on his breastbone; if he stayed awake, his hand, groping for the hilt of his short sword, set up a feeble rattling at the scabbard; both sounds Mik found distracting. But one morning the sisters Alexander came to report that their father had passed away in his sleep. The sculptor's bed was used as his bier and he was buried amid cackling and wailing in the quarry near his blacksmith wife, his rock carvings their happy epitaph. After that, Rose, who had been looking for an excuse, went to sit in the chair beside Mik, and the two would stare out of the window at the fireflies thronging the jakfruit trees, and Mik, oblivious of his companion's splendid breasts, would talk.

In fact Mik had not, during his last absence, spent all his time warring. Towards the end he had arranged for his second son, Attila, a fierce and fecund young man, to assume command of the Rose Boys while he himself went in search of peace. He travelled to the very tip of India and from there turned around and started back northwards. He stopped at all the important shrines, chiefly but not exclusively (*Eclectic Trotter, Idolater*) Christian ones. On the way north he did stop in Madras to ask after a Mrs Llewellyn and her daughter, but he learnt only that the woman was long dead and the girl sold into slavery. Heartbroken, he was of a mind to end his days as a coolie in the new icehouse on the Kistnampet beach, but an inner prompting spurred him on. His pilgrimage had only just begun: he climbed Adam's Peak to kneel by the giant footprint of our first father, he stood in the blest shade of the Bom Jesus Basilica, he kissed the pickled corpse of St Thomas the Doubter, and still he pressed northwards across rivers and ravines that he had once charted as a young surveyor with a boy and a pony. Finally he reached the high Himalayas, where he stood rapt, gazing at the blue and silver bosom of Lake Mansarovar. There at last the peace entered his heart and he returned to civilization filled with a horror of war. His pacifism, hot and inconsistent, manifested itself in a kind of internationalist zeal: his talk ran chiefly to his travels by land and sea, and he spoke of the remotest countries with a zest that brought them glowing into the room where he sat. You would have supposed that he visited Lithuania expressly to turn wolves inside out like gloves, and that he once cured and threw away a golden fleece in New Zealand for a dare; animals, at any rate, did not qualify for the new pacific order. When he told his tales he grew so heated that his bullet head shone like polished brass, but suddenly in the middle of a story he seemed to catch at a tuneless crooning in the air, and his voice would falter and break off. Then his skin took on the colour of ash and for a long time he was silent, staring accusingly at the forest beyond the dairy till his eyes filled with tears.

He was not always in his chair. By day Rose had her work to do, and Gipsy pottered about in the New Armoury bending bayonets into garden-shears and melting pistols down to spoons. He rejected, in a long indignant eristic letter, an offer to become the Nakhlau agent for a rocket manufactory at Phapamhow, and he turned his father's powder magazine, the Life-Giving House, which had become a hunting-lodge, into a waystation for incorrigible travellers. It was he who planted the Asoka trees along the Trotter Road. Between the kitchens and the glacis of the saltpetre hill he set up a sugar-cane-press to which he harnessed a camel that he had once liberated but which returned voluntarily to its old quarters. The press lasted a solitary week because the beast died in harness, but it supplied Rose with cheap sugar for a season, and the fibre waste gave Mik the idea for the invention of his old age.

The salamander

Of all vulgar errors, the most vulgar and erroneous is the belief that the salamander is a balloon. Almost as fanciful is the notion that it is an animal, real or mythical. It is true the salamander has a belly which holds water and a tube which passes through, and it cannot be denied that the creature has three legs below and a neck above. But let us not jump like lemmings (which are no relation) over the cliff of conclusions. The salamander is neither vegetable nor animal, but mineral. It was invented in the middle of the nineteenth century by General "Gipsy" Trotter to demonstrate the peaceful uses of fire. It is a drum of iron sheeting with a funnel or chimney passing through its centre (thus from the upper elevation we see a circle within a circle). The drum is filled with water, the chimney with kindling. Thus the fire, when it is lit, is not under the water but *in* the water (in a metal sleeve) and the heat is distributed outwards, not upwards. Nor is costly fuel wanted: any trash will do, as who should say, history books, vile novels, worthless paintings (as who should say, certain self-portraits), broken lance shafts, globose butts, cigarette butts, indigo stubble from the final crop, sugar-cane fibre from the press. The drum is covered, except at the chimney, to keep the heat in. When the water is found to steam it is drawn off by a tap or stopcock at the bottom. This is *bath-water*, the product of heat used for peaceful ends. The salamander is now available from J.c. Solomon & Son, who are in the usual place near the Residency.

(CHRONICLE RESUMED)

Working in the city, Thomas Henry chose to live at the edge of Sans Souci in the Life-Giving House. He turned out the travellers from what had only recently become a serai, and found his new lodgings satisfactory: if the furniture was spartan, the ride to work was halved and he got there on time. His punctuality was not a matter of conscientiousness; he simply wished to keep his job, and he kept it not because he liked it (he did not) but because there was no money left at Sans Souci. The cane-press was defunct, only one of the ice pits was stocked, and he seemed incapable of living within his means. Besides, he was now married, and Philippa looked close to giving birth. She had married him without a murmur, drawing one side of her mouth into a meek smile. Six months later, the shape of her belly told Rose (who remembered a ballooning of her own) that the moderate Thomas Henry had laid on twins: one would be too few and three too many. At the wedding he had eaten his customary two gulab jamuns and looked unflappable, telling himself that if marriage had its disadvantages, there were also its advantages. The bride, whose plain features were miraculously transformed (here too Rose had been at work), had no opinion; after all she had honoured and obeyed the groom since he stood as high as her shoulder. But in her confused guilty way she had sensed, even before he came to her on the wedding night, that a vein of turbulence ran under the Middle Trotter's wonted calm.

By day Thomas Henry sat at his desk in the city, his pen automatically transcribing words and figures while his eyes roamed the office. Packed into the Writers' Building were a dozen clerks (they were no longer called writers, but the name of the building stayed) who sat at desks which dovetailed with one another in order to frustrate supplicants entering at the main door. Along the walls and at intervals across the hall were black-varnished shelves bursting with files, many of which spilled out their contents for want of a simple tie. Overhead the pankhas flapped, their ropes stretching across the hall like rigging to disappear through china-smooth holes in the wall beyond which, in the verandah, sat the tribe of pankha-pullers. Occasionally the breeze plucked a bill from one of the untied files and sent it spinning across the room. That was usually when a pankha-wala woke up with a start after nodding off: the rope slackened, the pankha slowed to a halt, a sharp curse flew, the pankha jerked into motion, a bill or receipt came floating down.

The Fourth Trotter looked around at his fellow clerks (he had found himself a desk in the middle of the hall). They sat with their heads bent, their pens scratching; unlike him, they had not developed the art of automatic writing. Thomas Henry, who could copy with his eyes closed, wondered briefly whether they did not dream of their wives as they worked. He certainly did, frequently and with a passion that could shake his neat regular script. Looking down at his page, he was dismayed to find these irregular passages— sometimes a word crept in which bore no resemblance to the original, and was not even to be found in the dictionary—but was powerless to control their irruption. He frowned, creasing for the first time his composed forehead. Was there a pleasure in the immoderate for which his past had not prepared him? He kept his daytime fantasies from Philippa and checked them when he could, but his severity on himself, he saw, was only another form of immoderation. He tried another kind of dreaming, but that only made him discontented with his lot. Instead of undressing his wife he began to wish he was in the superintendent's chair, or in the covenanted civil service, or somewhere else altogether, winning a medal for some noble deed or invention. The pankha, he mused, looking upwards, was already invented; so was the steel-nib pen, and ink and blotting paper and the paperweight, not to speak of the file. His grandfather had just patented a water-heater, his great-grandfather had invented an array of strange devices, among them the filing cabinet (which had not caught on in India), even his wife's grandfather was said to have invented the dumb-waiter. What was left?

He went back to dreaming of his wife, how he would go home tonight and blow out the candle and whisper immoderate nonsense, now hot, now sweet, in Philippa's ear, until she lay back and forgot about the debts mounting on all sides. And as Thomas Henry dreamed, the pile of papers on his desk began to swell.

How red tape is made

I wish to shew how red tape is made. Safflower and saffron, bright adept, are notable dyestuffs for making yellow. Silk (for aerial balloons) and other materials may be dyed with them. It is a well-known fact that if the yellow is rinsed out of the fabric thus dyed (let us say silk, cut up in the Balloon Room by the thrifty), the colour that remains is not white but *red*. Thus, if the adept object to the colour yellow on principle, his wife may rinse it out of his garments, leaving, say, red pyjamas. Pyjamas, virtuous adept, are an excellent invention, though some count them a hindrance, finding the draw-string a great nuisance in the dark. For such, the drawstring is best removed altogether and put to some other use. It may, for example, be taken to the office to tie files withal, a use that will soon catch on among clerks, an apt and willing tribe. This is one way.

The other way is to go directly to J.c. Solomon & Son, situate by the Residency, just where the road turns away. At this moment, J.c. the elder is busy supplying all the haberdashery needs of the ladies of White Town, Nakhlau. Quantities of embroidery silks and tapestry cloth, to say nothing of needles and thimbles, are being sold daily to the bonneted ladies of this and the surrounding stations, ladies who sit at home, in the Residency or in the cantonments across the river, embroidering roses and forget-me-nots and jonquils and thatched cottages with gardens in which further bonneted ladies sit embroidering roses and forget-me-nots and such. Lately, however, the men of White Town have begun to require their wives and daughters to work, in a variety of stitches, improving mottoes such as: OLDE ENGLANDE, MOTHER KNOWS BEST, OUR FATHER, A SHEPHERD'S PRAYER, HOME SWEET HOME, and WOMEN AND CHILDREN. Especially, of late, WOMEN AND CHILDREN. The cross-stitch, much favoured, is meticulously worked, but the underside of all embroidery is a fright. When you have your tape and scissors hie you home, sharp adept, stopping only to pick up one of those bottles of sweet red which lie in bins carelessly strewn between shelves of groceries. Buy some provisions too, since it is time for stocking up. Who knows, with the temper that shows in the bazars these days, what might happen? Why, even J.c.'s shop could be looted, though it is right next door to the Residency (just across the way)! Take your tape and your wine and your plum duff and hurry home: time is running out. It is exactly one hundred years since the Battle of Plassey (1757) when Clive opened Bengal for the British. The centenary will be celebrated with fireworks, so get you home and bolt the door. To calm yourself pour a glass of sweet red and proceed to cut the tape into lengths twice the width of an office file, plus a little for the bow. If your hand shakes and a little wine is spilt, no matter: the tape is stained and you are saved a hazardous journey to Dilawar Das & Son, Dhobis and Dyers, who are of course rogues. This was the other way.

One way or the other, it is likely you will have to wait until after the troubles before you can popularize your invention. A trial, however, is in order. This is what I wished to shew. So do that. But do it quickly. Time is short. Tape or not, it will be a red year.

(CHRONICLE RESUMED)

The pile of papers on Thomas Henry's desk grew taller, but it suited him well enough, since the buff of the files matched his skin and he could idle without being noticed. His pen had slowed a little with the onset of summer, and the tiny heat blisters between his fingers were itching as if he lacked distractions. But Thomas Henry's brain ranged much farther: when he was not tumbling Philippa (her twins were a year old and already she was making more), he was leading a charge, all unclerically. And yet there *had* been a clerk who covered himself with glory on the field, a clerk who at twenty-five became Britain's chief military commander in India—Robert Clive! As impulsive a scrivener as ever brandished quill. Twice attempted suicide, both times the pistol stuck. Duellist, debtor, dandy; hero of Arcot, victor of Plassey, nabob par excellence, astonished by his own moderation. Ah, to be moderately immoderate! History had obliged the young Robert with a war. Would it, a hundred years on, oblige Thomas Henry? The Middle Trotter sat and dreamed. If someone—a trader, perhaps, in search of a permit—came to his desk, having negotiated the maze, Thomas Henry could now spread his hands and point at the mountain of files in front of him. Each one was impossibly knotted with a drawstring of red tape.

Meanwhile, Mik sat in his chair and discoursed on peace until one night Rose interrupted him with a tale of her own. Her interruption was unusual enough to surprise him into listening. That evening at dinner, she said, there had appeared on the long table in the Glacerie, among the breaded chops and boiled beans, a small pile of dry wheat chapatis. Rose, who never made unleavened bread except for lunch (dinner being a strictly European affair), was puzzled, but said nothing. It was only after she had them removed that she remembered Philippa's visit that very morning—to report exactly such an appearance on her table at the Life-Giving House.

The tale ended there, but Mik was already on his feet. The travelling pile of chapatis could mean only one thing—and it confirmed reports that had reached him of disaffection in the Company's army. There were still men who kept Tartar Sahib informed: they told of sepoys refusing to handle the new Enfield cartridge because the caps, which had to be bitten off before loading, were rumoured to be greased with the fat of cows, sacred to Hindus, and pigs, unclean for Muslims. When Rose had gone, Mik wrote a memorandum to the British Resident in Nakhlau advising him that unless certain immediate steps were taken, the sepoys would revolt and be joined by the populace, making things unpleasant not only for Europeans but for Anglo-Indians as well. The same night he despatched the memorandum to Thomas Henry at the hunting-lodge with instructions to pass it on to the Resident the first thing next morning. Thomas Henry did take the memorandum across the Ice Bridge to Nakhlau, but by tiffin it had found its way into a file securely bound and knotted with a red drawstring. The file was not Thomas Henry's, so it seemed the invention was catching on. In the memorandum, Mik had begged the Resident to advise his senior military officer to withdraw the new cartridges from use until such time as the chapatis that were now making their rounds should appear spread with ghi.

A note on ghi

Also GHEE, clarified butter. Clear and liquid in summer, white and solid in winter, it is not to be confused with the fat of cows or pigs (see LARD). It is used for cooking by the fortunate few, but also for spreading, when heated, on fresh rounds of unleavened bread (see CHAPATI) sometimes with unrefined sugar (see JAGGERY) sprinkled on top. All manner of sweets (see AMIRTI etc.) are doubly delicious when made with pure ghi. It is also wonderful when poured liberally over lentils, pulses (see DAL), and the like, after a pinch of cumin seed or asafoetida has been fried in it. All in all, it is a good thing. Enough cannot be had of it. The term *ghi* is sometimes indiscriminately applied to all solid cooking oils, including those of vegetable origin (see HYDROGENA-TION). Such a definition is misleading and pernicious, for not all vegetable oils (see VANASPATI) are of vegetable origin. Certain manufacturers have been known to mix in beef tallow imported under a soap licence. There is no telling what the wicked foreigner will stoop to. Best to buy from the Alexander sisters, who are in the new place (at death's door, if truth be told) in the Rib. A daughter, the strapping Alina, has taken up the burden: she milks the buffaloes and mans the churn. Go to her. Ghi is seldom eaten plain: why not mix in, say, sugar and semolina flour (see SUJI)? Suji halva is the excellent result, so rich it needs no accompaniment, though some use puris (see PURIS). Spoon it onto a banana leaf (see BANANA) or grease-proof paper (SEE PAPER), but on no account cartridge paper (see MUTINY).

(*CHRONICLE RESUMED*)

On the twenty-ninth of March, 1857, a sepoy of the 93rd Native Infantry stationed in Nakhlau refused to bite—

—*Narrator? This greased cartridge and chapati affair*—
Stale, Cup-Bearer?
You said it, Narrator, not I. I have heard it before. It seems as if every story-teller—
Agreed, my Cup, we will scrap it. But I will have wasted a note on ghi.
A note on ghi is never wasted, Narrator.
Well said. Very well, fetch me a bottle of Marsala from the Solomon shop before the looters get there, and I will say no more about greased cartridges and chapatis. Good man. What—wounded!
A scratch, Narrator. Everything but this was taken.
Stout heart! Now listen. I have heard from the adjutant bird that it happened in this way.

(*CHRONICLE RESUMED*)

Mahavir Pandav, sepoy of the 93rd, had been drinking. On his way back from the bazar, he stamped up and down in front of the quarter-guard, jeering at the sentry and calling on his fellow soldiers to rise up against the foreigner.

"Remember, your caste is in danger from those greased ——s! The British intend to convert all of us to Christianity. What are you? Cowards? Are you asleep? Rise up now! Already there is resistance—or have you not heard of the dry ——s that are appearing everywhere?"

The guard wavered, but did not throw open the armoury. Pandav's jeering grew louder. In a little while a British officer came on the scene and ordered the guard to arrest sepoy Pandav. The guard refused. The lieutenant stood irresolute a moment and then went in search of his commanding officer. Colonel Willis, he was told, was at Sans Souci visiting his old friend, Gulabi

Trotter. Riding out at once, the lieutenant carried the news there himself, breaking into one of Mik's discourses on peace. Under other circumstances Willis, who had been nodding off, might have been grateful for the interruption; today he turned to Mik for more. The name Gulabi Trotter still carried weight, he proposed, and besides Mik spoke the vernacular as well as he spoke English: a speech in Hindustani might save the situation, since the soldiers were not yet openly mutinous.

Mik agreed. The officers rode on ahead while he hobbled off to the military museum, where he drew on his brittle boots. Then he saddled his old mare, who looked enquiringly at him, and rode to the hunting-lodge to call out his grandson, Thomas Henry. Together the two men galloped through the fading light to the cantonment, Thomas Henry wondering whether his hour had come and Mik trying to work the tranquillity of Lake Mansarovar into a Hindustani speech. When they drew near the quarter-guard, the sight of a soldier drunk in uniform drove all thoughts of peace from Gulabi Trotter's head. He dug his spurs into the mare and charged, mouthing foul oaths and waving his sabre above his head as he used to many years before when only a cadet.

Mahavir Pandav stopped his harangue and turned to meet the attack, snatching the sentry's musket. He was a tall man with moustaches that rivalled Mik's.

"Grandfather, his musket is loaded!" Thomas Henry called, reining his horse aside.

"Damn his musket!" Mik roared and galloped on.

"He is taking aim at you, Grandfather!"

"If I fall, Thomas Henry, you will cut him down!"

But Thomas Henry, civilian-and-clerk, had no sword. He had barely had time to pull some clothes over his pyjamas and to snatch up an enamel washbasin as a kind of shield. The basin fell to the ground as he caught a glance of angry enquiry from an officer of the 93rd. What business did a civilian have there? What, for that matter, was a retired commander of irregular horse doing there?

The second question was curtly answered: at that moment a shot rang out and Gulabi Trotter sagged in his saddle. The mare, remembering an old lesson, rode on and straight over Mahavir Pandav.

Ten days later, Mahavir Pandav was court-martialled and executed. He died calm, aloof, and unrepentant, with the slightly knowing look of a martyr. Mikhail Trotter, also known as Gulabi Trotter, Gipsy Trotter, and Tartar Sahib, died on the same day of a bullet wound in the abdomen. His doctor, Hakim A. Ahmed, nephew of Hakim Ahmed, was unable to help him with his roots and powders, and he seemed disinclined to help himself. He lay in his reclining chair in the East Tower with Rose always at his side. Once he wished he could extend the armrests on his chair so that he could put his feet up without taking his boots off, but just then he died. The inventing of the railway retiring room chair was left to epigoni. As his soul slipped away in what looked like a puff of smoke, he took Rose's hand and kissed it for the first time. The old delicious resistance was gone, and Rose thrilled at the contact, but Gulabi's lips were already cold. By his express wish Mik was cremated and the ashes placed in an urn in the military museum, which he asked to be renamed the Abode of Peace. One part, however, escaped burning, because when the body had been washed and laid out on a block of ice Hakim A. Ahmed took a razor and made a significant excision in the name of science. And for many years after, there stood beside the urn in the museum a decanter filled with clear alcohol in which, like a wrinkled blue sea horse, swam Gipsy Trotter's foreskin.

Within a week all the Alexander sisters were dead, of grief or of choking or of self-inflicted wounds. The muscular Alina, who for many years had stood over the milk churn in their stead, dug a dozen graves beside the eight in which her hot-blooded brothers lay buried. Afterwards she levelled the soil in the Crocodile Wing and returned to the churn, sweating because it was the middle of April. She was a large-boned obdurate woman who smelt of custard and wore wooden slippers with a spool-shaped toe-grip. Her Greek forehead was narrowed in the middle by a cowlick, and short sight made her squint her startling grey eyes. She could not read, but her shoulders were like bookshelves; her chest was as solid as a tree trunk and her forearms were alive with unpredictable muscles.

It was quiet in the dairy with the old ladies gone. She missed their husky chatter and the way they had of cracking their knuckles in unison. But in the morning when the buffaloes started their bellowing, Alina was comforted by routine. She would kick the old leather medicine ball across the floor (it came from the gymnasium into which the Alexander-Trotters had moved), sit down on it beside a buffalo, remember the bucket, get up again to fetch it, remember the well by the jakfruit tree, swill out the bucket and set it down with a clang under the udders. Then she went to work, her head on one side for the creature to lick, her forearms rippling as she plied the black teats. Mesmerized by the jets of milk that alternately purred at the bottom of the bucket and drilled against its side, purred and drilled, purred and drilled, she would drift off and dream of her railwayman who had gone off to Allahabad and was building a track that would bring him back again. In fact Philip had promised to come back before it was finished, on leave. *Leave!* It was a word that never failed to delight Alina, who had milked the buffaloes every month including Sundays, for years; but now she had no one to use it on. Her brother, Cyril Brendish, worked in the telegraph office and had taken up lodgings with another tele-graphist at the greyish edge of White Town. Lately his visits were shorter and less frequent, and he brought such alarming news of unrest in the city that Alina had begun to wish he would not come at all. The only other people she saw were Farida and Rose; from one she fetched the ice for the dairy and to the other she delivered the milk for the kitchen.

One morning after the milking was done she walked up the Steps and across the Water Court to Farida's tower. Farida was not in, and the ear-ring on which hung the last of the Sans Souci keys, the key to the ice pits, was not on its nail. This was curious, because on Wednesdays the two women usually went down to the ice shed together for the block that Alina carried all the way back across Sans Souci on her shoulder. On the dressing table below the long mirror in which Farida daily discovered ruin and decay, was a fragment of ice. The moat of water around it had spread to the pins and jars and comb that lay on the tabletop and trickled down to a pool on the floor. Alina was used to the chaos in the room: candle ends, cotton swabs, cakes of mouse-bitten soap, and fragrant corks formed a kind of stubble through which she had learnt to walk, but the water was new. She called softly: "Farida!" There was no answer. The curtains, bleached and fraying, stirred and became still again. Alina turned and went back downstairs to the ice pits. The sun had come up. From half-way across the Ice Court she saw that the second pit was open: the lid leaned back on its hinge gleaming like an archer's target. Strange, thought Alina. Ordinarily Farida left the least manual task to her, and besides, only the first pit was functioning. Still more strange, the door to the ice shed, which stood over the first pit (it was where the ice was weighed), was also ajar. From it there unrolled a carpet of mist, white in the morning sun.

Alina came up to the shed and stood in the doorway, feeling the cold damp breath spread over her face and arms, which were bare to the elbow. It was a sensation which always gave her pause, the goose pimples down her front while the morning sun, already warm, shone on her back. She might have been divided exactly in half: the lobes of her ears frozen, the cartilage at the back flushed and red. She stepped across the threshold and glanced around, her shadow framed in gold on the opposite wall. Except for the light reflected off the wall and caught in a block of uncovered ice, the rest of the shed was still dark. She called, "Farida!" No answer came. A block of ice shifted slightly, but there was no other sound. She glanced at the heavy scales. They were swaying gently, breathing almost, but empty. She decided to look in the second pit. As she turned she was grabbed roughly by the arm and pulled back in. She screamed as she swung around and went instinctively for her assailant's throat. Her grip was so sudden and unshakeable that the man dropped his hatchet and grappled with her wrists, but Alina's grasp only tightened and she shut her eyes and began to pray with intense concentration. Presently the man stopped struggling and she realized that the trembling in her hands was her own. The body grew limp and suddenly heavy and she pushed it away; it fell back into the godown. Alina lurched outside, slammed the door and drew the bolt. From inside there came the sound of ice blocks falling. For a moment she saw nothing but a few stray tadpoles of light that swam towards the edges of her vision. When she could see again, she crossed to the second pit and automatically shut the lid, catching a glimpse at the bottom of a Farida who was broken past helping, little more in fact than an indigo dress and sheaves of long white hair. Alina went to the heap of broken marble where the Corinthian pillars had once stood and brought back a capital with which she covered the pit mouth. Then she ran sobbing in search of Rose.

The previous night Rose had had another visit from Philippa, who told of how on her last trip to the village some boys had thrown stones at her and called her a firangi. Philippa was accustomed to unwelcome attention: when she went to the city, to the new market called Hazratganj, the Europeans sneered at her while the Indians did not hide their puzzlement at the sight of a dark-skinned woman in a foreign dress. Lately there were no Europeans to be seen and the Indians' perplexity had turned to scorn. The boys in the village had come up behind her and chanted: "One more week, one more week to live!" On her way back through Trotterpurwa, Philippa had stopped at Wazir Ali's and asked him to make up a set of Muslim clothes for her family and four other women. The son of Zuhur Ali, tailor-and-balloon-maker, worked all day on the order with his sons and delivered the garments the same evening, though he suspected payment would be even longer coming from the Life-Giving House than usual.

"There's a burqa for each of you," Philippa told Rose, pleased to have acted independently. "Thomas says we must all go to the Residency without delay. He says it's being fortified by the English. They expect an attack any day now."

"Why not go on Sunday, after the service?" Rose could never believe things were as bad as they were said to be.

But the next morning Alina came running in, weeping hysterically.

Rose hugged her and stroked her hands until the young woman grew calm. "We go to the Residency this evening," she whispered. "We'll be safe there." She became practical. "We must take only what we absolutely need. I'll bake the jewellery into a few loaves of bread."

While the bread was in the oven, Rose went to the North Tower to prepare Bulbul for the journey. Bulbul was not in her swing. The water that

Rose had changed only yesterday stood a little lower in the bowl; the saucer of pumpkin seeds was overturned. Rose climbed to the very top of the stair, wheezing and crushing pumpkin seeds underfoot as she went, but Bulbul was not in the loft either. Several dusty canvases lay scattered about the studio floor, stuck together where the corners overlapped and gathering mouse dirt (*Aesthetic Justice, Rich Deserts*). From the lintel of the only open window streamed a long feather, improbably orange; when the room breathed in, the feather trailed inside; when it breathed out, it fluttered crazily in the wind. A shadow fell across the room as a gust of loo slapped the shutters to one side, releasing the feather which went spinning through the air and was caught up in swirls of yellow dust. Rose watched it go, swooping and soaring by turns, until it disappeared behind the Rain Room. She looked down at the Gunpowder Court far below, leaning out to see if perhaps Bulbul lay there. There was something at the foot of the tower, but it was not a human figure, just a dark scalloped pit of sorts. A slow smile spread across her face as she recognized the grave she had dug with a teaspoon so many years ago when the North Tower had been her own prison. Nobody had bothered to fill it in, and the mali had simply ringed it with alternate red and white bricks.

Impossible to say whether Rose was helped along from behind. There were no witnesses, and she herself felt no more than the lightest of currents at her ankles. It may have been a mouse frantic among petticoats, or simply the room breathing out again, but she was wafted gently across the window-sill. She fell without a cry but with a considerable flutter of underclothes, each layer billowing up a paler pink than the one before until there were only her plump bare legs with their delicate twiglike ankles. She floated down into the scalloped pit and lay there trembling in the heat until gradually she went still.

In the Rib, Alina put together a bundle of her possessions from the gymnasium and went down to the dairy to rub noses with the beasts she had milked every morning for years. The buffaloes had already begun to sense a departure and foamed and bellowed and shook their heads while the cows turned on her their solemn glistening eyes. At the end of the line she looked out of a westerly window and saw clouds of smoke rising from the direction of the Glacerie—or was it the kitchens? So the sack had begun. She stepped out at an easterly door and made for the jakfruit tree by the well where she cut herself the largest fruit she could find—it was longer than her arm, wide as her chest, and evenly spiked—balanced it on her free shoulder, and set out. Short of the Balloon Room door she paused and called: "Rose!" Her voice lacked assurance, the sound creeping without an echo into a hollow in the shapeless walls. She crossed the Indigo Court and passed without knowing it the speaking tube to the kitchens which Fonseca had used in the old days to call up shaving water. At the North Tower she called: "Bulbul!" but did not even wait for an answer. She crossed the Audience Hall, taking off her rough shoes half-way, and let herself out by the Ice Door just as a man on horseback rode up to the Gunpowder Door. She made the Trotter Road and did not stop walking until she arrived at the Residency, six miles away.

The jakfruit

It is the largest fruit on earth. Actually it hangs just above, like an elongate watermelon, only it is twice as big, not as sweet, and the skin is spiky. Thus it makes an excellent weapon but only fair eating. When tender it is curried, when not it is hurled. Vegetarians, poor souls, find it wholesome but it can also be tiresome. The largest are positively boring, but they go a long way in a siege. The seeds are eaten like almonds, quickly. The tree is large and spreading, its trunk like the chest of a strong woman.

(CHRONICLE RESUMED)

The man on horseback was Thomas Henry, come to alert the women. He heard the revolving echo of Alina's footsteps in the Audience Hall but did not know which way to turn; by the time he tried the Ice Court, she was gone. Finding *Sungum* empty, he rode his horse once around the fountain, enjoying the thunderous accumulation of hoofbeats in the vaulted ceiling, a sound that drove out the last particle of moderation and filled his head with the conviction that his clerical days were done, so that he longed to be where the danger was greatest. He dashed upstairs to the military museum and seized a brace of his great-grandfather's pistols. Then he rode to the kitchen, which was still smoking, but found only an ovenful of charred loaves with gritty centres. The Balloon Room was empty, the dairy deserted. Thomas Henry turned his horse around and was galloping up the Trotter Road when he saw the old carriage coming the other way, driven by a woman he did not immediately recognize as his wife. Philippa had dressed in her new clothes and escaped with the children moments before a band of rebel soldiers arrived and began to destroy the old hunting-lodge. The sepoys, she said, were making for Sans Souci.

Thomas Henry turned around again, and the Trotters took the road that led past the tall silk-cotton trees, skirted the saltpetre hill, and ran through Trotterpurwa. To the left, the setting sun showed purple through a new pall of smoke: the Life-Giving House was on fire. Further west, all over White Town and at the edges of Black Town stood other columns of smoke, some already thinning into a general blackish-blue haze. Just short of the Sagarpaysans' village Philippa turned the coach off the road and over the grass into a guava grove. The family decided to wait till it was dark and then go to the house of Durga Das to ask refuge. The old dhobi-and-dyer stood in the doorway chewing pan with fastidious incisors; he guessed at once the purpose of the visit. He addressed Thomas Henry, who was standing in the shadows still in European dress and content as in the past to leave all such transactions to his dark-skinned wife.

"Sahib!" Durga said, professionally obsequious. "What to do? I too have heard that the soldiers are coming this way. For myself I have no fears— but how can I endanger my family? Now the potter next door, he has no dependents."

The potter, who had been listening, blew out his lamp and sat very still, so the Trotters were obliged to knock at Wazir Ali's door. The tailor received them cordially, reproaching them only for not having come to him directly. He had his wife prepare a meal and he gave up his own and his family's beds to the guests. Towards midnight they were wakened by a knock on the door: it was Dukhi, son of Durga Das, come to warn of immediate danger. Some soldiers, he said, had just been interrogating his father and were now busy with the potter, who was sure to break down and lead them to the fugitives.

In the bright moonlight the family slipped out of Wazir Ali's back door and returned by a roundabout path, accompanied by both tailor and dhobi, to the guava grove. As they reached the shadows two shots rang out in quick succession. Thomas Henry had emptied his pistols into a uniformed figure who looked set to challenge them. Several things happened at once: a screech owl began a demented screeching, the two young Trotters began to wail, and Thomas Henry's horse bolted. From up the road came shouts and the sound of running feet. Philippa pushed the children back into the coach, slammed shut the door, and took the reins. The coach was already rolling when Thomas Henry jumped up beside her; by then it was too late to change places. Wazir Ali raced off down the back lane, but was chased by a soldier and caught. When the dead man was discovered by his comrades, the tailor was brutally beaten and bayoneted. By then the carriage was pelting along the Trotter Road towards the Ice Bridge under a moon that in a little while showed them the smoking ruin of the Life-Giving House and beyond it, by the bridge, a group of men stirring at the sound of fresh prey. The men were dacoits who had ridden into town armed with spears and clubs as soon as trouble broke out. They ran onto the road as the Trotters approached, brandishing their weapons and shouting for the carriage to stop. Philippa urged the horses to a gallop and broke through the line, receiving as she went by a blow to the shoulder with a lathi. Two dacoits who were already mounted gave chase, one of them coming up alongside Thomas Henry and giving the clerk his first sword wound of the campaign. The other clubbed Philippa several times on the arm and back but she held on to the reins. The man launched himself at the box, fell short and found a lucky foothold on the carriage step, from where he continued to wield his club until the coach door swung open and dislodged him. He slid down to the road where a wheel passed over him, almost tipping the coach over onto its side. The dacoit on the other side rode on until he noticed the riderless horse and turned back to look for his fallen friend. After that the ride was a smooth one and the children's screaming subsided. Only when the Trotters got to the Residency did they discover an extra passenger: Dukhi, son of Durga Das, had come along. It was he who had shaken off the dacoit on the carriage step and comforted the twins, who knew his crisp starchy smell from his weekly visits to the Life-Giving House with a bundle of washing. A short plump sensitive man with small eyes and a keen sense of honour, he was anxious to make amends for his father's lapse in hospitality. He was still in the Residency the next day when the siege began.

The morning after the Trotters' escape, Sans Souci was pillaged. A second batch of sepoys arrived as the sun was coming up and rode directly to *Sungum*. In the Audience Hall they smashed all the wall mirrors and busied themselves with prising out bits of inlaid semi-precious stone from the marble. They darted from one spot to the next, impatient for greater treasure. The inscription around the fountain read, *If there be a paradise on earth, it -- ----, it -- ----*, but the soldiers, tired of jasper, were already in the gallery above, reaching for the chandeliers whose brilliants they plucked, imagining them to be of value. One group burst into the Spur and started a fire in the Room of Gilt Cages when they found that the bars were not of real gold. Retreating, they tossed a brass lectern in the shape of three monkeys out of a window and jumped down after it as the smoke poured out behind them. From there they ran to the Begam Kothi, whose dome and upper storey they destroyed, leaving the godowns where everything in the world was stored intact because already their eyes had strayed to the Ice Court. They took the Ice Bell carefully off its hook, carried it up to the balcony of the New Armoury and stood it on the balustrade; then, with a whoop, they slid it over the edge. It shattered on the basalt flags, sending up a fountain of splinters which dwindled to nothing in the midmorning sun. In the Water Court another group riddled the water-clock with musket balls at close range before running off down the slope and up the steps of the Rib. They tore through the gymnasium, overturning a row of iron beds that had not been slept in for some time. At the far end of the crescent they came upon a room filled with tents, which on inspection were found to house a curious stack of lumber. They paused, baffled by the alien shapes of the Great Trotter's unfinished devices, until one of the sepoys touched a coil that sent a cold fire racing up his arm. Enraged, he struck back, while his companions fell on the other contraptions, hacking lustily at the knobs and wires. In one corner stood a dozen flasks of Burma mercury that they took for wine and smashed when they discovered their mistake. The liquor flashed across the floor in elastic globules that split and joined up and split again until the whole room was alive with tiny skipping lights; then, because the Rib tilted fractionally toward the Crocodile Wing, the scattered droplets, some smaller than a pinhead, began to roll across the floor joining up again until the whole silvery mass lay dusty and quaking in the original corner. From the gymnasium the men climbed to the roof of the Rib and ran exulting along the crescent back toward *Sungum*, detained briefly by the stone observatory, which they took to be a children's playground. Then one of them, looking up, pointed to the Audience Bell at the Crown and set off a fresh race to the towers, one group taking the blue tower while the other took one whose windows were barred all the way up. There was nothing to delay the first group, but the second came upon a room at the top strewn with foul paintings that they scooped up and tossed out of the one open window. The canvases, brittle as old leaves, floated down to cover the grave where Rose lay, but already the soldiers were scrambling up the steps of the Crown. Three of the four arches remained, poised dizzily far above the Audience Hall dome; the fourth had collapsed with the West Tower. From the centre, where the arches joined, hung the bell. The men stopped short of the top, except for the one who had first sighted the bell and who now decided to test it. He knelt at the top, leaned over, reached down, and tapped the metal. The bell remained dumb, refusing to answer even when struck with the heel of a boot. The men gave up and turned to go. As they did, the bell decided to fall. It fell without a turn, crashing through the once mica-tiled dome of the Audience Hall with a din that sprang back up and shook the towers; it broke through each floor of *Sungum*, braying insanely as it went, leaving a hole where the fountain had been and another in the library floor below, until it burst into the tahkhana where, with a final clang, it came to rest at the foot of the plinth. The soldiers gave chase, drunk with adventure and giddy from the twisting stair, but at the hall level they were checked: there seemed to be no stair leading down, and yet the hole in the floor showed at least one more level below. Rope was fetched from the village, because here at last, they were sure, was treasure. Two men volunteered to go down. They were lowered one by one while the others held the rope or lay at the lip of the crater and shouted advice. At the first level the volunteers passed rows of shelves radiating outwards; then they seemed to pass through a space of blankness so dark that they were greatly relieved to arrive at the tahkhana and step onto the plinth. The long leaden casket they found was empty save for a pile of grave-clothes at the foot, neatly folded. Lit for the first time in half a century through the holes in the floors above, the room looked more than ever like a cold chimney: even the bat dung had crumbled into an odour that clung to the damp walls like soot. The men overturned the coffin, gave the rope a tug, and were hauled slowly back up. At the top they were searched by their comrades but had nothing to show. One man, remembering the shelves at the first level below, flung a firebrand down the crater, which ignited the drifting pollen in a single blinding flash radiating outwards from the empty centre. The smell of charred ghosts and the sound of cries thinner than the lightest paper rose out of the crater and ascended to the ceiling in a grey cloud which escaped through the new smoke-hole in the dome. Their eyes suddenly heavy, as if they had been ages reading, the soldiers spilled out of the Gunpowder Door and made for the lawn. They sprawled there, gazing up at towers which threatened to topple over as the clouds drifted behind them. A kind of sluggish exhilaration flooded their veins, urging them on and pinning them down to the grass. They had taken nothing of value. The very cooking pots from the kitchens had already found their way into various huts in Trotterpurwa, while the cattle from the dairy were dispersed through the surrounding villages. They had even missed two brass coins that had once weighed down the eyelids of a distinguished corpse and now lay on the floor of the tahkhana among marble chips from the fountain and mica tiles from the roof. A drop of rain fell from a cloud no bigger than a split pea. One man rose and strolled over to the unfinished Chaldean sundial and bent to look closely at it; its oval face lit up his own with a brassy glare. Casually, he put his shoulder to the slender column and leaned with his whole weight against it till it snapped off at the base and thudded into the lawn. The wrestler fell with it and he and his friends laughed uproariously. When they had rested, the men sent for four bullock-teams from the village and harnessed them to the big gun, *Urban*, which stood in the centre of the lawn. The gun in tow, they set off up the Trotter Road to the siege of the Residency.

The siege of the Residency at Nakhlau

In the entire history of warfare, from antique times to the present day, there is no purer example of heroism against overwhelming odds than that presented by the defenders of the Nakhlau Residency. From the 1st of July to the 25th of September, 1857 A.D., three thousand souls, two-thirds of whom were civilians or

WOMEN AND CHILDREN

*held out against a foe ten times their number. During the
87 days they were invested, they endured a ceaseless barrage
of cannon and mortar fire and repulsed four general assaults
and innumerable sorties. The beleaguered force numbered
130 Officers, British and Native; 740 British and 700 Native
Troops; and 150 Civilian Volunteers. There were 237 women,
260 children (not counting drummers), 50 boys of St Aloysius's School, 27 noncombatant Europeans and 700 non-
combatant Natives, with perhaps half a dozen others. The
first relief, under Generals Porlock and Feverfew, proved a
qualified success, the relievers being themselves besieged with
the original garrison for a further 53 days until Sir Crawley
Campelot arrived on the 17th of November. The enemy's
numbers are variously put at between 40,000 troops with
44 guns (including the great gun, Urban, cast by Colonel
Trotter of Sans Souci) and 400,000 troops with 4,400 guns
and Russian military advisers.*

—*The Guide to the Nakhlau Residency,* by
COL. A. E. POUGH, Nuntio Press,
Nakhlau, 1946

(*CHRONICLE RESUMED*)

Apart from the officers of the Tirnab Irregular Horse under Brigadier
Gray, the regimental drummers, and the fifty boys of St Aloysius's School in
the charge of their principal, the Anglo-Indians in the Residency were for the
most part uncovenanted clerks like Thomas Henry, surveyors, telegraphists,
railwaymen and their families.

Philip Kahn-Trotter, railwayman, was not among them. He had been
one of the prisoners taken at Allahabad, where he was put to work making
gun-carriages for the rebels. In the Residency, his sister Philippa and Alina,
his intended, prayed that the railway line had not reached Kanpur, where it
was rumoured a complete massacre had taken place. The garrison there had
surrendered and been offered safe conduct, but as they were boarding their
boats down by the river a few stray shots were fired, it was never known by
whom. The firing developed into a confused battle in which all the men and
a few women were killed. The remaining women and children, some two

hundred of them, both British and Anglo-Indian, were kept prisoner for several weeks in a house called the Bibighar. In mid-July, as the British relieving force approached, it was decided that nothing was to be gained by keeping hostages. Ordered to kill the survivors, the sepoy guard refused, emptying their muskets into the ceiling of the Bibighar. Upon which five butchers were fetched from the bazar, two Hindus, two Muslims, and one unidentified man, and let into the house with their knives. Next morning, the bodies were thrown into a nearby well. The well, whose horrors, unlike those of the Black Hole of Calcutta, were real, would one day disappear from Indian history, proving that while Britons were skilled at seeing what was not there, Indians would become adept at not seeing what was.

Alina's brother, Cyril Brendish, was one of the last to come into the Residency, having waited at his post to send off the telegram that disarmed the Punjab. THE CITY IS IN FLAMES, he tapped, THE SOLDIERS HAVE MUTINIED AND ARE BURNING DOWN THE BUNGALOWS . . . MR TODD IS DEAD I THINK . . . HE WENT OUT THIS MORNING AND HAS NOT RETURNED . . . WE ARE OFF. Moments later the wires were cut, but Cyril was on his way. Without stopping to shut the door, he dashed to his superior's house, collected Mrs Todd and her baby, and shepherded them to the Residency by a back road.

The scramble over, those who made the Residency bedded down for the siege. The Trotters found accommodation in the Post Office near the edge of the entrenchment; the inner buildings, better sheltered from the enemy's artillery fire, were kept for the families of Europeans of the better sort. In the beginning an air of adventure eased the settling in, cheering the children, but once the heavy guns began their pounding, anxiety consumed the smallest faces. As the first shells fell, tearing up the neat garden paths, bruising smooth plaster and taking the tops off shade trees, the besieged began to walk with a stoop which never left them. In after years, Dukhi, who came out of the siege without a scratch, would assure his wife that his back was bent from long hours at the dhobi ghat, but when he went to collect his pension he was put in mind of the falling shells and snipers' bullets of that distant dreadful summer. For a week there might be a lull, then the barrage would begin again, roofs, walls, pillars, and whole houses disintegrating in time to let the monsoon rain in. At first, blood and bone surprised the civilian accustomed to the charm of skin, but by the end of June such innocence looked impossibly remote. In the hospital, which stank of bandages and rotting flesh (it was set up in the former banquetting hall), the younger boys of St Aloysius's sat pulling the pankhas and fanning the wounded against the flies and heat. The older boys helped defend the most exposed part of the garrison, the southern face, alongside the Sikh Cavalry and a detachment of the 32nd Foot. The Aloysian Post, as it came to be called, stood directly across from the houses of J.c. Solomon & Son, which had been looted and taken over by the mutineers. During the first two months of the siege, an African eunuch from the Nawab's court occupied the tower of the elder Solomon's house and trained his musket to such effect on the defenders that he was nicknamed Bob the Nailer. On the twenty-first of August he was finally silenced, his tower being blown up from underneath.

How a mine is sprung

I wish to shew how a mine is sprung. To start with, good adept, you must have a Mutiny (or at least a War of Independence). Otherwise, complications occur which are not easily explained away: property damaged, life lost, men and women (and some in between) hurt. Other essential ingredients are gunpowder, a fuse of sufficient length, a match, pickaxes, spades (as who should say, shovels), pans, beams, supports, patience, pistols, dice, and a demijohn of sherry. All the ingredients were available in the old days at J.c. Solomon & Son until their shops and houses fell into the hands of the rebels (or freedom fighters, restless natives, African eunuchs, or what you will). The last-named is a particular nuisance, nailing people when they least expect it. Ordinarily he looks after the Nawab's harem, singing to the ladies in a high sweet voice and nailing nobody, but now he seems to have tired of the old life and wreaks his vengeance on an unjust world.

Do not despair, good adept: help is at hand. Keep your head low and run to the banyan tree near the Post Office where they are busy manufacturing fuses, shells, cartridges (they have just two moulds), and the like. Captain Dashery is there, the mining expert; and just beyond is the magazine, where gunpowder is plentiful. Digging tools are many, and you have a formidable digger in the Post Office, Alina by name, a lady who lives on jakfruit and has immensely powerful forearms. Before the troubles began she buried a dozen mothers in one morning and eight brothers in a day, and since the siege she has been much in demand in the churchyard beyond the sheep slaughterhouse where every night the victims of cholera, smallpox, and the day's fighting are sown. Leave the mining to the experts, sharp adept: the rebels have theirs in the mining tribe called Pasis, the defenders have Captain Dashery of the Engineers and Alina Alexander-Trotter. It is for you to man the mines. This is how.

Crawl as far as a given shaft will go, taking with you your ancestor's pistols and one or two Sikhs for company. Like you, they are thirsty for adventure, so pass the bottle freely—moderation is a thing of the past. You are now in the *mine*. If you hear pickaxes picking their way towards you, expect a *countermine*. When mine and countermine meet, the earth falls away and enemies stand face to face. This is called an *encounter*. Here is where the pistols and the Sikhs prove useful, the latter especially, for they have a noble tradition of challenging the enemy to single combat. However, down below there is little light for histrionics, so fire away with your pistols, stout adept, hurl abuse (here again your companions are useful), and generally rattle your sabre. Sometimes it happens that tunnels will fail to meet and will proceed happily alongside, the one in the one direction and the other in the other. This is called a *miss*. It could extend for a mile. Eventually, of course, one must decide whether or not one is directly under one's target, let us say, the tower of the elder Solomon's house where there might be, perhaps, an African eunuch named (say) Bob. Let Captain Dashery lay the charge and set the fuse—no easy task in the rains. When all is prepared, the Captain will return to the mine-head at the Aloysian Post to see if Bob is *in*. To his cost, the answer is *yes*, and the garrison loses one of its ablest defenders. Let Alina bury him, cunning adept. It remains to put a match to the fuse. The elder Solomon's house and tower melt away, and with them Bob the Nailer. When the dust settles you are covered in glory.

This is how a mine is sprung. Do it as I have shewn and the Aloysian Post will be a safer place for all. Réclame will surely follow, but will it suffice, now that moderation has been cast to the winds? Wait and see. Defend God. These days He is being undermined by Geology.

(CHRONICLE RESUMED)

Food, almost everyone in the Residency agreed, was more precious than gunpowder. Barely a mile from the garrison, in his newly built Kaiserbagh or Caesar's garden, the Nawab was undoubtedly of that opinion. Every August it had been his practice to put on the robes of an ascetic and sit under a large mulberry tree near the western Mermaid Gate. Ochre-clad, ash-smeared fakirs from all over Tirnab came to celebrate the annual Yogi Fair: no one without a begging bowl was admitted, and a prize went to the man who had practiced the fiercest austerities. This year, since everything was upside down, the Nawab proclaimed a feast, put on his favourite wife's clothes, and danced for the ladies of his harem, who wore for the occasion the uniforms of men soldiers. Afterwards he went in to them and expired with his mouth full of Turkish delight, while the remains of the feast—saffron tandoori chickens and buttered nans, sweet rice and golden laddus—were carried to the housetops adjoining the Residency and displayed for the enjoyment of the besieged. The garrison watched gloomily from the roof of Mrs Sago's house near the Baillie Gate, and that night many of the servants who had remained loyal to their beleaguered masters were lured away.

At the opposite end of the Residency from Mrs Sago's, the Financial Commissioner's house was well stocked with wines, puddings, pâté de foie gras, salted meats, tubs of ghi, raisins, mango paste, and even a sack of cashew nuts. With the prescience of a gourmand, Mr Gubbins had laid up stores on earth long before the siege (*Prudent Shopman, Figural Genius*), but it had to be said he kept an open table. On any given day an American or Australian dentist (the country teemed with them) was to be found visiting at dinnertime. Across from Gubbins's house in Sikh Square, the Sikh cavalrymen, disdaining rice, ate dry chapatis; elsewhere, the servants who remained drank rice-water, leaving the rice for their masters. The Trotters ate a thin soup made of sheep's feet in which shreds of jakfruit floated. Since the twins died there were fewer mouths to feed, but Philippa's belly was again swelling. Thomas Henry gave up his crust for her (a crust which as often as not she had saved for him) because he loved her immoderately. Cured of restraint, he dreamt extravagantly of food, but still more extravagantly of the history he must somehow make before the days of plenty returned.

The siege dragged on from month to month, flies and heat by day, mosquitoes and heat by night, and at any time a shell that might blow away an arm or a leg and send the victim to that dreaded staging-post, the former banquetting hall. Those who felt themselves cheated by hopes of an early end to the fighting began to wish they had died at the start; one or two grew reckless. To discover unexpected depths or shallows in oneself became a daily risk. Tempers grew short, soldiers became contemptuous of civilian volunteers, volunteers mocked at non-combatant civilians, and everybody mistreated the servants. There were private rewards beyond sacrifice and duty faithfully performed. One former builder found revelation on the rooftops of the crumbling buildings which he repaired openly and with zeal, careless of the snipers' bullets which fell around him as he worked. A drummer invented a new kind of spoon. Thomas Henry began to sing. He had lately taken up with Signor Beberelli, a round-cheeked Florentine alabaster merchant who wore three cartridge belts, a curved sword, and jungly moustaches, and the two could be heard all the way across the low ground from the Naubat Khana or Music Hall, the Italian trilling his rare counter-tenor, while the Middle Trotter's basso ostinato wrapped *Tom Bowling* in all the murky pathos his hot heart could muster. By day his feats of daring grew more prodigious, by night he dreamed with such intensity that his pillow glowed. Some of his energy must have communicated itself to his sleeping wife, because Philippa, whose sleep had once been perfectly blank, began to dream, in black and white, of twins.

Then came the change. At nine o'clock one night in late September, the stars being auspicious, the rebels wheeled *Urban* into position on the Kanpur Road opposite the Kanpur Battery, elevated the barrel as far as it would go, and packed in a massive charge of gunpowder. Then they called their priests, who recited a prayer, stuffed the great gun's mouth with forty pounds of sweetmeats, and stood back. A fusee was put to the touch-hole and the gun belched fire and sugar, recoiling from its deed with a roar that woke sleepers roundabout for miles. In moments the east face of the Residency was smothered in a vapour of burnt sugar. When the brown fog lifted, the trees which had long since lost their foliage and stood gaunt and charred for as long as anyone could remember, wore a mesh of fine white hair which glittered in the light of a small high moon. The children in the Residency came up and touched the hair: it stuck to their hands and could be removed only with the tongue, where it dissolved in a prickly mist of sweetness. But then a long and bitterly contested night assault followed, which ended in the small hours with a sudden shower of rain. When the sun came up the next day only the angular black trees remained of the collective dream.

After that the wind changed. Things began to go wrong with the besiegers (*Prodigal Gunners, Criminal Rite*) and right for the besieged. Sorties out were successful, enemy guns were spiked, spies came in with news of a relieving force. A blue-bull wandered out of the Chinhat forest and up to the Baillie Guard Gate; ravens dropped buttered nans. Two more general assaults were repulsed; Thomas Henry struck a true note in the Naubat Khana; a dentist lost an arm. People continued to die, it was true, deaths more or less painful, and Philippa had the calf of her right leg blown away, but she miraculously survived the bleeding and there was no gangrene.

On the twenty-fifth of September, Generals Porlock and Feverfew, who had forced a march from Kanpur, broke through the rebels' lines and into the Residency. They were themselves besieged together with the original garrison, but they brought with them food, ammunition, powder, medical supplies, and new faces. For a further six weeks the combined forces held out, fighting continuing above and below ground, and the hopes of the survivors sinking again. When Philippa, who was now far gone in pregnancy, had a dream. It was in colour; but more startling was the fact that she herself was in it; until then her dreams had been peopled exclusively by others, chiefly her husband-and-master and her dead children. Now she appeared boldly, even immodestly, swimming in a foreign landscape, effortlessly displacing the pellucid air high above a range of mountains, her eye sweeping the purple crags for the source of a skein of blue smoke whose track she followed with the lightest flick of her toes. She awoke, or half awoke, with a droning melody in her head that was bound up somehow with the skein of smoke. It was coming nearer, she said, humming the tune for Thomas Henry who heard in it the skirl of bagpipes. Then it struck him: General Sir Crawley Campelot and his Highlanders were at hand. The story ran about the Residency, but it was not until the next day, when the same melody was carried across the city by a gust from the south, that Thomas Henry's rendition of it was connected with "The Campelots Are Coming." That night a spy returned with confirmation (it was Dukhi) and the Middle Trotter stood justified: his wife, Thomas Henry Trotter's, was gifted with special powers. At dinner he gave up his rice ration for her, a gesture which brought tears to his eyes.

How History is made

I wish to shew how History is made. Understand first, good adept, that there are no sides to it. Front and back there be, certainly, which the vulgar call past and future (the one with buttons and the other not), and also top and bottom, which some call class (the one with epaulettes, the other not). But sides, no. No circumventing it, sharp adept: the fabric extends endlessly, defying the lateral cut. In this present sorry business, for example, neither side (so-called) will budge, foreign or native. Show them, good adept, the middle path lit by the lamp of self-interest. After all, you have no concern with either: the one would kill you and yours if he could, the other would chain you to a desk, an uncovenanted one at that. Consider your predicament well. Go to the Naubat Khana and pace there, turning it over in your mind, your newfound hatred thickening like water held in the mouth. Remember also that the siege will soon be over and opportunities for glory will be thin on the ground (or under it for that matter). One cannot be ever mining.

For the making of History you need: a friend whose hand is steady (it does not matter greatly if it be blue), a sword, a shield, curl-toed shoes, a red shirt (this you already have, but cut off the European collar), a cream turban, a jaggery-coloured jacket, a jamun-coloured (*Eugenia jambolana*) cummerbund, some lampblack or burnt cork, a little mustard oil, a blank sheet of Trotter paper, a pen, the juice of a lemon, and a quill tip—the entire feathery portion being cut off since the situation is ticklish. All of these ingredients except the first might have been had from the Solomon establishment, but alas, that is already history. (It may revive some day, who knows?) Meanwhile, you must go from hut to hut in the Residency confiscating the necessary properties. When you have the costume in one place, you need a green room, so go to the sheep slaughterhouse and there disguise yourself. You now look like a cross between Rana Partap and Garibaldi (though, it is true, the latter will fumble with Madame History's buttons for another year or two). Your face, hands, and neck blackened, you are as dark as night (which has fallen), darker even than Dukhi Das, Dhobi & Dyer of Distinction.

Now you are ready, bold adept, to carry the message. To be sure, Dukhi could carry it with far greater safety alone, being Indian, and your presence could endanger his life, to say nothing of the mission, but consider the History waiting to be made. Accordingly you will already have gone to the garrison commander and reasoned with him; so earnest were you in your entreaties that he succumbed. The message, writ small in lemon juice upon a square of paper no bigger than a postage stamp, has been rolled into a tiny cylinder and inserted into the quill tip, and the quill tip lodged in Dukhi's rectum. It warns Sir Crawley in dog Greek not to take the route through the city by which the first relievers, Porlock and Feverfew, suffered heavy losses. Deliver it successfully and History is made. The Victoria Cross is yours—the first ever awarded to a civilian—and you will henceforth be known to the world as the *Guide of Nakhlau*, or simply, *Nakhlau Trotter*.

This is what I wished to shew. Do it in one night. Do not tell your wife.

Extracts from My Path to the Victoria Cross, *by Thomas Henry Trotter (Nakhlau Trotter)*

By five o'clock I was trembling so violently I rushed from the room, heedless of the officers' eyes upon me. Ever since the notion seized me I had been in a fever of indecision. Could I—nay, dare I—risk all, even to my life? Might I attain that which all men seek to attain—the acclaim of their fellows for some honourable deed, some feat which distinguishes them from the common herd of mankind?

I made my way across the low grounds of the Residency to the Naubat Khana, or so I must have gone, putting one foot before the other, for I scarcely knew how or when I arrived, being only conscious of the journey I must make. Under those twisted rafters where it had been my wont to sing [*sic*], I paced back and forth in the greatest confusion. I will not trouble the reader with my heart's dialogue, nor should I wish to inflict upon him the enormous weight of oppression which burdened my soul. The solitary witness of my suffering was a nightjar which flew a short way off and sat watching me. Whether he mocked my distress I knew not, but it was he helped form my resolve. At last I stopped in my pacing and stood still, fists clenched and teeth set. All at once I, who had been a monument to Placidity, threw myself intemperately upon my knees and swore to go. The decision so relieved my heart that tears streamed from my eyes.

. . . .

At the beginning of the siege I had been too ill to go out with the soldiers to spike the enemy's guns. When I heard tell of how *two men* spiked a gun beyond the Cawnpore Battery against incredible odds, I was so moved by their gallantry that it was a task for the doctor to prevent me from leaving my bed. Had he not sat upon my chest to quell the commotion there, my heart would surely have burst from its ecstasy of enthusiasm. As it was, the rapturous convulsions eased themselves at my eyes. . . .

. . . .

It remained to persuade Dukhi Das to allow me to accompany him. He knew me from before the siege, having been a dhobi or washerman to the family, and played some small part in our safe arrival in the Residency. In September he carried a message out and returned to Colonel Inglis's satisfaction. Notwithstanding our acquaintance, he demurred in the strongest terms, declaring it madness to expect my European features to go unnoticed in the city. I then approached General Feverfew himself and entreated him to send me, reminding him that a message of such urgency concerning a new line of advance might appear suspect from the hands of a native. I humbly adduced my knowledge of the native tongue and also of the city where I had worked so many years as a lowly clerk. Finally I produced a lime, a half-sheet of Trotter paper and a clean nib, whereupon he was convinced, and sat down to write in a mixture of Roman and Greek characters one of the most momentous letters ever penned. When he had finished he rose and addressed me in words which ring in my ears to this day—"Noble fellow, you will never be forgotten!"—looking the whilst at me with such feeling that tears rose unbidden to my eyes.

. . . .

The most painful of all my tasks remained. I must bid my dear wife goodbye, whom I loved more than life itself, my precious helpmeet, mother of our beloved children now dead, yet, it has pleased God, mother-to-be of many more. She was in our room preparing—as well as she might in her condition and with the meagre rations to hand—a few coarse chapatis for our evening meal. I sat down upon the bed unable to speak the few lines I had rehearsed for the occasion. When she called me to break bread I turned my head away to hide the emotion welling up at my eyes. I kissed her quickly upon the brow, and pleading some duty in the mines, rushed from the room before the floodgates should burst.

. . . .

At a quarter past eight we slipped out by the Redan and hastened down to the sands of the river. There, within sight of the Iron Bridge, we undressed, my companion's swart complexion providing a stark contrast with my own, which was blackened only at my face and hands. Placing his clothes upon his head, Dukhi Das stepped boldly into the stream and waded across. I followed with all haste, but no sooner did I enter the water than I found my courage so chilled that had my helper not been too far gone I might have called him back and abandoned the enterprise. Instead I threw away the sword and shield, howbeit with the greatest reluctance, for although I could not use them they

made a fine show. I was not half-way across the river when I had occasion
to rue my rash disposal of those weapons, for coming towards me I perceived
a large mugger or crocodile, unmistakeable from the fearsome arches of its
breathing apparatus. But Providence so ordered it that at the same moment
there came floating by a charred corpse which I pushed towards the creature.
He opened his jaws to receive it, and by this burnt offering my life was spared.
On the farther bank we dressed once more in the shadows of a mango grove
and proceeded as far as the Stone Bridge, where we were challenged by a
native officer who demanded to know who we were and whence we came.
We said we were unfortunates from the village of Chinhut journeying to
Barrah Bunkey to inform my sister of the death of her son at the hands of
the English. He bid us go, saying that the times were black but soon the
foreigner would be cast out. We crossed the bridge and entered the heart of
the old city which was uncommonly quiet, betokening the onset of winter,
when the people retire early. Some of the houses were still lit with clay deeyas
left over from the Hindoo festival of Deewallee. Against the remonstrances
of my companion, I stopped to buy some monkey-nuts from a vendor, for
by now I had a not inconsiderable hunger. I ate a modicum of the roasted
nuts with salt and powdered chilles and gave the rest to Dukhi Das who
partook heartily enough once we were in the shadows. Indeed the food must
have worked upon his appetite, for it was he who found an excuse to stop at
the next sweetseller's and fill his puggarree or turban with puffed rice and
the white sugar sweets which the Hindoos make in the shape of various
animals and birds for the Dewallee festival. I took two, no more, when pressed,
thinking of my dear wife, whereupon tears rose to my eyes and flowed down
my cheeks.

. . . .

At length we came upon a mango tope where we rested, but upon
emerging into the moonlight we were hailed by a picket of rebel soldiers.
Here my companion for the first time lost heart and was for flying, but I
remained calm. They surrounded us and asked the most uncomfortable questions, roughly put and pursued with evident suspicion. We gave the same
account of ourselves as before, whereupon they tired of their game and sent
us on our way. As we left, one of them who had been looking hard at me
called us back, but his comrades bid him leave us be. Thereafter we passed
through green fields whose freshness was a source of the keenest delight after
long months of confinement in the Residency. I pulled up a young carrot and
washed it in the dew, but could not eat more than two mouthfuls, though it
was crisp and sweet, for the thought of my dear wife choked my throat and
brought tears to my eyes.

. . . .

CHAPTER XLVIII

In which I accost a cultivator—He is lame—He raises an alarm—
The village dogs—I fall into the Gundah Nullah or Canal—Ice upon its
surface—My shoes worn down—My feet raw and swollen—I skirt the
Dilkhoosha or Heart's Ease—My companion tempted—Another picket—
More dogs—A dragon?—A churail?—Villagers fleeing with their chattels—Dacoits—I fall into the Canal again—My feet bleeding—My companion rests in a haystack—I keep watch—Two pickets, their campfires—
Scratched in a sugar-cane field—We lose our way—Two dragons?—I
fall in the Canal—I lose my shoes in the mud—We enter a village—I
grope in the darkness of a hut—A young woman's thigh pressed—She
awakens—I beg her not to betray us—She anoints and binds my feet—
The stepmother—We hurry away—Village dogs—Their diet—Their
guile—Vultures—Nesting habits—*Gyps indicus*—I fall into a blind well—
Rope and bucket—The rope just short—A mighty leap—I fall back—
Angels—Sand in my eyes—A great weariness—My companion rests—
Further longueurs—My companion sleeps in a pea-field—My vigil—
Geese above—Shots fired—A chase—Slough of Despond—Wading two
hours—I begin to feel the cold—A sneeze—*Who goes there?*—Friends!—
My companion falls in a faint—I bear him up—My feet bleeding—I meet
the Commander-in-Chief—He takes me for a native—I declare myself—
His astonishment—He takes my hand—His memorable words—Tears
rise to my eyes.

(*CHRONICLE RESUMED*)

The message delivered, Thomas Henry spent a week recovering from
his night's adventure. A semaphore signalled the success of the mission to
the watch at the top of the Residency tower and Philippa, who had supposed
her husband on duty within the fortifications, was informed of his safety some
five miles away. She heard the news through a mist, smiling her one-sided
smile: her labour pains had begun.

When the relieving army struck camp, the Middle Trotter kept close to
the Commander-in-Chief, expert by day on terrain that had tricked him by
night. Sir Crawley's plan was to feint a northwards thrust while the bulk of
his force made a wide curve around the city and approached the Residency
from the east. Detained briefly at the Dilkhusha Park, where the Nawab's
deer furnished a venison breakfast, the main force entered Sans Souci from
the south. It skirted the aerolite and the jujube groves, preferring the brittle

salt flats to the desert for marching, and met the first sepoy resistance at the
Begam Kothi. The rebels were driven back across the Ice Court at bayonet
point, retreating to *Sungum*, from where they peppered the foreigner with
musket fire through the embrasures of the South Tower. A battery set up at
the Begam Kothi pounded the tower with oddments from the godowns and
flushed them out in forty minutes without severely damaging the building or
depleting Sultana's hoard. The mutineers fell back to a stronghold beyond
the Ganda Nala, and Sir Crawley set up his headquarters in the pentagonal
North Tower. The same afternoon Thomas Henry showed the General to the
top of the stair, from where he pointed out the salient features of the land
beyond the canal and indicated the route suggested by Feverfew.

The next day the relieving force made its final push to the Residency.
Crossing the canal, it met the fiercest resistance yet in the Sikandar Bagh,
where there was slaughter on an epic scale. In a single savagely contested
courtyard two thousand dead and half-dead lay piled, five and six deep; on
those same grounds in years to come, the city's botanical gardens would
greenly doze. Howitzer shells, chainshot, sword hilts, stones, empty powder-
horns, and rockets of terrifying inaccuracy cut a swath through the retreating
sepoys. Sikandar Bagh, Kadam Rasul, Shah Najaf, Moti Mahal: one by one
the rebel defences were abandoned. From the other side, the garrison marched
out of the Residency and advanced across ground vacated by the besiegers.
There remained a narrow corridor between the relievers and the relieved
which at length the sepoys yielded, withdrawing southwards to the Nawab's
palace in Kaiserbagh. Then, through a breach in the defensive wall on the far
side of the corridor, there appeared Generals Feverfew and Porlock advancing
to meet their deliverer. Without warning, Thomas Henry dashed out across
the middle ground to meet them, running out alone ahead of the troops and
braving the stray bullet to lead the relieved generals to Sir Crawley. Upon
which, the life seemed to go out of all present—all except the Guide of
Nakhlau—leaving them frozen in postures worthy of a painting in the heroic
style.

(INTERPOLATION)

Concerning Mr T. Jones Barker's painting The Relief of Nakhlau

I don't know where the original is, but if you're interested there are two
prints of it—yes, not one, not three, but two—facing each other in the model
room of the Residency, identical in every way, even in the brown freckles of
age, framed in glass so that they reflect one another, locked in an infinite
series of mute exchanges inaudible to the visitor and practically invisible as

well since the room is lit from a clerestory and the light falls directly down, bounces off the glass, and blinds the viewer. Which, when you come to think of it, is probably just as well. The prints, "Engraved in the Highest Style of Art" (so proclaimed the publishers, Thos. Agnew & Sons, in their advertisement), could hardly hope to escape the sin of the original, an oil. But let's look at the work.

Too big, to start with, so we can imagine the artist, a sort of frail pink snappish wafer of a man, the very antithesis of, say, Jean-Honoré (*The Swing*) Fragonard, painter-and-martyr, who died of a seizure while eating ice cream.

Then it's—confessedly—a compilation. No harm in that, as such, since some of the best miniatures are compilations (though Ivor, my Ivor, might not agree: "A pastiche," he'd sniff, the filthy purist, as if that was saying something). Anyway, Mr T. Jones Barker was never anywhere in thumbing distance of Nakhlau: *The Relief of Nakhlau* was done "From Drawings and Portraits made for the Author expressly for this picture by EGRON LUNDGREN." Fair enough. Not the worst of faults by any means—except in the circumstance: the borrowed pieces are put together by a vulgar realist suddenly confronted with the mythical. The result? Victorian melodrama, familiar enough from its modern Indian incarnation in the Hindi film industry. Mr T. Jones Barker's picture is a gigantic prototypical film poster, gauche, garish, scheming, ferociously symbolic. In fact, the original *Relief of Nakhlau* is probably in Bombay, where it had better remain.

But let's look at the artist's proofs in black and white.

In the centre stand the three generals, the two on the left looking forgivably relieved, the one on the right (Sir Crawley) sternly relieving. Hats off all round, all eyes on the heroes, even those of the dying, to stage left and right, and the elephants and histrionic camels. Sorry—not quite all eyes: Gunga Din the bhisti (grandson of Justin's Gunga) has his back to the great men, but his loyal eyes are glazed as he stoops to pour water for a wounded highlander; and on the other side, grubbing in the mud over a few pieces of silver, a couple of wild-eyed naked badmashes whom the publisher's Key (the Agnews forget nothing) describes as "Natives Quarrelling over Plunder." Lots of heavy drapery dangling from heaven knows where, stuffed animals, wooden crowds, canvas minarets, tin swords—standard oil painters' props filched from museums and menageries and stuck onto the canvas so that they all point to the centre.

But the centre—that is, the heart of the centre—the very middle, is empty. Or is it?

Look again. Sir Crawley is fractionally right of centre, the relieved generals fractionally left. All the big shots of the Defence are propped like wax dolls on either side. Well, then, what in the name of T. Jones Barker is that blur at the centre of the centre? Everybody who was anybody in the siege is recognizably there—everybody except the Guide of Nakhlau. Where is Nakhlau Trotter? Could he be the blur? Is that grey smudge the Middle Trotter, his makeup imperfectly removed, traces of burnt cork lingering on the forehead, his middle-sized nose foreshortened to nothing, his mid-grey eyes fixed on the viewer, on posterity, on History?

Yes, the Key agrees, it is he. Of all the figures in this trumpery painting, this hideous piece of razzmatazz, his is the most convincing, the least stuffy. The most ghostly of them all, he remains the only one alive, the only one who looks out at us with humid expectant speaking eyes. Not all the artist's massed incompetence has snuffed him out.

It might be History's revenge on Thomas Henry, Middle Trotter, to have placed him so far to the middle as to be virtually invisible. But then the saving grace of a bad painting is its blanks and empty spaces, those silences which a miniaturist makes his own, those minute shadowy gaps which an oil painter smears with his lard-based atrocities. After all, the best part of a Bombay movie (supposing one were forced to go) is the relief in the middle, full of chips and ice cream. In a way that he least expected, the Middle Trotter *is* the relief of Nakhlau: he's the relief of *The Relief of Nakhlau*.

(*CHRONICLE RESUMED*)

As he ran forward across the open ground ahead of the troops, bullets whizzing around him, Thomas Henry's brain was filled with the most delicious visions. All the antique heroes of Greece and Rome passed before his eyes and were found wanting when their deeds of valour compared with his. Horatius, Aristomenes, Mincius, Deucius, Themistocles, Gallicus the Younger, Caius Gumptor—all fell short. Would there be a statue of him in Nakhlau? Thomas Henry wondered. Horatius, he recalled, had been granted a piece of land, and every Roman contributed the cost of a day's food for his reward. Would every Briton subscribe the cost of a day's food to reward him, Thomas Henry (*Fond Trotter*)? Or at least the Victoria Cross—might that be his (*Canny Clerk*)?

When suddenly he remembered his expectant wife. Leaving the generals to their devices, Thomas Henry went scurrying across the pitted ground between the Moti Mahal and the Kurshaid Manzil, past the Bridge of Casks, the Chhatar Manzil and the Lal Baradari, the Tehri Kothi and the Naubat Khana, through the Baillie Guard Gate, past Mrs Sago's, around Dr Fayrer's, under the banyan tree and in at the Post Office where in a dark corner, among foul rags and dishcloths spread on a string cot, Philippa Trotter had just given birth to a child. It was not the expected twins, but it was big enough, and a girl. Thomas Henry bent over and kissed the glistening forehead of his wife, who smiled back at him out of one side of her mouth. He took up the new-born creature and held her, despite her extraordinary weight, high in the air, his eyes shining. She gave a watery gurgle and brushed repeatedly at her caul. The eyes, he saw, could not have been further apart without opening on the side of her head. There was never any doubt in her father's mind as to what she should be called.

Before the Residency was evacuated, Thomas Henry's daughter was taken to a well near the treasury where a garrison priest, lacking a bucket, marked a cross on her forehead with his own spittle and named her Victoria.

> *Tell me, Narrator, have we come to the end of this Mutiny business? To tell the truth I would like something a little quieter.*
> *We are done with howitzers and mines and rockets, gentle Cup. In a little while you shall have all the silence your heart desires.*
> *I stand relieved, Narrator. Here is a shy little liebfraumilch, very modest and retiring.*
> *The vulture, Cup-Bearer, has told me this. Listen.*

(CHRONICLE RESUMED)

The garrison and the relieving force withdrew the next day, allowing the Residency to fall into the hands of the mutineers. The British would not return to Nakhlau until the following year, some four months later. In the city there was subdued rejoicing at their departure, but preparations began for their inevitable return with reinforcements fresh from Europe. A cloud of yellow dust squatted over the city as earthworks were dug along three lines of defence. Troops were drilled, stocks laid up in the Kaiserbagh Palace. Sugar prices shot up, ghi disappeared from the market. Winter vegetables—cauliflowers, cabbages, brinjals, and carrots—ordinarily plentiful and cheap, grew scarce; even turnips and white radishes fetched their growers good prices when they were not commandeered for the army. One no longer saw stray goats and cattle: no hoofed creature was safe from the commissariat's agents. Those families who could afford to left the city, travelling northwards across the Iron Bridge or the Stone Bridge or the Bridge of Casks; many who could not afford to followed and perished on the road. Those who stayed built false walls and floors in their houses which they whitewashed two and three times. Already the sound was fading: one day the whole caste of whitewashers found that the usual flopping slap had gone out of their brushes.

In March, with the heat and flies, the British returned. Once more they advanced from the south and then looped around the city, attacking from the east and north, but this time their boots made no sound as they tramped across the Iron Bridge. The sepoys fought silent suicidal battles but were pushed back from palace to palace; their musketry, like that of the invader, had lost its crackle, showing only in the puffs of smoke that ran up and down the line. Shells rained down on the city, bursting without a sound, though real blood spattered the whitewashed walls. Bayonets did silent work in sepoys; in civilians they barely squeaked. And even when the rebel leaders were blown from cannon, the explosions could only be told from the sulphurous cloud that spurted from the gun, shot through with gritty bits of red. The shade trees of the city's famous gardens wore silent emblems of justice which swung from short ropes in the afternoon loo, inviting bluebottles. Overhead the clear sky was dotted with circling vultures, graceful in the air and patient from the glut of corruption. The stench was so bad it hung in mauve flags above each private death; only the dogs and rats and crows seemed not to mind. The attackers ran noiselessly about their business with embroidered patches on their breast pockets which read: WOMEN AND CHILDREN. Those who were new to the country, having neither women nor children there, wore the badge on their sleeves. In the circumstances, megaphones were issued to the officers and ear trumpets to the men, but the commands died on the air, and the auditory aids were soon abandoned. The officers, in any case, were not always the most backward among the avengers-and-looters.

The shops in the newly built Hazratganj were the first to be stripped, but the trail of fallen merchandise led quickly to the Kaiserbagh Palace—silver hookahs, ewers, tooled brass kettles, lacquered trays, wine jugs encrusted with garnets, candlesticks, telescopes, shawls, rugs, rich stuffs, fragrant inlaid woods and ivory-handled knives—shed by men whose piratical uniforms grew more fantastic by the minute. In the palace the fortunate found ropes of pearls, swords and daggers whose hilts were balanced with rubies, a gigantic jewelled salt-cellar which they smashed, two stools with golden legs, a navel-jewel of deep blue with the legs and tail of a scorpion in silver, an old clock in the shape of a leviathan that punctually swallowed a British marine. For those who came late there were mirrors and pier-glasses to fire at, a shrubbery with china jardinieres to club down, and a troupe of eunuchs to flog; the mirrors and vases collapsed in silent showers of light, the eunuchs danced a dumb charade of pain for a pair of pink-faced sergeants who warmed to each other at the end. Other soldiers struck at Chowk, the shopping centre of the old city, and worked their way along the narrow street from the Akbari Darwaza, through which the Great Mughal was said to have passed, to the Gol Darwaza at the other end. They burst into patrician homes where a family that had refused to leave the city might be seated in silence; when they left, dressed in tiger skins and prayer mats and carrying silver pan-boxes, the women of the house were beating their breasts and wailing soundlessly. In the jewellers' shops the looters cut themselves on broken glass, turning the emeralds red; one man covered his fingers with so many rings that he found it impossible to loot efficiently for the rest of the day. His companions rushed down the Chawal Wali Gali or Rice Lane, terrifying the prostitutes and ripping open rice sacks which the Sikhs had told them concealed pearls of price.

The silence continued for the rest of 1858. Months after the corpses were cleared away, it took its toll on victor and vanquished alike, contempt and fawning becoming the unspoken mode of exchange. That summer the Viceroy "Clemency" Coningsby appeared in Nakhlau, but when he lifted up his hand words failed him; the Vicereine kept a handkerchief to her nose. In White Town homes, when servants were beaten, the stick fell without the usual whack. In the city, men broke down in public, offering the embarrassed street a silent gaping mouth; a woman appeared shaking uncontrollably with sound-less laughter. After the monsoon, in the kite season, boys flew a few tentative kites, but they were still black. Only the boldest bought string coated with powdered glass for kite fights or chased a loser's kite as it dropped out of the sky into the next neighbourhood. There were no crackers at Divali, but once, towards the end of November, a sugar-cane vendor's cry astonished the city. "Come snag your kites!" he called, waving a purple cane with a tangle of leaves at the top, and the idlers round about, delighted more by the sound than the sense, applauded the wit with guffaws and clapping until they realized that the sound had not yet returned for them.

At last, at the beginning of the true winter, the smallest sounds began to surprise the townsfolk: a bucket put down at a well, the beating of a wicker fan against a brazier. But as late as Christmas Day a pin dropped in Chowk could be heard six miles away in Sans Souci.

"Did you hear that?" Thomas Henry asked his wife.

They were sitting at breakfast in the Rain Room as if they had never moved to the Life-Giving House. The old hunting-lodge at the edge of the parklands was a blackened ruin; when peace returned to Nakhlau they had had to move back nearer *Sungum* to find another place. Of all Sans Souci only the Glacerie had escaped damage, being the most northerly of the buildings and thus sheltered from both the sepoys' rage and the British line of advance. There, in a suite at the Old Armoury end which communicated with the roof and the godown, the Fourth Trotters made their home. Breakfast, by the inflexible rule of the place, was eaten in the Rain Room on the roof; lunch, in the cool basement where the ice had been stored in the old days; and dinner, still a formal event, in the main hall. It did not matter that Thomas Henry was a long way from the Writers' Building: he no longer worked there. The uncovenanted civil service was no longer for him. It was history, along with much else, and yet there were times when the Middle Trotter found himself missing his modest desk, his mousy ledgers, the fawn-coloured office paper, the khaki files, and the red tape that had once held his life together. Now Nakhlau Trotter had to endure the turmoil of fame. Not that he undervalued himself: his impetuous grey eyes, prone to sudden irrigations, still scanned the past for parallels in History. Hercules, messenger of Thebes; Hannibal, chill wanderer; Horatio, saviour of Rome; Gog, Magog, Tubal Cain, paraded before him and went their way diminished. He had heard over the past summer a rumour that the government of the land (Tirnab, along with the rest of British India, had now passed formally under the British Crown) was seriously reviewing a proposal to extend the award of the Victoria Cross to civilians. What had once been a fanciful notion presented itself to Thomas Henry as palpably as the thirteen-month-old daughter, his own Victoria, playing at his feet under the breakfast table.

"It sounded like a pin," Philippa answered. "They can't *still* be looting in Chowk?"

"Chowk?" Thomas Henry was nonplussed. The pin he could understand: lately a pin to him was something that held up a medal. "Chowk!" he repeated. "Whatever are you dreaming of, my dear?" He shook the creases out of the newspaper he was reading. "I said, did you hear this about the Victoria Cross? It looks as if the government have made up their minds."

Philippa had heard the story before. It was an old newspaper, because supplies of most things were not back to normal yet. She smiled her crooked smile as her eyes wandered over the breakfast plates on which a rime of grease was already forming. There had been eggs because it was Christmas even though the prices at the new Solomon establishment in Hazratganj were worrying. But things were expensive everywhere, and besides how could one grudge the old man the few extra coins when he gave such generous credit? The wine, which Thomas Henry was drinking more freely than when he was an uncovenanted clerk, had not been paid for for months, but the Solomons seemed not to mind. Their bread was not as fine and white as before, but these were hard times. Had Philip not wandered in the other day, there would have been no goose. She had given her brother up for dead, and so had everyone else, including his intended, Alina. In fact he had three times narrowly missed death, first in escaping from his captors in Allahabad for whom he was forced to make gun-carriages, then from Kanpur where he survived the riverside massacre by floating off in a burning boat, and finally in the jungle where he was mauled by a panther. For months he had remained a fugitive, first from the sepoys and then from the British, who he feared would punish him as a traitor. Necessity had made a hunter of him; a sense of special deliverance had made him religious. God, he was convinced, had singled him out for preservation so that by his witness others might be brought to Him. The gun-carriages, however, weighed on his conscience, and it was that burden as much as his privations in the wilds that gave him the haggard look of a prophet. In later years the Trotters called him Philip the Baptist, but Alina was quite happy to marry him all the same. Philippa smiled when she remembered the shriek from the dairy the day her brother came back from the dead; it was the first sound heard in Sans Souci since the silence began to thin. Philip and Alina were to marry in the new year. By then, thought Philippa, the bells of St Aloysius's cantonment church will have found their tongues. Her smile lengthened on one side until a spasm in her leg reminded her of the calf that had been blown away. She would always walk with a limp.

Meanwhile, Thomas Henry had put down his paper. In his mind's eye he was nearing England, at which point in his itinerary he usually stood up and strode about the room, pent on deck for too many weeks. He leaned on the back of his wife's chair as if against the taffrail, staring across the breakfast dishes at the cliffs of Dover. Forcibly reminded of his presence, Philippa leaned on the table and took up the thread of his daily discourse, narrowing her eyes and craning the entire length of her soft dark vulnerable neck till she saw, or seemed to see, the white cliffs in the distance.

"Think of England!" Thomas Henry coaxed, and his wife obeyed. She saw meadows and apple orchards and cottages thatched with snow. She found herself struggling up a familiar garden path, her skirts snagging on a thorn bush. She recognized the cottage, the door, the latch, but as she went to lift it, it drew away and left her with a stark vision of greasy plates. She could only whisper in remonstrance: "Thom! The *servants*!" But the Middle Trotter was too far gone to care. His own helping vision was of Windsor Castle, where a dumpy monarch smiled for him alone as she lifted the sword from his shoulder. "Rise, Sir Thomas!" she seemed to say, when suddenly the breakfast table came to life and began to pummel his knees.

It was the real Victoria, his daughter. He had quite forgotten that she was playing at his feet under the table. Alarmed at the rattling dishes overhead, and sensing in that moment the conception of siblings-and-rivals, the girl struck with all her might at the guilty quaking legs, careless of wounded calves and feet, howling all the while on a high virtuous note which did bring one servant running.

She need not have vexed her little brain. The result of the Christmas breakfast trauma was not a rival. The twins who came would never shake her from her place in her father's heart, for the simple reason that they could never be called Victoria. They were boys. But they were called Victor—both of them, black and white—the first of a long line of Christmas Victors who would eventually stretch to the very end of the dining table in the Glacerie. There was also another result. When Victoria grew up she kept the legs of every table, carved or not, breakfast or bedside, carefully concealed with yards of white linen that hung down to the floor. But that was many years later, though not as late as the plague of dust. As for Philippa, she would struggle up the crazy paving of an English garden walk many a time, always disappointed at the last moment, though never again at the breakfast table. Only the Middle Trotter's surmise was rewarded—at least in part. If he didn't rise Sir Thomas, it did happen that he sailed to England (leaning on the taffrail as the ship drew near the cliffs of Dover) and was decorated by the hand of his sovereign whose name honoured the cross at his heart. If the pin on the medal slipped from the royal hand, it was a minor incident which only the perverse or superstitious would have seen as an augury, because Thomas Henry himself stooped to pick it up and bore the good lady no grudge in after years. Nor did he make any mention of the slip in his book.

He was writing one. In the new reading room of the British Museum, sandwiched between two grave black-coated men, the Middle Trotter sat musing. The man to the left, the more bushily bearded of his neighbours (*Brutish Barbarian, Unkind Cut*) and cursed with a bulging forehead, was proofreading his *Critique of Political Economy* and already making notes towards his *Capital*; the man to the right stroked a long straggling beard in a vain attempt to conceal a prognathic jaw (*Satanic Simian, Hairy Ape*) and gibbered softly to himself over the proofs of his *Origin of Species*. In the middle sat Thomas Henry, with his middling beard, about to start the book that would change the world.* He ran his eyes over the hunched figures all around the circular room, starting with the man on the left and coming around by degrees to the other, as once he had looked over his fellow clerks in the Writers' Building at Nakhlau. The drones! What did they know of mining and sapping? Had any one of them smelt gunpowder? Or spiked a gun? Or carried a sword? Soft hands, lily livers! And here he was among them, Thomas Henry, man of deeds as well as words—a Babar, a Julius Caesar, who balanced pen with sword. He slid away the dictionary of classical allusions, blew gently on the blank sheet of Trotter paper before him (it had a piece the size of a postage stamp taken out of the upper left-hand corner), and wrote in upright capitals that he underlined twice:

---

* Not one of these grave gentlemen, secure in their discoveries, would have guessed that the most revolutionary book of the century was already in the press. That same year of grace, 1859, saw Mrs Isabella Beeton publish her magnum opus, *Mrs Beeton's Cookery and Household Management Book*, at the tender age of twenty-three (*Kitchen Copernicus, Gastronomy Galileo*). For an example of her method, ravishing in its simplicity yet heavy and satisfying in the result, see her Delhi Pudding, made of brown sugar, currants, apples, suet, and flour.—E.A.T.

MY PATH TO THE VICTORIA CROSS

The book did well, considering. It even inspired his brother-in-law, Philip the Baptist, to start on a book of his own. He had got as far as a title, *The Valley of the Shadow, Or, His Hand Revealed*, and for many years after he returned to the railways he would toy with it, removing or putting back a comma while lecturing the trolley team about something called the Machinery. He would sit beside the railway track at the end of the day's work, his mouth full of jungle fowl and toast dipped in tea, and say: "It's the Machinery that's holding things up," taking care to explain that he did not mean the *Deus ex machina*. The body of the book, he was confident, would write itself, being an exact and minute demonstration from true life of the intervention of God in the affairs of selected men. But the Machinery was a problem. Later on, it became the Apparatus; he had been talking to a pastor who had read the German exegetes.

The brothers-in-law were not the only ones whom fate had turned authors. Everybody who could write (and some who could not) was busy writing or dictating his version of the Great Calamity. Memoirs multiplied beyond the number of surviving memories; eyewitness accounts soon exceeded the number of remaining eyes. From unlettered soldiers to judicial commissioners and the wives of judicial commissioners, everyone had a story to relate, full of wonders, atrocities, and providential escapes. Generals and generals' aides, special correspondents, alabaster merchants, clerks, drummers and tars—all spent 1859 scribbling in penitential silence, though the sound had long since returned to Nakhlau. Sometimes it seemed that there was only one man who was not writing a book, but this man was in fact a ghost who had written books enough to last many lifetimes. Munshi Nishan Chand, librarian of Tirnab (that was), who had just closed his one hundred and fifty-seventh year, had nothing more to say. He had seen the palace library ransacked, and not by men hungry for his works, but by looters-and-arsonists who found in it fuel for fires to be lit elsewhere. He had himself been mistaken for a stick of furniture and tossed onto a bonfire at the western Mermaid Gate. In his last moments he reluctantly discarded the theory that the British were a handy tool. As his foreign pyjamas caught, he was grateful that his habitual posture, which kept him folded in half, saved him from the indignity that he had heard overtook men laid out on their funeral pyre: the fire made the corpse sit up.

Writers were not the only ones making hay. No sooner had word of the conflagration reached Calcutta than merchants began to offer Mutiny bargains: cut-price memorials, monuments and tablets, toy Enfields and trick greased cartridges, Mutiny telescopes, Mutiny muffins (at Ferdinand Fonseca's Fine Foods on Park St), Mutiny matches, Mutiny alarm clocks, Pandy cigarettes

and dart boards, and decks of Mutiny playing cards in which Mahavir Pandav
was the knave. In London there was the Mutiny pub lunch and the Mutiny
March, mutiny field glasses and campstools, buttons, wallets, boots, hats, and
haircuts. One undertaker offered mourning at reduced rates for grieving relatives, swearing that the sheen on his bombazine lasted longer. It was no
wonder Mr T. Jones Barker, looking over Egron Lundgren's sketches of
"Natives Quarrelling over Plunder," decided he could paint.

> *Narrator. Here is a little bribe, some Ben Shalom pressed from Jaffa orange peel.
> Let there never be another Mutiny story!*
> *I'll drink to that, Cup-Bearer, but I must confess I am not sanguine. Where there
> is life, there is, alas, another Mutiny story. But hear now what the dove told
> me.*

(*CHRONICLE RESUMED*)

It was a lasting peace. All across the city craters were filled in, bullet
holes patched up. Buildings were repaired and replastered; those that the army
engineer pronounced unsafe were demolished. Three wide military roads were
cut through the heart of Black Town (a term now considered outré), and the
bazars around the Residency were cleared away. The Residency itself was
left as it was, bullet- and shell-riddled, except that lawns were put down and
cypress avenues planted. A low wall was built around the entire grounds, and
although there was no sign at the gate that read, as at Kanpur, NO NATIVE MAY
ENTER, none did apart from the gardeners. Obelisks were raised and tablets
set in them to mark notable or cherished spots, such as:

> ☞ HERE FELL SO AND SO
> ☞ HERE SUCH AND SUCH PASSED
> ☞ HERE THE ENEMY SPRUNG A MINE
> ☞ HERE MRS TROTTER HAD HER DREAM

Here on Sunday evenings the rulers came to breathe the cool, instructive air,
to offer up thanks for deliverance, and to ask strength to forgive. For the new
Nakhlau, adjacent to the quondam White Town (now called the Civil Lines),
public buildings of bulk and utility were planned: a post office, a courthouse,
a college, a hospital, a waterworks. They rose up, exotic but working witnesses
to the municipal virtues of the Peace. And new cantonments were laid out,
just in case, nearer the city and aligned with the military roads.

One day the railway arrived with a fiery clanking, and Grey Town too
was transformed; overnight Anglo-Indians went from clerks to railwaymen.

Philip Kahn-Trotter and his kind built, staffed, and ran the line. It came up out of the south and cut across the desert extremity of Sans Souci between the aerolite and St Aloysius's School, making a level-crossing at the Trotter Road and traversing the parklands to the south of the Ice Bridge before coming to a halt at the Charbagh or Four Gardens Station. The beginnings of a railway colony now abutted the canal across from the squalid terraces which marked the seamy side of Grey Town. For the rest, Sans Souci remained much as the sepoys had left it, except that the seasons smoothed over the destruction. A hardy black moss rounded off the tops of broken walls, lakes of feathery white grass filled the open spaces between buildings, and the least watercourse was marked with the plant the villagers called Shameless, with its silvery blue leaves, milky stem, and white trumpet-shaped flowers. Philippa, who was not sure she didn't prefer the wildness of mint jungles and spreading thickets of lantana, nevertheless had the sunken garden weeded and planted with portulaca, balsam, and zinnia, whose hot colours were more satisfying than those in the English garden of her fantasy. She also tended Mik's grotto, and in a meditative mood would sit in its shade by the Persian rose-bush which had grown up out of a scalloped pit at the foot of the North Tower. The blooms were white in the morning, pink by noon, and at dusk, when they were poised to fall, carmine. In the midst of the general decline, they brought a kind of consolation for which Philippa was grateful.

Philip and Alina were married in the new cantonment church where the bells were deafening. A week later the whistle of a steam engine carried all the way across the parklands (it scared old Munnoo to death) announcing that Philip was off to push the line out westwards. The builders of the railways could be separated from their families for as long as three years. Alina returned to the dairy, where already there were six buffaloes and two cows about to calve. She was accustomed to work and solitude, though there was help and company in an old widow from the village who came to clean out the cowsheds. Budhiya, the daughter of an irregular marriage between a poulterers' client and a grooms' client in the Great Trotter's day, took no fee beyond the day's dung. Every morning she shaped the dung into biscuits which she slapped onto the crumbling walls of the Crocodile Wing where they sunned until ready for use. When the caste Hindus of the village burnt down her hut one day for some esoteric transgression involving a well, she came to live at the far end of the old dairy in a smoke-blackened room and was happy to be nearer her work. She would not touch the cows' teats, although she knew that caste rules did not apply at Sans Souci. When a calf died she skinned it and stuffed it with straw and propped it up near the mother so the grief milk might sweeten quickly; and on special festivals she painted the animals' horns red. During the milking she sat at a distance and shouted intimate questions at Alina until a close friendship grew up between them. She admired her mistress and modelled herself so carefully on her that when Alina became pregnant she did too. Both women were delivered of sons (though Budhiya had to cut the cord herself), but there was never any danger of the boys' being confused, since Alina's son, Alex, had a high profile. As for Jivan, the shastras declared that the issue of a fallen woman of the untouchables must go down one rank, and he was duly demoted.

In the Glacerie, Philippa's pregnancies would recur punctually for many years to come. Once she even fell pregnant while Thomas Henry was away, simply by thinking of England. She put each set of Victors, black and white, into the previous Victors' clothes and planned to make clerks-and-writers of them; when the oldest set invented the paper clip, their future seemed settled. But then Philip came home on leave prating of outer signals, down lines, bogeys, buffers and thrust, and the boys' heads were turned. There was never any doubt after that that they would follow their uncle into the railways. And follow they did, after a boyhood in which they stood one behind the other in descending order and chuffed up and down the Ice Court, stretching, as the years went on, to infinity: coal and steam, coal and steam. Their arms, bent at the elbow and held rigid as pistons, rocked to and fro as their boots scraped the flagstones in double time and the steam escaped them: *Koo-oo-ooo!* Chhuk-*chhuk-chhuk-chhuk*, chhuk-*chhuk-chhuk-chhuk*!

Their father, ever since he came back from England with his Cross, was a celebrity. The name *Nakhlau Trotter* caught on, so much so that people no longer even thought of his great-grandfather (*Great Trotter, Blessings on His Name*) when they used it. As a reward for meritorious services rendered, the government elevated him to the covenanted civil service, making him an Assistant Collector on a salary ten times higher than his previous one. He was admitted to the European Club in the former Umbrella Palace (though he could never bring his sable wife), and once while there, to his signal gratification, an admirer confessed in his ear that some acquaintances had come in "only to see you." "Only to see you": another phrase was stamped on the Fourth Trotter's memory, and not even an incident a little later in the evening could erase it.

It was an old planter at the next table. He had lost his wife in the troubles and sat daily in the same wicker chair drinking four-finger pegs of whisky. This evening he was startled out of his musings by a whack which told all present, and finally himself, that he had brought his stick down on the nearest waiter's turban. The bearer, a loyalist who had served in the Residency (only his kind had been hired by the club), was shepherded away to the pantry, where the other bearers gathered around him whispering. A group of sahibs had formed around the planter, whose cry, "Brutes, brutes!" feebly stirred the hanging cigarette smoke. Thomas Henry, the man for an emergency, sat unmoving in his chair when his listeners went over to the old man. His eyes had followed the shivering bearer to the pantry door and returned to the planter: strangely, neither man could excite the Middle Trotter's sympathy. He read in the eyes of the English a reluctant kinship with the bereaved; on the other side, the bearers seemed to have melted away for the moment. The only relief Thomas Henry could find was in the blank gaze of the bartender, a whisky-coloured Anglo-Indian who stared shortsightedly into the crystal glass he was polishing with a soft white napkin.

He had not been one of the vengeful, Thomas Henry, and he took no part in the looting. The Cross was compensation enough, and the Assistant Collectorship paid handsomely, though not well enough to pay for fine wines and a family that threatened to grow indefinitely. There were times when the Middle Trotter, now within the covenant, coveted a full Collectorship. Fame had its costs. The number of bottles on the Trotter table at dinner multiplied thanks to visiting well-wishers, overnight tourists, and tribes of tardy journalists in search of a story. Thomas Henry was happy to tell his, but it was fortunate that J.c. Solomon & Son were liberal with their credit. At three in the afternoon he might send a peon to warn his wife that guests were coming to dinner and require her to order and pay for nuts and fruit and sweetmeats as well as a choice roast from the market. He had brought back from England a copy of *Mrs Beeton's Cookery and Household Management Book* for her (*Devoted Husband, Selfless Spouse*), and he expected results. Economy was, after all, the wife's province; he brought home the rupees, she must manage.

Philippa managed. There was a cook, and even a bottle-washer to help, but it was her job to train them (the old ones had been carried off in the troubles or gone over to more prosperous households in the Civil Lines), to supervise, to keep accounts, to plan immoderate meals, to scold the shopper-and-haggler for inflating his commission. She cut down on meat, introduced radish leaves, switched (*Faithless Spouse*) from pure ghi to vegetable oils. She dismissed a slack servant and dusted the furniture herself, limping around the Glacerie apartment with a feather duster. Victoria, now a young woman, refused to have anything to do with naked tables (she would shortly invent the tablecloth) and her mother sympathized: the poor girl's hands were plain enough without housework to ruin them. As an economy measure Philippa had already reopened the chicken run in the Comb; in the mornings the Victors were sent chuffing off to collect the eggs. At night she poured cheap sherry into some of the more impressive bottles from J.c. Solomon & Son (*Cup-Bearer!*) but still the totals were alarming. She reread Mrs Beeton on the domestic budget, on sharpening pencils, on carrot-ends and tripe and fried potato peels, but the money was gone by the third week of the month, and she still had to pay the mochi for resoling all the Victors' boots. Floundering, she wrote a daughterly letter to Mrs Beeton, addressed simply, *England*, unaware that the lady was her junior and in any case prematurely dead (*Immortal Englishwoman, Chiefest Bess*). When no reply came, she went and sat under the Persian Rose.

Still nothing happened. It was not a promising day. A party of guests was expected from Roorkee, Englishmen all, including a small bearded man who dabbled in silly verse, was confessedly a "Dirty Landscape Painter," and was said to drink heroic quantities of sherry. The meat the shopper-and-haggler brought back from the market had had to be returned; one could not serve the English a tainted roast. While she waited, Philippa decanted and blended some more sherry

—*Cup-Bearer, I shall flog you and flog you in the English way until your bottom bleeds! O my sweet Ganymede, fetch me the malacca cane!*—

The shopper-and-haggler came back with word that all the choice cuts were gone. "Well, bring anything!" Philippa scolded, and the third time the shopper-and-haggler brought back eight trotters. Philippa clouted the man, flung the goats' feet into a corner where they lay clicking disconsolately, and went back to the Persian Rose. Delhi Pudding with goats' feet! She sat unmoving till dusk, when a carmine blossom detached itself from the branch and fell into her lap. As she gazed at it a glassy stillness came over her and her head grew clearer and clearer until it might have been a mirror of the sky.

That night Philippa's meal was highly praised. The Middle Trotter looked across at his wife with tears in his eyes, while the small bearded painter-and-versifier (a sugar-refiner's son gone wrong), who was jolly enough on his tenth glass of sherry, recited an impromptu composition.

(VERSE)

> The Trotters of Sans Souci
> Are nifty as nifty can be,
> Where others make glue
> These serve you a stew,
> The Trotters of Sans Souci.*

---

* Mr Montagu, understandably, renders *nifty* as *thrifty*. —E.A.T.

(CHRONICLE RESUMED)

The stew was a curry, but Philippa blushed invisibly and made a curtsey. She ran to fetch a sheet of paper from Thomas Henry's bureau and asked the poet (expansive on his eleventh glass) to write down the verse for her, which he was delighted to do. Cheers, bows, and an encore followed, during which Thomas Henry inwardly rehearsed a sticky moment on his famous night journey. He handed cigars, signalled the bearer for port, and began. Philippa slipped away to record the inspiration that had come to her sub rosa in the little garden at the foot of the North Tower. Seated at the bureau with the barley-sugar legs, she smoothed back the sheet of Trotter paper which had a piece missing from one corner and wrote out, under the signature, *Edward Lear*, Rose's recipe.

How Trotter Curry is made

I wish to shew how Trotter Curry is made. Ordinarily it is served at lunch. In setting out the recipe I follow the revolutionary path of Mrs Beeton, in whose book the *ingredients* were first separated from the *method* and tabulated at the head, thusly:

    2 large onions (or 4 middling)
    8 cloves garlic, crushed
    2 tablespoons fresh ginger, crushed
    3 teaspoons coriander powder
    2 teaspoons turmeric powder
    2 teaspoons cumin powder
    1 teaspoon red chilli powder
    1 teaspoon salt (or less, to taste)
    2 tablespoons oil
    8 trotters (sheep's or goats', no other), singed, scalded and scraped or
      skinned

Slice, sharp adept, one of the onions and set it aside. Chop the other and grind it with the garlic and ginger into a paste. Mix in the spices, adding a little water if you wish, a dessertspoon perhaps. Next fry the sliced onion in the oil until golden brown. Add then the spice paste and fry on low heat for 5 minutes.

Add then the trotters and brown them on high heat for (say) 10 minutes, stirring frequently. Cover the trotters with water (just) and add salt if you must. Simmer, good adept, for 3 hours, 2½ if patience be lacking.

Serve with fine white Basmati rice from Dehra Dun, or else chapatis spread with ghi (see GHI). It is a gravy, really.

This is what I wished to shew. So do that. Do it periodically.

(*CHRONICLE RESUMED*)

After that, Trotter Curry became standard fare in the Glacerie. It upset Victoria (she was growing up strange) but it made men of the Victors. A whole generation of railwaymen grew up on it, virile and dependable, so that there was truth in the claim that the trains of India ran to time on goats' feet. And Philippa was always grateful to Rose's shade.

She was not the only one to visit the bush. Thomas Henry, whose vision of his foster-mother's splendid breasts still troubled him, was sometimes drawn there of a Sunday. The bush never dropped a blossom in his lap, but he did conceive while seated under it the notion of building a memorial to old Rose. Having discovered the pleasures of extravagance, the Middle Trotter was constantly finding new ways of living beyond his means. Labour was cheap and plentiful among the Sagarpaysans, and he knew of a couple of stonemasons who could be persuaded to work for the old family on a rum ration. Of course the stone need not be transported, as of old, all the way across the Sea of Rains: the memorial would have to be built near the quarry. And so work began on the rocky ridge in the forest, looking out one way over the Kirani river and the other at *Sungum*. The memorial, Thomas Henry let it be known, would honour all who died in the troubles, on both sides, but especially Rose, Bulbul, Farida, and the Second Trotter, Mik; however, since it stood in the forest where his father fell a quarter of a century earlier, it might as well honour the Third Trotter, Charles, and for that matter all the Trotter dead. In fact it was Thomas Henry's half-formed wish to be buried there himself. Like the Nawabs of old, Nakhlau Trotter was building his own mausoleum.

The dome was only half completed when a man arrived from Nakhlau with a letter. Victoria, who seemed gifted with special powers, had predicted a visitor at breakfast and was at the Gunpowder Gate, waiting. Philippa took the envelope from her, trembling because she thought it might be a reply from Mrs Beeton. But it was a local stamp. Inside was a bill from J.c. Solomon & Son, who regretted that further credit could not be extended the Trotters owing to a record of payments that was, "to put it mildly, complacent."

That night Thomas Henry also brought news. When they were in bed he rolled over and said: "My dear, guess what!" Philippa could not guess. "The furlough's been granted—it came through today. I've written to the P&O in Bombay to book three starboard berths. Now that the Suez is open, the passage will be half as long, so we'll have longer in England. Victoria, naturally, must be presented at court. But the Victors will have to be left behind, with Alina, maybe. There are simply too many of them to take." Philippa absorbed this second shock of the day. England! And at once she felt a tickling in her belly as if she had swallowed a tadpole with her bedtime soporific. The English garden of her muscular fantasies swam before her, suddenly attainable, and for the first time since her marriage she travelled without a snag up the crazy-paved path, lifted the latch on the cottage door, passed through, and dissolved into nothing on the other side. When she opened her eyes, Thomas Henry, impetuous as ever, had got there before her and was fast asleep. It was then that she remembered the Solomon bill.

The next morning he hardly looked at it. The figures at the bottom had a fatuous cast; there was something unconvincing about the way they crowded together, hoping to intimidate by sheer numbers. Obviously the Solomons were not serious: the bearer could be asked to come again or fobbed off with a note of hand and the whole business settled when they came back from England. All the same, Thomas Henry halted work on the cenotaph, which was little more than four walls of pink stone that would always lack a dome. Among the Sagarpaysans it came to be thought of as Gulabi Bibi's tomb, while the woodcutters said the girl buried there died a long time ago. As for the cowherds, they knew that the tomb had always been there. The Fourth Trotter, packing for England, put Rose and the Solomons into a mental file, tied the knot, and forgot about them.

Victoria, now sixteen, surprised everyone by refusing to go. Onto a furtive wilful childhood there had of late been grafted the stubbornness of a gnostic. She wore no colour but violet, verging on black, and pulled her hair severely back just when young women were beginning to pile on curls. With lumpish intransigence she would wait hours for a sign before starting some trivial task. In the middle of lunch, at which she ploughed through mounds of brinjals, she might suddenly toss her head and sniff the air elaborately for a hidden gate. Lately she had acquired from somewhere a book of theosophy which made, and showed how anyone might make, startling divinations concerning other ages and other dimensions of the present age. She said she foresaw some calamity, a rock or shoal; something humped, anyway. Her mother flared up at the prophecy, but was relieved even so at a passage saved. Thomas Henry could deny his daughter nothing. It was decided that Alina would come up from the dairy and live in the Glacerie. There she could chaperone Victoria and look after the multitudinous but actually quite regular Victors, while her own brood, spaced evenly at intervals of three years, would have the benefit of company. In addition, a tutor should be found who would groom the (it had to be admitted) plain and backward girl into a refined young lady. No expense would be spared on that account: Victoria's accomplishments must not end with spreading tablecloths and working twelve-foot-square counter-panes on tiny crochet needles. An advertisement was accordingly placed in the *Nuntio*, and notices were sent to the Calcutta papers.

Governesses came and went over the next few months. Some were English and lasted no longer than the interview; they had not supposed they were to teach a black child. Others, French, Portuguese, or Anglo-Indian, stayed a day or two before being frightened off by the queer girl. Either they had found her up at midnight table-rapping (through a cloth) or else she was out in the noonday sun feeding the crows. One lady fled without taking the old Erard piano which, determined to last, she had brought for her pupil's instruction. She had been sitting in her room the night before, darning her stockings, when the candle went out just like that and the room was filled with drooling hairy presences. Moments later, there was Victoria on the thresh-old with a lantern held under her chin, asking could she be of assistance? The last of the governesses gone and the day of her parents' departure approaching, Victoria made another announcement. She saw, she said, a man coming. On the chosen day she went to wait at the Gunpowder Gate, but it was only the man from J.c. Solomon & Son with a final reminder. Her brothers chivvied her about it, easing a long-held grudge which their mother, curiously, seemed to understand. The man returned the old note of hand for part of the debt and said his master required full payment. Without looking into his bankbook, Thomas Henry wrote: "Pay to J.c. Solomon & Son," and copied out the entire amount of the bill. The man went off satisfied. That afternoon the sky grew dark by teatime and Victoria, who had met her brothers' teasing with a long cold stare, went up to her room and fastened the windows. She spread a fresh cloth on her table, drew up a draped chair, and sat with her black stockinged legs pressed tightly together and her hands folded in her lap. In a little while the windows were rattling and although the door was bolted, the fringe of the tablecloth had begun to stir.

Forecast of a plague of dust (Proceedings of the All-India Pantheosophical Society, Nakhlau Chapter, 1873)

12. The next and last plague, coming after the plague of locusts, and related to it in form but not substance, is the plague of dust. Abhayanka has mentioned it in his *Mystic Defile*, as also Master Tzu Win-li in his *Secret Voices of the Desert Whale*, and Nostradamus of Meiringen bears witness to it in *The Dark Haven* at the eleventh chapter. Our Rosicrucian brethren have noticed it in the vicinity of the Great Pyramid. Madame Blavatsky has seen it in other places at other times. It is now overdue. It comes out of the desert mostly, but since locusts make deserts of the most fertile land, it may originate any-

where. Its colour is between black, yellow, and white, and it combines the gross qualities of each. It is of the twelfth plane, dust being the lowest form of matter, lower even than dung (which may, however, when dry, mix with it as it flies). The hornet is its sign. It corresponds below to the twelfth plane of essences above (which comes after that of subtle bodies), namely, ether, whose sign is the tablecloth. The antagonism between them is one of innate contradiction. In the present age, dust has the ascendency. Its note on the piano is the lowest, its enemy or antidote a roll of felt. April is its month, but May and June, when the Great White Plain is driest, are susceptible. Those born in these months have crystal springs of resistance, but the divining rod must be grasped firmly at the base of the kundalinic spine.

(CHRONICLE RESUMED)

All through the storm Victoria sat with her large plain hands folded in her lap and her thoughts concentrated on the base of her spine. First the sky rained locusts whose wings beat on the windowpanes with a greedy sound. After an interval came the dust. It came out of the desert where the sand beneath the prickly pear called snake-hood cactus had been edging in for days. A twist of dust rose up and vanished, reappearing in another place. Soon numbers of dust devils had sprung up across the desert roundabout the aerolite, spinning, tilting, weaving in and out, colliding with one another and passing easily through as they skipped towards the Sea of Tranquillity. The whirr of locusts' wings gave way to a bass drone which set the lowest string on Victoria's piano vibrating. Sweeping across the ice pits, the dervishes stormed the ruined roundhouse where the bees were so incensed that a squadron of them zigzagged insanely across the Ice Court before returning to bury their stings in the fleshy limbs of the Oracle tree. Here the storm paused, gathering itself up, clouds of dust billowing higher and higher until the whole mass tottered and fell upon the towers. Dust burst in at the Ice Door and quickly carpeted the floor of the Audience Hall. Outside, it raced up the sheer walls of *Sungum*, straining at the shutters and smothering the dome; where the bell had left a hole it poured in and plunged three storeys to the tahkhana far below, which it filled to the depth of the plinth in minutes.

For an hour and a half the storm raged, shaking Sans Souci to its foundations before vanishing in a puff of dust on the Plain of Cannonballs.

Afterwards it was hard to tell where the locusts' work ended and where the storm's began. The Victors crept out in a row, red-eyed and gaping; they had taken shelter with Philippa in the old ice godown while Thomas Henry searched for them from room to room. In all directions the trees were bare, the bushes picked clean. Not a blade of grass remained for miles—even the bamboo clump near the tea-house had been nibbled down to the woody sections, while the mehndi-hedge maze was a cage of bones. And as far as the horizon there lay the dust, inches deep, the colour of history. Everything man-made: buildings, gateposts, flights of steps, the fallen sundial, was mantled in it. The elephant graves to the south were levelled, the Tank had lost half its depth, while here and there in the endless beige expanse a dimple showed where a well had been. The tall antlered silk-cotton trees wore on every branch and twig a ridge of beige dust that looked to Philippa like the snow of an England which at the height of the storm she had half expected never to see. With Thomas Henry (who burst into tears at finding his wife alive) she limped up the Gunpowder Drive, staring at a world transformed. Behind them, in single file, came the Victors who no longer dragged their feet but lifted them up high with each step as if walking in a kind of tropical snow. Their mouths hung open, echoing a larger silence. It was not complete silence, as in 1858, but sounds underfoot were muffled and ashen. As the Trotters reached the first of the silk-cotton trees, a branch fractured in the storm came crashing down through the lower branches with a noise like a locomotive and fell with a hush into the powder below, springing back up and turning over softly at Thomas Henry's feet.

Victoria was not with the rest of the family. They had caught sight of her at her window, flicking aside the curtains with a triumphant look, her wide mouth stretched in a smile. The dust, she knew, was everywhere in Sans Souci; she did not need to go out to look. But as far as she could tell, not a speck had penetrated her skirts or touched a single table-top. As for the man, she did not bother her head with proofs. The rest of the family came upon him at the Gunpowder Gate, standing there alone, epaulettes of dust on his sloping shoulders and a green patent rain-gauge in his hands.

T. H. Montagu

> T eetotal Trotter!
> H ardly Trotter!
> E gghead Trotter!
> O economic Trotter!
> B ald-as-a-bandicoot Trotter!
> A ugmented Fifth Trotter!
> L ocust-without-wild-honey Trotter!
> D ry-as-dust Trotter!
>
> H istorical Trotter!
> O ssified Trotter!

R ickety Trotter!
A ttic Trotter!
T one-deaf Trotter!
I llegitimate Trotter!
U nlikely Trotter!
S tand-in Trotter!

M endacious Trotter!
O dd-man-out Trotter!
N o-thank-you-but Trotter!
T rotter without the T!
A postate Trotter!
G ruel-thin Trotter!
U n-Trotter!

(CHRONICLE RESUMED)

"Can I help you?"

Thomas Henry's voice came out in a shout. He held out his hand at once to make amends.

"No thank you, but—" The stranger's voice trickled like sand from the corner of a practiced smile. He took the Fourth Trotter's hand and continued. "—I think perhaps I can help *you*. Theobald Horatius Montagu"—a bow toward Philippa—"at your service!"

And the next they knew, the man had turned the line of Trotters around and was marching them back up the drive while he explained the virtues of the patent rain gauge.

"—nay, gaug*es*. In a climate such as this, if rain-gauges were comprehensively installed on a large estate such as this by a progressive family such as this"—here he rolled an admiring eye down the row of diminishing Victors—"satisfaction will surely and swiftly follow."

Thomas Henry took to him at once. There was for a start the coincidence of their initials (at least to their given names). Then there was the Horatius. And besides, the man had a suavity of address that was soothing coming immediately upon a bewildering act of God (*Posturing Satan, Carpetbagging Rogue*). Philippa was less sure, but softened to him when he admitted to being a Calcutta Anglo-Indian even though his suit and certain accents in his voice suggested North America. The rain-gauge was indeed from Cleveland, Ohio, but the man did not profess to have been there. As for the puffing Victors, they were always glad to see a new face: when they saw their mother relent, they brightened up at once and began to drag their feet again. It was doubly disarming when the man confessed that he was new to the job of salesman, assuring them at the same time that his confession was not in itself an old confidence trick. He had never sold a thing, he said, though that was not for want of trying or travelling. He had placed two rain-gauges, but one was left in Jamalpur on credit, and the other he had purchased himself. In fact, he did not *really* recommend it to the Trotters—

"—that *is* your name? I took the liberty of reading the plaque on the gate."

"Trotter, yes, quite so!" Thomas Henry apologized for having forgotten. Something about the man always had you wanting to accommodate him. He held out his hand once more, adding: "Thomas Henry."

"Not *Nakhlau Trotter*?"

After that, Thomas Henry would not hear of a hotel.

They went in for dinner at eight. Victoria came down wearing, to every-one's surprise, a gown of yellow silk that she had made herself from pieces found in the Balloon Room. Thomas Henry presented his daughter, gamely enough; not even her choice of his hated colour could offend the doting father. Mr Montagu made his pedantic little bow and then—whether from the yellow lights that burned in the girl's eyes or from the painful spark that flew when their hands met—took a step back. Victoria did not flinch: she was used to little shocks.

Philippa produced river fish and sweet potatoes at which everyone except Victoria felt obliged to nibble because the guest ate so sparingly. It *could* be the bones, Philippa told herself. Victoria as usual serenely engulfed her food: it might have been her holy mission to devour and transmute the dross of the world which swam doomstruck towards that open mouth (*Gorgeous Eater, Mystic Whale*). While she ate, the family heard Theobald Horatius's story.

Born in Bunkeegunge, he had been educated at the Lower Military Or-phanage in Calcutta and then on a scholarship at a college established by Jacob Kahn-Trotter on his return from England. He was an historian by training, and until lately, by profession. A matter of principle—some difference with the head—had compelled him to resign his lectureship at the same college, a decision taken before he had properly considered the alternatives. Obliged to look elsewhere for an income, he discovered that history teachers were in sufficient supply in Calcutta. (*Where are they not?*) Letters to the presidencies of Bombay and Madras brought letters of rejection (*Sagacious Bombay, Far-seeing Madras*), while those to upriver districts were lost in the post (*Worthy Postmen, Illustrious Dak*). Eventually, his funds running low, he happened to meet, on an early constitutional around the Maidan, an American man of business. The Bronxman, complete with cane and dachshund, turned his head with talk of commissions, advanced techniques, patents, travel, and the vision of a conglomerate of firms that would in the not distant future honourably swallow up the Army & Navy Stores presently enjoying transitory success. A small deposit was required: beyond that a candidate for salesmanship need only be unattached and willing to travel. He would be trained at no cost for three days, at the end of which his rote-learning would be put to a test (Mr Montagu blushed to say he had secured the highest mark). Then he was free to go. Travelling upriver, the historian-and-salesman found no buyers for the rain-gauge. Across the countryside from Bengal to Tirnab the rains had failed, the crops and cattle were dead, and famine ruled the villages. Yet stocks were bountiful in Calcutta and it was reliably known that the government continued to export rice (*Monstrous Misrule*). At length the powers were prevailed upon to import rice (*Benevolent Despots*) from Burma—while the export continued from Calcutta—and to distribute it at relief works set up throughout the afflicted provinces.*

Thomas Henry was deeply moved by this account of human suffering. He determined, the tears rising, to write immediately to the government sacrificing his furlough and offering his services on half pay as a volunteer. Philippa, who saw a green isle once again begin to shrink and sail away, said nothing. The stranger looked down at his buttons, ivory on a beige suit. Buttons were his failing—in fact, Philippa had at first sight taken him for one of those box-walas who came around with European needles and thread, garters, lace, hairpins, and endless boxes of buttons. Mr Montagu wore his entire stock on his coat, down to a small cluster, like a pallid rose, on his lapel. Buttons apart, he was blandly, even professionally, nondescript: a slight bald man with even ivory-coloured teeth and the kind of sketchy distracting beard that might be shaved off in a minute to evade the police.

"A drop of port?" asked Thomas Henry, dabbing his eyes. The decanter shone through his tears like the Grail. He had suddenly remembered his duties as host, and was ready to pour.

"No thank you, but—"

There was a moment of stunned silence up and down the table. Dinner without port to follow! But the guest had not finished speaking.

"—a little dry sherry would go down very well—the drier the better."

A bottle of dry sherry was found, and the exquisite red olorosos pushed to one side where they glowered richly. Thomas Henry's faith in the man

---

* Three years later, a biased Viceroy wrote home of these relief works: "The people on them do no work of any kind, are bursting with fat and naturally enjoy themselves thoroughly." Lord Lytton, *Letters of the Earl of Lytton*, Vol. 2, p. 79. Photographs of this Viceroy, of which there is a glut, explain his attitude most eloquently. The reader may profitably compare photographs of Lytton's good-natured successor, Lord Ripon.—E.A.T.

was briefly shaken; as Middle Trotter he liked a blend of sweet and dry, inclining as the years slipped by towards the sweet. He recovered over cigars, helped by the young man's interest in the minutest details of the Siege. And shortly, Nakhlau Trotter was slipping out of the Residency for the fiftieth time on his heroic night journey, while before him, with the rapt humility of the man of words come face to face with deeds, Mr Montagu sat motionless, his beige eyes enlarged behind thick glasses and fixed shrewdly on the past. Occasionally he might interrupt, avid of fact: "Now this second attempt was at seven o'clock, would you say—or a quarter past?" And the Middle Trotter, his own eyes damp with self-reproach, would refill the glass of vanishing dry sherry. Never before was so much demanded of the telling: each footfall of that November night's journey must be accounted for. The eastern sky was whitening over the Indigo Court (Victoria, then the Victors, and finally Philippa had long since gone to bed), but the stranger sat on, thirsty for more. One might as well have watered the desert. At last Nakhlau Trotter was obliged to let Dukhi Das reach safety, a thing he never did until the second night's instalment so that his audience might be kept on tenterhooks and then rewarded for their patience. But the stranger's curiosity was inexhaustible. So far they had covered a single day: what of the other days of that historic siege?

But for the furlough, Thomas Henry might have been tempted. As it was, the tickets were already bought, train and ship. History, he knew, with the security of one who had made a bit of it, could wait. Two days later a wire came from the government: the Middle Trotter's services were not required for famine relief. Philippa's island hove back into view as they boarded the Deccan train. At Bombay, another telegram was waiting for Thomas Henry. It was the bank, to say that his cheque in favour of J.c. Solomon & Son could not possibly be honoured. But the Fourth Trotter was already too far gone; he cabled back a small amount, all he could spare for the moment, and the Trotters set sail. Victoria was not with them after all. According to plan, Alina had moved into the Glacerie as her resident chaperone, and as to her mental guidance, a tutor had been found. There would be no singing or piano, but she would start, the coming Monday, her first lessons in history.

The lessons, at which Alina or one of the senior Victors was always present, were held in the Rain Room on the Glacerie roof. Between master and pupil was a wide table, decently covered, on one side of which stood the blackboard and on the other a high-backed chair for Victoria. At the door, placed there by the Victors, was the medicine ball, but Alina, who had taken to wearing saris, preferred to sit on the floor nowadays. Mr Montagu delivered himself of his lessons in his ashen voice, gazing out across the Sea of Rains that his coming had turned from indigo to a uniform beige. A stick of chalk blanched his fingertips, shuttling from hand to hand at first slowly and then with mounting speed until a lunge at the blackboard snapped it in two and sent the pointed end ricocheting about the room, proof that history in its academic mode was not without its perils. But the master did not look his pupil in the eye, remembering too well the yellow lights that burned there; easier to scan the drab expanses beyond the old indigo baths for hints of a deep bruised blue. Already he knew something of the history of the place. The pupil sat unmoving in her chair, her massive craggy hands folded like sleeping mountains in her lap, patience in the set of her huge forehead. Sitting there in one of her violet gowns which the tea-coloured morning light gave a bronze cast especially persuasive at the folds, she might have been the statue of herself. Very rarely, when the emotion wrung from some hoary date carried Mr Montagu away, his voice ran up above its habitual chalky whisper and glanced off the blackboard with a chilling screech. Then the yellow irises contracted sharply, but no other movement betrayed Victoria's irritation.

There was one moment, however, which could move the girl and which drew her back to the history class day after day. It came at the end of the lesson, when Mr Montagu was gathering up his books and moving swiftly around the table as he made for the door. He was never more than half-way across the floor when Victoria found the duster, a strip of coarse green felt backed with wood that rested on a runner at the bottom of the board. Without rancour or vengefulness, but with evident pleasure, she would seize this weapon and begin to wipe, starting at one corner and working her way across the board in sweeping arcs, obliterating kings and battlefields and charters, revolutions and timid reforms, until all was once again a virginal black. Then, where another child might have been tempted to blow the fresh chalk-dust to the ends of the world, Victoria brought her fleshy nose down to the runner and breathed in, deeply. It was a kind of sigh in reverse, a snort almost, and when it was finished the smallest particle of dust had been spirited up those gaping nostrils. Mr Montagu only once waited to follow the spectacle to its close; after that he turned and ran. Had he been more attentive, he might have learnt to read against his blank board the obscurest characters of desire.

Victoria herself could not understand it. She went off to her room, where she pounded the black keys on her Erard repetition-check-action piano, the spoils of an earlier war, and wondered why she kept gravitating towards the lowest note, a white one. Here was a campaign whose conduct for the first time simply baffled her, and yet the feelings it aroused had troubled her from earliest childhood, long before the shameful red tides that Philippa explained as Eve's punishment. Once, playing in the mud, she had cocked her head like one of those stray dogs to listen to a tiny distant sound and been immediately ashamed of her beastliness. Her second sight when it came gave strength, because the shadowy figures she began to glimpse were allies against the beast, leaning towards her from beyond, offering disbelief. Now, just when she had begun to master the art of swallowing up the world, a speck stuck in her throat. She who had exuded confidence in yellow the evening of Mr Montagu's arrival, exulting in the prospect of an equal battle (the governesses had been routs), suddenly found herself slipping. She banged harder at the keys as awareness grew until suddenly she kicked back the piano stool and slammed the lid down. The whole instrument trembled at the terrible knowledge—she not only longed to engage with the devil: she longed to let him win.

Knowing nothing, the historian suspected nothing. Each day he walked from the Begam Kothi, where he had taken up residence, to the Glacerie and back, scattering dust as he went. At the first sight of a cloud in the sky he set up his rain-gauge beyond the old lotus pond between the maze and the nearest of the mango topes, expecting mango showers. When the true rains came, the dust settled, releasing a sweetness long suppressed as Sans Souci had its first wash since the plague. Trees began to leaf and there was new grass between the buildings, though in the sunken garden there formed miry pools of beige batter in which a locust's wing might glint as the sun topped the Glacerie. Arrested by a flashing angle of incidence one morning, Mr Montagu stooped to pick up a wing and held it up against the light exclaiming to himself. There and then he decided to invent the glasshouse. Since the grounds all round appeared to be returning to a hateful monsoon green, here was a way to preserve an arid plot close to his heart, planted with cactus, tumbleweed, and assorted desert flora.

He did it modestly in the backyard of the Begam Kothi, although there were more salubrious sites. As a guest-and-tenant he could hardly impose a new structure on Sans Souci, especially as the owners were away. When the folly was built, from a stack of panes found in the godown of the Kothi, Mr Montagu found that he could not stand up in it, but it was not for living in, he told himself, much as one might wish to. The roof up, he began on the floor, taking extended walks in the desert and filling his pockets with sand when he thought no one was looking. Next he took to bringing home suitable plants, slipping perhaps a snake-hood cactus into his shirt, or some sterile lichen scraped off the aerolite. Later, he promised himself, he would send for spiny quince from Baja California, lithops from the Transvaal, and sand-cabbage from the Gobi Desert. And when all was flourishing aridity, he would push a desk and chair under the sloping roof of his solarium and sit there in the noonday sun, writing history.

*And now, O Cup-Bearer, the shoe is on the other foot: I shall ask you
  a few questions.*

Such as, Narrator?

It is for me to ask. Are you prepared?

I am.

Then answer. Who first made Sans Souci?

The Great Trotter made it.

For whom?

For Trotters.

For Trotters only?

*For Trotters and Fonseca-Trotters and Kahn-Trotters and Alexander-Trotters
  and combinations thereof.*

Well answered. Give me the begats.

*The Great Trotter, Justin Aloysius, begat Mik, Next Trotter, who begat Charles
  Pote, A-Trotter, who begat Thomas Henry, Middle Trotter, who begat Victoria
  and the Victors and is now abroad.*

Each was steward-and-husbandman?

Some better than others.

But the vineyard prospered?

The vineyard prospered.

And it was good?

It was very good.

Then tell me: who first brought Care to Sans Souci?

The Devil did.

His principal name?

The ANTI-TROTTER.

His other names?

Theobald Horatius Montagu.

Was he a Trotter of the flesh?

In no part, form, or substance.

What was the state of Sans Souci before he came?

A state of bliss.

And after?

A state of desolation.

Its colour?

The colour of dust.

Which is?

Beige, dun, ivory, or bromidic.

Its smell?

Rank.

Its sound?

Ashen.
Its texture?
Sandy.
Its shape?
Scroll-shaped.
Its taste?
Ashes in the mouth, ashes in the belly.
This foul substance is called what?
The foul substance is called History.
And its opposite?
Is the Chronicle.
Which may be illustrated?
Profusely.
Is colourful?
In the extreme.
Has flavour?
Honey in the mouth, honey in the belly.
Its smell?
Ambrosial.
Its texture?
Smooth but sometimes sticky.
Its sound?
Ethereal.
Specifically?
Soprano.
Not male alto?
Never.
Female soprano?
No.
Male soprano?
Yes.
Not castrato?
Not quite.
Its shape?
Spherical.
Its supreme exponent?
You.
Does it usher in a new age?
It ushers in an age of promise.
Which is the end of what lie?

It is the end of Historie.
Go up, Cup-Bearer.

(CHRONICLE RESUMED)

To keep the air in the glasshouse dry in the monsoon, the historian burnt a charcoal fire in one corner (*Gnostalgic Satan, Infernal Gnick*). On one of his walks he had found an old fire-bucket lined with clay in the Balloon Room. A window in the glass roof, propped open with Gibbon, let out the fumes, assorted prickly cactii covered the floor, and a writing desk stood just inside the door. When he was not sitting at it or teaching in the Rain Room, Mr Montagu spent his free hours exploring Sans Souci, his brain fired by the thought of so much unwritten history as he wandered among buildings crumbling away like Imperial Rome.

At the opposite end of Sans Souci from the Begam Kothi he found the Crocodile Wing in a state of almost complete dereliction. To judge from the bleached floor, the roof had fallen in many summers ago, perhaps in the bombardment. Giant pats of dung suggested an elephant stable, a smoke-blackened room conjured up branding irons. Satisfied with his notes he turned away just as Budhiya crept back into her hovel. The cows grazing at the edge of the forest looked up and followed his departing form with little jerks of the head, but before he was out of sight they shook their tails and went back to grazing. On the other side, in the old Elephant Wing, he would find evidence of crocodiles. Another day he walked westwards as far as the mock ruin and was again deceived. He stepped inside. A single branch of the overhanging Oracle tree remained stubbornly alive, although its blossoms, fleshy and pink in midsummer, lay in withered swirls like crepe on the floor of what had once been Alexander's studio. Driven across the flagstones by random gusts they sent back a mutinous whisper: *Thus far and no farther.* The historian, who took the scrooping for an invitation, sat down to rest for a moment when suddenly a bee falling out of a dream veered crazily down from its nest and stung the hand he held up against it. Wounded as much by the treachery of the past, Mr Montagu went doubling back across the Sea of Tranquillity to the Begam Kothi in search of a female key: the ones on his chain (Sans Souci keys as well as his own) were skeleton males and would not do. He was running up the steps, not daring to look at the spot, when he caught sight of something else that made him forget his pain. Glittering in the dark of his drawing room was a pair of yellow eyes which rose and floated towards him as he entered.

It was Victoria. Unchaperoned, as far as he could tell, his own eyes getting used to the dark, and wearing her customary violet with black trimmings. Only when she spoke did a face begin to coalesce around the eyes.

"Mr Montagu—"

But he led her at once to his study, where he drew the table across the door before she could follow him in. Inside, he could not stand upright, and since he could not very well sit, he leaned across the desk, which was covered with books and letters, maps, pamphlets, blotting paper, sand, calendars, a tiny minute-glass, an inkstand, pins, a watch, a ruler, a penknife, pens, several crumpled stiff handkerchiefs—everything, in short, except a tablecloth.

The shock to Victoria was like that of a human limb bared suddenly, only here were four legs, turned and black-varnished, their tendons tapering downwards to an ornamental bole under each of which there stood, motionless and turned slightly outwards, a cloven foot. Her own support failing as she recalled another trauma of four legs from out of the buried past, she leaned heavily on the desk and came face to face with the Beast. He shifted uncomfortably, shedding a penumbral dust which settled on his shoes and crept under the girl's skirt. Victoria shut her eyes tightly and went on.

"Mr Montagu, the Victors have gone, they've disappeared, they've run away with Alex and left a note, Aunty Alina fainted and all, so I came to get you."

Mr Montagu could feel only relief: a couple of boys run away—was that all! And here was his hand, which he now dared to look at for the first time. It was worse than he expected, the skin ballooning yellowly around a tiny embedded dart. Boys, he reasoned with his pupil, couldn't be helped; now *bees*—had she perhaps on her person (he looked away) a female key? He held up the hand for inspection. Victoria, who carried not only keys but ointments, fetiches, tiger balm, a fly-whisk, and a dram of sherry, produced a female key and took his hand. Pain, her roughness said, is immanent in things: swallow it. She placed the hollow head of the key around the sting and pressed without mercy. When the key was removed, a little red moat showed where it had dug in. In the centre on a bead of risen flesh lay the drawn sting. She breathed it in and thumbed a gout of ointment on the spot. Then she whispered two syllables, cupped her ear to catch a response, and shook the fly-whisk lightly on either side of the hand. Finally she offered her patient a drop of sweet sherry, to which he murmured, "No thank you, but—" and could go no further. They walked in silence to the Glacerie.

The boys were gone all right, but not all of them, it appeared. A row of younger Victors wandered in from somewhere looking like a train without an engine: it seemed only the oldest pair were missing.

"I *thought* there'd be more where they came from," Mr Montagu ventured, recovering. He spoke softly because Alina was there, and her firstborn, Alex, was gone too.

Alina had always feared something of the kind. The boy's hero was his telegraphist uncle, Cyril Brendish Alexander-Trotter, who had sent the famous telegram that disarmed the Punjab army in the Mutiny. Now Alex was gone, leaving a curt professional-looking note of his own:

AM GOING JOIN TELEGRAPHS STOP VICTORS GOING RAILWAYS STOP

And they had gone.

"Where'll he get his milk?" Alina whimpered, as if it were not the land of the cow.

"Madam, please!" Mr Montagu begged. "He'll be back in no time on leave with his wages in his pocket. Besides, the country needs our men to set an example."

Alina was not comforted. She cuffed the next of the Victors and wailed: "What'll Philippa say?"

The Victors, caught off balance, went down like dominoes, but were only hardened in their resolve to follow their brothers into the railways when the time came. They were unmanageable at the best of times, especially at mealtimes, since no one really knew how many of them there were. After grace some ran along under the dining table, rapping knees with soup spoons while others engaged in bread-and-water fights above the board. Knives flew through the air, tin plates turned into shields, napkin rings went skittering along among the dishes. At the far end, in a zone of relative peace, a young coal-Victor might be showing a young steam-Victor how to somersault his dessertspoon into a water glass by bringing his fist down onto a strategically placed fork. Since their parents left for England, the battles had grown to epic proportions, and Mr Montagu, who dined with the Trotters in the Glacerie, was secretly relieved that the ringleaders should have taken themselves off. Even Alina, who saw her Alex as having been led astray, did not really think Philippa and Thomas Henry would mind. Victoria was safe, and that was the main thing.

In the event, Philippa would say nothing. A few weeks later a letter arrived from the Middle Trotter telling of how his beloved wife had gone ashore with him at Alexandria where she had fallen from the back of a ruttish camel. After weeks of suffering, she had succumbed to injuries and been laid to rest in the foreigners' cemetery on the Cairo Road. After that, England was out of the question, and Thomas Henry was waiting for a berth in a ship going home. Unfortunately, eastbound ships were at present packed with young ladies carrying their hopes and reticules to Bombay, Calcutta, and Simla; failing Simla, there were always the plains.

The letter was unaccountably four months getting to Sans Souci, and it was strange that Thomas Henry had not preceded it.

"You see," said Mr Montagu, when the letter was read, "if a telegraph line were put through we could have had the news in a day." About progress and the future he could be cavalier.

Alina, who had still not forgiven the intruder for calling her boy a man, sniffed. Victoria simply asked: "What's ruttish?," causing her tutor, who had finished, to fork a piece of carefully pared away fat into his mouth. Lately— she dated it from the time the Victors ran away—the red tides had stopped, sparing her much discomfort but leaving her strangely unquiet. Her palms had begun to sweat, her throat grew dry and her breath at times sounded like all the Victors chuffing at once. Whenever Mr Montagu appeared these days, the symptoms were heightened and it was all she could do to keep from moaning. She would have liked a whole hive of bees to envelop him so that she could, making amends for roughness past, remove the stings with boundless tenderness from every swollen part.

As for the historian, he knew nothing and suspected less. He returned to his afternoon walks, to the saltpetre hill, to the stupas, to the jujube plum groves, and around the Tank which since the dust storm looked like a pan of bromide. Once he burst through the jungle onto the quarry, but a glimpse of Alexander's sculptures sent him back to the glasshouse for a week. After that he concentrated on *Sungum*. He stood before the water-clock, which Thomas Henry had set going again, and poked it till it stopped. In the Audience Hall he stared awestruck down the crater, marvelling at the force that had smashed through the dome above and the floor beneath. He found the military museum where he gazed upon cabinets of pistols with seemingly endless varieties of butts, muskets without number, powder flasks, and a left-handed sabre. Dust had crept in under the glass, coating the green felt with a beige pollen, the scent of which sent a thrill through him. On one shelf stood a pickling jar with a blue sea horse swimming in alcohol. Like a certain pope of old testing for the authentic relic, he unstopped the jar and, assuming a judicial air, proceeded to make a trial of elasticity. The thing snapped in his hands and he returned it guiltily to its home in two pieces. He climbed to the top of the North Tower where he discovered a worthless sheaf of miniatures with calligraphy in the Persian script, somehow overlooked by earlier thieves. In the South Tower he found an old volume of political discourses propping up a wardrobe.

One morning he decided to tackle the lower storeys, darkly visible through the crater. The only stair leading down, he deduced, must have been blocked off by the collapse of the West Tower, therefore anybody who wished to penetrate below must enter by a skylight. He chose one that opened onto the

Indigo Court, knocked the glass in, and peered inside. It was probably a good way to the floor, but the dust and gloom made him reckless. He grasped the cord on the skylight and let himself down, face to the wall, his feet kicking uselessly at the pointing on blocks of hewn stone. Half-way down (or so it seemed: he had made a guess standing at the edge of the crater) the cord broke, and he braced himself for a long fall, but his feet met the floor almost at once and he fell back onto his hands. When he looked up, the skylight glowed at perhaps twice his height, pouring a soft blue light into what gradually took the shape of a cubicle furnished with a desk and a tilted chair and a tubelike contraption whose funnel overhung the desk. Inspecting the tube, he found at the mouth a prism on whose surface there appeared, as he blew away the cobwebs of three-quarters of a century, the image of a man upside down and wigless and falling through the air. It was very strange, but he was drawn away by what was surely the scent of books. As he stepped out of the cubicle he saw the shelves. From the nearest one he took down a volume at random and fondled it, running a long finger down its spine with a frisson at each delicious bump. He half opened it, still in the dark, and then, eyes closed and nose positioned, clapped it shut and drew a long breath. The snuff of ages shot up his nostrils and flared among the fine bones of the sinuses, an atom, a galaxy exploding, and Mr Montagu came as near as he would ever come to the little death. Returning to himself, he saw in the middle distance a column of white light wreathed in a slowly moving mist. It stood at the far end of the row of shelves shining like—like, he hesitated, abashed at the extravagance of the image—ice on fire. He began to move towards it, noticing as the light grew stronger that the shelves on either side of him were stacked with charred books that looked as if they might disintegrate at the slightest touch. To the soot and ashes were added, as he approached the source, dust of a familiar colour, and through the skeletons of burnt shelves he saw other rows of shelves, similarly burnt, all of which appeared to be converging on the pillar of light.

When he reached it it was no mystery at all. It was simply the hole in the floor of the Audience Hall above, where he had stood earlier. The midday sun had let a shaft of white light through the breach in the dome far above, directly down, through the space where the fountain had once played and again through the breach in the library floor. Going to the edge of the well, Mr Montagu looked down and saw at the bottom in the brilliant light a plinth of white stone far below with a fragment knocked out of one side, and beside it a greenish bronze bell, its tongue lolling indecently, its shell cracked, like a giant turtle half buried in mud. He walked around the hole warily, shielding his eyes, when suddenly the icelight flicked off, leaving only the frail falls of luminous dust that surrounded it. It was easier to see now, and looking down he saw at his feet several dangerous-looking cracks in the floor radiating from the hole. He stepped back quickly onto something that lay on the floor, a pile of books, it turned out, unburnt but covered in dust. He was going to pick one up when he remembered the one already in his hands. He blew gently on the rich binding and read, in his small Persian, *Ni'mat-Nama*. He turned the pages with growing impatience. A recipe book! He frowned. Receipts for making plantain fritters—and illustrated! He snapped the book shut for the second time and laid it on the nearest shelf, grunting. Then he turned to the pile on the floor. They were obviously modern, mostly scientific publications in many languages. But what were they doing in a separate pile, unhurt, when the rest of the library, except for the outermost shelves, was burnt to ashes? Who had brought them to the edge of the crater like some pagan offering and left them there apparently unread? He shook his head, and since the problem seemed to have no present solution he began to think of making his way back. But now a fresh problem confronted him: which way led out? Which way had he come in? All the shelves were identical, radiating from the centre. He chose one and began to feel his way along it, running a finger along the charred books and unaware that each one collapsed in a puff of ash at his touch.

He had not gone far when he began to sense that he was not alone. The feeling grew on him, slowing his footsteps until he came to a halt in the darkness. As he stopped, there came from behind him a sharp report like a single clap followed by a soft sliding sound. Then, silence. He paused to master his breath, turned, and felt his way back, padding softly in the dust. Where the shelves ended he stopped and peered out into the clearing at the centre. There was no one there, and no sound—unless he heard the echo of a pair of leather chappals stealing away somewhere up above. He emerged from the shadows and walked around the hole, keeping an eye on the shelves. It occurred to him that someone might easily dart out and push him down the well. At the pile of books he stopped. A new book lay there, its wrapper free of dust and bearing a triangle of postage stamps that showed the same sovereign in black, pink, and green. And then it became clear—the footsteps up above were the postman's. Evidently books kept arriving at Sans Souci in response to long-standing orders and generous advances even after the library had been destroyed. The postman, accustomed of old to being met at the main door, nowadays simply let himself in, crossed the Audience Hall floor to where the fountain once stood and tossed the books down the crater to the first level below.

Mr Montagu took the liberty of opening the parcel. It was a book by a certain J. Gierke, entitled *The Ice Age*. Something in the title appealed to the historian in an archaic, indefinable way, so much so that he looked sideways and slipped it into his shirt. As he did so he caught sight of the large recipe book he had placed on a nearby shelf and decided to try that row. It brought him to the cubicle where he had started (*Book of Books, Shewer of the Way*) and in gratitude he put it back in its place on the top shelf, resolving at the same time to catalogue all the remaining books in the library. He pushed the desk up against the outer wall, placed the tilted chair on it, and drew himself up through the skylight, his hands bleeding because the skin was dry. All the way back to the Begam Kothi he was too preoccupied to notice the slivers of glass that had entered his palms, slivers which Victoria would have given much to extract. What tormented him was an immense burden of unwritten history awaiting its chosen pen. And for the second time that day he stopped in his tracks and abandoned himself to a bookish ecstasy. An idea had come to him (*Solitary Mote, Pale Loiterer*). From that moment on, he would have no rest until he had written, for all time, the history of Sans Souci.

Interloper, Snake in the grass, Dust devil

INTERLOPER! SNAKE IN THE GRASS! DUST DEVIL! ARCH FIEND! ARCH TEMPTER! SERPENT IN THE GARDEN! SEDUCER! BOUNDER! LECHER! CAD! THUG! DECEIVER! FATHER OF LIES! BANDED KARAIT! SNAKE IN THE DUST! BANDIT KARAIT! INTRUDER! IMPOSTOR! PRETENDER! POSTURER! BOGUS SALESMAN! PETTY CROOK! CHARLATAN! WHITED SEPULCHRE! ASP IN THE BOSOM! LYING TOAD! PHARISEE! DISSEMBLER! MOUNTEBANK! HUMBUGGING TUTOR! CORRUPTOR! FALSE FRIEND! CUCKOO! HAWK CUCKOO! CROW IN PEACOCK'S FEATHERS! IN DOVE'S FEATHERS! DESPOILER! DEFLOWERER! HISTORIAN!

(*CHRONICLE RESTORED*)

"Historian!"

It was Thomas Henry, back from England. He had had to take a ship from Alexandria to London in order to get a berth back to Bombay, so full were the ships coming east. And even then he was obliged to travel by one of the ships of the notorious Fishing Fleet, on the starboard side, subjected on the way to the attentions, not altogether unwelcome, of a hundred young women sailing to India to find husbands. The attentions withered on the vine when he let fall that he was an Anglo-Indian, and Thomas Henry found to his moral dismay that once the Mediterranean of his bereavement was behind him, he was inclined to conceal the fact and use the old card, *Nakhlau Trotter*. It almost worked, but Bombay rose up and put him in his senses. He could not very well turn up at Sans Souci in crepe with a new wife at his side. So he exchanged addresses with the girl of careful grammar on deck and they promised gloomily to meet, knowing the odds against it. The girl moved away, hope returning as she scanned the line of white faces at the dock. She could not be expected to know that many of the ladies among them were waiting to board a ship going the other way with the closed shrinking faces of what their martial countrymen called Returned Empties.

The Middle Trotter knew how they felt. When his tikka-gadi rolled up the Gunpowder Drive, all the sights he had known and shared with Philippa bowed him down and left a vacant space in his chest. But his troubles were not over. There was something different about his precious daughter as she came slowly down the Glacerie steps to greet him. He stared at her, frowning, and then his mouth dropped open: her belly was plainly—too plainly—big. She was joined by a haggard Alina, who stared accusingly at the historian standing on the bottom step. Mr Montagu simply hung his head, content to take the blame. He knew it took a man, and since he was the only one around, what could he say? Told the truth, he would have laughed at the notion that a pinch of dust creeping under the girl's skirt or an inhaled beesting, could make a difference.

"Lecherous Fiend! Seducer! Cad! Arch-Bounder! Arch-Cad!"

Thomas Henry was running out of steam, his heart not really in it. Nothing really mattered now that his helpmate was gone. He could not bring himself to address Victoria, and he heard the news about the oldest Victors in silence.

"You will marry her, of course," he concluded in a low voice as he made for his rooms, turning once to add, "on Saturday."

On Saturday, along with the priest there came a peon from the office with a government letter. Thomas Henry set it aside until after the wedding, there being a few things to attend to first. The cake in the shape of *Sungum*—ordered from J.c. Solomon & Son, who had recently opened a bakery at the nearer end of Hazratganj—had still not been delivered at half-past four, and there appeared to be an additional celebrant, a Protestant minister sent for by the groom. Mr Montagu, it turned out, was not of the true faith (*Double Deceiver, Thug of Thugs*). In the event, there were two services in the chapel where Alina placed a vase of daffodils on the altar and Victoria retaliated with marigolds. The bride was dissuaded from playing her own march on the Erard piano of her stolen youth, but her yellow gown was countenanced because it helped set off the groom's dismal beige. Not that many were present to judge, since there had been no time for invitations. The remaining Victors stood in a long fidgeting row that disappeared at the far end of the Audience Hall; they were vaguely aware that their queer sister was in trouble and darkly pleased by the fact. Alina sat in front with her brother Cyril the telegraphist, her husband Philip the Baptist, and their son, Alex, the men all in station on leave. She herself might have been taken for the bride's mother, except that she wore one of the saris she had lately acquired. A dark yellow glow of mustard oil hung over her and she smelt of fresh coriander (she had turned vegetarian). Her glossy greying hair was scented with aloes, parted down the middle and done up in a bun. In the middle of her forehead was a bindi. Having given away his daughter, Thomas Henry went and sat in a separate pew across the aisle from Alina. He had never had much to do with his cousin, and the gulf between the Assistant Collector and the dairy-woman was widened by this going native. Alina's Hindustani had become fluent, too fluent, and she insisted on being called not Aunty Alina but Alina Aunty. So, after the ceremony she went her way and Thomas Henry his, and the celebrants got their fee and departed. The Victors had already pulled out, since there was no cake to keep them. The newly-weds made their way to the Begam Kothi, having exchanged vows and changed a name. As he walked, Mr Montagu was shaking less from nuptial dread than from his brush with the truth.

The day before, he had gone to Thomas Henry and confessed his desire to write, now that he was to join the family, the definitive history of Sans Souci. The Fourth Trotter, who had once half contemplated the project himself, gave the historian a listless hearing and then turned to look directly at him. Only a Trotter, he pronounced carefully, could undertake that sacred task. So after the wedding, when the chubby Catholic priest placed his matrimonial register before the couple, Mr Montagu took the step. As the blotting sand fell away from the page, the priest's lips parted in wonder and his cheeks puffed out, for all the world the picture of the North Wind on an old map. For there before his bulging eyes, beside Victoria's signature (a whale with spout and fluke) was the lie—an entire fictitious continent drawn in the groom's own hand—Theobald Horatius *Trotter*.

Four months after marriage changed Mr Montagu's name he had a son, thin as pencil lead. Victoria was for calling him Peter, but her husband (*Self-styled Trotter*) favoured the more Protestant-sounding Paul. He felt he had conceded enough in the register of marriages and was now entitled to a decision in the register of births. So the boy was called Peter, the second of many baffling losses in an unequal mating.

"Peter Augustine Trotter," Victoria repeated, pleased.

Her husband returned to history, content to wait. Less patient was the boy's grandfather, who now had nothing to do. Ever since the government letter he had been out of work, missing his dak-box and the files tied with red tape that he had promised to spend the rest of his career undoing. The truth was, though few knew it yet, Nakhlau Trotter was under suspension. During the year of his furlough a complaint had been brought against him by J.c. Solomon & Son and grave letters had passed between officials concerning his habitual indebtedness. The specific charge was that of "Conduct

unbecoming a Gentleman, in passing off on an ignorant native a Promissory
Note which Mr Trotter must have known was absolutely worthless." Thomas
Henry hotly denied the charge, pleading forgetfulness, but his adversary, a
Mr Charles Curry (*Delectable Dun*), marshalled an array of witnesses and proofs
that convinced the government. Assistant Collector Trotter was asked to tender
his resignation and file his pension papers.

It seemed that fate had once again conspired with circumstance to make
a writer of Thomas Henry. He wrote an endless stream of letters, to Collectors,
Commissioners, Chief Commissioners, Lieutenant-Governors, the Viceroy's
Secretary, the Viceroy himself, the Home Government, his Gracious Sovereign. From the highest places he got no reply, from his immediate superiors
correct and sometimes reproving letters. It was the temper of the Peace, cool
clear and solid, like a paperweight: flattened by it, Nakhlau Trotter could have
little sympathy for the strange British guilt and lacing up, for visible justice
and the meaning of example. In the end there was nothing for it but to comply,
and he filled in the required form, listing in the column "Identifying Marks"
every wound received in the service of Her Majesty: a bullet lodged in the
neck, a sword cut across the back, left earlobe shot away, dagger cut at the
base of the thumb, nicks to right and left. He was on the point of listing his
wife's leg wound when, for the first time since Alexandria, he saw her. She
was sitting opposite at the bureau, looking sadly at him, her shadowy features
scattered across a wide tract of air so that she appeared twice her normal size.
Under his gaze she began to shrink, dwindling finally to a point of light in
the glass paperweight. Thomas Henry was left with an unbearable loneliness
which turned at length into a sense of the futility of things. He inked the
fullstop, signed his name without the usual flourish (abbreviating it, in fact,
to *Thos. Henry*), and sent off the form.

The mood did not last, because the next morning Nakhlau Trotter hit
once more upon a gesture. He went to his almirah and fetched out from under
a pile of shirts a small square silk-lined box. Then he took yet another sheet
of paper and began a final letter. It was addressed to the government that had
brought so much humiliation on a man who deserved only honour. He was
returning—the Adjutant General would please find them enclosed—the Cross,
the medal and its three clasps, awarded him for valour. Until he was cleared
of the charge of dishonourable conduct he could not bring himself to wear
them. And may the agitation and grief caused by the surrender speedily
overtake the man who had done him this injury. Thos. Henry read through
the draft, crossed out the word *speedily* and wrote instead, *never*. The effect
was immediately improved, and tears rose to his eyes. He gummed the flap
on the envelope and sent for a servant. He had written his last letter.

A headline (from the Nakhlau Nuntio)

VICTORIA PROCLAIMED
EMPRESS OF INDIA

Disraeli acts:
"You have it, Ma'am"
2nd January, 1877

(*CHRONICLE RESUMED*)

Just when he was learning to forget his Victoria Cross, Nakhlau Trotter picked up the paper and saw that Victoria of England had been proclaimed Empress of India.

"Did you hear that?" he repeated, shaking a dog-ear into the page and peering over the top. But Philippa was not with him in the Rain Room, and the recollection, always delayed as he grew older, soured his breakfast.

VICTORIA. Nowadays the mere sight of a capital V was the thorn in the flesh. Victoria! What misery hoarded in that hollow sound! Never again for him the brisk Greek syllables: Phi-li-ppa! No. Victoria, Victoria, the mournful Roman sound must toll through Sans Souci, and now, thanks to the Earl of Beaconsfield, all through the land. Thos. Henry groaned. His daughter's misconduct still rankled, and he thanked God that her husband's modified initials, like his own, were an upright T.H.T., without the slightest trace of an acute angle about them. As for the Victors, he relegated them to those distant tracts of Sans Souci that lay along the railway line, an arrangement that they wholeheartedly approved of. Only recently the runaways had been back with pay in their pockets, swearing that it was an impossible thing to sleep without the soothing hiss and clank of a locomotive. When they left they took with them the two oldest of the remaining twins, promising to return regularly for the rest. Thos. Henry's only stipulation was that the contractor for the building of the Railway Colony be someone other than J.c. Solomon. For that gentleman he had conceived a hatred unequalled even by his loathing for Benjamin Disraeli.

To ease his bitterness Thos. Henry began to take a little eau sucrée at bedtime. It helped him sleep and now and then infused into his dreams a happiness and colour denied his waking hours. It was also his succour when he wrote the first of his vindications: *GUILTY or NOT GUILTY? Nakhlau*

Trotter's Defence against Charges of Misconduct. The work was published by the New Nakhlau Steam Press and some copies went as far as the British Isles. Encouraged by the response, he wrote a sequel in the third person entitled with grave finality: *The Verdict.* This time the run was smaller, and a single copy reached London, where it was deposited in the British Museum. Not content with refutations and justifications in print, he began to restage old battles, at first in his head and then out loud. What would have happened, he demanded of Philippa's chair, if the Trotters had not stood firm in the Mutiny? Cousin Cyril's telegram would never have been sent and the Punjab would have risen up. A Punjab rebellion on top of the others would have spelt the death of British power in India—the British said so themselves. And where would the Residency garrison have been without the Guide of Nakhlau? For a moment there flickered at the edge of Thos. Henry's vision a blue hand. The Guide's guide, Dukhi Das, Dhobi & Dyer, had received no Victoria Cross for his exploit. A small pension was his, and in better days Nakhlau Trotter had been known to fulminate at the Nakhlau Club that his companion deserved better of the government. (History had not been kind to Dukhi either: the very year of his nighttime exploit saw the production in Europe of synthetic indigo, and already demand for his dye had slackened.) Nowadays Thos. Henry no longer went to the Club. Since the Curry affair he hardly went to Nakhlau at all, and because he entertained no visitors he did not need the former supplies of wine from the city's largest supplier. Instead he turned increasingly to eau sucrée.

To occupy his time and to swell his pension, Thos. Henry began to consider starting up his grandfather's cane-press. The machinery was undamaged, all that was needed being a little oil. That and a camel or, camels failing (the last one had done), a pair of bullocks. The sugar-cane crop along the Cranny river was especially fine that year; by December Sans Souci could theoretically supply not only the needs of the Fourth Trotter's bedside glass but a good portion of the Nakhlau jaggery market as well.

How jaggery (or gur) is made

I am pleased to shew how jaggery (or gur) is made. It must first be defined. It is not refined. It is the yellowish brown cake, usually crumbled, formed from the heat-reduction and consequent solidification of the juice of the sugar-cane. This was the definition. Take now a camel, stout adept, and tie it to a stick. To the other end of the stick—which must be horizontal—attach a cane-press. If you already have the press you will need oil for the oiling, the machinery being old. Go to Suresh, the bania in Narhi who is opposite the temple, or else to Teli Mahesh, his son, who is threatening to open a new dry goods outlet in Hazratganj just where the road starts (next to Ferdinand Fonseca's Fine Foods). Do not go farther, for then you will surely fall into the clutches of that evil merchant J.c. Solomon. These days there is no & Son, though he is said to be waiting for one. Long may he live to do so. Go, ample adept, to Suresh or his son. All your oiling needs are met there, and more. Mustard oil, Brahmi Amla oil, ghi, vanaspati, tallow, sesame oil, cottonseed oil, groundnut oil, oil of Ulan, Three-in-One oil—he has them all. At times it seems Suresh is awash with the stuff and Mahesh is in a state of extreme unction. Oil, slick adept, the machinery and set the animals going. Round and round the camel goes (or bullocks go), round and round the gear-toothed wheel and crusher. Into the crusher insert sticks of sugar-cane. A beaked pan catches the juice, a runnel carries it away to a larger pan. If you lack an evaporating pan there are some beyond the aqueduct and the mulberry trees at the bottom of the slope, but scrape off first the encrusted indigo. The principle is the same. Stoke the fire with the woody cane pith that comes out on the other side of the press, boiling the juice until it thickens, going from yellow to golden brown. Pour it then into moulds and allow it to cool. When solid, it is stacked in rounds. Crumbled into nuggets, it is called jaggery (or gur); powdered it is gur shakkar. Both are available at Suresh's, but for some reason a few yellow split peas invariably find their way into his gur shakkar, perhaps because pea flour is cheaper and easily mixed in. Best produce your own and have done with adultery. Do it, sweet adept, without delay, before the devil tempts.

(CHRONICLE RESUMED)

Having purchased his machine oil, the Fourth Trotter paused. He took a guarded sip at his drink and considered the prospect of turning Sans Souci into a sugar factory. Crystal vistas opened before him, tall chimneys, saw-toothed factory roofs, steaming refineries, a branch railway line, an entire industrial town.

Act, Thos. Henry! Strike now! Begin! All India waits.

The Middle Trotter took another sip and toyed with his glass, dimly aware that the fate of his house hung in the balance. He stared into the limpid elastic circle of eau sucrée. From humble beginnings might come a sugar empire stretching as far as Cape Comorin, swallowing up Calcutta, Madras, Bombay. All to be directed from Nakhlau—once sugar capital to the world—from Sans Souci, from here, his chambers in the Glacerie.

A knock sounded at the door. He hid his glass.

"Who is it?" he called.

It was Mr Montagu.

(VERSE)

Unmake the Ruinous Tempter,
Smite hard the Blinding Satan:
Stand firm Backsliding Trotter—
Rue not the Road Untaken!

(*CHRONICLE RESUMED*)

Looking back, Thos. Henry was never certain whether he did agree to the ice factory. He recalled in a haze, as if it had all happened somewhere before, his son-in-law's discourse on ice, interlaced with sparkling formulae and conjurable German names such as Linde and Gierke. But as to the actual permission, he could not be sure. The point was, work had begun, and the site chosen (on the best historical principles, he was assured) was the Glacerie. Apparently his great-grandfather had stored ice there in the godown; the presence of certain shelves of enormous width suggested it, and scattered wood-chips, shavings, sawdust, and gunnysacks clinched the matter. Why history should have to repeat itself, he (who thought he had made it once and for all) could not understand, but the historian-and-ice factor persuaded him it was always so. And before long the cane-press was broken up and converted into a Persian wheel powered by two bullocks that conveyed water from the Glacerie well to the reflecting pool around the Rain Room on the roof. From there the water descended through a series of pipes and filters to the liquid ammonia plant where the German cooling system was so severe that an exhaust pipe was needed to let out the extracted steam. From morning till night this pipe, which opened just under Thos. Henry's window, released at intervals of three seconds a plume of punctual steam, and with the steam a manic earsplitting hoot. Hell, Thos. Henry decided late in life, could hold no torments to match those on earth. He found it grimly amusing that his brother-in-law, Philip the Baptist, now retired from the railways, should be eternally spouting Damnation and the Four Last Things. Hell, as far as he could tell, would be a perfectly habitable resort until a freezing mechanism were installed.

Philip took his taunts patiently, half his attention, as always, reserved for his book. The critical apparatus to *The Valley of the Shadow, Or, His Hand Revealed* had swollen marvellously in recent years, until the text itself looked like a mere preface to the machinery that followed. Eventually the signal he was waiting for came, and he stopped writing. The New Nakhlau Steam Press rejected the work, but the American Baptist Press published it. A representative passage, printed on the back cover, ran: "Captains Lumsden and Crow's escape was indeed marvellous, but such escapes are in the order of things since some must get away. Mine was of another order. Why was my executioner delayed? Who called him away after he had despatched the others? Why was I singled out? Whose hand stayed his sword? The Hand, can we doubt, . . ." But people were losing interest in Mutiny accounts. Mr Montagu, who could never resist a footnote, assured him that the apparatus was fine and dense, *dense* being a favourite word with him. He reviewed Philip's book for the *Annals of the Tirnab Historical Society*, but Philip was tempted to believe that he did so in order to receive a free copy. In fact a reviewer's copy did thump down onto the dusty pile in the library, but Mr Montagu, who never read the books he reviewed, was too busy with Gierke's *The Ice Age* to notice.

Made bold by his success with the Glacerie (Sans Souci ice was travelling to Nakhlau once more) the historian began to speculate more dangerously. Writing the history of Sans Souci, he found himself lured further and further back in time. Not sufficient for him to start with the Great Trotter (*First Trotter, Edenic Man*); no, he must find a past beyond that blessed past. Early in life he had come to think of Time as a cool withering breeze and learnt to turn his back on it, marching into the past with gently lifting coattails. Since the Gierke episode, not even the sanctum of prehistory was safe from the prying of the historian-turned-geologist (*Overnight Evolutionist, Tissue of Lyell*). The land around Sans Souci, he discovered, showed evidence of glacial activity. The aerolite was not a meteor but an erratic boulder transported there by an ice sheet; the elephant graves were not elephant graves but drumlins; the hot salt flats by the railway line had once been caked with ice! All the available tokens supported a hypothesis that Sans Souci marked the southern extremity of an ice cap which during the last great ice age covered much of northern India (*Brain-fever Pedant, Lunatic Fringe*). And seated in his solarium Mr Montagu inscribed the first paragraph of his apocryphal book, writing lies with the fluency of a busy man. Dashing to the Glacerie that day to check on the Linde plant, he stumbled on a technique that he took as a sign. Ice, he discovered quite by accident (he had tripped over one of the galvanized tubs and shaken its contents), was like lies: it need never be cloudy. If you agitated it during the freezing, it came out crystal clear.

But there was one task that proved too much for Mr Montagu. He abandoned, with a show of reluctance but once and for all, the education of his wife. His former pupil returned blissfully to her state of animal intelligence, diving deep down to a fathomless darkness, a vast blue whale rejoicing to have escaped the hunter's keen harpoon. Content to suckle young Peter Augustine, Victoria continued to devour the visible world and to see things that others born without cauls could not. Lately there had been added to her ghosts and fairies something new. It was an inanimate object that travelled twice daily, morning and evening, along a fixed course three feet above the ground with no apparent support. It seemed nevertheless to be acquainted with at least one Sans Souci custom, because although it came and went across the Sea of Rains, it passed obediently through the Indigo Gate, respecting the unwritten law by which all residents pretended to see a fence on either side of the gate. Once through, it crossed the Indigo Court, mounted at unusual speed the steps leading up to *Sungum*, glided across the Audience Hall and out at the other side, crossed the Ice Court, passed through the Ice Gate, and, veering round toward the Begam Kothi, disappeared just beyond the cesspool at the corner bathroom. Victoria described the object to her rationalist husband as a white enamelled vessel with a blue rim, slightly tapered like an overturned Pilgrim Father's hat. But when she pointed he saw nothing.

"I'm telling you, it's there, men," she insisted.

"My dear," was all Mr Montagu would say, but when he found she was neglecting the child to lie in wait for the object, he decided on the camera.

It was not his first experiment with light. Earlier, in rummaging through one of the guest suites in *Sungum* he had come upon an old camera obscura left there by a forgotten visitor. Tempted, he had set it up beyond the Tank, inserted a sheet of paper, and proceeded to trace a view of Sans Souci. Discouraged by the result (*Shrewd Judge*), he put the box away and did not give light another thought. In those days he had been a bachelor and poor. Now that the ice was doing well there was money to spend, and he bought a German camera off a visiting colleague from Basel. The next day he set up his tripod outside the bathroom and waited, ducking every now and then under a black cloak that covered his head and shoulders. In a little while Victoria came round the corner, her eyes following an invisible trail that appeared to travel a short way ahead of her, three feet off the ground. When the line of her sight intersected a point directly in front of the camera, Mr Montagu removed the lens cap, counted to three, and replaced it. Then he took the camera off to a darkroom that smelt of bromide. In the afternoon he emerged with a photograph. It was slightly blurred because the subject had moved, but an historian was trained to interpret phenomena blurred by time, and there was no mistaking this photograph. The object was, as Victoria had described it, a brilliant, almost blinding white—it was a plain unadorned chamberpot. It was not unsupported, for behind the object was a subject, and it was this that was especially blurred. All the same, through the smudge of ghostly waving lines there shone a face which for the first time in its life was made visible. It was Jivan, the sweeper-and-emptier, Budhiya's son, a man of so degraded a caste the very untouchables lorded it over him. He was, or had been until now, an unseeable.

The discovery turned Mr Montagu's life upside down. To start with, he set aside the history of Sans Souci so lately begun (*Fickle Scholar, Yet Not Unredeemable Wretch*) and began a series of social pamphlets on the evils of caste. True, he later returned to the Trotter book (*Stubborn Scribbler, Incorrigible Worm*), but to his passion for history was appended a social guilt that lasted to the end of his days. He also came to respect his wife's gift. How did she see what his trained eye could not? More to the point, how could he not see what was under his very nose?

As for Jivan, his view of things remained unchanged: the drains, the cesspool, the long path to the midden where he emptied the familiar hanks and coils and red monthly-pads, the same path back (which he usually covered at high speed), the extinct crater in the middle of the Audience Hall which he used in emergencies, the back of the Begam Kothi, the commodes, the broom corner with its long- and short-handled brooms, its dustcloths, and its cobweb-brush, a long bamboo pole with a ragged halo of bristle at the top. His perspective on most houses was fixed, and it always unsettled him to discover that a house had a front. He tended to avert his eyes if not actually to shut them and hurry past, hoping not to be seen. It had not occurred to him that his precautions were superfluous; until the camera arrived, nobody, not even his mother, had seen him. Had she known of the photograph she might have asked to see it and died content. As it happened Jivan could not make out the photograph at all; he would be lucky to see himself before he died.

The experiment had another effect on Mr Montagu. His appetite for photography grew until he began to stink of bromide as well as ammonia, and he was constantly hunting for objects to wave his lens cap at. In a Begam Kothi which, thanks to the Great Trotter's first wife, Sultana (*Cup of Grace*), still held a replica of everything in the world, he did not lack for studies. But since new forms were constantly coming into the world, not least from his wife's womb (she had just had another son), he wished to capture those as well. Accordingly, he turned to portraiture.

(INTERPOLATION)

Who killed the miniature?

Who killed the miniature? But let's start further back—we're on historical ground, after all. Well, then. Who created the miniature? Who gave it life? A fat man, of course, no marks for that, and let him be nameless since there were so many of him and so much to each. Mughals, Pekinese, Andalusians, Rajputs, Alsatians, Venetians, Javans, Cumbrians, Koreans, Muscovites, Garhwalis, Nakhlavis, and the rest, good livers all, exuding respectable miniatures of hunts, castles, temples, feasts, festivals, pilgrimages, toilettes, trysts, battles, pageants—*general* views, that is, from a generality of fat men. But now. When does an art form come into its own? When does it find its true voice? When it learns to distill from the general. So we come to particularity, though it's not just that. Character counts. A pea has particularity but it's low on character. For a combination of the two, you must go to the single human sitter, the individual subject, and you come up with, money apart, a miniature portrait. (You can work from a mirror if you wish, but self-portraiture has its risks when it comes to identification.)

So the art of the miniature finds its voice in the portrait: crowds, pavilions, trees and birds, rocks, hills, and lotuses are all very well in their way, but the acid test is the portrait. And who is the father of the miniature portrait? A Trotter. Or at least, the next best thing, the French rendering of Trotter, namely Petitot.

M Jean Petitot, Franco-Swiss miniaturist, painter of the portraits of Louis XIV of France and Charles I of England, among others. Received into the bosom of the Catholic church in 1685 and dying, despite rumours to the contrary, in the full light of the true faith. Justin's ancestor, if you recall. The first great portrait miniaturist (*Proto-Trotter, Apt Forerunner*).

The last great miniaturist is, naturally, also a Trotter, but unlike his illustrious predecessor he is forced into hiding for his faith, painting in catacombs by the light of a 40-watt sewer bulb, braving ridiculously narrow manholes in foreign countries where not long ago he breakfasted on hand-dipped chocolates, the toast of society. Well, let it be. I make no complaint—it was good while it lasted. Now there's just this illustrated chronicle to finish, its endless repetitions waiting for their final release, the nirvana that comes with perfection, its many sitters—some of them not yet born—waiting for their ideal expression. Repetition is the twentieth-century miniaturist's lot in a fallen age, a perfectly honourable lot, I might say, until Orangemen and Interpol and hired thugs like Carlos get involved.

But now I'm straying from the subject, and sitters don't like to be neglected. So back to the miniature. Who killed it? When? What was the weapon?

Full marks—the *camera*. The nineteenth-century camera, and behind it the Montagus of this world. Dry, literal, joyless, prowling shutterbugs. Smash their cameras for them and you get no gratitude. Instead of kissing you and embracing the world, they creep off somewhere and grow another.

(*CHRONICLE RESUMED*)

Running into his father's darkroom one day, little Peter Augustine knocked over the camera. Mr Montagu, who didn't much like the boy anyway, lost his temper and drubbed him energetically. Then he stood him in a corner while he spent the afternoon trying to repair the damage. It was no good; the lens had a Y-shaped crack right across it. But the ice was doing well, and when the next visitor from Europe came by, he bought himself another. With the replacement he did a series on his new son, named, to his Protestant satisfaction, Paul. He favoured him shamelessly, docking Peter's pocket-money and paying it into a waiting account for his brother. The photo series on the growing Paul (sometimes it seemed to his parents that he did not so much grow as burgeon) came out well, though it was no credit to the photographer, who had simply to make intriguing noises from under his black cloth, like a pilloried ostrich. It simply happened that Young Paul, despite the handicap of his name, was a handsome child. It was as if the full moon had fallen into the cradle, or else a round of creamy Camembert lay among the pillows. As he grew he waxed handsomer, though Victoria was not so sure. She preferred the slender fingers of her first-born, a boy whose long sly hands already betrayed a sensual curl which she did her best to straighten with prayer and a laundry mangle. She let him play the piano all the same when he returned from St Aloysius's School in the afternoon. He would go on, she did not doubt, to the seminary and thence to Rome; already, though she had not breathed a word of it to anyone, his mother had begun to nurse the Highest hopes for Peter. Paul, on the other hand, his father had decided, would be sent to the hills to a Protestant boarding school where prefects and rugby on the gravel would make a man of him. Like all scholars, Mr Montagu wished to protect his son from books. For the present, though, he made a fine if restless sitter for the camera. Until Alex Kahn-Trotter, runaway telegraphist, came home Mr Montagu had a captive subject for his bromidic rites.

Unlike Jivan, the sweeper-and-emptier, Alex had no problems with visibility. Born with a high profile, he carried it as he grew up as if personally responsible for its many excellences. He was said to have resigned from the telegraphs over a dispute involving the dress code, but he may have been looking for his chance. He was the despair of his old mother, Alina, and his father, Philip the Baptist, warned him that there was no room in heaven for young men who smelt of carnations. He wore expensive ties, an apricot waistcoat, a windowpane checked jacket, narrow bottle-green trousers, and glossy button-boots. A pair of wide insouciant eyes stared out from under a white pith helmet, strangely grey against the damp tobacco-coloured skin. Once in a while they might be pricked with anxiety when Alex thought a speck of dust had settled on one of his wide slightly upturned lapels. He smoked a meerschaum, tucked a cream parasol under his arm, and carried a short horsewhip, as if he were dressed for a picnic and had decided at the last minute to go hunting instead. For all his horror of dust, he did not mind Mr

Montagu, and stranger still, Mr Montagu on his side took to the flamboyant young ex-telegraphist who wore every colour but beige. They had one uniting bond: Alex had no objection to being photographed.

Since his departure from the telegraph office (a desertion which so distressed his terse Uncle Cyril of the famous telegram that he said "Pity!" and died), Alex had fallen in with a group of progressives in Nakhlau who were starting to make noises about political representation for Indians in the government of their own country. He did not understand this representation very well, but the idea was new and glossy and his friends were for it. Because of his outgoing nature, his easy and familiar manner, and his many associates in Nakhlau, Mr Montagu decided to make him a kind of unofficial sales representative for Sans Souci ice. The job suited Alex well. It allowed him to do what he did best, hobnob with a cheerful aimlessness, and it kept him in ties. Wherever three or more persons were gathered Alex was present, no dinner party among the progressives being complete without his profile and his charming small talk. He was all for parties, so when the formation of a Congress party was announced, he was naturally among its most enthusiastic supporters. And sales of Sans Souci ice continued to climb.

He soon found a way of attending British parties too. His Indian and Anglo-Indian friends were amazed at his effrontery and some professed disgust, but it was quite simple: Alex became a photographer. It meant borrowing Mr Montagu's camera for the day and abandoning the horsewhip, but both were managed after a tussle. When he heard of a British garden party he arrived at the house the day before and presented his card, which read simply:

ALEX KAHN-TROTTER
Photographer
Sans Souci, Nakhlau

The next day he turned up nattily dressed, with a long black box which contained his equipment. He would make a brief tour of the garden, assessing porticos, pillars, and hollyhocks for suitable backgrounds. Then he would set up his tripod, mount the camera and go off and enjoy the party, mixing easily and smiling his winning smile as he told stories of shikar or life in the Foreign Legion. It was impossible to snub him. Given a cold shoulder, he simply turned to another group and engaged them in effortless, usually one-sided conversation, eating and drinking all the while. When the party was breaking up, he would suddenly turn professional and clap his hands softly from behind the camera. Gradually his equipment grew more complicated as he started to experiment with canvas backdrops showing either bulbous Muslim domes and palm trees or else severe Greek temples and cypresses, and sometimes, when the party was large, both together. He was tolerated because of his name and connections, but then certain telltale clouds began to loom. There were never any in the blue skies of his canvases, but when he developed the photographs there invariably hovered, just above the subjects' heads, a small blank balloon sometimes with a trail of tiny bubbles leading up to it, as if the whole company were posing underwater and someone had let out a breath. At first the clouds were easily disguised (Alex put them down to grains of silver on the photographic plate) but later they grew bigger and more numerous, eventually turning into blotches and smears that would spell, among other things, an end to his second career.

It was in the month of February, when the bubbles were still only small, that Victoria heard about the Ilbert Bill. She was sitting on the verandah eating early gooseberries four at a time because the child required it (she was carrying her third and praying for a girl). With each green burst of juice she shuddered from head to fluke like a whale leaping clear of the water. Alex and Mr Montagu were in the garden discussing politics. It seemed that the Viceroy or one of his secretaries had proposed a bill that would allow Indians to try Europeans in court. Mr Montagu, dry and sesquipedalian, approved of the enlightened measure because it showed the British government was sincere in its declared intention progressively to admit capable and upstanding Indians to positions of considerable authority. Alex liked the idea because his friends were for it.

"And you, my dear, what do you think of it?" called Mr Montagu over his shoulder.

Victoria and Alex exchanged a surprised glance, and Alex smiled mischievously. Complicity, even ordinary communication between them was unusual, but here was a situation without precedent. Mr Montagu was one for pronouncements, not questions. On those rare occasions when he asked your opinion, he laid a bony finger on your shoulder as if conferring a knighthood, and always interrupted before you had said two words. This man was asking his wife what she thought of the Ilbert Bill! Alex's smile broadened, but now Victoria was concentrating. Involuntarily she crushed a handful of gooseberry capes and with the other hand brushed away the fine papery debris that fell into her lap. She sat very still, staring out between the verandah pillars at the men on the lawn, and spoke deliberately.

"If it's what I think it is—"

"My dear—"

"*I said*, if it's what I think it is, I'm against it. And you can stop your grinning, Mr Smart Alex. It's not right for servants and all to go judging their masters. I wouldn't want an Indian to sit in judgment over me, and that's that."

Mr Montagu turned where he sat and looked hard at his wife. He had never known her to express herself with such conviction about matters outside her experience. Had he looked into the future he might have been perturbed, but trained to examine the past, he saw only a passing upheaval. For Victoria it was the beginning of a sea change. She had for the first time acknowledged a solid world outside. After that she was less inclined to dabble in the esoteric arts, and her faith, while continuing steadfast, grew by degrees more conventional (*Politic Body, Catholic Soul*). The change had something to do with little Peter, whose religious instruction she took in hand the moment he returned from the school across the railway tracks. She had second thoughts about the piano and substituted the black book in the chapel, but the boy had time only for the first and last pages and said that music could better fill the space in between (*Extremist, Enthusiast*). He got his knuckles rapped for his paganism by a mother who was still not accustomed to the role of teacher, but inevitably some of the pupil's worldliness rubbed off on her; in the small parts of his mother's education Peter seemed to succeed where his father had failed. Victoria no longer rapped tables, though she continued to drape them with stout linen and ate off them with an undiminished appetite. She would grow larger and darker with each successive child, and her prayers for girl-children would be abundantly answered. And she would always date her conversion from the Ilbert Bill.

The bill aroused other people too. With Victoria firmly against it, virtually all the rest of Sans Souci followed suit. Her multiple brothers—the last two Victors had grown up and chuffed their way across to the railway colony by the line—were unanimously opposed to it. Behind them stood their multitude of wives brought home from Bombay, Calcutta, Madras, and the many little stations and rail-heads where the railways had penetrated, and their broods of steam-and-coal children. With every passing year the colony expanded, new bungalows with red tiled roofs, macaroni chimneys, and Anglo-Indian gardens going up along the track at the far end of the babul-treed parklands to the west of the Trotter Road. From any one of these houses one might hear, at all hours but especially at night, the soothing clank of buffers and the delicious steely grinding of brake-blocks clamped on errant rolling stock. In the centre of the colony there rose, like a church without a steeple, the Railway Institute, edged with dahlias and complete with bar and billiard room, badminton court and bandstand. At one end of the long colony was a railway school which feuded with the nearby Free School, and at the other, up against the track, was a new cemetery with two identical marble crosses and room for many more. The two youngest of the Victors had drowned in a boating accident before they could join as firemen on the Calcutta line. They hadn't liked the Ilbert Bill either.

Also against were the majority of Fonseca-Trotters, grandchildren of Ferdinand, the Fine Foods purveyor, three of whom were managing the bakery at the head of Hazratganj that was doing well enough to cause the last surviving Solomon terminal indigestion. The Alexander-Trotters, fierce Attila's progeny, who had come home to roost from the many marches of India where Trotter's Horse raised its standard, and rented terraces and tenement-bungalows beyond the Free School, were against. At the opposite end of Sans Souci, in the Rib, there was some division among the Kahn-Trotters. Philip the Baptist was against and his wife Alina for, while their son Alex was for and his steadier brother, Zacharias, who had become a canal engineer, was against. In the Glacerie, Thos. Henry, slowly going deaf, was decidedly for: he would have given up his eau sucrée for a chance to be a magistrate prosecuting a European, especially if the defendant were an Englishman named Curry (*Vengeful Thos., O Unsucrée!*)

All summer the controversy raged. In September the againsts met in the Railway Institute. There was hardly room for them all—it might have been a social—and extra chairs had to be fetched from the school. Through the evening they argued heatedly about the best way to defeat the bill. Ladies of every complexion, from coal to steam by way of ash grey, rose to declare that they would sooner perish than be tried by an Indian. Their husbands sweated and cried *Hear, hear.* A Calcutta man with Rangoon in his eyes spoke reverently of Derbyshire. Philip Kahn-Trotter spoke about the manifest will of God with respect to certain races. Victoria said nothing but sat violet and unsmiling, lending her considerable weight to the proceedings. As Thos. Henry's daughter, she was raised up higher than the rest, her cane chair having been placed on the stage where amateur Gilbert and Sullivan musicals were sometimes performed. Although not yet thirty, her cheeks were beginning to sag and two frown marks showed between her barely visible eyebrows. The women pitied her for that and because she breathed heavily and was saddled with a father, a husband, and a cousin who were actually *for* the bill. But if Victoria needed their sympathy she did not show it, and the ladies withdrew their offers in a huff. Victoria sat on unmoved, massive and statuesque, stirring only to tuck a wad of wilting cucumber sandwiches into an empty corner of her roomy mouth. She was growing perceptibly all the time, so that when she left the meeting she was broader than when she arrived, and yet she moved with effortless grace, swimming through the humid air. The meeting concluded on much the same note as it had opened: those present were against the bill. But an association had been formed, the Trotter Association, and it was decided that the President would write a formal letter to the government. A party of younger Victors was for railing to Calcutta to hiss the Viceroy, but maturer heads prevailed. Chuffing and hissing would not be necessary, they said, and they were proved right. By Christmas the Ilbert Bill was withdrawn and the following year the Viceroy was on his way back to England. The association always looked upon those events as a Trotter victory. It assured the British community of Nakhlau of the loyalty of all Trotters, threw a party and invited officials to view the charter enshrined in the institute. But the British did not come, and afterwards they were seldom invited.

Their loyalty pledged by proxy, Alex and Mr Montagu missed the institute celebrations. Alex would have liked to attend, but Mr Montagu assured him that there was another party in Nakhlau and he brightened up. Besides, it had come to his ears that the Victors meant to scrag him for his scuggish stand on the bill. Valuing his striped blazer, he went with Mr Montagu and was signed up as a member of the Nakhlau cell of the Indian National Congress party. His dues were paid by Mr Montagu, who also became a life member. Since there were commemorative photographs to take, Alex had to leave his hunting crop behind and carry the camera. For the first time he had Mr Montagu in front of the lens, a reversal of positions that the historian noted with a jiggle of the foot. When they developed the picture it came out sharp and clear, without any of the bubbles Alex was accustomed to finding on his society photographs—though there was a blur at Mr Montagu's cocked foot. But at the next British garden party the old blotches were back.

In time, the tiny white bubbles leading up to the blank balloon were replaced by a tusk that pointed to one or another pair of sealed lips. Alex disguised the patches as clouds, as smiling suns and languid moons, ringed Saturn and winged Mercury, but his cutomers began to notice and to warn their friends. And the time came when he was turned away without an appointment. Not all his shikar stories and winning ways could overcome the fact of leprous spots on his photographs. It was only when he invented the enlarger that he began to make out at the centre of each balloon a word or phrase that made him furious. The word appeared just as it might in the best dictionaries, followed by italicized abbreviations, an explanation, and in parentheses: (*derogatory*) or simply, for convenience: (*derog.*). Mr Montagu was at a loss; the words he dealt with were of another order. But Thos. Henry, sounded out, had an explanation. "Ever since the Suez Canal," he shouted, "they've started marrying their own kind and calling us names. D'you hear me?" De Lesseps had much to answer for in Thos. Henry's book. It was enough for Alex. He tore up his visiting card and was about to put away the camera forever when Mr Montagu restrained him. "Why not just keep away from the *Civil* Lines?" he suggested, giving the word an ironic sibilance. Alex's professionalism revived, but the wounds took a little longer to heal. After that he attended Congress party meetings with a new sense of purpose, and when a national convention was announced for Nakhlau he gave himself fully to its organizing, even to supplying free ice.

The day after the convention there appeared in the *Nakhlau Nuntio* an article by one R.K. It reviewed the meeting and the delegates in a high satirical mode seduced here and there into moralizing and peevishness. Among the delegates whose presence was noted was Alex Kahn-Trotter, described as "a half-caste." Alex flung aside the paper in a rage and presented himself at the *Nuntio* office without his camera. Horsewhip in hand, he demanded to see the editor, and in the exchange that followed he flicked the man on the ear. R.K., who happened to be in his old office next door (he was getting ready to leave the country), scampered off to get the Superintendent of Police. When word got out, the British were up in arms. There was no record now of balloons, but the air was thick with cries for justice. The Superintendant of Police threw Alex into the city jail, where the Jail Inspector, Dr Hall, was a special friend of the wounded editor's. Dr Hall came daily to torment the upstart, asking him Dr Johnson's definition of a half-caste and making other jests that needed no enlarger to spot.

"Dr Johnson is an old fogey!" Alex bellowed through the bars. "How does he spell *reindeer*?" (Mr Montagu had taught him that one.) His pulse slowing, he continued: "I will have my people called by their proper name, which is Anglo-Indians. The descendants of the Saxons and the British were called Anglo-Saxons, their descendants with the Normans were called Anglo-Normans, and we are the Anglo-Indians."

"And the descendants of the French and the Indians, are they Franco-Indians?" jeered Dr Hall. He had heard of the Great Trotter. "And are there not then," he continued, "Luso-Indians and Hispano-Indians?"

Alex thought for a while before replying. Afterwards, because he was not a man of ideas, and knew it, he was always proud of his untutored reply.

"No," he said, "because they no longer speak French or Portuguese or Spanish, but English." He had summed up his people.

He had other visitors, including Mr Montagu, who came to the cell bringing books without illustrations and smuggling in a rusk. All this, he assured his impatient young friend, would pass; the month would soon be history. He sounded almost gleeful. Realizing that Alex might not have the stamina for longer works, he brought him collections of short stories, among them (quite by chance) a book of Alpine stories by the same R.K. called *Plain Tales from the Hills*, of which Alex picked the shortest, "His Chance in Life," a heartwarming piece about a climber. Inspired, he spent the rest of his time in prison writing a song.

On the day of his release, Alex was met at the jail gate by a committee of his Congress cronies who garlanded him with daffodils and took him back to Sans Souci in a procession of carriages. Mr Montagu met them at the Gunpowder Gate, where the Sans Souci gate plaque was still caked with dust, and they swept up the triumphal drive together. A feast had been prepared in the Glacerie, where the whole company fell to, devouring pea pulao and chicken curry and the famous Nakhlavi rice pudding called firni with such zeal that an onlooker might have supposed that they had all been in prison together and for longer than a month (*Congress of Epicures, Bodies Politic*). Afterwards there was much wassail, toddy, and arrack or rice wine being brought in when conventional stocks failed; after that there was weeping, and still afterwards, singing. Mr Montagu, who earlier had carefully cut off the parson's beak, now looked on, sipping his dry sherry and sighing with satisfaction at the passage of time. Insulated from the pandemonium by deafness, Thos. Henry presided, looking mildly surprised at each outburst of silent laughter and nursing a grudge behind his eau sucrée: he had been warned not to attempt his Mutiny story. At two in the morning Alex got up onto the table and stumbled along over dinner plates and cut-glass to the Nakhlau end where he turned and sang the defiant song he had composed while in jail. It was an interminable ballad with garbled lines and the suspicion of a tune, and it was made even lengthier by the insertion of a chorus and between every line of the chorus a refrain which his audience took up and stretched to stupefying lengths.

(VERSE)

Oah you can take me Toddy Tippling
Any time, men;
Quench my thirst with Muddy Rippling
Any time, men;
But don't give me Ruddy Kipling
And his Firkin Plurry Nipling
Or by Jingo-Jakko, Whipling's
What you'll catch, men!
What you'll catch, men,
What you'll catch, men,
Or by Jingo-Jakko, Crippling's
How you'll end, men!

—Chorus to "Arrack Room Ballad"

(*CHRONICLE RESUMED*)

Then he collapsed in a heap among the crumpled napkins and had to be carried back to his room, moaning as he went, "I'll *kibble* him! *Please* let me!" Mr Montagu claimed afterwards to have put himself to bed, but he had already lost some of his credibility. The other revellers left at dawn.

"Bringing home Indians and all," Victoria rumbled at her husband the next day, looking blacker than ever. "Is this the way to bring up children? What sort of example you setting, men? What if the boy saw?"

She meant Peter, though Young Paul was also in the room. And in fact Peter had seen. He had slipped out into the chill night in his pyjamas, making his way around the Spur to the Glacerie from where the sounds of merry-making came. He paused by the sweet peas that grew black, white, and grey in the moonlight, spilling their fragrance onto the cold porch of the old Cock Hall, but the laughter and the singing and the warm boozy fug that poured out of an open Glacerie window drew him on. For a long time he shivered at the window, listening to Uncle Alex's song and filled with a nameless desire. Then he did a strange thing. Although it was still early February, he took off his pyjamas and slippers and loped across the dew-crisp lawn back to the Begam Kothi, naked under the full moon. The next morning he had his first taste of spirits when Victoria dosed him from her Maxwell's Compound bottle with a tonic that tasted very like brandy. Floating blissfully all day, it struck him as unfair that his mother, so agreeably provided, should grudge her husband a second dry sherry. But after that the battle lines were drawn.

It seemed that the couple disagreed on principle, though each one was simply following an inner and quite independent compulsion. Whenever Victoria complained about Indians, Mr Montagu quoted one of his anti-European works, of which he had acquired a small collection. He might produce the Haitian, Antoine Firmin's *De l'égalité des races humaines*, and translate a passage out loud as he read. If his wife praised the English for their far-flung empire whose geographical extent was unmatched in history, he would smile mockingly and say: "You know, geography is everywhere but history happens only in England!" He would hold up Republican France as an example. When it was reported to the French Senate that the colonies were endangered by the principle of *Liberty, Equality, Fraternity*, what had a Deputy cried? "Perish the colonies rather than a principle!" *That* was talking. Not that he was pro-French. His great hero was another Haitian, the eighteenth-century revolutionary and enemy of Napoleon, Toussaint L'Ouverture, whose portrait graced the Begam Kothi drawing room. Victoria responded with an oleograph of Disraeli on the opposite wall. "How," Mr Montagu waved his hand dismissively at Beaconsfield, "do these British keep their empire? By the simplest geometry." He sent Young Paul off to fetch his geometry box. When it came he selected two instruments and held them up by turns, gesturing.

"Divide. And rule."

"Filling that one's head with don't know what-all nonsense," Victoria scoffed.

Young Paul stood there thinking his father the cleverest man in the world. It was to seal his favoured son's esteem that Mr Montagu yielded to a shameful encore, fishing out still another instrument and adding: "That is how you encompass the world."

There was, however, one Englishman who turned their quarrels around. It was Charles Darwin (*Proto Carlos, Carlo Pithecus*). Mr Montagu contended that here Nature had thrown up a brilliant exception on those isles; his wife saw in the scientist a bogey—that was, until she heard the story of his conversion. At his death, the story went, the heretic had humbly recanted all his former blasphemies. How Victoria got her information remained a mystery, but it was a useful trump card because the tradition of the deathbed conversion took root in the family and Mr Montagu was powerless to check it. Whenever the children were present Victoria brought it up and all her husband could do was wriggle (*Corrupting Worm, Diabolic Germ*).

When the time came for Young Paul to go to boarding school, his father personally saw to the readying of his uniform, which he had tailored by Zafar Ali, High Class Tailor of Trotterpurwa. Victoria, perhaps out of guilt, stuffed the trunk with pound cake, ginger biscuits, and kal-kals. "The *small* box is for the tuck, my dear," Mr Montagu pointed out, but for once Young Paul was on his mother's side. He shed no tears when he waved his parents, having already before him in his mind's eye a breakfast cup of Darjeeling tea with a lump of yak's butter floating in it. He would have no trouble at school, unlike Peter who was also in Darjeeling at the seminary across the valley. Walking in the garden, the young seminarian might stop in his tracks and wave a hand through the air to test the fluid space he had just passed through: *where* was reality, inside or out? Young Paul would have laughed. Peter's letters home were full of vapid warblings about the strange new hill birds; Young Paul was more sensible. After the first few times he devised a method by which the first and greater portion of a letter home was taken up with detailed explanations of precisely which letters were being answered, when they had arrived, their order, their dates, their postmarks, any discrepancies between dates and postmarks, any confusion arising from such discrepancies followed by general observations on the state of the post. By which time barely half of the letter-hour remained and was filled in with remarks on the weather, including temperatures, maximum, mean and minimum, humidity (always high in those parts), cloud formations and rainfall. It remained to ask after his parents' health and to assure them that his own was variable, depending on regular parcels of food.

At the Seminary of the Elevated Host, Peter was beginning to have his doubts. The discipline of the place grated on him, and its rigid demands on his faith irked a mind already half surrendered to vague oceanic feelings. His consolation was music, the great music of the European church which he would immerse himself in and prolong in his head hours after it had ended. Invariably the brothers found him drenched and shivering in a pew long after mass, the notes still racing across his glazed eyes. They put him on the organ so that proximity might wither the disease at the root, but he played with an impious frenzy that was disturbing to watch. The pedals were his rack and he burnt his fingers on the black keys. It was there that he discovered, in the fat frowning tide of sound, a note so intensely hot it was cold to blueness. It kept him in the seminary, it and a sense of guilt. To ease the confusion in his head that brought on migraines that threatened to split his skull, he took to drinking unconsecrated wine; then he drank whatever he could lay his hands on. "Better to have known nothing," he slurred, swigging what looked indistinguishable from Maxwell's Compound. "Better not to have been." But to consider the casual optimism that inflicted life on him was to blame, to add to the weight of his guilt. He considered hanging himself above the altar just before matins, but his courage failed him and he left that rite to another seminarian many years later in a Nakhlau chapel. He returned to the torment of that nameless longing that had gripped him at the Glacerie window the night of Uncle Alex's release from jail and still teased him with the possibility that there might be something worth living for. And then there was the thing expected of him: he must go to Rome just as his mother wished, propelled by her secret yet all too indicative hopes.

He did go, but not to Rome. A piece of land beyond the forest was mortgaged—the river still shifted further out with every passing year—and a Victor accompanied him to Bombay on the railway. He drank and was sick all the way to Italy and never got beyond Naples. There he was buttonholed by an artist wearing three shades of yellow, a frothy young man who mistook him for an Ethiop and wanted to know about Abyssinian fertility rites. Peter, who had taken the stranger for a fey Frenchman, learnt that he was English, an illustrator of some notoriety fled to Italy for his health and, he hinted darkly, his safety. Between introducing Peter to opium and fornication, he drew ithyphallic ink sketches that he threatened to burn some day. For Peter the blend was like ice on fire floating on nothing: the first time he was rocketed back to the Glacerie window whose nameless presentiment was disappointingly fulfilled. Together the two men went in search of the old town of Fescennia, famous for its graffiti and its wild harvest dances. "I will call you

Chico Sgarra," the artist declared on the road, "and you will call me Cucorogna and we must let nothing come between us except a delicious little nun." The nun was found, but Peter, who had fallen instantly in love with the moody Englishman, now came under the spell of their new companion, a girl of seventeen whose hair was only just growing back. In the tussle, Lucia, elfin and green-eyed, with elbows like alabaster, won. Cucorogna wandered off, and for months after they were married the couple lived in a Neapolitan hostelry washing empty wine barrels by day and grappling with one another's language by night. When the child was born, Lucia's tender Naples yellow breasts swelled a little and she said she craved papayas. "Let him get a little older," Peter agreed, "and we'll go home." The convent had given Lucy a fright, and now she wanted to see the world. She liked the sound of Sans Souci and was convinced that time and unalterable facts would win over Peter's disappointed mother. She was not the first outsider to misconceive Victoria.

Yet another son, Narrator? Something in the water, perhaps?
In the wine, more likely, Cup-Bearer. Fetch me some papaya juice, and let it be
from a female tree. Good man. Now hear what the Seven Sisters told me.

(*CHRONICLE RESUMED*)

All the time her sons were away, Victoria was rearing daughters. Faith, Hope, and Prudence, who came in a row, were already in black stockings and frocks. Then there was a gap, of some ten years, before Dulcie came. The older girls were sent to the convent school, St Cecilia's, where they proved clever in botany, in zoology, and in geology, in that order. Demure and diligent, they were patted by the nuns and pinched by the other girls, so they kept apart speaking a patois of their own making, passing notes in code and dreaming up chimerical inventions that would bridge their favourite subjects. Intelligent bronze artichokes, mechanical Venus flytraps, and potted shuttle-cocks filled their notebooks, complete with drawings, specifications, and no-menclature.

They were not the only ones with schemes. Long after he retired from the railway, Philip the Baptist, in a fit of bucolic senescence, invented the cow-catcher. He produced twelve to start with before going over to the railway track to check. When he did he found that the world was moving on and the more advanced engines were already fitted with cow-catchers. The cows themselves were growing canny, and his brainchild lay unused in the Comb until many years later when the British Other Ranks came. At the railway end of Sans Souci the Victors were also busy, but there too there were problems though the project was nothing more complicated than a chair. As it happened, the legs, produced by one team, were too short; the back, produced by another, reclined too far; the sloping cane seat brought in late in the day was slippery as a slide; and the arms, which came last, when it was too late to do anything about them, were broad and flat and extended so far forward that one could put one's feet up on them without taking off one's shoes. Thus was born the railway retiring-room chair. But once again someone had got there before, and railway retiring-rooms throughout India were already filling up with recumbent transit passengers in positions of more or less ridiculous repose. But the most extraordinary sight of all was Victoria on her bicycle.

Ever since Mr Montagu extended and metalled the Trotter Road to create the Lower Trotter Road, his wife got it into her head that she needed exercise. Unlike the mermaid in the story, her own legs, she was sure, were slowly growing together and the pain was like dull knives. She sent away to Suresh the bania's son with her request, but bicycle oil was Teli Mahesh's limit. Finding him unwilling to deal in machines, she switched loyalties to Uberoi & Uberoi, coming Sikh entrepreneurs-and-local agents for the Army & Navy Stores of Calcutta. The brothers, who had bought out J.c. Solomon, promptly delivered a tubular bicycle made in Holland on the most improved principles and fitted with the latest in twin-petal hygienic saddles. And Victoria began to ride. Each day from seven till eight the people of Sans Souci were treated to the spectacle of the grande dame exercising. Impossible to tell under all those skirts how she pedalled, for she refused to wear bloomers, but somehow the machine was propelled, faithfully carrying its enormous burden. The first time Mr Montagu saw her coming out of the desert up the Lower Trotter Road, he thought it was a black cloud and felt justified in his rain-gauge. But then the cloud took the shape of a whale on a bicycle and he watched it leave behind St Aloysius's School, bump across the railway track at the level crossing, roll past the aerolite, bowl along the salt flats, sail across the Sea of Tranquillity, scud between the old ice pits and the jamun (*Eugenia jambolana*) grove, and disappear behind the mango tope. "Well, if it keeps her happy," he murmured.

He was not unhappy himself, although heavily outnumbered by females in the Begam Kothi now that his sons were gone. Letters from Italy were few and evasive, and they never seemed to shake off the Naples postmark. Presently, gently, there was mention of a wife, and later on a child, but Victoria had already stopped reading. "A letter from your son," she would say to her busy husband, as if the papal hopes had been his, and there it would lie because the historian was a busy man. Apart from his daily trip to the rain-gauge to gather rainfall data, there were other tasks. The ice, for one, wanted closer attention because there were now competitors. The brothers Uberoi, who had started out in scrap iron and gone on to the retail trade, were now setting up a factory just across the Ganda Nala with the newest generation of American ice machines. True, their water supply could not be relied upon and it was certainly not as sweet as Sans Souci water, but they were nearer the city, and many old Trotter customers were stopping there. If an ice godown could be set up nearer Nakhlau—perhaps in the burnt-out shell of the powder magazine called the Life-Giving House—it might be an answer. Mr Montagu made a note of it. His memorandum lists were long, multiplying by the hour. At present he was busy electrifying Sans Souci, replacing the exquisite old oil lamps and pankhas with vulgar incandescent lights and ceiling fans (*Philistine, Parvenu*). In Nishan Chand's cubicle in the library, where there had been a mirror-tube, he put a wattless bulb. The Begam Kothi got a tiled roof and a new bathroom where the historian was learning to overcome his dread of water. There were also repairs to the fabric of *Sungum*: a rail around the hole in the Audience Hall where the fountain had been, beams to reinforce an excavated staircase, buttresses. Quite forgotten was a pane for a broken skylight in the library (*Vandal, Ostrogoth*). He built stormwater drains to the north and south of the two wings in expectation of a downpour that never came (*Prodigal, Profligate*). He petitioned the government for the return of the great gun *Urban*, and had it reinstalled in the Water Court (*Gunrunner, Warmonger*). He catalogued the remaining books in the library on a new system which used a magnetic bar-code instead of numbers, but abandoned the scheme on the pretext that it was ahead of its time (*Preliterate, Troglodyte*). But in the midst of all the fuss—he was also delivering lectures at the New Nakhlau Christian College on the influence of the future upon the past—his glasshouse languished and there was little time for his history of Sans Souci (*Worthy Steward, Fit Husbandman*).

His comfort was that from all reports—including the boy's own—Young Paul was doing well at school and expected to matriculate with the highest marks. His latest letter expressed a wish (it was actually a stated intention) to study medicine in England. Mr Montagu was put in a quandary. In the first place, his xenophobia was aroused. Why England? Why not Haiti, Germany—even Scotland? Next, when he cast his eye over the ice account, he found it was beginning to show signs of depletion although nobody but himself managed the ice. It was almost as if a ghost were tampering with the figures. He began to suspect old Thos. Henry, who lived on in the Glacerie and might have a grudge. But the Middle Trotter was unapproachable, having gone completely deaf. The fact remained that the ice was not doing well of late thanks to the Uberoi factory. And yet how could he deny his favourite son's wish? He regretted having recently bought, at a price, a set of moving-picture machines from two visiting French brothers. At length he ground his even teeth and made the necessary deduction; at least the boy was not going in for dentistry. That summer, Paul was sent to England on a handsome stipend: while the Trotters of Sans Souci were beginning to feel the pinch, the scion was sent a comfortable allowance each quarter, which he spent on dessert wines and acknowledged in his businesslike letters along with notes on the English weather (of which there was a lot in those parts) and his variable health. On the way over, he too had an amorous encounter, but unlike his older brother he knew where to get off.

They might even have crossed each other somewhere in the Red Sea, because Peter and Lucia had at last decided that the child was old enough to make the voyage to India. When they arrived at Sans Souci there was no one to meet them at the Gunpowder Gate, although the same gate had seen a spectacular farewell, with fireworks, for Young Paul. At the Begam Kothi, Victoria, who had had no trouble seeing Jivan's pot, was temporarily afflicted with her old blindness to material things. She looked straight through the small family and it was for Mr Montagu to make small talk about Rome. Since no one present had ever been there, the conversation quickly grew thin. Presently, Peter, Fifth Trotter, wondered where they should stay, and Mr Montagu suggested the Japanese tea-house at the far end of the sunken garden. And there they went, taking with them their single trunk and a quantity of sheet music.

Peter Augustine Trotter, failed priest, lived on toddy and music. Vocally a baritone, he naturally fought shy of singing and preferred to play, having lost none of his enthusiasm for the organ. Since there wasn't an organ at Sans Souci he was obliged to go in search of one, and the circumstance helped him to a job. He became an organ tuner. Unwelcome at the Roman Catholic church, where his reputation preceded him, he attended the various Protestant churches by rotation and might have become permanent organist at any one of them had it not been for his habit of turning up drunk and making no distinction between sacred and secular music. Sometimes he appeared late, in time for the recessional, and sometimes not at all, preferring to play at night, when he stood on the pedals, pulled out at the stops and thundered the overture to *La Vie Parisienne* until the terrified chowkidar summoned the police. So he remained an organ tuner, and since organs were far between he was obliged to travel, disturbing the local peace where he went. Even so, it was necessary to include pianos in the realm of his expertise although he would confess: "Strictly speaking, you know, the principles are different." They became a familiar seasonal sight in all the small towns of north India, the itinerant tuner, his Italian wife, their athletic half-deaf son, and the dog, Offenbach. The railway hotels no longer protested over the animal; one even improvised a kennel every August. But mostly they slept on trains, to economise, or in

railway retiring-room chairs in the neither-here-nor-there retiring-rooms kept
for those who travelled, as Trotters always did, Intermediate.

In between tunings the family returned to Sans Souci, to the tea-house
where Peter drank, with Alex at his elbow, every concoction under the sun
except the one his Italian wife had learnt to drink: tea. She made it the Indian
way, with the leaves and milk and sugar and cinnamon and cloves all stewed
together for an hour, but Peter swore he could not keep it down. He seemed
to have caught Cucorogna's moody disease, slipping from merriment into
gloom without warning. Once when Alex asked him, after a couple: "Tell
me, was it a civil wedding?" he replied: "Oh, I wouldn't go *quite* so far—but
they tell me it was not *al*together uncivil!" And he looked at Lucia and roared
for several minutes until the laughter dried on his tongue and he was obliged
to run some toddy over it. He said nothing for the rest of the night, staring
morosely at the fresco of some pilgrims trooping into a curly-roofed shrine,
until Alex rinsed his glass and left. Lucia was no help at such moments. Her
English was limited and a slight, never-voiced disappointment with Sans Souci
had made her more reticent than ever, though she clung to her husband like
moss. It was moving, the way the Fifth Trotter wept when he had finished
beating her, their blows slipping easily into wild love-making. During their
scuffles the quiet half-deaf Eustace as usual said nothing, but crouched in a
corner with his junior hockey-stick and trained it like a rifle on his father.

Alex's question did not spring from idle curiosity. He too was in love
and, after years of bachelorhood, contemplating marriage. The problem was
that his bright particular star was from an orthodox family. Converted Hindus
from Bengal, they seemed unable to leave their brahminism at the church
door and had continued for two generations to marry within the old caste. A
Kahn-Trotter, therefore, especially one who had been in jail and did nothing
in particular for a living, was hardly to be encouraged as a match for their
daughter. In fact, Alex had simply been hired to take a photograph of the girl
so that families who were eligible might view her. Suchita, educated to a mind
of her own, thought differently, and she could not but be impressed by a
photographer who promised her a picture of herself that would actually move
and that would one day make her a star. "It's like being a great stage actress,"
he explained, "only you can sit in the audience and watch yourself perform."
No mirrors were involved, he promised: during the viewing she could sit as
still as she liked and her image would continue to move. But the experiment
would involve many sessions, since a row of several hundred tiny photographs
was needed. His blandishments prevailed, and Suchita began to skip her history
lectures at the New Nakhlau Christian College. Alex would be waiting around
the corner with the carriage (it pleased him to act as a sort of chauffeur for
Mr Montagu) and the two would dash off to Sans Souci for a rendezvous

with the Lumière motion-picture camera. Then they would dash back, always a little late, so that Mr Montagu, his lecture delivered, would be pacing the long verandah wondering what had become of his colourful driver-and-agent and why he found it irritating that his best student, a handsome enough girl, should have stopped attending lectures.

It was a civil wedding. Alex wore a magenta waistcoat of shot silk with lacquered buttons, a biscuity brushed velvet jacket (tailored by Zakir Ali, High Class Tailor of Trotterpurwa and pressed by Dara Das & Sons, Cleaners and Dyers) and a hat to match. In his buttonhole he wore a single white carnation, and a promise of coral tinged the ruffle of his pocket handkerchief. He had combed his remaining lock of hair so that its strands were evenly disposed on the glistening dome of his head, but mostly he kept his hat on. His lower half was clad in burgundy trousers with darts in place of pockets, English buttercup yellow socks lent him by Peter, and patent leather shoes of withering lustre. Suchita wore a white cotton sari edged with red and kept looking behind her. But it was only Mr Montagu, who was surprised to find her there. He wore his usual beige and was the only witness. Elopement meant that there could be no festivities, but in any case Victoria would have allowed none at Sans Souci. It was not simply that she disapproved of her cousin's conduct, because in other circumstances she would still have sniffed: "Marrying Indians and all!" and then given in to a feast. After all, her own wedding reception had not come off, and she had not lost her appetite. There was a grander, more tragic reason for her refusal, and it appeared that same morning in the *Nuntio*.

Another headline (from the Nakhlau Nuntio)

VICTORIA REGINA
IS DEAD

———————————

The end of an era

———————————

Our darkest hour
23rd January, 1901

———————————

(CHRONICLE RESUMED)

For the rest of the year all entertainment was forbidden at Sans Souci. Even the film that was to prove so popular had to be screened privately on a whitewashed wall from which the still pictures had been removed. It was

a short flickering affair of no more than three minutes' duration and it showed
a single continuous action, a girl skipping with a rope, but people never tired
of it. Suchita herself could hardly believe it, though she sat very still the first
time. There she was on the wall hopping up and down, and there was the
rope, now down below her feet, now hidden behind her back, now up in the
air. It was difficult to tell whether the jerky motion was due to the nature of
the subject or the state of the art, but one complemented the other. The
following year, when the ban was lifted, Victoria set her face against the
motion picture. "Playing God," she snapped, "and all." But when Alex showed
the film in public the Sagarpaysans came in droves to sit on the Steps and
watch the miracle performed on an improvised screen, a bedsheet stretched
on a bamboo frame. And even in after years, when Alex had moved on to
more sophisticated camera work, the Trotterpurwa audience would chant, in
the boring bits or when the reels were being changed: *I-skipping rope, i-skipping
rope!*

The rope trick attracted much attention outside Nakhlau from both oc-
cultists who mistook its uncanny nature and sceptical hypnotists who chose
to scoff. The founding members of the Congress party, who combined politics
and metaphysics with the greatest of ease (*True Forerunners, Way-Shewers*)
asked for a private screening but could not agree on an auspicious date. Sir
Arthur Conan Doyle, always open-minded, wrote a letter of congratulation
from the bottom of his garden at Hindhead. When the workings of the machine
became widely known, fakirs and freemasons appeared from nowhere and
prowled the corridors of Sans Souci with anxious accusing eyes as if the age
of the arcane were threatened. Mr Montagu undid a button and spoke of the
rewards of technology, but agreed that perhaps things were moving too fast.
The future lay with the Alexes of this world. But people in Bombay were not
impressed: what could Nakhlau offer that they couldn't better? They produced
a six-minute sketch that included twelve mimed songs, two fistfights, a chase
across mountains, a pair of billing doves, two gun battles, a daring rescue,
thirteen rapes, and not one kiss. Not to be outdone, Madras produced a twelve-
minute mythological that encompassed the *Ramayana* and the *Mahabharata*
and included a large cast with stiff wire tails. Calcutta retaliated with a trilogy
of one-minute art films, but by then Alex had turned to slapstick comedies.
Mr Montagu, who despaired of ever getting back his expensive bioscope,
returned to speculative history, but there was this difference, that he began
to introduce into a hitherto materialist lump some slight leavening of Spirit.

Aspects of the World-Historical Water-Spirit (Weltgeschichtlicher Wassergeist) *revealed*

Hegel, Montesquieu, and other Europeans have made passing observations on the phenomenon of the World Spirit (*Weltgeist*) and the World-Historical Spirit (*Weltgeschichtlicher Geist*) and I do not propose to dispute with them. We too have our philosophers (who were anciently discoursing on the banks of the Ganges when the likes of Hegel were rubbing sticks together in caves far removed from Plato's). . . . The essence of the World Spirit, it seems to me, has not yet been adequately distilled. If it were, it would appear not as air, which is merely the sustaining or inspirational element of life, but water (*Wasser*), which is the origin of life. The earth's surface, after all, is four-fifths water, a proportion which holds equally true for the chosen instrument of history, namely the human species. The Spirit moves in the first place on the face of the waters, the waters, that is, of its sublime but necessary alienation. . . . Reflecting upon itself, the spirit is actualized as a negation, namely matter, and subsequently history, which progresses through time towards its final dissolution (the verb is significant), which is to say the negation of the negation in the restoration to itself of spirit. Water is thus the solvent or end as well as the source or origin of life, the deluge as well as the well-spring. The stream in the desert and the flood in the plain are exemplary symbols of the dialectic of history. The World-Historical Spirit of Hegel is therefore better described as the World-Historical *Water*-Spirit (*Weltgeschichtlicher* Wasser*geist*). . . . Wherever the sprite appears, that nation or people is dominant in world history, but such dominance is transitory and, with one exception, never to be repeated. . . . It first appears in the desert watered by the four rivers, the Tigris, the Euphrates, and two others, one flowing from China and one from India. . . . With the passing of the Garden of Eden, it is borne into the Persian Gulf and enters the Indian Ocean, an eddy reaching the Indus Valley, but the main current being drawn into the Red Sea. The isthmus of Suez is no barrier to the sprite, for an ur-Suez Canal has been dug four thousand years before de Lesseps. A thousand years the Water Spirit frolics in the eastern Mediterranean, between Alexandria, Tyre, and Ithaca. Somewhat shorter is its sojourn in the central Mediterranean where it voyages between Rome and Carthage, and shorter still its time in the west. . . . By 1492 it has passed between the Pillars of Hercules, by 1588 it has turned north to sport in the English Channel as far as the North Sea. Here it resides a further three hundred years at the close of which it is found to have travelled to the North Atlantic, roughly midway between the mouths of the Thames and the Hudson. There it will appear to the unwise to reside indefinitely, but the World-Historical Water Spirit is nothing if not fickle. Already it has sent scouts to find other routes

to other bodies of water. At the time of writing one has discovered the elusive Northwest Passage to the greatest of oceans, the Pacific, where a decisive encounter is shaping in the Sea of Japan. Already the sprite has been sighted between Vladivostok and Yokohama. . . . Let the entire century now begun be an Atlantic one; the one that comes after will be a Pacific century. Up and down the China Sea the sprite will sport, riding dolphins, startling Russian whalers, playing ducks and drakes as far south as Botany Bay. . . . But the dialectic has not yet run its course, for the Pacific is itself a passing phase. One last hurdle remains before the negation of the negation by which the World-Historical Water-Spirit comes into its own, redeeming both itself and the stubborn Object which it absorbs into the purest Subjectivity. Its passage to the Absolute is first hindered by the Indonesian archipelago whose many arms and inlets lure and deceive, but at last the Straits of Malacca yield their secret and the balmy Andamans beckon, pointing the way. True, at so great a remove in time, prediction is hazardous, but with the aid of data patiently gathered from the patent rain-gauge, calculations may be attempted. The year which ushers in the Aquarian age may be expected to vary, but by all that is apparent the World-Historical Water-Spirit (*Weltgeschichtlicher Wassergeist*) will on the twenty-first of [*illegible: June?*] burst into the waiting Indian Ocean.
—Abridged from "Historiography and Prognostication: the case for a *Weltgeschichtlicher Wassergeist*," *Journal of the Asiatic Dowsing Society* 62 (new series), January 1904, pp. 1–21.

(CHRONICLE RESUMED)

In later years, Mr Montagu was ashamed of this, his only satisfactory essay and would have given much to suppress it. The fact that he had correctly predicted the Russo-Japanese War of 1905 mattered little compared with the fear that his patriotism had not been ardent enough. And yet there were times when he thought it too naked, its metaphysical weeds too transparent coming from a materialist. He bought up and destroyed as many copies of the issue as he could find, but inevitably some eluded him. It may well have been that his inquisitorial impulse stemmed from a more radical fear, for the Anti-Trotter had been vouchsafed (perhaps in the bathroom, where he spent up to ten minutes a day washing away essential oils) a glimpse of the dissolution of History. Whatever his motives, he turned his back on the article and began to write in the style of Vladimir Ilyich Lenin.

The year the Japanese navy scuttled the Russian fleet in the Sea of Japan (thus proving to the world, to the historian's confused satisfaction, that an Asiatic power could defeat an European one) there occurred another event of political significance for Mr Montagu and the Congress party. On the seventh of August a pledge was taken in the Calcutta Town Hall to boycott British goods, chiefly the cloth of Lancashire whose mills had destroyed the Indian textile industry. Millions of independent weavers had seen their livelihood succumb to duty-free cloth woven in Britain from Indian cotton and sold back to India at wondrous profits. In Nakhlau the local branch of the party called on all patriotic citizens to stop buying and selling British fabrics and to wear homespun khadi instead. As the weather grew cooler, symbolic bonfires of Lancashire cloth were lit in public places. It was true that some traders tossed only the cheapest bolts of imported cloth onto the flames, but the demand for the better quality fabrics nevertheless suffered a slight fall. Mr Montagu was obliged to have a new set of clothes made up by Zakir Ali, High Class Tailor of Trotterpurwa, and he was pleased to find his preferred shade of beige in natural undyed khadi. When he was at home, he wore his old European suits; when he went to Nakhlau to deliver his lectures or on business, he wore a khadi achkan. Victoria snorted, but let it go because his legs at least were covered. It was not a dhoti anyway.

For Alex the dilemma was sterner, and he compromised by giving up English cigarettes and his favourite Britannia cream biscuits instead (*Freedom Fighter, Patriot*). He lost a few friends by his decision, but there were many others who saw his plight and recalled his solidarity of old. He attended the bonfires dutifully all the same, despite the jeers of the crowd. Once in the heat of the moment he took off his foreign coat and threw it onto the fire, but it only succeeded in smothering the flames just as the police arrived, and the gesture took on an ambiguous cast. Afterwards he retrieved the coat with great tenderness and had it relined with contraband Japanese silk to the historian's satisfaction. Now that he was a father, Alex could not afford to go throwing away clothes. His moving-picture shows brought in some money, enough to keep the girls, Anita and Sulekha, in red floral kimonos smuggled in at Calcutta, but he had to think of the price of film. It was fatherhood and professionalism, not the party, that eventually took the colour out of his clothes. There were other side-effects too. As he began experimenting with longer feature films, a new jerkiness came into his step. He began to hurry about from place to place, in black and white, his head nodding and bobbing as if on a spring. His wife, Suchita the film star, found the puppetlike twitchiness at first amusing and then trying, especially as she herself, who should logically have developed the celluloid symptoms, moved quite normally. Alex was conscious of the disease in a furtive glancing way, but could do nothing to control it; when he looked back on his youth, so colourful and debonair, and so agonizingly recent, he groaned out loud. But the groan was little more than a bleat: the fact was he was losing his voice and would not regain it until a competitor launched the *Fanfare Talkies* in Nakhlau. His wife claimed she could not hear him at all, but ears were not her strongest asset. When he looked at Young Paul, newly returned from England with a medical degree and an extraordinarily high polish, Alex felt a twinge of envy. The doctor had taken to calling frequently, at all hours, at the Kahn-Trotter residence in the Rib. Not that there was any curable illness in the house. The calls were social. He very rarely had anything to say to Alex, no doubt because these days Alex's replies barely crossed the space between their chairs. When the girls came in to show off their kimonos, Young Paul hardly noticed. But he seemed to have much to say to their young film star mother.

Young Paul had picked up a first at his university and never ceased to shine. The very brilliantine in his hair was more brilliant than other men's, and yet he managed it so that its lights were discreet, not showy. He wore dark socks and his shoes were black mirrors over which he was in the habit of bending and smiling so that it seemed at times his mouth opened downwards. Even his sharkskin suits tailored in Bond Street, London, got up a sheen, though never vulgarly. There was no flash about the man, no glitter; he simply glowed. Along with his first he had picked up a reputation for women, which he always modestly denied. At university he despised the artistic set but tolerated artists' models, although himself a medical man. On his return to India, by way of Paris, he set up as an eye specialist, but knew about and treated ear, nose, and throat, and other complaints too. His surgery was at the edge of the Civil Lines, and he lived in Sans Souci in the Comb, adjoining the New Armoury, where he refurbished a set of rooms to suit his tastes. His patients were chiefly Indian and Anglo-Indian, with a sprinkling of Europeans, though never European women. Once when he examined an Englishwoman, the European community whispered and shook their heads, because although he was white everyone knew him to be part-Indian. He never forgot the incident, and yet among their men he moved easily. He knew the Lieutenant-Governor and numerous British civilians; often they and a Parsi taxidermist made up a pig-sticking party (*Unnatural Trotter, Vicious Sport*). Shikar quickly became a passion with Young Paul, the jungle and the marshes to the east of the Tank being near at hand and rich with game. When it crossed his mind that perhaps he should have stayed on in England and done it properly with scarlet and horns, bellowing *tantivy* and *taiyaut* and *hoicks*, he would ask himself: "What's in a fox?" Already he had left- and right-barrel tigers to his name and was buying an elephant gun. His father, who had welcomed him home from England with a peaceable fireworks display, was taken aback by this bloodthirstiness, but shut his eyes to it. When the gunfire from the jungle beyond the Gulabi Manzil grew intolerable, he wound up the gramophone and put on a record from his collection. However much he professed to despise Europe and its works, *these* works (and he had the best tunes) were sublime, a solace beyond understanding. He began to wonder if he hadn't been mistaken in the other, musical son.

Peter, however, was drinking too heavily to make the kind of music his father collected. He had given up playing church organs and seldom kept his tuning appointments even in the nearer towns. He dusted off Victoria's old piano in the Glacerie (she had not touched it since the day it told her of her darkest need) and hauled it down to the tea-house where he found the black keys hopelessly out of tune and spent a week restoring them. In between he drank and scuffled with his wife and then played on her tenderly with fingers that his own mother had turned into tuning forks. Afterwards he got up and drank some more and sat over the keyboard hunting for that blue-grey note he had found and lost many years ago at the seminary. Until one day he found it again. He played it once, twice, to make sure, by itself and in a series, and yes, there it was. He began to improvise, ascending and descending by way of its icy blue, stretching out some notes, syncopating others, introducing a bass rhythm, flopping onto two adjacent semitones at once. Mr Montagu, who was coming by to make amends, paused at the tea-house door during one of these dissonant sessions and saw that he had been mistaken. He shook his head and wandered off in search of his daughters.

There were four of them now: the ten-year gap after Prudence had been ended by Dulcie, who came into the world round, white, and spongy and kept that shape through childhood. Nobody in Sans Souci, from the Rib to the railway colony, had produced a boy for as long as anyone could remember. It was, Trotters agreed, the water, and Victoria drank as much as everyone else put together. Faith and Hope were already out of school and showed no inclination to marriage; Prudence, in her last year, was more interested in metals than in men. Faith, the botanist, was the witty one who told wry cruel stories with a straight face, her acid tongue the result of Victoria's craving for early gooseberries the year of the Ilbert Bill. Hope was growing up gloomy and querulous, her bitterness the consequence of a pregnancy binge on raw liver. Prudence was shy, not much to look at and notoriously heavy-handed with the saltshaker. Not marrying material, Mr Montagu saw, coming upon them as they sat in a row on cane mondhas, pressing leaves, dissecting frogs, and examining old coins. Not yet out of their teens, they were already the Maiden Aunts. They had the chaste serenity of certain kinds of music, and Mr Montagu, who had once believed himself destined for bachelorhood, gazed at them with a reluctant admiration. What was strange was that Dulcie, the product of a whole basketful of jamuns (*Eugenia jambolana*) and temperamentally quite different from the others, tagged along with her older sisters and insisted on drawing up a mondha beside them. There was always a gap between her chair and theirs, but all the same she was in line. She did not flirt with her father after the fashion of little girls (she was almost five), and it looked as if her natural sweetness would drive many a young man to desperation when she grew older. She was not, however, destined to be the youngest. Victoria, for all her talk of her legs joining up, was pregnant again, and the historian, schooled in the repetitions of the past, saw more daughters coming. Only this time his wife's belly was twice as big as usual.

In the Comb, the walls were filling up with trophies that would have distressed old Sunya the egg-brahmin who had given the place its name. Today the visitor who climbed the staircase at the elbow where the crescent joined the wing would be startled by a raging elephant bearing down on her with its trunk uplifted, its mouth open and one mammoth foot poised for the crushing. Recovering, she might peer at the plaque underneath with its long narrow strip of electroplated metal engraved with the legend:

HOSI SODAWATERBOTTLEOPENERWALLA, B.SC. F.R.T. TAXIDERMIST, HAZRATGANJ, NAKHLAU

Continuing along the curving verandah above the old stables toward the New Armoury end where Young Paul had his bachelor suite, the visitor would see mounted along the wall to the left and the pillars to the right, a variety of heads. Along the wall there were tiger heads with yellow marbles for eyes, crocodile heads (the jaws wide open), boar heads with broken tusks, pig heads (*Savage Sport*), panther heads, cheetah heads, hyena heads, jackal heads, fish heads, turtle heads, seal heads, a complete yeti, and a Giant Panda head. On the pillars were the horned heads of barking deer, antelope, chital, swamp deer, musk deer, fallow deer, reindeer, moose, bison, blue-bull, a yak, and a leering goatish head. In places the verandah was virtually impassable for the antlers. Then there were the birds—but by now the visitor would be overwhelmed or impatient and would knock, boldly enough, at the door where the crescent ended.

"Why, Suchi!"

Only a gentleman could have expressed the right degree of surprise. Young Paul had been waiting.

"I had to come." That was from a later film script.

He invited her in at once, shut the door behind her, showed her to the comfortable sofa, put a cushion behind her, and told her that her eyes were wasted on a faded jerky old cameraman. And who should know about eyes if not the eye-specialist.

Meanwhile, Alex and Mr Montagu were involved with planning a major Congress party demonstration of defiance in Aminabad Park. Aminabad was the city's bargain shopping centre. If you wanted European goods, you went to Hazratganj; if you wanted traditional Nakhlau goods, you went to Chowk; at Aminabad, located between the two, you got both at half the price, as Victoria knew. With Christmas coming up, she picked a day for her gift shopping and served notice on her husband.

"My dear, I have an appointment in the city," Mr Montagu pleaded.

"Good," said Victoria.

"No, no, I mean another appointment. And besides," he indicated her belly with a fastidious hand, "in your condition . . ."

But Victoria would not hear of changing the day. Time was short enough and there was still the big breakfast to prepare for. Finally Mr Montagu agreed to return from his appointment (he dared not say what it was) as soon as he could to pick her up.

Victoria ran her eye down the list of names and likely presents. It was not a long list: her brothers, the Victors, were not on it, since they chose to spend the day with their families or at the Railway Institute, where there would be dancing; Peter, her first-born, did not exist; and there was nothing you could give Young Paul that he didn't already have. The girls, then, were the problem, the older ones refusing to drop hints and Dulcie reluctantly copying them. Well, they could get sober dress lengths, of good quality British twill, and so could she herself, from her husband. Grandfather, as she called Thos. Henry after the children were born, could do with a walking stick: he needed to get out. Alex and Suchita warranted a counterpane, their girls tablecloths. Philip the Baptist had asked especially for something, she couldn't remember what, and Alina, who had grown very feeble, would probably be in bed. Mr Montagu would get his beige hankies.

On the chosen day Mr Montagu was late. Victoria waited in the bedroom, lying back on the made-up bed, breathing heavily and looking at the wall-clock from time to time. Minutes stretched to half an hour, an hour, two, two and a half. At three o'clock she decided to go without him: the best of the winter sun was already lost and it would be cold coming back. She put on her shawl, had the carriage brought round and was helped into it by a mali and the driver. An hour later she was in Aminabad, where a large crowd was gathering in the park. She took no notice of the chanting; she had already ignored a policeman who suggested she go back to Hazratganj. At her customary shop she found the owner getting ready to pull down his shutters. "Already, Mr Haq?" she demanded. Mr Haq was an oval fair tight-skinned man, thin only beside Victoria. "Madam, the crowd . . ." he began, when, looking at her, he saw her condition. He ushered her in, turned the lights back on, leaving all but one of the shutters fastened, and offered her a seat on the padded bench set up against one wall of the long narrow shop. Always a leisurely shopper, Victoria began to consider and point at this and that bolt of cloth on the shelves along the opposite wall. The bolts came down and were unrolled with practiced abandon as Mr Haq forgot his nervousness. The round ones rolled smoothly across the padded platform between customer and shopkeeper; the flat ones made rapid trajectories, flapping like startled pigeons. It was an old ritual: the more insouciant Victoria became, the more briskly Mr Haq shamed her with unlikely offers. In a little while there were more fabrics on the platform than on the shelves. Twills, seersuckers, silks, bombazines, summer drills, winter tweeds, poplins, gauze, linen, muslin, calico lay entwined on a fantastic sargasso sea. All were of the best quality, with the new, slightly waxy smell of the Lancashire mills, and each one had been lightly considered and rejected. At last there remained one bolt of cloth on the shelf, and even before Mr Haq took it down Victoria knew it was for her—for her, that was, and for her daughters. It was a violet twill, durable, dark, conservative. The shopkeeper, who knew her tastes of old, handed the bolt over without unrolling it; there would be no need to measure and cut. Victoria stroked it triumphantly and nodded. She was about to pay for it when a man ran into the shop, snatched it out of her hands, and ran out again.

It was probably the shock. Victoria sat unmoving for a few seconds, digesting the action. Then she lurched out of the shop after the man, but he was off, already bobbing across the park with his prize to where a bonfire was burning. Several other men were making for Mr Haq's shop, but Victoria stood in the way, her massive violet frame palpitating as she cursed them to the fifth generation. "Sons of owls!" she panted. "Great-great-grandsons of owls! Scum of the earth! Guttersnipes! Tartars! Cream of Tartars!" Behind her Mr Haq was handing out conciliatory bolts of foreign cloth. It was not his best cloth, but then not all the takers ran in the direction of the blaze. And then it happened: the cramps began. Victoria heaved herself back into the shop, fell onto the platform among the wreathed fabrics, and began to wheeze. Mr Haq, who guessed what was happening, raced outside but did not know which way to turn. The carriage stood waiting but there was no sign of the driver; that good man had gone to warm himself at the blaze. Mr Haq begged one of the bystanders to go and fetch a doctor or a midwife, bribing him with a roll of seersucker (*Liberal Mercer*). He asked a would-be looter if he had no shame ogling while a ladies was therein in family way. He was also, in a corner of his mind, worried about the new danger to his stock from an old and trusted customer. But there was nothing to be done about that; he was too courteous to go back in.

Inside, the labour was excruciating but short. Before the midwife could arrive Victoria had given birth to twins and cut the cords with Mr Haq's imported Turkish scissors. The scene in the shop was horrific: an ocean of blood, placental jelly, and white ropy fluids on which there floated, besides Victoria herself, two new creatures so covered in slime as to be unrecognizable but evidently, audibly, alive. "Never again," Victoria promised. She left in a little while, despite Mr Haq's protestations, and tottered to the carriage supported on either side by the shopkeeper and the driver, whose sleeve felt unusually warm. When she was seated, two bundles were brought out of the shop and placed in her wicker shopping-baskets. As the carriage rolled past the bonfire, Victoria, reclining with her head rolled to one side, saw in the twilight a pale dusty man past middle age, haranguing the last of the crowd. It was Mr Montagu.

His wife made a spectacular recovery. For the next three days she kept to the bedroom (her husband, banished from the conjugal bed, now slept on a chesterfield in the drawing room) and admitted no one except the khansama. "*Only* Chotey Lal," she warned, and the cook entered trembling to hear her discourse on potato lions and butter peacocks. The day before Christmas, Victoria swung out of bed to personally oversee the preparations for the big breakfast. The morning of the Great Day found her in the Glacerie before anybody in the family was up, inspecting the long carefully covered table. Sadly, several of its leaves had been removed since the departure of the endless Victors, but it took four cloths to cover what remained. She walked up and down its diminished length, straightening a fish-fork, patting the daffodils in their vases, primping a fleur-de-lis-ed napkin. She flicked murderously at a speck of dust on her plate and stood back to admire Chotey Lal's magnificent mashed-potato lion, stiffly couchant in the cold morning light. In the middle of the table, carved and stuck with tail-feathers, was the butter. The place smelt a little musty from disuse, but shortly there came from the old kitchens the rich sizzle of fatty meats for the biryani, the sweet intoxicating reek of burnt onions for garnishing the pulaos, aromatic kababs, fragrant stuffings, a promise of creamy cheese sauce for the fish, heavenly custards, beatific blanc-manges, rosewater for the syrupy sweets. Everybody from inner Sans Souci would be there, including the three nameless ones from the tea-house, though they were relegated to the outer darkness at the Old Armoury end.

It was then, counting the settings, that a thought struck her. She swam back through the pearly light to the Begam Kothi and woke Mr Montagu, who was asleep on the drawing room couch. It was time for church anyway, though his service was, typically, later.

"What do they look like?" she asked, shaking him.

Mr Montagu found his glasses. "Well, they're girls, to start with," he mumbled. "Twins, but one is, well, pale—you know, like me . . ."

"So the other's like me, is it?"

"I'm afraid it's worse than that." Mr Montagu hated being woken early.

"She's a little . . . red, in some lights. Pomegranate red. But it's all right, my dear, chin up. They're both doing well. The ayah's been very good."

Secretly Mr Montagu was well pleased. Although the girls were still too young to flirt with him, they were both clearly—you could tell the way they held onto your finger—the marrying kind. After four precocious spinsters that was something to be grateful for.

Table-talk

—Can we say the grace?
—He went on and on about poverty. My carnation was wilting. Hello, Peter! Didn't see you at church, you devil. Lucia. Merry Christmas, Eustace!
—I say, Alex, we heard about your bonfire.
—Shh! Chup, men. Don't get the Old Vic worked up again. All bloody hell broke loose when Monty got back, I'm telling you.
—We heard it from the tea-house.
—Tea-house! The dash buffaloes broke out of the dairy, men!
—It's bloody freezing in here. I could do with a nip of something.
—Can we say the grace?
—That Chotey's quite a sculptor. That looks like a real lion.
—What's my Anita crying about?
—Eustace gave her Chinese bangles for Christmas. Her arm's gone all white.
—You watch out there, Eustace.
—Give him a clip on the lug, Anita.
—Merry Christmas. Looking delicious. Where've you been all my life?
—*Can* we say the grace?
—Look at Uncle Paul—he's making eyes at her.
—Why was *I* spared? The Hand of God. If they would *read* the Apparatus.
—Can we say the grace first? The children want to start.
—The dandy broke down. That's why we were late. Hub came right off.
—All lies.
—Excuses, excuses.
—Chico?
—Cara?
—Mother want grace.
—I heard her. That potato lion looks like a bloody lamb.
—Ours was all about giving. The gift of love. By the way, sotto voce and all, your eyes . . . Look, why don't you come over afterwards and gather some rosebuds?
—Mr Montagu, will you *please* say the grace.

—My dear, your father should, by rights.

—Oah foah! Grandfather, please will you say the grace?

—Eh?

—Can you say the *grace*. The *children* want to start.

—The children . . . ? Yes, yes. They're looking very nice.

—*Mr Montagu.*

—My dear, my throat.

—Yes, yes, your throat! You can shout all day don't know what-all kinds of seditiousness against the King, but when it comes to saying a little grace—

—Asking grace, my dear. And please, we've thrashed that business out.

—Yes, thrashed it out, thrashed it out. Leaving your wife to suffer in the market.

—My dear, please.

—All right, then, say it.

—But yours is so much more . . . graceful, my dear. "For these and all thy gifts—"

—Just *say* it, men.

—All right, close your eyes, girls. "For what we are about to receive, may the Lord make us truly grateful, for Christ's sake, Amen."

—Ah-men.

—Ay-men.

—Ay-men, ay-men, Rat-Catcher!

—Stop that, you two. Now, I'll have some fish.

—Certainly, my dear. Faith, pass your mother the fish.

—NOT GUILTY!

—Tea! At ten-bloody-thirty in the morning my wife wants tea. A full-blooded Italian! Take her pulse, somebody. Is there a doctor—no, on second thoughts. We'll get a bottle of the real stuff. Chotey Lal!

—Baba?

—Ek-do botal lao. Aur suno, whisky gilas.

—There will be no drinking at this table.

—Victoria!

—You heard me. And no politics.

—NOT GUILTY! D'you hear?

—Never mind, we'll have it in teacups. Chotey, *special* chai!

—This cold is bad for my chest.

—Nothing like a good BONFIRE for that, Uncle.

—Shh! Peter, don't get Vicky going, men.

—It's a minute blood-vessel that helps to nourish the eye of the foetus.

—I say, this biryani is damn good with *tea*.

—And no bad language either.

—What's left, for Pete's sake? Father, Alex has been telling me all about the BONFIRE.

—Hm-hm!

—Is that a goose?

—Uncle Paul shot it.

—Yes, as a matter of fact, I did. It comes all the way from Siberia. They fly south when the marshes start to freeze, right over the Himalayas and plonk into our jhils in time for Christmas.

—Poor old goose.

—NOT GUILTY!

—They're best roasted over an OPEN FIRE.

—*Curry!* Fine sort of name for a man. Mouse, rather.

—What sort of name is Trotter?

—Solomon, Disraeli. All the same.

—He was a good Prime Minister.

—No POLITICS, remember?

—Hmf.

—What happened to the Solomon property after the old man died?

—Those Sikh brothers bought it, the Uberois.

—Have you seen their ice? Like monsoon clouds.

—Wonder if it'll rain before New Year's.

—Looks like it. It's all those volcanoes going off in Japan.

—Japan. Now there's a country for you. Jolly good pasting the Russians got.

—Never trust the Russians.

—No POLITICS, eh?

—Eyes, darling, I think your husband wants you.

—What is it, Alex?

—

—You'll have to speak up. I wish they'd hurry up and invent the talkies.

—I SAID, ANITA'S NOT EATING.

—You don't have to shout. Sulekha, give her the pope's nose.

—Parson's beak!

—Pope's nose.

—You should have bought that property, Father.

—The ice is not doing well enough for that, Young Paul. Winter, you know.

—Only to be expected. What we need now is a bloody good FIRE. Father knows how to light one.

—There isn't a chimney.

—Outside, I meant. A PROPER FIRE. We're not English.

—What are we?

—It's a pity *some* people aren't. Or they wouldn't go dancing around bonfires like savages.

—My dear, the Angles were rubbing sticks together without results when the people of this country had a university.

—No wonder they're so seditious.

—It's a sort of granulation on the surface of the eye. Wordsworth had it. So did this boar, thank God.

—Not seditious, just patriotic.

—Burning cloth is patriotic?

—If it's destroying our industries, yes.

—Anyway the boar had a bad case of it. Or I'd be minus a leg.

—Nice gabardines and all. You think these people can make cloth like that?

—They've been making it for thousands of years.

—All rubbish. The British are teaching them to make things properly. They're here to civilize them. Could you pass the fish?

—They're here to civilize themselves at our expense.

—They're here to civilize them. Pass the fish.

—I hit it in the thorax. The next shot went into the pinna, so the mask was spoilt anyway, but *it kept coming*! Thank *God* for trees, I tell you.

—I'm going to do that walk again. I'll show them.

—Which walk, Grandfather?

—Peter.

—That night walk with Dukhi—he's no more, poor soul—out of the Residency. Did I tell you about it?

—Some custard, Grandfather?

—You told us.

—Well, let me tell you about it.

—You *told* us.

—Eh? Yes, it was cold. November. And I fell into the canal.

—You're drinking a lot of tea there, Peter.

—An old Roman failing, my friend. Tea and continence, hah!

—*Nakhlau Trotter* they called me after that.

—Peter, sing us a song.

—Anyway, let me tell you about it.

—Peter. Sing *Pole Fishers*.

—PEARL Fishers.

—There will be no singing at this table.

—One of the First Trotter's wives choked at table.

—What rot. Just because she was fat!

—She fell out of a window.

—The First Trotter had only one wife.

—He was a bachelor.

—Then how . . . ? Stupid ass!

—Mummy, Dulcie's hogging the honey roggen.

—All right, then, a Negro spiritual.

—She's buried down there.

—*He's* buried down there.

—There's nothing down there.

—Is nothing sacred?

—"The Old Folks at Home." How does it go?

—"Oh darkies, how my heart grows weary . . ."

—It's *pole*. Like in a fishing rod.

—Where's Zacharias?

—He couldn't get leave.

—*Still* building the Upper Ganges Canal? You'd think he'd have got lower down by now.

—He never takes leave.

—S-Solomon!

—Lucia looks a bit pale. I'd say Eustace takes after his mother.

—He'll get a bloody hiding if he does. He's going to be a musician.

—Who was it married a bugler?

—Dulcie's musical.

—My teacher said I would sing in Vienna one day.

—I say, Peter, where's the potato lamb?

—It's bloody extinct. By a process of natural selection. DARWIN wrote a book about it. *Oranges and Peaches*.

—I've read it.

—Hope's read it. Mummy, there's only *so* much custard left.

—I know it too. It's called *The Origin of the Species*.

—Shh, men, you'll get Vicky worked up.

—It's not *the* species, stupid ass. It's *The Origin of Species*.

—It's *the* species. That's us. He says we're descended from——

—*Stop* that wicked talk, you girls, or you won't get your presents.

—My dear, just when it's getting interesting. You must let their minds——

—Let their minds, nothing. Seditiousness and unpiousness, that's all they'll learn from you. Bonfires! You should burn some of those books of yours instead of all that lovely cloth.

—How's the bioscope doing, Alex?

—Not too much happening, men. Cast's on strike. In any case the rolls are getting too expensive—when you can get them. Sometimes I think it would be better to open up a theatre and just show pictures.

—Need a pianist?

—I *say*, men!

—Ungodliness everywhere ever since that machine came into the house. Next they'll want to film the Prince of Wales.

—Well, my dear, I'd better go turn the other machine on.

—Today! You heard that you-all? He's going to turn the ice on today. You see what happens when he starts going around with heathens.

—I'm afraid it's necessary if we're going to eat like this again. You should see the ice account.

—Come on, then, Grandfather. You'll soon have a nice present.

—You're giving me a stick, aren't you? Like last year. You think I'm old and feeble and I should get some exercise, no? I'll show you.

—When's tea?

—Ask Peter. He's the expert on tea.

—Let's go out in the sun.

—After you.

—Nice gloves, men. Where you got them?

—Uberoi's, where else.

—Smart buggers.

—Coming?

—I can hardly move. Foof!

—You! Look at *this*.

—Hold the door.

—Match?

(*CHRONICLE RESUMED*)

The crash came the following year. It came for no particular reason, a long winter, a short summer, increased cartage costs, the collapse of a newly repaired godown, the fickleness of customers, the wizardry of the brothers Uberoi, inept management—but each contributed its share. What was certain was that the ice had failed. The plant worked at half capacity for a while, then even that was halved. Mr Montagu declared he would never compromise on quality, that he would rather be right than rich, but the fact was that the market was cornered. Production did not cease altogether. The Glacerie continued to produce ice for Sans Souci. Some of it went to the village of Trotterpurwa, some to the dairy where Alex's steady brother, Zacharias, had taken over immediately after retiring from the Upper Ganges Canal, and some made its way along the branch road to the railway colony where the institute, the canteen, and the school needed a block each. One summer a large block was needed for laying out Philip the Baptist whose executioner was not, this time, called away. His wife Alina was spared till the following winter when it was not necessary to draw on the dairy quota. The domestic needs of the various establishments around *Sungum* were modest: the Begam Kothi took a canister, the Kahn-Trotters in the Rib did likewise, the tea-house three took less than was needed, and Young Paul in the Comb rather more. But one person steadfastly refused to touch ice, and even though he died in the hot weather there was no need to indent on the Glacerie whose infernal machine had made him deaf.

In his seventy-eighth year, Thos. Henry, Fourth and Middle Trotter, decided to repeat his celebrated walk. For some years he had put it off, accumulating in the process a succession of unused Christmas walking sticks. Then, in 1911, the year of the Delhi Darbar, although he was not strictly old, he began to weaken. Ever since his surrender of the Victoria Cross he had had no use for royalty, and here were the first British sovereigns to visit India, George V and Queen Mary, right next door to Nakhlau. They were only there to dignify the transfer of the capital from Calcutta to Delhi, but it was enough to arouse all Nakhlau Trotter's old suspicion and mistrust. He had bad dreams which his nightly glass of eau sucrée was powerless to prevent and he concluded that if he didn't do the walk right away he would not be allowed to keep its anniversary on the ninth of November. And yet he needed help. Dukhi Das, the Guide's guide, was dead, and his own son-in-law, the historian, was hardly walking material. His grandson, Peter, the true Fifth Trotter, was a complete stranger; in any case, by all reports he was seldom capable of walking in a straight line. "Not that that's in itself a disqualification," mused Thos. Henry, remembering the route to be retraced, but it was support, not abetment, that he needed. He found it in Eustace, Sixth Trotter. The choice was not strictly dynastic. Apart from being an athletic young man, Eustace knew, if partially, the curse of deafness, and the bond between two beings compelled to inhabit enclosed private worlds was a natural one. They understood each other without having to speak, and their necessary gestures were identical. And so, leaning on his muscular young confederate, a walking stick in his other hand, Nakhlau Trotter set out to repeat history.

They chose a night in June and took a tonga to the Residency. Eustace, as eager as his great-grandfather to test himself, told nobody. He had grown into a graceful animal, lightsome like his mother but with short stubby fingers and nails like two-anna bits. He had also her girlish features and her reticence. The school's best boxer and fullback captain of the Aloysian hockey team, he did not know what it was to be fettered. Bored with a class at school, he simply walked out; called back and caned, he didn't flinch and was not one for grudges, but the next time he walked out again. If a lesson was interesting he sat motionless, breathing lightly at long intervals, his slightly yellow eyes level, his good ear cocked. The night walk was welcome, though it was not (his instinct told him) going to be the severest of his trials. They slipped out together beyond the Redan and made their way down to the river, where Thos. Henry stooped and dipped his fingers in the stream. Then they crossed by the bridge, since wading was out of the question. On the other side they found the grove where Nakhlau Trotter and Dukhi Das had dressed before crossing back to Nakhlau by the next bridge. They passed through the city and emerged into the fields on the other side. By now Eustace was virtually carrying the Guide, making no complaint. They found the canal, the village of the sleeping young woman, now a great-grandmother, the barking pi-dogs, descendants of the ones that set up a terrific cross-country barking on that historic night so long ago. And then, left alone for a moment just before dawn, Thos. Henry fell into a dry well.

When Eustace returned with a rope, it was morning. The fields in that part were riddled with blind wells and each one had to be shouted into. To manage the pain while he waited, Thos. Henry imagined himself in a mineshaft waiting with pistols loaded for the enemy to break through. Schooled in patience, he listened for and heard the stroke of the pick, saw the earth on the other side falling away, bringing his quarry closer. He began to help the other along, poking with his stick at the soft wall of the mine in the direction of the fated digger. It was like tunnelling towards some once-blinding insight, now covered over by time and only dimly remembered. With each stroke a little dark earth fell away and one was visited by the sensation of approaching clarity. On and on, every fall of earth an advance until only a veil of wasp-clay divided one from the other: the next stroke—the next breath—would bring one face to face. With expectation so complete, one was content to put down one's tools and await the transfiguring plenitude of that encounter.

The dust from the collapse of the well rose to the surface like a wraith and was dispersed across the field. Eustace saw it too late and took his secret back to Sans Souci, aware that nothing could be done. On his own he decided that after he left school he would join the provincial police force and trace people who simply disappeared. When Victoria found her father missing she suspected the boy had something to do with it, but could not question him because, like the rest of the unholy family, he did not exist. A search was mounted, an advertisement placed, but Thos. Henry was never found. After a year he was presumed dead. Those who remembered the Siege of Nakhlau took out a subscription and put up a tablet in St Thomas's, the Protestant church to which, since the coming of Mr Montagu, Nakhlau Trotter had inclined.

A memorial

IN HONOUR OF ONE
WHOSE NAME SHOULD NEVER BE FORGOTTEN

THOS. HENRY TROTTER
WHO
ON THE NIGHT OF THE 9TH OF NOVEMBER 1857
WITH THE DEVOTION OF AN ANCIENT ROMAN
TAKING HIS LIFE IN HIS HANDS
WENT FORTH FROM THE BELEAGUERED RESIDENCY
AND PASSING THROUGH A CITY THRONGED
WITH MERCILESS ENEMIES
DID SUCCESSFULLY GUIDE SIR CRAWLEY CAMPELOT
AND HIS ARMY
TO THE RELIEF OF THE GARRISON

(*CHRONICLE RESUMED*)

It was unfortunate that just when peace was returning to the Glacerie (the ice-plant now worked half a shift) Thos. Henry should not be there to enjoy it. But that was one of the ironies of fate on which Mr Montagu found new time to reflect. He returned to his glasshouse where the unfinished history of Sans Souci lay yellowing in the sun and took up where he had left off. It was the best an historian could do. He ignored Justin Aloysius's gastronomical feats and dwelt on profitless experiments with mould or the collecting of lacklustre artefacts. The bequest of a school occupied him for an entire chapter, while of breakfasts and recipes he made no mention. And he closed the first generation by dismissing the balloon-over-Ganda Nala account of the Great Trotter's accidental death. People don't just disappear, he wrote. It was a sad commentary on the makers and recorders of history that Nakhlau Trotter, so lately disappeared, should already have been forgotten.

After the twins, Pearl and Ruby, were born, Victoria kept her promise. She never again admitted Mr Montagu to her bed. Not that he would have made much progress had he insisted on his husbandly rights. The fact was, Victoria's legs had at long last joined up and the old knifelike pains gone away. The process was invisible to the world because her dresses continued to trail on the ground while other hemlines were beginning to rise, though she did concede a plain lace trimming at the cuffs and below. She suckled the twins without looking at them, and when they were old enough to walk she put them in dark gaberdine, sent them to the Free School, and forgot about them. She also put away the bicycle in one of the Begam Kothi's many godowns, but since walking was evidently difficult for her nowadays she got about in a bath chair. Her favourite route no longer lay along the Lower Trotter Road but the other way, past the Ice Gate and the New Armoury, through a passage at the elbow of the Comb, around past the Steps and down, rolling the last stretch through the Water Gate, to the Tank. There she disappeared into a bathing-machine that stood among the toddy-palms at the edge of the water. Many lumbering minutes later she emerged on the other side, hidden from view, and slipped heavily into the water. She spent hours together in the Tank, buoyant and streaming, grateful to be freed at last from the crushing gravity of land. Nobody was allowed to come near during those hours, but ever since the bicycle there had been no dearth of theories. Once the young Kahn-Trotters playing on the other side were startled to see a white waterspout shooting into the air at intervals across the green surface of the Tank. They told Alex about it and for some time he toyed with the notion of a cinematic *Moby Dick* with Mr Montagu as a pale Captain Ahab. But then war broke out in Europe.

The historian was against it. Unlike the European, Hegel, who saw in war the mainspring of history, Theobald Horatius Montagu was a pacifist (*Peacemonger, Beige Funk*). The war was simply another example of the barbarity of a supposedly civilized people who now wished to entangle the rest of the world. Victoria thought differently, and so did the railway Victors' sons who volunteered to a man. All over India their relatives were enlisting in thousands and being shipped off to the Levant and Europe. A Trotter accounted for the first zeppelin brought down in England while another brought down the first zeppelin over France; fatal balloons, one way or the other, seemed to run in the Trotter blood. Young Paul was among the first to enlist, even though he felt responsible enough for the swelling in Suchita's belly to wait around until a boy who looked nothing like Alex was born. The girl-plague at any rate was ended, and not too soon either. Eight out of ten Anglo-Indian men of fighting age left their wives and sweethearts and marched with jerky steps not unlike Alex's onto the troop ships.

Alex was not among them. He was just beginning to count himself lucky to have been sent daughters when the boy, Cedric, was born. Stung, he made a documentary called *Cannon-Fodder*, which was immediately impounded, although even if the censors had let it through it would not have been a box-office hit. Unlike the average war documentarist of the time, Alex refused to fake battle scenes: his film consisted of twenty minutes of uniformed men marching jerkily past a stationary camera. It proved to be his last. The public was not ready for avant-garde statements on the screen. Once, in a moment of weakness, he was tempted to make a romantic feature using little Pearl, the fair one of Victoria's twins, but thought better of it; experience had made him wary of starlets. They did a few takes, and the girl was clearly a natural, but *Pearl of the Orient* was never finished. For the rest of the war he showed other people's films in a rented hall in Hazratganj called the Odeum. With Peter at the piano the show sometimes started late, but both made a satisfactory living. When the war ended, a documentary of the soldiers coming back would not have lasted ten minutes. Among those who failed to return were numerous Trotters who in the moment of their death were transformed into Britons. Their records and posthumous awards stated, concisely, "Born in India."

Young Paul did come back. He had seen active service in Mesopotamia with the Medical Corps, performing operations of Jesuitical complexity under canvas with his customary rate of success. His hand was as steady under fire as it was when he went boar-hunting at home, and he came back with a commendation, glowing. It was indecent, some people said, the way his success succeeded. Then he applied for membership of the Nakhlau Club (where Thos. Henry had been admitted) and was blackballed. "There is another club," he was told, "for Anglo-Indians; go there." His father might have spared him the humiliation had he known. "When it suits them we're British," he said, "when it doesn't, there is another club." What nettled him most about his own potential exclusion was that, despising clubs, he would never have wished to join in the first place. There was no way he could demonstrate his indifference—and now here was a son of his who had actually applied! It was beyond belief. The other Trotters who had returned from the war to their Railway Institute and the Residency Club behind the 'Ganj simply nodded their heads and smiled as if to say he should have known better: the bullet that might have turned Young Paul British had missed its mark, and that was that. He should think himself fortunate to be alive. Even Suchita the starlet, who was happy to have him back, scolded him for applying. "What you want to do there," she said, rubbing his temples, "that you can't do here?" But the headache would not go away. "I'll Balkanize him!" he said through his teeth, meaning the blackballer. His temper was already famous, and it was made no better when he realized that his position as luminary of the community to which he did belong was being threatened by a competitor.

Things had moved on while he was away in Mesopotamia. Under the leadership of a man called Gidney-Trotter, the various Anglo-Indian associations around the country had agreed to come together. They had been joined, moreover, by another remnant, called the Domiciled European community because they no longer had any family ties with Europe, who had for years kept to themselves. The merged Anglo-Indian and Domiciled European Association of India was now lobbying for the entire community at a time when the British were listening to the needs of minorities. "A ploy," Mr Montagu warned. "You play off minorities against the majority and prolong an unjust rule." Young Paul remembered a lesson taught him out of a Globe geometry box long ago. He had often wondered afterward about the protractor. Now that its use was becoming clearer, he wondered whether it wasn't time to do some geometry of his own. As a boy he had spent much time sharpening pencils, but invariably broke the lead with one twist too many. The Nakhlau Club had been that extra twist, and yet he suspected that success might still be snatched from the jaws of a small defeat. As usual he was right.

He did a tour of Calcutta and saw poverty among the Anglo-Indians there. He made notes on the housing question; in some slums there were whole families to a single room. He wrote letters to the national papers describing what he saw and what he would like to see. Coming from an eye-specialist, such views were bound to interest. He quickly got a following and began to address gatherings in Anglo-Indian clubs and Railway Institutes across the country, from Simla to the Kolar Gold Fields, from Bombay to Rangoon. He was humble with the lowly, breezy with the daft, solemn with widows who wanted more housie because they had missed the full house last time by a measly "Legs, 11." He terminated his long and energetic bachelorhood by finding a Domiciled European wife in the famous Belle of Bangalore. "Such a nice-looking couple!" people sighed, although Young Paul had lost much of his fat. It was already the Anglo-Indian shibboleth: a couple was either nice-looking or they were not. They spun around dance floors together, shimmying on talcum powder, gliding on a silver note. It was a coup: Young Paul had staged a merger of his own, more palpable than that Gidney-Trotter's. The blackball was forgotten and he began to glow again. His partner, too, would be glowing from a dance, but when they went up for the prize Young Paul took the opportunity to make a campaign speech in which every sentence began with *I*. The next year he was elected without serious opposition and his acceptance speeches showed his syntax had not changed. In the years to come his speeches were so liberally laced with *I*'s that a disgruntled faction from Calcutta began to call him the I-Specialist. It was a label that caught on just when Gandhi arrived on the scene.

For weeks Mr Montagu and Alex had one topic of conversation. The small frail Indian just come from South Africa had stopped in Nakhlau and addressed a gathering in Aminabad Park. The rally was well attended, though the only ones there from Sans Souci were Alex and Mr Montagu—and Eustace, Sixth Trotter, on horseback and in uniform. He had kept his promise about joining the police. Few beyond the front row could hear the speaker, but he made a profound impression by his simple presence.

"Here," Mr Montagu said, "is the man we have been waiting for."

"That scrawny little thing!" Victoria sniffed when she saw Alex's photograph of the man. "Like a cross between a spider and a bat."

"My dear!" Mr Montagu glanced at his own legs. "The country needs precisely such a man." When he was on the defensive he put in a *precisely*.

His wife looked assessingly at him. "There are enough funny little men in this country," she said, "to go letting in South Africans and all."

And she went off to the Tank. Immersed in the mottled grey-green waters, she pondered this fever called politics which seemed to have the men around her in its grip. She thought of the man called Gandhi. What did he want—what did he have to offer? It seemed self-evident to her that if a man must enter politics and court the public's favour, he should be nice-looking. Like, she had to admit, Young Paul. She sent up a spumy jet and dove deep down. Perhaps she had been wrong about her second son, just as she had been deceived in her first. There was after all something appealing in Young Paul's prosperous, well-fed (at least when compared with the other) deportment. A natural leader, he got things done. He had promised to clean things up, and there were devilish things in Sans Souci—moving pictures, electric fans, strange discordant music from the tea-house—that wanted cleaning up. Something in Young Paul's scrubbed manly looks suggested that he meant business. He had, in the midst of all his politics, found time to shoot a crocodile that had strayed into the Tank during the recent flooding of the Moti Ganga river. He kept the military museum, once dust-ridden, spotless (so it was said), oiling and cleaning the weapons there with joyful diligence. And with his dutiful wife, the Belle of Bangalore, he had produced a nice-looking boy, Marris, who was baptised in boiled water and caused a sensation by wailing in italics.

Back from her swim, Victoria went to hang out her towel to dry on the clothesline which, like most things since the bath chair, from hat-racks to sideboards, had had to be lowered to her level. There on the line, conveniently at her height for examination, but just where her towel normally hung, stretched a long white piece of homespun cloth. Victoria frowned.

"I thought the table-cloths went to the dhobi yesterday."

Mr Montagu came to the rescue. "They did, my dear. That is my dhoti."

From the railway track beyond the cemetery there came the distant clang of loose shunting.

"Your what?"

"Dhoti, my dear. It's a kind of—"

"I *know* what a dhoti is. What I want to know is, what you intend to do with this one."

"Well, my dear, I could sit on it and fly to Arabia."

"Very funny. What are you going to do with it?"

"Well, *wear* it, of course. Alex—"

"You wear that table-cloth and I'll leave this house."

"But my dear, it—the Mahatma—"

"My-dear, fy-dear nothing. You heard me. This is not an Indian house."

But the matter did not rest there. Mr Montagu insisted that the garment be given a trial before being thrown out. He invited one of his Congress friends over to show him how the thing was tied. When it was on he walked stiffly up and down the verandah, his pale calves twinkling in the dusk.

"Very fine, Sir, very fine!"

"You flatter me, Nigam Sahib!"

"Flatter!"

"Yes!"

Mr Montagu took another turn, pleased.

"I think he does flatter you."

It sounded like Victoria, but she was nowhere to be seen. She may have been behind the fly-screened double doors. Left in the dark, the two men grew apprehensive. The historian knew Victoria; his friend had heard. Mr Montagu sighed and began to loosen the tuck of the dhoti. He was no longer young.

"Well. Sorry for the trouble, Nigam Sahib."

"Trouble!" Mr Nigam shook his head gleefully. Then he added: "But I suppose the shirt is not correct."

"Not correct."

"And then the mosquitoes."

"The mosquitoes."

"And the general discomfort."

"The general discomfort."

"Unpleasantness . . ."

"Too much . . ."

"We will meet tomorrow, then?"

"Tomorrow."

"Sir!"

"Sahib!"

At dinner Mr Montagu ate determinedly, fortifying himself. It was a fish fricassee, Victoria's favourite, with mashed potatoes, mashed pumpkin, and mutilated spinach. There was a caramel custard afterwards, which Hope saw at once was not burnt enough. Wines were a thing of the past, ever since the ice crashed, but there was ice for the water. The twins were squabbling as usual, while the older sisters, who showed no restlessness though they had lived at home for upwards of thirty years, were set more than ever in the mould of the Maiden Aunts. Dulcie, who normally filled the gap, was in

England on a music scholarship. The girls ate their chosen portions, rejecting this, heaping up that, while their father for once tried everything. The only male at the family table, he was accustomed to the glassy treble concert of female voices into which would enter from time to time Victoria's sombre whinny, crossing immense distances, it seemed, like the call of the great whales. It was only when he was pressing the napkin to his lips that Mr Montagu realized his wife had not spoken throughout the meal. Then he looked across at her plate and saw that she had not eaten. She caught the glance, a child pouncing on attention long overdue.

"Yes!" she bayed, stirred to an unknown depth by her sacrifice. If no one noticed she would risk the ignominy of display. Pride was not her sin. "Yes. Was it good? Had your fill? Done well? Some more pumpkin? A little more fricassee?" Her broad lower lip trembled at the word.

Mr Montagu refused to be drawn.

"No? *No! No* more spinach? Are you sure?"

It was still a dispute between husband and wife, and the girls' chatter went on. But Victoria meant to widen the action.

"*No*body for more?"

The chatter continued.

"Very strange. Funny. One minute we're *all* gobbling away and the next we haven't got room even for this tiny little bit of fish that's left in the dish. Of course, if I'm making too much I can always tell Chotey Lal to cut down. On everything. He gets his share anyway. *He*'s not greedy. Sits there on the ground and eats with his hands. Maybe we too should be sitting on the ground! Why are we sitting at the table? Maybe some people would like to eat with their fingers. Why not get some brass thalis and little-little bowls from Suresh and sit on the ground and eat and do don't know what-all like Indians. No more fricassee for dinner. Curry and rice like at lunch—only sitting on the ground and making little wet-wet balls with our fingers. Yes. Let's lock up all the cutlery. Sell the table. Just keep the cloth. For wearing. Easy to sit on the ground when you're wearing a table-cloth. Even if the cloth doesn't cover, doesn't cover—everything. Who cares? And if you don't know how to tie it, get some Congress pan-wala to show you. Maybe even one who's come from South Africa with all the latest fashions. Yes. Maybe this Gandhi will come and show some people how to tie their table-cloths personally. And then we can all sit on the ground and spin cotton and eat with our fingers and do what-not and serve the country, no? And read fat-fat books about how bad England is and talk don't know what-all kinds of seditiousness about the King. And give away our nice china and all—no, break it up, and make a bonfire with our foreign cloth. In fact, break up everything. What about those funny-funny English records? And the gramophone—that's English. Don't know why some people want to listen to all these English things. Why don't they get a Japanese gramophone if Japan's such a great country? No. Just cheap English goods, no? Maybe I better go and start throwing out some of those records. They're only English . . ."

Her chair scraped back, but at that moment there came a crash at the opposite end of the table. Mr Montagu had brought his fist down beside his plate. The girls' chatter was instantly silenced by this unusual display. The ice in the ice-bucket settled a little. Pearl and Ruby stopped quarrelling and looked at their father. The crash surprised Mr Montagu himself, and having got his audience he did not know what to do with it. Prudence, who liked to help out at such moments, could think of nothing to say. Mr Montagu shifted his feet; the floor seemed to have risen alarmingly under him. He cleared his throat. It was plain that he must justify his energy; he could hardly speak of his record collection, though he had meant to say that they were German, the music was German. He found himself saying, in a louder voice than usual: "I would follow the Mahatma to my death!"

Victoria stared at him unimpressed, the yellow lights on in her eyes.

"Maybe," she conceded, unwilling to pursue the theoretical. "But if you wear that table-cloth in public, I'll never eat another mouthful again."

She was close to tears, but it was a statement, not a threat (*Heroic Matron, Ultimate Sanction*).

The next day Mr Montagu gave away the dhoti. But he kept the gramophone, and there were times when he played the Haydn Trumpet Concerto late at night outside Victoria's room though he would rather have been in bed himself, asleep. He never forgot the moral muscle of his wife's declaration—was it moral?—and once suggested at a local Congress party meeting that here perhaps, in the hunger strike, was a useful political instrument. There was nothing like it in the Globe geometry boxes from Britain. But by that time Gandhi was a long way off and the idea was squashed.

Mr Narrator, pardon me, but are we ever going to progress beyond the age of history?

Restless Cup, stolen drink has pickled your brain. Or how could you have missed two generations, the one after history and the one after that? Decadence began fifty pages ago, and after that—

Is there life after decadence, Narrator?

There is not only life—but bring me the sweetest maraschino and you shall see.

Three ages side by side?

That is called a synchronicle.

A sin chronicle, Narrator?

The maraschino, my impatient Cup. You are not yet ready for self-rule. Now. I
have heard from the peacock that it happened in this way.

(CHRONICLE RESUMED)

The next year Pearl disappeared. She had grown impatient with Alex's
progress on the film that was to make her the child star of the East: already
her childhood was behind her. The Free School had been a terrible bore,
except once a year when they put on *Trial by Jury*. Then she was in her
element, the leading lady who better than any of the cast could keep the
clipped Anglo-Indian accent out of her solos. A wild beautiful girl, she had
elbows like watered silk and a neck like a white swan's. Her chest, quite
unswanlike, was always a worry, but on stage it could be plumped up, and
she sometimes left the stuffing in when the show was over. In the large old
days, with old Rose (*Buxom Confectioner, Gulbadan*), there had never been any
question of *suppressio veri*; with Pearl it was more than often a case of *suggestio
falsi*. Then there was the Alpine Snow which she applied as if she could never
have enough. Talcum powder for her downy neck, half limes for her elbows,
scents, creams, rouges blossomed on the dressing table as rapidly as Hope
confiscated them. When the dreaded blue moons appeared on her nails, a
chain of cigarettes smoked in the cemetery by the railway tracks turned them
yellow. Finally she disappeared, leaving a jar of vanishing cream for Ruby,
her twin-and-enemy. Ruby said (and everybody knew) she had gone to Bombay. Victoria, who wished she had taken an interest in the child sooner, baffled
the curious with a confounding dictum. "She is," she pronounced, "a girl of
unimpregnable virtue."

Two weeks later, Pearl sent a postcard with the Gateway of India on it
from a Colaba address. It was a tissue of plans and relayed promises. She had
met a gentleman who was very handsome and very kind and very good who
was going to take her to England very soon. Then she wrote from another
address about a film in which she had a part that might lead to another part
in another film. Neither her father nor her brothers must come to get her, she
warned, because very shortly she planned to move again. This time it would
definitely be to England, where the studios were much better. The Maiden
Aunts shook their heads and looked pained. Beauty apparently had its pen-
alties, and great beauty must suffer soonest. Their own faces were of the
enduring kind, rescued from plainness by a serenity that each one privately
could tap but which they sometimes squandered on collective judgements.
Bombay, even London, held no charms for them: the Botanical Gardens, the
zoo across the Ganda Nala, the Provincial Museum, the local Anglo-Indian
girls' school, employed them, and they returned every day to the Begam Kothi

where they sat in a row on mondhas, looking out across the arid Sea of Tranquillity—Dulcie's chair, as before, at a short remove from the rest. Back from England, Dulcie was the only one who troubled with her hair, which she wore permanently set in the scalariform style of Albert Hall divas. When Pearl's last letter arrived she sympathized but closed the gap a little between her mondha and the rest, at the same time looking uncertainly the other way to where her remaining younger sister was shelling peas. Ruby would never disappear, but she was, no doubt about it, the marrying kind.

One day the British Other Ranks came. They came, three of them, a sergeant-major, a corporal, and a private, having heard Mr Montagu speak at a meeting in the city. Their mission as Fabians was to assure the historian that not all Europeans were bad, and that some—including soldiers—believed in independence for India. Mr Montagu received them seated beneath the picture of Toussaint and listened with one ear. He had not stopped collecting anti-European tracts any more than he had given up buying European records. He was about to usher the men to the door when Victoria appeared there, an idea illuminating her ordinarily sombre face. She had had enough of the Haydn Trumpet Concerto and had hit upon a piece of revenge that was economical, regular—even punctual—and did not need to be wound up each time like a gramophone. It was moreover productive (and not only of noise) without recourse to complicated wiring. Victoria's fear of any machine more sophisticated than a bicycle had not abated. (Thirty years after they were installed, she refused to sleep under one of Mr Montagu's electric fans: the magnets, she was sure, would twist her dreams, and besides the fan shaft with its vicious spike did rather resemble a harpoon.) The present scheme involved no mechanical device, yet it would work like clockwork.

"There," she pointed, and although Mr Montagu refused to lift a finger, work on the chicken coop was begun that same day. Ruby was already clearing the ground; even before Pearl ran away she was the family workhorse. But today she had help: the Other Ranks in a demonstration of good faith had rolled up their sleeves and got down to work. The old fowl run in the Comb, which had been started by the egg-brahmin, Sunya, and revived by Philippa, was not near enough. The new one would stand just behind the Begam Kothi, between the glasshouse and the sprawling thickets of lantana that had grown up outside Mr Montagu's bedroom. It would take the shape of a long low bunker reinforced with iron (at last a use was found for Philip the Baptist's twelve cow-catchers), cemented outside and plastered in, with vents along the arched roof and a low door at either end. The job was hot and heavy, with the result that first the sergeant and then the corporal stayed away. For the plastering, Ruby had only one helper, the private, Thomas Atkins. A week after they went in, there was nothing to show for it; by the end of the month they had still made no progress, and yet to judge from the sounds that came out of the vents it was hard going. All through the summer, work inched along while Victoria sported in the Tank sending up blissful jets of water. It was September before the first fowls were let in, together with a cock that crew, dependable as a muezzin, at five o'clock in the morning, an hour whose existence Mr Montagu had hitherto been content to take on faith. To Victoria, an early riser, the sound was music, though she would have liked to get at the eggs. Ruby, whom she had counted on, was no help. Her belly had grown so big that to crawl through the hatch was beyond her, while her husband (they were married in the cantonment church at the height of summer), once the laziest soldier in the British army, did not wish to lower his standards in retirement. Afterwards, when they were living in what was left of the old Elephant Wing, and Ruby had four sons to care for and was working as a nurse in the civil hospital besides, Thomas Atkins could be found with his feet up on the henhouse, lolling under the laburnum tree that had grown up there, his face lit with the glow from the long lanterns of yellow blossom, his lips in an O as he whistled a familiar vacant tune from back home which he embellished with trills of terrifying jollity. He was too lazy to invent even the hammock. A mongoose got the eggs; then, growing bold, it got the hens. The plastering was never finished—for that matter it might never have been begun. It was too dark inside to tell, and besides, Thomas Atkins submitted, who ever heard of plastering the inside of a henhouse? Already, as was inevitable at Sans Souci, a hyphen had appeared after his surname, a burden he thought quite sufficient. In time Thomas Atkins-Trotter came to be simply Tat, for Ruby. He in turn called her, with some justice, Tit, preferring that to her own acronym because he was actually fond of her.

Things had not gone well at the Odeum in Hazratganj ever since the brothers Uberoi opened the Fanfare picture house next door. The Fanfare was new, had a bright foyer, padded seats, and a chrome refreshment stand where the prices were twice those at the Odeum. People started to go there instead, and others came just to watch them. For beggars and rickshawmen, who were never allowed to gather outside, it was enough to catch a passing glimpse of the electric chandeliers. Seeing the writing on the wall, Alex sold out and took his pianist across the road to where a new restaurant had opened. The Coral Gables was in need of a manager and Alex, the old charm working, got the job. He decided at once that if the restaurant was to succeed it must have a dance floor and if it had a dance floor it must have a band. Then it could expect to attract not only the British and visiting Europeans but Anglo-Indians and some modern Anglicized Indians as well. Peter was approving. After many near-misses he had discovered, barely a month after it was invented in New Orleans, jazz. Formerly, as a moving-picture pianist at the Odeum, he had found the changes of mood too many and too quick; one barely began to develop a theme when the scene changed. With the new music it was different, the melody either clinging or convulsive, but amenable to elaboration, not to speak of moody improvisation. He advertised for players and found numerous applicants among the Fonseca-Trotters: it was scandalous how many clarinets and trombones you were starting to find in the city of the shehnai. They rehearsed fox-trots, rumbas, and rags for two days and two nights to the general astonishment of the waiters, until on the third night their black-and-white lounge suits were ready. The lights went up, Peter took an unsteady bow, and Nakhlau (or that portion of it that could pay) was treated to the spectacle of an Anglo-Indian band playing Afro-American music for a clientele that included Oriental Jews and resident Armenians. At one table sat the Parsi taxidermist who had abandoned his father's profession, and his wife; at the next was stationed a burly Panjabi civilian in a Bond St suit of archaic cut; the other tables propped up a miscellany of sad Sahibs. On Saturdays there were working Trotters who ordered a drink and nursed it through the night. Peter, who didn't have to pay, rested a glass on either side of the keyboard. He was regularly deposited outside the tea-house at Sans Souci at three in the morning, insensible, but sometimes he slept in the restaurant, his forehead resting on the black keys so that he woke up with a corrugation on it like a sinister caste-mark. That was how he came to miss the delivery of his second son, Albert, born three decades after Eustace.

The birth carried Lucia off, and Albert went through life with a matricide's conscience. Because his arrival was unexpected, a midwife could not be found. Eustace, who was home on leave, ran to the Begam Kothi for help, but the Maiden Aunts were of no use. Finally, Victoria heaved herself into the bath chair and grumbled: "Where's this tea-house?" It was a major concession; until that moment the tea-house had not existed. Eustace propelled her there at high speed, swinging the chair up the three steps from the lawn by main force. In the middle of the circular room was a bed. On the bed lay Lucia in labour. For the first time since the girl came to Sans Souci, Victoria looked at her and took her hand. A middle-aged woman smiled back. "Today I cannot make for you the tea," she said. Victoria patted her hand and took out the old bag which in the spirit days had held everything necessary. It was all still there. Lucia seemed to be waiting for Peter, but at three o'clock Albert pushed his way into the world and eased his mother out of it. Victoria released the lifeless hand and laid it across the other on Lucia's chest. Then she smoothed the sheets, cleaned off Albert's tiny anguished-monkey's face with the fly-whisk, and took him back with her to the Begam Kothi. Eustace went along, ostensibly to wheel the bath chair back, but he had taken up his one boyhood relic, the junior hockey stick, and carried it with him. He went to the Coral

Gables to call his father, but the pianist had already left. When Peter entered the tea-house there was no one to warn him.

At first he thought it was a hallucination, his wife lying there composed on the bed. He shook her once. The body yielded to his pressure, but when he withdrew his hand she was still. The shock reduced everything to one object, the woman on the bed; then there was a consciousness which could say, "She is dead." That person began to whimper, his own body growing faint and unreal. One part of him stood inert; another part, where anger was growing, had begun to break things. There was little enough that had survived past rages, but this time he did it thoroughly: the chairs, the table, the pictures, a cupboard, two cups, the four willow-pattern saucers, Eustace's bed, a shaving mirror. He emptied the one trunk onto the floor and kicked the piles of sheet-music about, deliberately, in no hurry. He got under the Erard piano, lifted it up, carried it to the door, and rammed it through. The wood splintered as it struck the bottom step and he saw the splinters come up white through the varnish. On the lawn where it fell a black lung of sound rose up, filled to bursting, and disintegrated into points of light. The breaking part of him went out to the custard-apple and pelted the piano until all the fruit was gone and creamy blotches slid down the black legs. Then he went back in and joined the other part that stood defeated among the broken things. She was still lying there, the bed a miracle of calm untouched by the wreckage. He whispered, "Lucia." She sat up and looked at him. But when he crossed to her she was lying there as before.

They buried her in the tea-house, taking up the bricks in the floor and replacing them, when she was interred, with a many-coloured mosaic of bits of broken china set in cement. The work was supervised by Victoria, who chose a pattern that she said was Italian. Not long after the workmen went away, china-mosaic floors became the vogue in the houses of the new gentry in Nakhlau, but it was a rare householder who buried an Italian underneath. At Sans Souci there were now two Italians singularly interred, but most people had long ago forgotten about Signor Marazzi sealed up in the music pavilion. Peter's band found itself another pianist, a teetotal Fonseca-Trotter, added a domiciled West Indian Negro saxophonist from the Third Lane in Calcutta, and changed its name from the Salt and Pepper Saraband to Ferdy Fonseca's Oriental Swing Band. Their reputation spread to Delhi, where a hotel offered them twice as much as Alex could afford, and they were replaced by a two-man team whose morale was not improved by a new piece of slang that came back from the capital: *to Fonseca, to have Fonsecaed, let us Fonseca this night away*.

Peter hung around Sans Souci for a month or two, sleeping at the Kahn-Trotters' and smelling of petrol, until one day he turned to Alex and shook his hand solemnly. "There's room for one more here, men," Alex said. Suchi nodded formally; she would rather have had the other brother stay. But Peter lowered his eyes and walked off to the railway track. He must have followed it west as far as Charbagh Station, because one of the railway Victors, a guard, afterwards swore he had seen him on a goods train carrying tinsel to Bombay. Another Victor, a ticket-collector in Bombay, said yes, he had let him through on a Nakhlau platform ticket. There were reports that he had formed another band in the big city; conflicting accounts had him working in a distillery; still others claimed he had reformed and opened, with the help of the Salvation Army, a tea stall. The truth was that he had joined a band on a ship bound eventually for New Orleans and sailed across the Pacific and through the Panama Canal. At Veracruz he had got drunk in a sleazy hotel and failed to come back on board; when he did find another ship going his way he got drunk on board and failed to go ashore. The ship left New Orleans for Rio de Janeiro and Buenos Aires. In Argentina he was taken for a Hindu and denied entry by an old statute. He took a ferry to Montevideo, where he passed himself off as a Greek and was allowed in. On his first Saturday there he died in a barroom, falling backwards over the bar-stool and choking on his vomit because his foot stuck in the footrail and the other customers were too drunk to notice. He was buried the next day, Easter Sunday, at the edge of the Indian cemetery in an unmarked grave.

The day Peter walked off towards the railway track Alex went back to the dressing room and looked in the mirror. He was, he decided, getting on. It was no longer possible to blame the crazing of the mirror silver. The fact was that under each eye there had appeared a pouch like a coin-purse finely netted with wrinkles. The eyes themselves were dull four-anna bits and the slack oval mouth, though wet and pink along the slightly jutting lower lip, was cracked and dry at the corners. The folds of his neck were puckered like the skin on boiled milk. No doubt about it, he was getting on. His daughters, Sulekha and Anita of the little Japanese kimonos, had children of their own. Sulekha, married to a Massey, had a boy, Reuben; Anita, married to a Hebron, had a girl, Soma; the two cousins (*Bathsheban Beauty; Babylonish Beast*) were old enough to laugh at their jerky grandfather. Something must be done. Not that it mattered to his ex-actress wife Suchita, who was beset by ageing problems of her own. (Alex knew that she continued to receive Young Paul when he was away at the restaurant, and he more than suspected that Cedric, bookish and flabby, was not his son.) It was for himself that he must act. He bought a new electroplated mirror and sent for an electrician who put in nine sockets around it on the wall and fitted each with a 40-watt bulb. Suchita took it as a gift, if an ambivalent one, and for a day or two she rubbed up against him and cooed: "You won't work on *Pearl of the Orient* again—promise?"

With Pearl six thousand miles away in England it sounded a bit thin. Then Suchita found her cosmetics starting to drain away. A bottle of almond oil, newly opened one week, was gone by the next. In the bathroom the cap was sometimes left off the bottle of hair dye. The sloping point on the lipstick had been blunted by a heavy hand. And every day Alex looked younger. The jerkiness went out of his movements, and although the colour had not yet properly come back into his clothes, there were days when the shock of his electric blue tie could be felt across a crowded room. One afternoon, as he stood managerially in the door of the Coral Gables and looked across the street at his old cinema house, he found that six workmen were lifting into place a gigantic signboard that was to join the existing one, put there by himself. The old one read, in blue and yellow, ODEUM; the new one, painted in matching letters, said: TALKIES. "That'll give those Fanfare buggers a scare," he thought, and noticed the passersby looking strangely at him. He went quickly back inside because he realized that for the first time in years he had spoken out loud.

Pearl arrived in London just in time for the talkies. Unlike her drunken older brother-and-failed priest, she had no trouble finding her destination: the Pine-wood Studios were her destiny. She was taken there by an important person who on the voyage home had preferred to keep his name confidential. Lord Greenham introduced her to an up-and-coming director in need of a swan-necked, raven-haired maiden for his projected *Dracula*. The part made no unreasonable demands on her talent: Pearl had simply to lie there and be bitten. People wanted a little blood, the director declared; it had been a long peace. The shot was tastefully done, with two tiny pomegranate seeds set like a jewelled clasp on Pearl's toothsome neck. It was a sensation. People fought bloody battles for tickets, and for months afterwards biting and being bitten were the rage. The next year Pearl took elocution lessons, and the year after that she made her first talkie. She took the script to heart, agonizing over the crucial scene in front of a mirror lit with twenty-nine 60-watt bulbs. Should she say: "*Ricardo!*" or "*Ricardo?*" That was the question. Then again, she might say, "*Ricardo!!*" or even "*Ricardo.*" In the end she said simply, "*Ricardo—*" and fell into his arms. It was a triumph of understatement; war clouds were threatening and people were tired of histrionics. After that, when people had nothing to say they said "*Ricardo—*" and fell into each other's arms. Pearl had her choice of films and contracts. In one year she made forty titles. Hollywood moguls, viscounts, Texas tycoons paid court to her in Belgravia. Unable to decide, she accepted them all. The last recorded duel in St James Park was fought over her; both parties recovered, but Pearl was already in California making *The Desert Queen*, falling in love with the landscape and deciding to stay. The only roles she refused outright were Eastern ones: even Sheba and Scheherazade were given to someone else, a blonde. When a friend, quite innocently, suggested a romance to be called *Pearl of the Orient*, she fainted away. And, unlike Alex back home, she was not looking forward to the coming of colour. Ah! if the world were an endless black-and-white picture! She sighed and shifted in her milk bath and was tempted to take a little sip. She hated this Eastman. Absently she rubbed her elbows with half-limes, an old habit; when she climbed out of the bath she was disgusted to find her entire body covered with milk clots. Things began to go wrong. That day she refused a B-grade Californian cowboy hero she had starred with in *The Log Cabin* because he said his first love was politics. Next she absentmindedly put phenyl in her bath instead of milk and broke out in a rash. There were chinks in her accent; colour was imminent; milk prices shot up. With the future looking impervious, Mr Montagu's daughter turned her talents to re-shaping the past. She took down an atlas from her custom-filled shelves and turned the crisp pages till she came to a map of the world. At length she found India, in pink, jutting like an accusing finger. What place on earth was farthest from there—farther even than California? Looking down into the Southern Hemisphere, she found two dots, also in pink, just off the coast of Argentina. The next day she called her agent and showed him exactly where she had been born. He said: "Jeez!" and read just above her yellow fingernail: "The Falkland Is, eh?" A Canadian himself. Then he remembered a letter that had arrived for her, from India. When he had gone, she opened it and read it at a glance. It was short enough. It said:

I KNOW YOU—RUBY

She had forgotten about Ruby. Ruby, the forgettable plodder with—now that she came to think of her—spectacular bunions and elbows like thimbles. As for that monstrous pair of yams her twin had developed at fourteen, well, sometimes one was grateful for small mercies. But what could she want? Surely she was married by now and provided for by some unfortunate rail-wayman with coal-dust under his fingernails and a handkerchief cap on his head? Finding her level. Kiddies, naturally—for those yams, six at the very least. So what was she after? To be on the safe side Pearl enclosed a hundred dollars in an envelope and addressed it to her sister at Sans Souci, Nakhlau, India. At Christmas she got a card: "From Ruby, Tat, and the boys (Thomas, Richard, Harold, and Ian) with *many* thanks." So that was that. For Pearl herself, children were out of the question. It was what had put Mr Ranger, the cowboy hero, on his guard even before she turned him down, though it was only interest that made him ask: "Don't they make 'em down Falk-lands way?" Actually he was happy enough on the range with his other Indian friend, and found her horror too obscure for his liking. Then came another letter which said:

FALKLANDS MY FOOT——RUBY

When it came to asking, three words seemed to be Ruby's limit. Pearl sent another hundred dollars, and back at Christmas came the cheery card. The pattern was set for years to come.

Colour arrived at last, and the directors' eyes were opened. They began to look elsewhere, knocking so rarely at Pearl's door that the house in Beverly Hills got the feel of a fake front in a studio set. Her latest husband was hardly ever at home. Sometimes she almost wished she had someone from over there to talk to—not Ruby, for sure, and probably not her other sisters either, the boring Maiden Aunts. But, maybe, Victoria. She wondered whether her mother might not be persuaded to come out on a long visit. Not *as* her mother, naturally: that, like children, was out of the question, with a mother as black as that. She could come as a companion or even as a maid. What was the Indian word? *Ayah.* Expense was no consideration, milk baths notwithstanding. The other day she had paid twenty dollars for a single mango so she could have a secret taste of home. The vendor, a Mexican, assured her that it came from India when she asked, and she believed him. There were some truths you could create if you simply believed in them hard enough.

The mango

Some (the Nakhlau School, for example) maintain that there is nothing that does not concern the mango, but others divide the world into that which concerns the mango and that which does not. The emperor Babar in his excellent work, the *Babar-Nama* (in some places it is quite dull), has many just observations on the king of fruit, but fails to rank the various kinds according to their merits—perhaps because he prefers the melon. Only the prejudiced would fail to agree that the Nakhlau *dasheri* mango is the king of kings. By all accounts, the United Provinces (formerly Tirnab) are the *dasheri* heartland with the heart of hearts in Malihabad, a mere two stations by train from here. They are brought here in the first instance, and thus Nakhlau is the mango capital of the world. The delicate *dasheri* is the sweetest of luscious fruits. It is yellow outside when ripe, the skin being thin and the seed flat so that the flesh between them is succulent. Two cuts with a knife make two cheeks and a seed. Mangoes are fine. Great care must be taken. It is of the cashew family, which is the richest and best of nuts. The flesh is also yellow.

Eaten before the first rains (or mango showers) boils appear, but prickly heat is worse. The blossoms are in April or May, depending. My brother, Eustace, knows where the best groves are. They are excellent plain, but not tinned, though my uncle, who is a specialist, says they are just as good from Manila in light syrup. This is doubtful. Those who say they grow in Mexico are great liars. Soak them well because of the bitterness like turpentine at the ~~nipple~~ head. ~~In classical poetry, breasts~~ Mangoes are a handsome fruit. They are best eaten by the dozen, but they are sold by weight. Fingers will do, by means of peeling, but then you must have a basin of water ready in advance. Sucking mangoes are cheaper. They are called *chusnis*. They are just as sweet as *dasheris*, but barbaric apparently. The emperor Babar preferred melons. He ruled from   to   . He was driven from pillar to post. Last summer we had mango ice cream twice. Pale ice cream is infinitely better than Uberoi's factory near the 'Ganj. For that you need saltpetre, sacking, and ice.* My grandmother smells of vanilla, from a Maxwell's Compound bottle, nevertheless the mango is the king of fruits. Some prefer it green with salt and pepper, but they are beyond the pail. You must wash your hands scrupulously afterwards or else the baby is thrown out with the bathwater. In short, the mango is the non-parallel, nutritious, and the *summum bonum*.

(*CHRONICLE RESUMED*)

Albert was precocious, but lacked stamina. His intelligence was of the order his headmaster was already beginning to call unsteady, and the boy hardly ten. At first his essays were read out to the class as models of restless enquiry; later they became examples of undirected energy and came back marked *Erratic* in blue, a colour he hated. There was no balance in him, his teachers complained: he would alight on a subject and find it momentarily engrossing—then he was off in a flash of wings. He knew a little about everything, from the desert fathers to the aurora borealis, but his eyes were always elsewhere. He made an impressive start but suddenly petered out; his father coming out in him, people said. People said a lot: it was the Anglo-Indian vice. Some said he would go on to university one day; others said he would go to the madhouse; everybody said it was his parents. What could you expect from a failed priest-and-itinerant piano tuner who ended up (it was said) in East Africa, and an Italian slut who (it was said) lasted six weeks in a nunnery? It didn't matter that the boy had no memory of either parent, having been brought up in the Begam Kothi by Victoria and the Maiden Aunts.

* Not to speak of sugar, cream, and milk, blended with eggs, mangoes, and patience. Penalty marks.—E.A.T.

His brother, Eustace the policeman, old enough to be his father, taught him to track and shoot, let him ride his horse, and showed him which were the best mango trees. Their rambles were invariably too long and on the way back Eustace ended up carrying his brother as a kind of delayed penance, keeping an eye peeled for blind wells and listening carefully as Albert gabbled on into his good ear. It was hockey that eventually separated them. Albert played it well enough, in his erratic way, using the junior hockey stick from his brother's tea-house days, but just when the goal was wide open he would lose interest and wander off to the Railway Institute to read a magazine. Eustace might have been patient, but now he was busy, his annual leave spent training with the Olympics hockey eleven. For the past few years Trotters and their kin, with a thousandth of the country's population, had made up half the national team. Eustace, as the team's goalkeeper, found Albert's attitude exasperating. "It's a matter of prestige, men," he said. "Can't you see?" He took India's hat-trick gold seriously. With forwards as good as the Trotter front line, his was a lonely job in matches, and it sometimes irked him that as goalie his function was limited to saving while the others dazzled with their stickwork. But Albert couldn't understand the fuss over prestige.

Closer to him in age was Young Paul's son, Marris. The cousins were roughly the same age but were bound by the contradictions they presented to one another, Marris forceful to overbearing, Albert a natural anarchist.

"Hullo, Half-Past-Eleven!"

Albert came up from behind and tripped his cousin as they were starting back from school. The other day Marris had, memorably, misspoken his age.

"*Hello, spirochete.*" Already Marris, baptized in boiled water, spoke only in italics. He was going to follow his father into politics, but through the law, not medicine.

"Pissed in the crater, didn't you?" There was a tradition among schoolboy Trotters that if you pissed down the crater in the Audience Hall your cock got cut off. There was something down there.

Marris ignored the jibe. He disliked crudity, which Albert knew.

"It was there only just now, wasn't it?" Albert taunted.

Marris's lips twisted down. He said in a bored voice: "*You coming to the mango party, spirochete?*"

"What mango party?"

It was now Marris's turn. "*D'you mean you don't know?*"

"Maybe."

"*D'you mean maybe you don't know or maybe you'll come?*"

"Oah."

"*Oh, what?*"

"Oah, I don't know."

"*D'you mean you don't know whether you don't know or you don't know whether you'll come?*"

"Maybe." Albert was peeved that nobody had told him, but he had only himself to blame. Everybody knew, and it was his policy never to bother with what everybody knew. He said grudgingly: "Where is it?"

"*Where is what?*"

"The mango party."

"*What about the mango party?*" As a lawyer, Marris would go far.

"All right—where, is, the, mango, party?"

"*At our house, naturally.*" The *naturally* signified his father's famous weakness for mangoes.

Ordinarily, from as far back as his university days in Britain, yellow was a colour distasteful to Young Paul. It might have been an atavistic link with Thomas Henry, but he avoided it in his own clothes, and the sight of it in someone else's—Alex's borrowed socks, for example—was enough to bring on a seizure. Sometimes he justified his cuckolding of the man by the colour of his socks. He forbade the colour in his household and even in Alex's wife, the now ex-actress, Suchita. Yellow journalism was his bête noire as a politician; as a medical man he dreaded yellow fever more than the black plague; and as an ordinary citizen he rated the Yellow Peril above the Russian menace. But when it came to mangoes, his resolve broke down. A Nakhlau dasheri touched some forbidden nerve in his constitution, making his pulse race and his glands slaver uncontrollably. He drew the line at chusnis, though. Chusnis were sucking mangoes, village mangoes, sweet enough but rustic, uncultured, growing by the roadside, cheap (you could get a whole basketful for the price of half a dozen dasheris), coarse, dehati, for villagers and vulgarians. There was something lascivious about the very act of preparing to eat them. He had seen it done once. You chose a mango from the tub where they had soaked overnight to rid them of their turpentine, and you began to squeeze. Since they were palm-sized, you could squeeze one in each hand alternately, setting up a kind of rhythm. You squeezed until the flesh inside was reduced to a pulp—you could hear it squelching there around the fat seed in nature's pouch. Then you bit off the top to make a little hole and spat out the cap thus removed. And you began to suck. After that, Young Paul had looked away. But every spring, when the white mango blossom covered the trees and its scent hung heavy on the night air, Young Paul's dreams grew turbid. And by day he longed for the very season his tight sweating body was ill equipped to take: summer. The fiendish heat of April, May, and June had to be weathered before the mangoes were ready; to eat them before the rains broke was to invite boils. And the hotter the summer, the better the fruit: a cool summer meant an insipid crop. By the end of June, when the first fat drop of rain came hissing down, Young Paul's dreams were entirely yellow. Worse, it was rarely the pale yellow of the delicate dasheri, but a coarser, more vibrant colour verging on orange. Sometimes he caught himself imagining what it might be like to succumb to a chusni, to go beyond the squeezing stage. The juice squirted, hot, sweet, and slightly stringy into your mouth, and you had to be careful not to choke on the seed. The pulp gone, you tore open the pouch, turned it inside out, and sucked it. Lastly, you sucked the hairy seed. Then you threw away both and started on the next. It was a messy business, and anyway, hardly the sort of thing for a party to celebrate Victoria's birthday.

"I'm not coming," Albert decided suddenly. They were nearing home when he broke away and wandered off. He was wearing one of the yellow silk shirts he had found in the Balloon Room. It was hot and sweaty and striped with dirt, but he liked the colour.

"*You'll be sorry*." Marris had no time for a hopeless case. He wanted to be early because he knew from summers past that ordinary people were transformed when it came to mangoes. Excepting, of course, his mother, the whilom Belle of Bangalore, who ate her mango cheeks with a knife and fork.

As it happened, most people had already arrived and were wandering up and down the curved corridor of the Comb ritually admiring Young Paul's hunting trophies.

"That's one hell of a bear, Young Paul," said one of the ancient Victors. They were all there—so far as one could tell—they and their balding sons and pomaded grandsons, all called Victor and all in the railways. Their wives and daughters were splashed around in bright contrast to their steam-and-coal.

"Yes." Young Paul hardly looked at the speaker. He was casually dressed in white summer drills and maroon socks. He rose, crossed to the thicket of antlers, detached a young Victor from one and dropped him on the floor with the air of a surgeon discarding malignant tissue. But he did it with a preoccupied air, looking the other way. On the sofa next to him sat the Parsi taxidermist and his wife, the latter conspicuous in an emerald green sari, flirting judiciously with her inattentive host. Each time he returned to his seat she gave a furry laugh and dug him in the ribs.

"You should mount one of them on the wall as a sort of warning!"

"*Victorensis horribilis*," the taxidermist offered.

Young Paul smiled shortly into the space between them as he ran his eyes over the gathering. Apart from the railway crowd there were the prolific Fonseca-Trotters, a handful of Alexander- and Kahn-Trotters, the women in saris, and a few unknown but undoubtedly agnatic Trotters.

"Where's Alex?" called Thomas Atkins-Trotter Sr, a stirrer. He had found the most comfortable chair. Ruby sat on a stool beside him.

"Putting on his face," ventured another of the Victors. Following some deep compulsion, they were falling into line like iron filings under a magnet.

"In Aminabad with his Congress friends," came from a Fonseca-Trotter.

"Listening to Indian music."

"Chewing pan."

"No, no. Fighting for freedom."

At that moment Alex entered with Suchita on his arm. His lips were freshly red, but not from chewing pan. He paused by the mirror on the hatstand and looked uncritically at himself, a dapper ancient growing younger every day. Suchita, several years his junior, had given up in the battle with age, but she stiffened when she saw the taxidermist's wife lean towards Young Paul. Their son, Cedric, followed, his nose in a book as he walked.

"Poetry, Cedric?"

There were howls of laughter from those near enough to hear, but one of the older railwaymen looked admiringly at the boy. Cedric had a chemistry exam the next day, but the book in his hand was, as the wag guessed, poetry. He scowled at his persecutors, who had already forgotten him, and found a back seat, his ears burning.

Young Paul was looking at his watch. On hot days it was not easy to lure Victoria away from the Tank, and today was a scorcher. The Belle of Bangalore, who during the past few years had been punctually producing sisters for Marris, sat beside the taxidermist, looking faint. He was fanning her gallantly with his own cane-weave fan. Beyond her sat the girls, wilting in silence; perhaps because their brother spoke with such emphasis they would always have nothing to say. On the other side sat the Maiden Aunts, articulate enough but in a coterie fashion. They sat, placid as ever, in plain saris, on the usual row of mondhas, except that for once the mondhas faced away from the Sea of Tranquillity. A store of green mangoes had been set aside for the older three. Fresh from baths, the company was already sweating, threads of caked talcum powder appearing on the ladies' necks. Now and again a man stood up to ease the plastered seat of his pants. A very minor Victor fell into a tub and was hauled out and kissed and slapped. At last Young Paul decided they should take the party Tankside. "If Muhammad won't come to the mountain," he grumbled, and the tubs were transported down to the grassed verge of the Tank. But Victoria was not there either.

At last she rolled up, dripping. "I thought you said the Comb," she complained. She didn't like to share her Tank.

People now felt free to notice what had been under their noses all along: a dozen galvanized iron tubs filled with three varieties of mangoes.

"Mangoes? I say!"

"Dasheris!"

"Langras!"

"Not safedas, surely!"

"No chusnis?" That from a young Kahn-Trotter. Young Paul glared at him.

"Mr Montagu," Victoria announced, "asks to be excused. He has some history to write."

At once Young Paul waved his hands. Everybody sang "Happy Birthday" for Victoria, and the eating began. The guests found plates and knives or not according to their needs. As a rule a lady cut her mango into two cheeks and a seed, while a gentleman peeled his and ate it like a peach. There was a children's tub somewhere. The same young Victor fell into it and was hauled out and shaken and slapped. No one but his mother noticed. Conversations grew thin and were largely exclamatory, the world reduced to luscious yellow mouthfuls on the banks of a still lake. The more serious eaters wore protective smiles each time they went back for more. Nobody noticed that the host was unusually restrained. He made his joke about the thousand and one ways of eating a mango, but few were listening. And nobody remarked when, with the failing light, he left. As for Albert, he was already a long way off. He knew of a chusni grove called Munnoo's tope on the far side of Sans Souci, below the saltpetre hill, where the sounds of the party could not carry to remind him that he had been forgotten.

It was late evening when he rinsed his hands in the Cranny river whose water, close to its spring in the hillside, ran deliciously cool. Above, a three-quarter moon was climbing up the east. The west was still vaguely lit by a band of hot yellow sky at the horizon broken by the jutting top of the tableland. He walked back along the remains of the canal that had once fed the indigo baths, a broken line of elevated pools that held water during the rains. The main body of the canal had run along the top of an embankment but portions were carried by pillars, twelve feet high, that formed an aqueduct. Some of the arches had collapsed, while the pillars remained standing like giant bird-baths. Whatever had destroyed the indigo works—an air of brooding tragedy hung over the place and made Albert look behind him—still breathed there. Most people walked a long way around to avoid it: most people, that was, except Albert. He dawdled in the shadows, looking through an intact arch in which the music pavilion was framed. He must go there sometime to investigate, he decided. Then his attention was caught by something else. From the top of one of the pillars came a slapping sound, like a stylite's lonely mortification of the flesh. And yet at the foot of the pillar was a litter of yellow pouches and hairy stones which Albert recognized at once. He looked up and saw, against the purple sky, sticking out over the edge of the canal, a pair of gun-barrels. Then a voice, drawling, possibly drunken.

"That tiger has my *name* on it, Hose."

Albert picked up a chusni stone and lobbed it back into the birdbath. Immediately he saw a figure lean over the edge, caked in yellow to the waist, like a mendicant. It was Young Paul. Albert darted under the arch, recognized. Another figure, similarly caked, leaned over the other side. He didn't wait. From overhead came two gunshots but he was already off, running nimbly through the dark, under cover of the embankment. When he stopped to look back from the old indigo shed, the pillar with its now barely visible figures did look rather like the ideal machan, where you sat up all night waiting for the kill. A thought came to him as he stood there: there *were* no tigers left, not even in the forest. Young Paul himself said so. They were all mounted on the walls of the Comb. There was another shot in the dark, and Albert felt a rain of pellets come down around him. Duckshot. He ran back home, cutting across the Indigo Court; he was the only one at Sans Souci who never obeyed the rule about the fenceless gate. At the Comb he heard the whilom Belle of Bangalore and the taxidermist's wife calling into the dark for their husbands. The mango party was evidently over. As he approached the Begam Kothi he heard another voice, unmistakably astringent. It was Faith. "He has the whole Tank in front of him," she was saying, "and he goes and drowns in a tub." It turned out that the very minor Victor had fallen in a third time.

And now, Mr Narrator, can we open up a window?

My poor steamy Cup-Bearer! Fetch me a chilled white, crisp and sparkling.

There will be no more decadence, Narrator?

Cup-Bearer, my hands are clean. Quickly now. Their faces are shining, their uniforms pressed. Smart Cup! Now listen. I have heard from the gaolbird that it happened so.

(*CHRONICLE RESUMED*)

After the chusni affair Young Paul could never wash his hands enough. That winter he lit the salamander twice a day for bath-water and used carbolic soap and a hard brush. He put away his sharkskin suits and had six khaki shirts run up with shorts to match. The shirts were long-sleeved, but he kept the sleeves rolled up and had them ironed that way. And about that time he developed his tilt.

For some years now he had been smiling with the right side of his face because that was the side that he considered to be the more photogenic. It was the side he presented to the press. Now he began to swing his right arm a little further than the left, with the result that his heel wore down more quickly on the corresponding shoe and he began to walk with a tilt. Suchita, whom he visited when he could, said: "Don't you start now! Just when *he's* got over his jerking." But Young Paul was powerless to correct his posture. He began to hold his head at an angle, and before long even his hair was parted on the right. What was more, he imposed his tilt on others, so that soon everyone in Sans Souci had developed a crick. As a politician he might have welcomed such loyalty, but as it happened, by the logic of opposites, everybody who talked to him had to lean the other way, especially his other son, Cedric, who was reading Lenin's *Imperialism, the Highest Stage of Capitalism*. Albert, who delighted in confusion, tilted sometimes to the left and sometimes to the right and had everybody, including sometimes Young Paul, wondering. Mr Montagu was the only one who preserved the perpendicular (*Fence Sitter, Dense Post*). What, the historian asked, had he seen in this son whose speeches grew more shrill and Germanic with the passage of time and still began with *I*? Young Paul's left eye had begun to weaken alarmingly, but since he himself was the leading eye specialist, there was no one he could see. The right eye, however, his sighting eye, remained true, because he continued to bring home big game in numbers that matched the rock inscriptions of ancient kings. After one such excursion (the bag being brought home as usual by his faithful servant "Joe" Hukum) Young Paul persuaded Alex to photograph him with his kill, which he laid out on the Grand Steps in front of *Sungum*: first the elephants, in the foreground, then the lions piled on them, and the rhinos disposed at the very top. Against the sky—the towers were blocked out— stood the hunter, shielded from the sun by a white pith-helmet and leaning, alas, a little to the left on his elephant gun. It was he who afterwards brought *Urban* around to the west side of *Sungum*, so that its massive barrel was not wasted on the fleur-de-lis-turned-fish Tank but pointed across the sunken garden towards the Gunpowder Gate. Thanks once again to the logic of opposites, the workmen misunderstood Young Paul, so that when the cement hardened around the wheels, the big gun was found to point a little to the left of the triumphal gate, at the nearest of the mango topes.

Mr Montagu liked his mangoes green, with salt. Now, ever since the closing of the curry mines, the Trotters of Sans Souci had bought their spices (and with their spices, their salt) in the market like everybody else. One day it occurred to the historian as he looked out across his beloved desert towards the salt flats beyond the aerolite that there was no reason he should not make his own salt. In fact he had simply to gather it, but what nature had freely given, the law in its majesty took away: it was illegal to make salt. The tax on salt provided the British government with crores of rupees in revenue, revenues which they would not give up without a struggle. Now it looked as if that was exactly what they had on their hands. In a small town on the sea-coast, the Mahatma (*Dandi Gandhi, Walking Stick*) had shown the way at the end of his famous Salt March. If the Gujaratis, renowned throughout India for adding sugar to their curries, could produce a champion of salt, who was he, Theobald Horatius Montagu, to lag behind? He would go on a salt march of his own.

No longer young, the historian decided to take one of his daughters with him as a prop. He could hardly ask Eustace, a police inspector, to cooperate in an illegal venture, and in any case he suspected the man had something to do with Thos. Henry's disappearance. It was not martyrdom he was after. "No doubt he'll come without being invited," Mr Montagu mused, with a frisson of patriotic anticipation. Prudence was the natural choice, but she backed out at the last minute, and it was Faith who volunteered. Unfortunately she happened to mention it in front of the khansama, who understood more English than he gave out, and the next day the entire Sagarpaysan population knew about it. Within a week people were journeying from distant villages to defy the government's ban and make (or gather) their own salt. Mr Montagu would have liked to wear his dhoti for the occasion, but secretly he was glad he had given it away because its absence spared him a moral decision. He knew he would rather face prison in trousers than come home to Victoria in a dhoti.

On the twelfth of March he set out across the Sea of Tranquillity accompanied by Faith and a host of villagers. It was already hot, so they rested under a pipal tree by the well with the stone umbrella (all that had ever been finished of the proposed temple in the large old days), and again under the tamarind trees beyond the elephant graves, where they came upon and were joined by Cedric the poet. By noon, sooner than Mr Montagu would have liked, they reached their destination. From every side people, clad mostly in white, were converging on the spot, some having swum across the river whose banks were dotted with young watermelons, while others came around the Tank driving donkeys fitted out with empty panniers. Ceremonially, Mr Montagu bent down and took his pinch of salt, half expecting a sigh to go up from the crowd. But the villagers were already busy scraping and shovelling, making lewd jokes as they filled their bags. It was rather like a country fair without the stalls. His own pouch filled, Mr Montagu turned, half expecting to find Eustace and a troop of policemen there. He was not disappointed.

The small force had marched along the Lower Trotter Road and come up under cover of the aerolite. Eustace, Sixth Trotter, rode forward on horseback and dismounted in front of his grandfather. The crowd fell silent. "Go on, then. Arrest me!" Mr Montagu urged. He had always been a little jealous of Alex's prison term. Now Alex could bring *him* books, and there would be a Congress reception committee waiting outside the jail on the day of his release.

Eustace may not have heard. He said in his quiet conscientious way: "Come this way, please," and led his aunt, his grandfather, and his cousin to one side. Next the accompanying magistrate read out something from a sheet of paper and stepped aside himself. After that the police charged, swinging their lathis. The crowd was dispersed, two heads were broken, and six villagers, including two Sagarpaysans, were taken into custody. Eustace and his men left with their prisoners and a half-laden donkey in train, while Mr Montagu, Faith, and Cedric made their way back to the Begam Kothi across a desert that suddenly looked very wide and still. Half-way across that barren expanse, the packet of salt slipped from the historian's grasp and fell unnoticed, bursting open to form a transient dune not far from where a gypsonometer had once fallen out of the sky and left a sugary stain on the sands. Over to the east, beyond the toddy-palms that fringed the Tank, shooting up at intervals from the surface of the lake could be seen a white waterspout, itself a moving palm tree. It spoke of the serene indifference of nature to the affairs of men, shaming the three adventurers into a silence beyond embarrassment. For his part in shielding his relations from the due process of law, Eustace was transferred to a district where there was no electricity and an abundance of dacoits.

Young Paul was not behindhand in his nationalism, only he tended to favour strength over passivity. Not every man could be a saint, he declared, in something of an understatement, but every man could be a soldier. Military obedience, not civil disobedience, was the answer to India's crisis. In the old Kaiserbagh throne room he gave a speech calling for a youth movement based, with reservations, on German Fascism, and stressed the importance of disciplined units of young men marching on ahead to show the way. The Trotters, who liked uniforms, applauded vigorously. In the nation to come, Young Paul said, all must pull together. However, as the representative of Trotters and their kin he wished to secure certain rights and assurances for Anglo-Indians in an independent India once the British had left. And just in case these guarantees—seats on the legislative councils, quotas of jobs, educational grants—didn't come through, he began to look into the possibility of an independent homeland for his community. Sans Souci was out of the question. It had shrunk in recent years as cultivators claimed land at the edges that had once belonged to their forefathers, and already there were squatters in the farthest outhouses. In any case the original title was always shaky, the deed being nowhere to be found; at any time the government, whether British or Indian, might simply revoke the grant. Besides, the place could hardly carry two hundred thousand people, the figure on Young Paul's All-India file—though no one had ever made a proper count. Better to start anew, somewhere else. It was then that he hit upon the Nicobar Scheme.

There, well down in the Bay of Bengal (at the rough antipodes of the Falklands) were these islands, a tropical paradise, rich in timber, coconuts, flowers, fruit, and fish, with nobody to make use of them except a few naked aborigines. Headhunters, it was said; at all events, savages. If the Government of India gave the Nicobar Islands to the Anglo-Indians, they could be transformed in a generation from a sinking scattered community to a wealthy unified one. At first, Trotters might hanker for the cities that had formed them, but in a little while they would remember that they were a frontier people: surveyors; dacoit-chasers; builders of railways, roads, and telegraph lines. In time a city would grow up; meanwhile Madras was not far away. There would be a government house, a radio station, a newspaper that he might edit, a port for the customs crowd and shippies and boatbuilders. Although the inhabitants of a small island, they could become a seafaring nation (there were precedents), and under the right leadership they would take their place among the nations of the world. Young Paul began to put out feelers. He wrote to the Government of India, and the Government of India wrote to the Commissioner at Car Nicobar. While he was waiting for a reply he began to canvass among the Trotters of Sans Souci for volunteers for a reconnaissance mission to the islands. A few unemployed Victors and Alexander-Trotters liked the idea and agreed to go for a period of six months during which they would report back on the feasibility of a larger settlement. "Try it out anyway, men," Young Paul said, clapping them on the back as he dropped into their lingo. A committee was formed, subscriptions raised, and tickets booked. Arrangements were made for purchasing tools from the brothers Uberoi; seeds and livestock would be bought in Madras. Then a letter arrived from the government. The Chief Medical Officer on the islands wished to advise prospective settlers that malaria was a present danger on those shores. After that the committee was divided, some volunteers withdrawing while twelve pressed on and made the journey. On arrival they were allocated plots of jungly land that looked worryingly unlike the featureless expanses of Sans Souci. By the end of six months, one settler was dead from malaria, one had disappeared without a trace, six decided to stay, and four came back to spend long hours in the Railway Institute.

Young Paul never gave up his Nicobar notion, his faith growing more stubborn the further the likelihood of a colony receded. Car Nicobar became a grail that went ever before him, a dream of a state in which his community throve without those invidious distinctions of caste and colour that crippled the rest of India. He was not the only one with a dream.

Cedric Kahn-Trotter, who had Young Paul's face (though he was black and tilted the other way), also had visions of a better lot for his people, only he saw a community—universally literate and without medieval fetters—ripe for democratic citizenship within a heterogeneous state. He deplored Young Paul's idea of an Anglo-Indian enclave with special rights and concessions. "Protection weakens a people," he scribbled in his notebook, the repository also of lurid confessions and apocalyptic poems encoded in the Cyrillic script. Trained in the sciences at school, he read poetry and Marx and asked unanswerable questions about justice. His putative father, Alex, who had never been past the university gates (where long ago he snatched his young wife), sent the boy to Mr Montagu, who put the works of M. K. Gandhi into his hands. Poring over them, Cedric lit upon a line of the Mahatma's that made sense: "Where the only choice is between cowardice and violence, I would advise violence." So the German and the Indian did concur in one respect— the recipe for social justice did not differ from land to land. It was like the valency of, say, a hydrogen atom, which remained the same across every border. All the while Young Paul was preaching nationalism, the boy with his face was learning to become an internationalist. When the Civil War broke out in Spain, he wrote a poem in solidarity with the republicans. And when his putative father died leaving him some money, he booked a passage to Barcelona in order to see for himself.

Alex did not so much die as wilt. Towards the end he gave up managing the Coral Gables on the 'Ganj, thus finally putting a stop to the Thursday night amours, punctual but flagging, of his wife the ex-actress and Young Paul. He kept away from moving pictures, but took to toying with the still camera once more. He used it only occasionally, because the equipment was heavy, and never professionally as in his younger days at Nakhlau parties: he wished to see no more bubbles, British or Indian, on his prints. In the photos of his old age (he did not speak of it as such) he confined himself to innocuous views of Sans Souci. He did, however, come up with a scheme for producing one last legitimate white cloud on a photograph. It was not an experiment, naturally, that he could prove to his own satisfaction; someone else would have to verify the result. Alex wished to photograph his own soul as it left his body. There was no need to dress for the occasion, since he was always already impeccably turned out, but a place must be decided upon in advance. Unlike the man who wished only to know the exact place of his death so that he needn't ever go there, Alex decided that the inevitable must be gracefully, even tastefully, accepted. A room must therefore be selected, much as one might select a coffin, and furnished with care. The old stylized Indo-Grecian canvas backdrops wouldn't do, since what was needed was a dark, preferably black, screen beside the bed against which the departing soul, presumably white, would be clearly visible. The camera would be set up directly across from the screen, and there would be an overhead pulley, attached perhaps to the ceiling fan, by which the lens cap could be manipulated without his getting up from the bed. At the foot of the bed would be a white screen on which Alex intended to show, while he lay dying, all the films he had ever made, spliced together end to end onto one large reel on the projector at his head. The pillow would be propped up a fraction.

On the chosen day—he could not tell whether it was he or Death that chose—Alex went for a last walk to the Begam Kothi, where he bade Mr Montagu goodbye and reminded him about the developing job. He left good wishes for his cousin Victoria who was away, swimming. The historian laughed the matter off: "Youngster!" he croaked, "I'll go before you." And yet, although he was right about their respective ages, Mr Montagu looked not very different from the salesman who had greeted Thomas Henry at the Gunpowder Gate so long ago. Time had been unduly kind to the man who so distorted it, its cool constant breeze buffing away the evidence of age. With Alex it was quite different, his face having been scored and scratched until it looked like the moving picture of itself run once too often through a shoddy projector. The pancake mask of makeup (*mockup*, he had called it in his cinematic heyday) filled in the deepest grooves but drew attention to the havoc underneath by being too pale: the face was of another colour from the neck, because Suchi favoured the lighter creams for her dressing table. When Alex wished his wife goodbye, she too laughed from the weight of that mortal embarrassment which the old will inflict. Alex was instantly ashamed of himself. Suchi, he saw for the first time, had two laugh lines around her mouth, three frown lines on her forehead, and four grief lines at her eyes. Nowadays she contrived to look neither happy nor angry nor sad but perpetually surprised because in this mood her wrinkles went away. Now he had caused her embarrassment, an emotion so complicated that it partook of all four states at once, and the effect was devastating. She went off to seek comfort in Young Paul, but Alex could hardly have left her without a farewell. His daughters refused to believe him, Cedric was nowhere to be seen, and the grandchildren simply giggled and ran off terrified because the very young can smell death. Rebuffed, Alex went to his room, shut the doors and windows, turned on the projector, tested the pulley, and climbed onto the bed, slipping the string from the camera around one patent-leather toe-cap. Then he lay down and composed himself, taking the Easter lily out of his lapel and holding it between the waxen hands that he folded on his chest. The film began to run, a brittle, much-scratched one which showed a young woman skipping. As he watched, his body began to grow lighter, as if all the gross matter inside were being transmuted into an ether contained only by the skin. The next time he opened his eyes, a round white window no wider than a ceiling fan appeared above him, filled with an imperishable radiance that was not blinding but soothing to the eye. It was like being a fly trapped in ointment gazing with many eyes up through the mouth of the jar at the soft heavenly vaseline-coloured daylight. Presently there appeared in the circle the faces of loved ones gone before, whispering and holding their hands out to help him up. Alex felt himself begin to float up towards the ceiling. When he looked back down at the body lying there with a crooked smile on its face, the lime-green suspenders peeping out above the neck of the waistcoat, he gave an unholy squawk. With the last ebbings of mortal strength he jerked his foot and tripped the string leading to the camera.

> *Excuse me, Director, but the whiff of decay is stronger than ever. I thought we had done with decadence and here you are serving me dolled-up corpses.*
> *My sweet Cup, a little patience—and a little tepid Horlicks while you're there. One more panel—no, two—and you shall have all that is wholesome. And when the time is ripe—forgive me—in good time, I shall show how death's sting is removed. But not yet. Now watch the birdie.*

(CHRONICLE RESUMED)

The photograph showed very little. Alex's late invention, the reflex shutter, failed to function: he had counted on a residual twitch in his foot but rigor mortis set in at once. When Cedric burst into the room, he saw nothing against the black screen except the outline of the body. He replaced the lens cap and turned off the projector, which had reached *Cannon-Fodder*. He knew that the man lying there was not his real father, though he had loved Alex in a way that he could never have loved Young Paul, whose face he recognized when he looked in the mirror. He had come running because while he sat in the South Tower eating cucumbers sprinkled with pepper and devouring an old book on statecraft he suddenly came upon a page that was black and smoking. The next day he buried his father and returned grieving from the cemetery near the railway track to help Mr Montagu develop the photograph. Two weeks later he sailed for Spain. And many years after, when Cedric himself lay dying of dialectical capitalism in New York, he remembered Alex's last photograph and wondered about the blaze of light. He had to his credit a dozen books of essays and sundry prose which he had to admit read better than his poems. They were impassioned pieces on the condition of Anglo-Indians and on Indian self-rule. On the first he maintained his position against protection; of the second he declared, on War Issue paper: "Indians would prefer the worst self-government to the most benign foreign administration." It was a sentiment few Trotters, and not all Indians, would have endorsed as Home Rule loomed, but Cedric was ahead of his time. Where Young Paul had trouble bending the fingers of his right hand, Cedric in his old age found it difficult to unfist his left. He had married an Englishwoman and gone on to live in New York, where he wrote on American Negro art. His son, Elgin, would return to India to become a well-known broadcaster for All-India Radio, but Cedric would die abroad with only the memory of a photograph to sustain him. To the end he needed that glow of faith to charge his restless doubt.

Mr Montagu put the radiance down to overexposure (*Blind Balaam, Sightless Saul*) and filed the photograph in the archives he was now urgently assembling. The death of Alex Kahn-Trotter was a spur to his history, reminding him that his own end might be near (*Dilatory Death, Live-Long Life*). He gave Alex a paragraph, noting his achievements in fashion and his pioneering work in photography and cinematography. He was forced to conclude that the last venture was a failure, but he did make special mention of another photograph which had himself at the centre. It was taken by Alex after a Christmas breakfast not long before his death, and it was to prove the last photograph of the Trotters before the dispersal.

It showed the entire family seated on the Grand Steps in front of *Sungum*, looking out across the fleur-de-lis-turned-fish Tank. Even Victoria had been persuaded to postpone her swim and pose with the rest; she agreed because she did not want a crowd of spectators. She sat there, an ancient child at the centre—on Mr Montagu's left—pouting like the last empress of China, her massive hands asleep in her lap. Her fingers were ships washed up on an atoll; the waves of her violet dress broke in plain lace, revealing nothing, while her eyes, never further apart, said: "Death is a waking—but hurry up, Smarty Pants." Mr Montagu sat with his legs crossed, reflecting on his history and jiggling one foot so that it appeared as a blur in the middle of the picture. Whenever he lied, or contemplated lies past and future, he stiffened his upper lip and wriggled his toes, the opposing currents in his blood spilling over in futile activity. Shy of the camera that he himself had introduced to Sans Souci, he was sure he felt a little of his being escape with each photograph, like sand running out. "Here is your hostage," his eyes pleaded. "Treat him fairly." (*Pseudo-Trotter, Changeling*) Behind him sat the Maiden Aunts, middle-aged and serene—except for Dulcie who looked adventurous, her carefully made-up eyes the only pair in the entire group that had strayed from the camera (they said: "Wait!"), her lips bruised from constant biting. Young Paul and his wife, the whilom Belle of Bangalore, sat with their punctual wordless daughters to the far right, the hunter-and-leader's eyes saying: "*I.*" On the other side of Mr Montagu sat Ruby and Thomas Atkins-Trotter and their straight-backed sons, Thomas, Harold, Richard, and Ian. In the middle, behind the Maiden Aunts, was Suchi with her two daughters and their husbands and their two children, Reuben and Soma (*Monstrous Uncle, Peerless Aunt*). Nearby was Alex's steady brother, Zacharias, and his numerous steady progeny. Their eyes said: "No time like the present," and they came out clearest. The railway Victors, balding and dependable, had the top step and went from one end to the other alternating steam and coal; the original generation were all dead. Alexander- and Fonseca-Trotters filled in the available spaces, among them Ferdy "Fingers" Fonseca-Trotter who had once played with Peter at the Coral Gables and now had his own legendary band. Cedric the poet was so far to the left he was barely in the picture; his one visible eye stared defiantly at the camera and said: "Fire!" Also on the outskirts were the servants, with Chotey Lal the khansama given pride of place among them and his son-and-apprentice one step down. Malis and masalchis stood stiffly further out, their faces dutifully expressionless, their eyes servant-blank for photographs. Young Paul's "Joe" Hukum was there, as was a short-lived experiment in a nameless leucoderma-speckled butler for the Comb whose turban, Marris said, concealed stolen eggs. And then there was a late Gunga, and a few Sagarpaysans including the dhobi, Darshan Das, and his two sons. At the very front, seated cross-legged in the grass on either side of their grandparents, were Marris and Albert, grinning. And then there was another face, a new face in between them at Victoria's feet (if feet they were), a young woman's face, smiling like the picture of ecstatic prayer that hung in Victoria's bedroom, her hair in waves down to her shoulders like a telephonist's, her forehead gently sloping, her nose slightly upturned, her hands as beautiful as Victoria's were plain, her ankles deliciously narrow, her elbows like milky marbles, and a look of quiet satisfaction in her eyes as if she knew the camera was a snare that could hold no peril for the virtuous.

What is wholesome

I wish to shew what is wholesome. I have no wish to shew what is not, but here and there what is not has proved importunate and the decadent has crept in. Now I make amends, doing penance the whilst. Cup-Bearer will flagellate me as I proceed. Thus. AH!

> *Milk is the perfect food, mothering and wholesome. The cream must be removed and no sugar added, as in the manufacture of gulab jamuns, etc.* AH!

Telephonist Trotters are not decadent. Their teeth are evidence, gleaming whitely as they make connections; their legs are pressed chastely together, slanting to one side. Their faces are shining.

> *Eggs, quarter-boiled or raw, are wholesome. They must not swim in fat in a frying pan because essential vitamins are lost, nor may they be baked with cream and topped with cheese and garnished with roe.* AH!

Sporting Trotters are not decadent. Their legs are evidence on the hockey field, where Eustace and his kin have won the third Olympic gold in a row. Their faces are shining.

Unmilled rice is wholesome. It must never be polished or the germ is lost, and on no account must white rice be lightly fried in quantities of ghi, then cooked in syrup (with saffron), and lastly have cashew nuts and raisins worked in, with beaten silver spread on top before serving. AH!

Military Trotters are not decadent. The Atkins-Trotter boys will serve faithfully and well in the highest places. Their brass is shining. Their sons will shoot down Pakistani jets. Their faces are shining.

Fish is wholesome. It must not be deep-fried in heavily spiced batter as (for instance) by a certain thela-wala on the Lalbagh Circle (opposite the Novelty cinema) and served on a bed of buttered white rice with sweet onions. AH!

Educationist Trotters are not decadent. Teachers, headmistresses, vice-principals, principals, inspectresses of schools bear witness. Dulcie has been promoted head. What if her lips are watermelon red and wounded? Her face is shining.

Lean meat is wholesome, the fat being pared away and never used for frying white bread for dipping in tea. AH!

Zoologist Trotters are not decadent. Hope has just published a paper on ant-mimicry in the grey humpbacked spider. Her face is shining.

Citrus fruits are wholesome. On no account must refined sugar be added. AH!

Botanist Trotters are not decadent. Faith is experimenting with a variety of seed husk that will make an excellent laxative. Her face is shining.

Pulses and lentils are wholesome. Dals made from them should be eaten plain before a triple tadka can be given with cumin, asafoetida and poppyseed fried in pure ghi. AH!

Museologist Trotters are not decadent. Prudence has unearthed some chalcolithic querns. Her face is shining.

Barley is wholesome. It must not be poured away. AH!

Nursing Trotters are not decadent. Ruby has the night shift at the Civil Hospital where she is matron. Her nurses are Trotters, showing the way (other Indian women consider the job defiling). Their faces are shining.

Spinach and other greens are wholesome. AH!

Railway Trotters are not decadent. The Victors keep the trains running on time and have yet to run a red signal. The loco firemen are a sight to see stoking the furnace in June. Their faces are shining.

Water is wholesome. It must not be confused with wine. AH! AH!

Canal engineer Trotters are not decadent. But then neither are customs officers or surveyors or waterworks clerks and the like. I rest my case: there are wholesome Trotters everywhere, nourishing the body politic.

Suggested stockists: For lean meat, eggs, and fish, the adept must go to the Saunders meat market in Kaiserbagh. Mahesh the bania-and-teli stocks pulses, lentils, and grains such as barley and rice, though he specialises in oils in the usual place (just where the road turns away). Fruit and vegetables are best from Kaiserbagh on that side and Narhi on this, though one day the Nishatganj market across the river will outdo both. Yadav, who milks the Alexander Cooperative cows, will bring you milk on his bicycle, which has a can on either side of the back wheel; the larger one is for the milk, though some allege it holds the water. Some go as far as the Ice Bridge, to Mansoor & Boy, Confectioners of Repute Since (circa) 1780. Mansoor claims descent from an earlier halvai of the same name from the Great Trotter's day. He is doing well enough to have opened a sweetshop-and-restaurant on the 'Ganj (just next to the Fonseca bakery). Best avoid temptation and stick to the Cooperative cows. Water, as such, is best drawn from the well near the Glacerie, which is said to be bottomless; the waterworks are not to be trusted.

This is what I wished to shew. So do that. Now I have done my duty, though it has cut me to the bone. When my detractors cavil and finesse, I will point to this plate and display my wounds.

And now, Cup-Bearer, you may put away the whip and fetch me something cool.
Lassi will do very well (it is wholesome), so long as the curd is fresh and the
clots smoothed away by assiduous whipping.
Narrator.
My sweet Cup, you have the wings of the Alpine swift! Come annoint my back
with a balm of balsam and turmeric, butter and honey, and listen. I have heard
from your kin that it happened in this way.

(*CHRONICLE RESUMED*)

It was the twenty-first of June and the heat was stupefying. For the past two days the ice in the Glacerie had refused to set. At dinner the night before in the Begam Kothi the jelly had had to be drunk out of bowls like green tea.

Today the sky at noon was the colour of glass, smooth and domed. Tiny white flurries of snow were falling out of it, swirling down in a kind of mad dance. In a little while the fall became more orderly though never as straight as rain: it was impossible to tell where a particular flake might fall, but you could keep track of it if you tried. The roofs of houses began to turn white, and an open field was covered over in silence. Ridges of white formed on the branches and twigs of trees that looked foreign and feathery. The edge of a doorstep was brushed with white; a line of scurf marked the jut of the lintel above. Along the sides of the church the window ledges were white, the fenceposts rounded off, the gate latch peaked, but above, the steeple continued black. Then the last straggling spore came to rest and all was still. A stagecoach jingling along the deeply scored road was already frozen in its tracks. There was snow on the top hat of the man in the box, snow on the hubs of the coach wheels, snow everywhere now except in the sky. The world was quiet and still and cold.

"Queenie."

The young woman pressed her nose against the glass and felt a chill run through it. She stared mesmerized at the purity of a world transformed, its perfection tantalizing because it shut her out. She would have liked to walk straight across that open field and shake the branches of the trees on the other side.

"Queenie!"

Queenie took the paperweight and turned it upside down. The snow leapt from its precarious holds on the earth and fell back into the sky. She shook the globe savagely, something she hadn't done since she was a child. The snow inside seethed and spun around the glass wall and flew across the tiny landscape in a demented blizzard. Then she put it back on its doily and went to answer Victoria's summons. To get to the old lady's bedroom she had to pass through the verandah where Mr Montagu's tuition was in progress. The three young men who came every evening were there, joined by a fourth, a most unusual figure. He was bright-eyed, black to blueness, and had long wavy hair that hung down to his shoulders: he might almost have been a girl, but the voice was a man's. He was saying something, but broke off to look up at her as she went by. The others did too, including Mr Montagu, but the newcomer was the last to look away. Queenie blushed and went in by the drawing-room door and on through to Victoria's bedroom.

She had come to Sans Souci a year ago as a lodger. Victoria had had a strange letter from Pearl in California which she did not read to the end but which made her decide to rent out her runaway daughter's room in the Begam Kothi. Like Mr Montagu's tuitions, started at about the same time, it would bring in a bit—now that the ice was reduced to a trickle—though hardly enough, considering the pittance her husband charged for his lessons (*Worthless*

Tutor). The two advertisements were run side by side in the *Nuntio*, one for a respectable working girl in need of lodging and the other for history students who wanted help. Victoria selected Queenie because she had a spiritual look and said *perspire* instead of *sweat*. The girl's parents were dead, and one of many brothers was, she said without elaborating, in business. They came from Burma side, originally, or it may have been Malaya. She was a well-fleshed young girl with ice-blue eyes pinched a little on the outside, a gently sloping forehead, and slightly puffy jowls as if she kept a lozenge tucked into each cheek. She brought few possessions beyond a snow-globe paperweight made in Japan and a Dutch-boy hanky catch for her pretty hankies, but the letter of reference from her employer said she was a steady worker. Five years as a telephonist had made her a skilled dreamer, half her brain sending instantaneous orders to her hands while the other half dreamt of a distant country, evidently not her mother's Burma, because in this other country it snowed in winter. Perhaps it was her grandfather's country, but she didn't know him. Occasionally she caught a glimpse of it, in colour, on a Christmas card, but otherwise it was black and white like the tiny world in the paperweight. Her friends at work were all going to this country if India became independent, because it would be short shrift for Trotters once the British left. Queenie listened carefully to their plans. Perhaps she would go too, though sometimes when she woke out of a daydream it seemed she had already been.

"What-thing, Aunty?"

"Come sit."

Queenie looked around. The only chair in the room was the bath chair parked next to the bed. On the wall was a life-size picture of a woman, not unlike herself, praying. There were two other pictures: a blond Jesus, and a Pears girl standing in her knickers in a sandcastle.

"Sit here on the bed, men." Victoria patted the counterpane. "So hot, no? The minute you come out of the water you're perspiring again. Makes you feel old-old."

"You should have a fan, Aunty."

"Me sleep under a fan!"

"Only in summer. We can push your bed a little to the side if you want."

"Maybe." Victoria wheezed and felt around for her Maxwell's Compound bottle. "This is the worst summer we've had since Faith was born. You're looking nice, though—the heat must do you good."

"No, Aunty."

"Really and truly. But you must get lonely sometimes, no?"

"Mavis is a good friend." Queenie shared her secrets with Young Paul's oldest daughter.

"Takes after her mother, that girl. The Bangalore beauty. But not as pretty as you."

"Aunty!"

"Truly. Like that picture. Oah ho, this heat! Last year it was quite nice at this time. Eustace was lucky coming home on leave then—the day before he came the rains broke. You remember him, no? Nice-looking boy. Quiet. But always going here-there-and-everywhere on that motorcycle. Needs to settle down."

There was a pause during which Victoria unscrewed the top of the Maxwell's Compound bottle, took a swig, and screwed the top back on. She looked at Queenie again.

"Put this over there, darling. Don't know why he doesn't find himself a nice girl. Shouldn't wait too long, or he'll end up like my first brothers. You didn't know them. Twins like the others, but never married. Used to live in the colony, that side. Anyway, Eustace wrote the other day. Coming again for his leave next week. Those Costello girls will come to borrow the mincer or something, any excuse, you wait. Ever since he went for the Olympics and all, he keeps getting pestered by who knows who-all. The wrong types. And such a shy boy. He needs a nice quiet girl who'll take him to church and make him happy. The girls these days. Don't know what-all's in their heads—bhoosa, I think. In the olden days we knew how to behave or we were thrashed. Our dresses always being repaired, they were so low. We used to sit on Saturdays and mend our hems. But now! Knees. And proper shoes, we had, mind you. Now, all vanity. No respect, no character, no religion. Not much time, you wait, before the End. Earthquakes, famine, and all happening all over. And see now in Germany that man talking about war. It's all written in There. The Antichrist and all. You wait. The Beast is opening his eyes one-one at a time. Maybe even today. We must watch and keep vigil, watch and keep vigil."

"Yes," Queenie breathed. She too prayed regularly and read the Book, but Revelation always gave her goose bumps.

"So, my girl, when he comes you can make that nice caramel custard you made. He just lapped it all up last time. And you know afterwards he asked me: 'Nana, you made it?' And I said: 'No, *Queenie*.' And he made his eyes like-this, like-this."

"War," Mr Montagu expounded to his tuition group, "is a European failing."

He looked over his glasses at each one of his pupils in turn. They were graduates from Nakhlau, cramming (with the exception of the newcomer) for a public service exam, and sensing that Mr Montagu's views on Europe would not go down well with the examiners, they looked worried. It would have been much simpler if war were an Indian failing.

"Twenty years ago," the historian continued, "we emerged from the bloodiest war ever waged on this planet—a European war. A war which they, with alarming generosity, called a World War. True, other parts of the world were involved, including ours. Tens of thousands of Indians went to their deaths for a cause they never understood, in countries they had never heard of, at the behest of a government that was not their own. Today we stand on the threshold of another such war. The nations of Europe, not content with sparring in the corridors of power, must draw blood in the cockpits of oblivion. And the scale will be greater than before—for that is their creed. Oceans of blood, a wilderness of bones, cities of Death. So be it. But must they be allowed to drag the rest of the world down with them? Barbarians! When Gandhiji was asked what he thought of Western civilization—what was his answer? You must write it down in your examination books. He said: 'It would be nice.' "

"But Mr Montagu, sir—" It was the young man with the long hair. "Surely the war to come is simply the working out of a larger historical impulse—an impulse not of nations but of classes, the consequence of a global struggle among capitalists—including Asian capitalists—the Japanese for example—for resources and markets that will extend their hegemony and for some short time their tenure, but whose indirect consequence must be the development of an international proletariat that will eventually spell their . . ."

The newcomer stopped. He was in fact a newcomer only to the evening tutorial sessions, being no stranger to Mr Montagu. Anil was the scion of the Trotterpurwa laundry establishment, Darshan Das & Sons, Dhobis & Dry Cleaners of Distinction. As a boy he was brought to Mr Montagu's notice by his father, the grandson of Dukhi, Thomas Henry's guide, who said: "The other one works. This one only wants to read." That was enough for the historian. He had the boy educated at St Aloysius's and afterwards got him a scholarship at the new Nakhlau University. As a result, Anil was comfortable neither at home nor in the polite society into which his education conveyed him. Since he preferred to be where he could talk of the things he read and the things he thought, he spent little time at home, but he met his friends on neutral ground, in the India Coffee House just around the corner from the main street of Hazratganj. While most of those friends had gone into their fathers' professions or into government service (or, like Cedric the poet, gone abroad) he had joined the *Nakhlau Nuntio* as a journalist. He attracted notice wherever he went, with his hair, his blue hand which fluttered when he talked, his feverish, dark brown eyes, and his secondhand ladies' bicycle, another gift from Mr Montagu, who had insisted that it be painted another colour, though not necessarily pillar-box red. He rode with a fluid unhurried motion, the tail of his brilliant white kurta flapping behind him and his eyes fixed on a spot that may have been at infinity or just out of reach. People took him for a musician—a vocalist, no doubt, since he carried no instrument. He knew Sans Souci well from Cedric's time; whenever he visited, Alex's grandchildren ran behind his cycle shouting: "Boy-Girl! Boy-Girl!" When he came to the Begam Kothi, Victoria had nothing to say to a man whose red lips marked him as a chewer of pan. "Chhi-chhi-chhi!" she said when he was gone. "Dirty-filthy habit." But Boy-Girl was not an indiscriminate spitter. When he came to visit Mr Montagu he shot his betel-juice out in one long red arc into the Ganda Nala as he sailed across the Ice Bridge.

Today he was calling on his benefactor after more than a year. Mr Montagu, who was always happy to see him, drew him into the tutorial group, and his happiness increased when the young man began, as he always did, to disagree. Secretly, he was proud of his creation, proud and a little afraid. When Anil broke in with his radical ideas the historian grew faint with nervous excitement, rebuking himself for his timid liberalism. Boy-Girl would have had much more to say about the true nature of the impending war had Queenie not passed through the verandah just then on her way to Victoria's room. He looked up at her and seemed to lose his thread. He found it again and said: ". . . their doom?" Then he fell silent and did not participate in the discussion on Hitler. Mr Montagu was disappointed; of late Anil had been an infrequent visitor. But the very next evening he was back, early.

Comrade Narrator, do I sense romance in the air in this late age?

You speak out of turn, Pleb Cup, and for that I will thwart your vulgar expectations. But a bottle of something bubbly will not be amiss. And a sweet pan, for afterwards.

Is this called introducing complications, Narrator?

So. You wish to learn my trade so you can supplant me, do you? Quisling! Fifth Columnist! Gossip Columnist! Ghost Writer! Are you writing a shadow chronicle there? I have half a mind to confound you by introducing yet another rival in Colonel Sodney Ravage of Bawana Junction. But the man is a professional romancer—I have it from the witless babbler—and not our kind of Anglo-Indian. So we will leave him half formed in some twilit dressing room of the mind where he hops from one foot to the other dreaming of Queenie while his Gurkha catamite lays out his socks. Hear instead what the sarus crane, who mates for life, told me.

(*CHRONICLE RESUMED*)

Eustace arrived home on leave a day late, so Queenie's special effort at dinner was wasted. Undeterred, Victoria woke him early on his first morning and sent him off for a walk down to the river with Queenie. "The best time of the day," she said. "Nice and fresh and the koel singing and all." Then she went back to bed.

Queenie and Eustace (*Sainted Mother! Holy Father!*) walked obediently out through the Kothi back gate and made their way around the Ice Court, along the Steps, under the English tamarind trees, past the inquisitive cows of the Alexander Cooperative (managed by the family after the death of Alex's steady brother, Zacharias), past the old dairy once called the Crocodile Wing by the Great Trotter, around the bamboo clump where the wing disintegrated into grassy mamelons, across the Sea of Rains, skirting what remained of the jungle, pushing through dewy bushes of rat-ki-rani whose tiny white stars were closing, the night's fragrance shed, and scrambling down at last to the Cranny river which wound its way southwards between fields stippled with tender shoots of sugar-cane.

(*VERSE*)

Romantic haven, trysting sward;
Fertile promise, sweet reward!

(*CHRONICLE RESUMED*)

The stream, at the best of times a modest tributary of the Moti Ganga, was reduced by summer to a narrow sleeve of water perhaps five feet wide. A pair of sarus cranes standing in the middle were barely in up to their knotted pink knees. On Eustace and Queenie's approach they launched themselves heavily into the air and flew off into the rising sun calling, *ré-ré-ré*. Queenie smiled and narrowed her eyes against the golden light. Beside her, Eustace (*Fated Trotter, Mated Trotter*) the goalie stepped back stiffly and watched with pained concentration as the birds made a wide circle and disappeared. The man who made four spectacular saves at Berlin was reduced to a lumbering crane himself. The presence of women made Eustace uneasy even in company: to be alone with one was misery.

"Pretty," Queenie murmured.

Eustace, suddenly the ornithologist, was too rapt to notice. After his hockey triumph he might have had his pick of the girls in Sans Souci, from the dairy to the terraces beyond the railway colony, but he fled on a solitary posting to Jhansi where he preferred to chase dacoits through the ravines on horseback. He had survived three ambushes and been wounded once in an encounter, but the only dacoit he was ever afraid of was a woman, the bandit queen Pushpa Devi. This morning, standing beside the harmless telephonist in the wide flat expanses of outer Sans Souci, he felt cornered. So this was what it was like. He had a brief fantasy of himself on his motorcycle riding at top speed along the Trotter Road, in exactly the opposite direction.

Queenie was not uncomfortable: she was dreaming. A light scurf of snow had fallen overnight and covered these fields, the Sea of Rains, the distant flat-topped saltpetre hill, the Cranny river. It was all white, and a mild sun was rising to the sound of strange birdsong, possibly an English robin. She gave thanks to God for his bright world; like Victoria she was constant in prayer. For a long time they stood side by side, one gazing at the sky and the other looking out across the fields, but both growing conscious of the silence between them. Eustace stole a glance at Queenie. She was, he saw, half his age. The side of him near her—it was his deaf side—had grown numb. If Queenie could have seen the goose pimples on her own arm she would have put them down to the snow, although the sun, barely a handswidth above the glinting Moti Ganga, was already hot. Eustace felt a stirring in him that started in his stomach and mounted rib by rib, locking his breath in at each stop until he felt he must do something or suffocate. He took a half-step back, then bounded the three or four paces down to the water's edge and hurled himself across the stream. Not quite across, because his run had not been long enough. One foot made the other bank, but he had not allowed for the slope, and he fell back into the shallow water where the cranes had been. Queenie gave a sharp scream at the fountain of sparkling water, but burst out laughing when she saw Eustace was out of danger. Eustace was also laughing, much louder.

They walked back to the Begam Kothi with the sun on their backs. Wet from the knees down, Eustace was steaming gently. Every now and then they exchanged a look and the laughter started again. The space between them had narrowed since their walking out, but it would not close completely until they were married. The banns were published in the cantonment church by the new padre, a rotund pink-faced major newly out from Pembrokeshire (*Blest Arrival, Ready Foil*) with a single change of cassocks and a trunkload of paperbound murder mysteries. After that the couple felt free to hold hands. Because Eustace's leave was ending shortly, the third banns were waived (in fact they were read on the second Sunday at evensong) and the wedding was set for the week before he was due to return to his wilderness posting.

"A sugary affair, largely attended," was how the *Nuntio's* roving reporter described the celebrations, causing much malicious amusement in Sans Souci because, as only the immediate family were present, the *largely* was taken to refer to Victoria. She had been sparing with the invitations, and one had certainly not gone to Boy-Girl, who gate-crashed all the same and was cordially received by Mr Montagu. The cake, from Fonseca's on the 'Ganj, was made in the shape of *Sungum*—an old dream at last fulfilled—and came complete with four towers, a piece of aesthetic license that Victoria corrected in the course of mounting it on a carom-board spread with a doily.

Conceptio

Eustace and Queenie retired to the Purple Suite, a lofty pleasance where giant sugarcubes marked as dice were strewn about the china-chip floor among bedroom slippers and garters and heterogeneous gametes. A scorpion crept into a dancing-shoe. A heap of jamuns (*Eugenia jambolana*) rode upon a black table. Next they climbed to a suite where red smiles blossomed from a book of pictures on a sofa. Clay oranges and peaches crammed the bookshelves; two cold cups of tea kept time. A hairbrush crackled on the duchesse and a stork in a black night-gown with sequins of rapturous pink pecked at the moon in a bucket. Rope ladders brought them to a yellow suite where a lizard slid behind the mirror. A jug of papaya-fool on the dresser wore a net of dust. The mangoes and jujube plums wore patines of patience. A hair lay across the carbolic soap. They climbed and climbed till they came to a terrace where blank-eyed statues turned away and clouds drifted through open windows. One room they found empty, another full of guns. Another was a labyrinth of mirrors, another held no surprises, another a basin of clear water. On a sheer terrace that lacked a balustrade they rolled bright marbles, the largest to chest height, some that diffused a milky light, one with a blue vein. Under their eyes a tender pipal leaf pushed up through a floor of seamless stone. At last they came to a septagonal pavilion where a fountain whispered to a swarm of tadpoles in a slime-green pool. Tall brass padlocks stood on either side of the entrance, sweating furtively. A fine white sheet was spread on the white marble divan. The pillow was stuffed with gramophone records, the latest. Newspapers came up by the dumb-waiter, but the date was always missing. Hot water rose from the salamander by osmosis, a tin peacock sang from behind a screen, and an everlasting candle smoked near the ceiling. Velvet roses were stuck like fountain pens in a flat dish with a rose-holder of frosted glass. A rabbit limped across the floor and snuffled at a bush of mint rooted in a ginger jar. From over the Indigo Court came three droplets of rain. A cloud of flying ants rose out of the dust of the Water Court and ascended past a window with no curtain. The pelmets were dripping honey. A towel-grip hockey stick flew in and out of the windows like a needle. The sun rose in silk on a kimono. The water-clock below had stopped at noon long ago. A cloud no bigger than a split pea was forming in the sky.

(CHRONICLE RESUMED)

Then Eustace came down and went back to chase dacoits. Queenie lingered among the pretty things (they were all hers now but she didn't touch them), wishing she could have gone with him. But Eustace had said: "It's all jungly down there—no electricity, nothing. And one shop only with just soap and matches. You wait here till my transfer orders come in December. This time they'll send me to a proper town and I'll come collect you. I might even be posted right here, to Nakhlau, God willing." So Queenie went back to the telephone exchange. Once she put in a trunk call to him but his voice sounded like a tin-opener going round, so she didn't ring again. It brought home to her the frightening thing about distance which she thought the telephone had settled once and for all, and it shook her faith in the country of her dreams.

That evening when she got back from work she sat at the dressing table absently pulling at the corners of a hanky. The table was bare except for a matching silver-plated brush-and-comb set and a mottled darning shell. All Pearl's cosmetics had gone with her, and the hours she spent in front of this mirror were now piling up on the other side of the globe. The mirror was a tall block of icelight reflecting the window behind her. Queenie had often meant to move it to a more sensible place, but today, when she had nothing to do, she found she could not stir. She gazed idly at a wasp that had alighted at the top of the mirror and was minutely examining the glass. It was a pretty yellow creature, hanging there on the edge of a cliff of light. It did a mincing, oscillating dance, swivelling its body while keeping its head still. Then, with exquisite grace, it began to rappel down the sheer crystal face, feeding on the light. It had almost reached the bottom when the invisible line snapped. She heard its wings, saw it veer towards her, and felt the immediate senseless pain of the sting. She cried out, not very loudly but loud enough to be heard, and was at once ashamed—because usually she took pain without flinching, but also because of the awkward place.

In the verandah Mr Montagu's tuition group leapt to their feet at the sound. Informed, the historian shuffled off to find a female key, sensing another pattern in history. "One minute!" Boy-Girl shouted to Queenie, and raced off home on his bicycle while the other students simply stood against their chairs and looked at one another. Victoria was probably still bathing. Boy-Girl was back first, even though he had had to ride all the way to Trotterpurwa. He brought with him an indigo bag which he gave to Queenie, whispering something into her ear. She returned to her room and applied it as directed;

already the pain was seeping out, leaving a pink freckle high up on the inside of her thigh. Mr Montagu returned with his key, which he left discreetly at the door before returning to the war in Europe. When Victoria came back from the Tank (nowadays an ayah wheeled her there and back) she began to rummage in her bag for the fly-whisk. "It's all right, now, Granny," Queenie said, embarrassed by the fuss she had caused. Since the wedding she no longer called Victoria *Aunty*. "My child, you can't be too careful," her grandmother-in-law warned. "People have been known to die from wasp bites." And she shook her fly-whisk over Queenie's lap like a bell.

By Christmas it was clear that Queenie was pregnant. She resigned from the telephone exchange and spent her days embroidering little suits for the child she knew would be a bonny boy (*Prescient Madonna, Mama Intacta*). Every day she would walk to the Gunpowder Gate, which was now little more than a single ruined column with a postbox clamped on, to look for Eustace's letter. On the way back she stopped at the rain-gauge between the maze and the mango tope to take the day's reading for Mr Montagu, who had grown very old and feeble and seldom emerged from his glasshouse. His history of Sans Souci had become a race against time. Time (*Tardy Reaper, Pinioned Chariot*) ran through his pockets and buttonholes like sand, spilling gently onto the glasshouse floor where his cactus plants throve.

"The cactuses are looking nice, Grand," Queenie said.

"Cactii!" the old man snapped, and looked impatiently at her.

"Zero point-six zero," she recited and wandered off. An above-average reading for winter.

Mr Montagu made a record of it in the rainfall register and returned to his manuscript. The history seemed to grow interminably: the more he wrote the more there was to write. Like Queenie's belly it swelled with every passing month, but where her work teemed with interest and new promise, moving steadily towards a full and glorious event, his was a barren round of dates and flimsy postulates, a flat expanse of maundering prose haunted by sterility and destined for oblivion

—*Wah! Narrator, Wah! Wah! Encore!*—

a feeble rhapsody in beige, conceived in hebetude and brought forth in despair. After the ninth month Queenie began to rest by the rain-gauge on her way to and from the Gunpowder Gate. The latest letter from Eustace said he was on his way home to be with her when her hour came. But Queenie knew she was not yet ready. In his glasshouse Mr Montagu grew more desperate, lunching at his desk on soft-boiled eggs and sucking the dribbled yolk off his cardigan as he wrestled with the past. He left glaring lacunae in the text, muddled the generations, misquoted, was cavalier with attributions, shuffled figures, bent facts. He concocted a strange theory that the Great Trotter's balloon ride took place, if at all, in winter, pretending that the season was preferred by balloonists (when in fact he chose it only because his birthday fell thereabouts). More serious still, he opened a vein of religious doubt that led back to the great man himself (*Exalted Trotter, Secure Soul*). By the tenth month he was fabricating impious theories that he justified with a battery of irrelevant footnotes.

By the tenth month Queenie, who was bigger than ever any woman had been except one (*Motherless Miriam, Cupola of Chastity*), was beginning to wonder. Eustace, transferred as he had hoped to Nakhlau, was likewise mystified. It seemed the hour was linked in some obscure way with the historian in his glasshouse: as long as he wrote on she was destined to wait. She sensed an impatience inside her, a joyful demiurgic will to live. By the eleventh month, when the heat was cruellest, she would stand at the door of the glasshouse and reason with Mr Montagu. But he drove her away. His pages were now covered with a kind of crabbed shorthand—and that in the form of jotted notes. When she insisted, he ignored her, and every day she stood there waiting on doomed history, a ripe fruit poised to fall.

On the twenty-first of June at ten minutes past ten in the morning she felt a kick. It was not a playful kick but a vigorous businesslike kick which said: "*Enough.*" It began one labour at the same time that it put an end to another. Queenie sagged against the glasshouse door, which swung shut from her weight. The impact dislodged the yellowed pigskin-bound volume of Gibbon from the vent in the roof and the vent clicked shut. Inside, Mr Montagu went on scribbling as before. Queenie crossed an endless field of snow to her bedroom where she lay down and began to moan. The labour lasted an hour and fifty minutes, during which time Eustace, who had shaved that morning, grew a white beard. At a quarter to twelve Victoria came in dripping and produced her bag. She had been lying on her back in the Tank when she saw a cloud rather bigger than a split pea moving towards Sans Souci. At the same time a great hush came over the world.

the water buffaloes lolling companionably in the mud began to roll their eyes squirrels ceased their harsh chatter the long whistle of a goods train approaching the moti ganga bridge ended abruptly the trains wheels still rolled but the sound was false like silk on steel silk on steel the rails turned to gold the sleepers stood up and gave praise all across the desert the dervishes stopped their dance the loo became a delicious cool breeze that stole across the sea of tranquillity and reached the begam kothi where it lifted the perspiration from queenies brow the house sparrows came and lined the bedroom skylight and peered in without the least ruffle of feathers in the nim tree outside the brain fever bird was comforted while high above the house the kites watched and kept vigil watched and kept vigil wheeling silently in a world apart the water in the ganda nala halted in its bed and began to flow backwards so that a few crocodiles were swept in from the river they travelled peaceably as toddy-palm logs weeping for joy and shedding no tears in the zoo across the canal the lions stopped their hollow roaring and refused to eat the kid thrown to them traffic in the city came to a standstill the traffic policemans hands were stuck at a quarter to twelve boy-girl was a statue on the ice bridge his betel juice frozen in a vivid red arc that stretched like a monochrome rainbow from his lips to the surface of the ganda nala

Then:—

¡HOH!

He enters the world with a laugh, like Akbar, like Zoroaster, like the Great Trotter (*that he is*).

His first syllable is honeyed perfection, forward or backward or upside down it sounds the same: already he has summed up the cosmos, passed judgment on the world and its contents.

His eyes are wide open, the one more brown than blue, the other more blue than brown, and the fingers with which he grips Eustace's hand are short, plump, and artistic.

His voice is cultured sweet and high: already he knows the ancient poets, Virgil, Firdausi, Kalidas, verbatim.

He begins to sing:—

(VERSE)

O Eugene, Thou art a Great Master of Fame!
Canst sugar enow heap on Thine Awful Name?

(*CHRONICLE RESUMED*)

Then he calls for paper, paint, and brushes and executes a marvel among paintings which shows his father with a venerable white beard and a towel-grip hockey stick, his mother in powder blue, mildly perspiring, gazing at him with worshipful eyes, her legs pressed together and slanting from a telephonist's stool, and himself in the centre on her lap executing a marvel that shows his father with a beard and his mother perspiring and himself, his lips parted in song. The age of the photograph is past, its patron lies dead; the age of the miniature is beginning anew. There will be no vulgar snapshots of this family, only paintings.

After that the Seventh Trotter, Last and First Trotter, lay down and kicked his heels and cried in order to pacify the adults around him. And Sans Souci went back to its daily round. Because of the heat it was necessary to hurry with the burial of Mr Montagu (who was found dead at his desk of heatstroke and asphyxiation). When the discovery was made, the Maiden Aunts fainted away—all except Prudence—and Victoria was noisily sorrowful, blubbering uncontrollably at the sight of a face worn smooth by time and aphasia.

They shall obtain joy and gladness, and sorrow and sighing shall flee away.— Isaiah 35:10

That night Young Paul and Eustace arranged for ice from the Uberois because the water in the Glacerie tubs refused to set.

All Nature seems at work.—Coleridge

The next morning the hearse, an American import, took Mr Montagu at high speed to the cemetery.

History is bunk.—Henry Ford

There the earth was hard from six months without rain and the grave-diggers stopped at five feet.

Completed labours are pleasant.—Cicero

At length the service was concluded, a few choice clods were hurled into the pit, and the earth closed over the Anti-Trotter.

Death alone reveals how small are men's poor bodies.—Juvenal

And now, Freeman Cup, an eau-de-vie of raisins, for the millstone has fallen from my neck. The generation of history is past, the age of new promise begun. My head feels light. Pleasure me.

But the age after decadence, Narrator—there was one, surely?

Constant Cup, there was. Come take my hand while I tell you of the age after decadence. Listen. I have heard from the shuttlecock that it happened in this way.

(*CHRONICLE RESUMED*)

Her husband dead, Victoria began to discover the depth of her love for him. She stalked through the rooms of the Begam Kothi repeating: *And all the place is dark and all* . . . It was the Tennyson whose name had once been her armour against Darwin, but now the old feud was forgotten as she went from room to room expecting to find, if not her beloved husband miraculously restored, some morsel of forgiveness. Once it seemed she had tracked him down when a curtain refused to part, and she addressed him anxiously through the veil, but it turned out her bath chair wheel was holding down a fallen hem. After that she gave up her quest, but she kept the glasshouse as a kind of cenotaph sacred to his memory. In it she preserved the least scrap of paper with his handwriting as well as others that he cherished, including one with a ghostly watermark and a piece taken out of one corner. The desk was kept exactly as he had left it, his manuscript that ran to some four hundred pages being placed in a drawer in case some future antiquarian should be interested (*Fond Spouse, Folly's House*). And she locked the door against intruders, although already tiny green shoots and glossy chocolate leaves were pushing up from under the sand. In the Begam Kothi she daily dusted the record collection that she had once come close to throwing out. She even overcame her fear of machines by learning how to operate the phonograph, and every evening at bedtime she wound it up and played the Haydn Trumpet Concerto. It was not long before she grew to like it (it had a nice lolloping beat) and kept time with her large plain fist on the arm of the springy coir-stuffed sofa. Sometimes at the climax she was moved to throw back her head and reach for the top note herself. Then she would turn off the machine, wipe the needle, put away the record, and go to bed. She no longer used her old bedroom, having transferred all her things, including the picture of prayer, to Mr Montagu's room, where she slept in his bed, directly under the ceiling fan.

There was one other major change in the tenor of Victoria's life. She no longer went to the Tank. She still bathed regularly, using a whole cake of soap each time, but in the bathroom, where she took to a sitz bath and an enamel mug for pouring water over herself. For her eyes, still yellow and moving steadily further apart, she used an eyebath of violet glass. From early childhood, Little Eugene Aloysius (sometimes called the Little Trotter) marvelled at the sight of his great-grandmother bathing her eyes with this curious oval cup, itself a miniature sitz-bath. When Victoria put it to one of her wide yellow eyes the eyeball was reduced to a green gooseberry at the bottom of the cup. At five, Eugene stole it from her table and saw all of Sans Souci shrink into a tiny perfect cameo: the blue eye turned *Sungum* into an ice palace, the brown gave it a satiny bloom, purple and sweet. A year or two later he heard a strange high ululation coming from Victoria's bathroom and was tempted to peep. With the blue eye he saw a frozen mermaid through a crack in the door; shifting his head a fraction, he saw with the other eye a whale in a sitz bath. It was Victoria, huge and disturbingly naked, her folds and flaps and fins glistening darkly as she poured mugs of water over herself and sang a hymn in her high quavering comb-and-tissue-paper voice. Little Eugene ran off, the blood roaring in his ears.

At first his care was given to a Muslim ayah with elbows like raw silk and a piece of netting always in her hands. She stood him on an old pallet of mango wood—because he fatly refused to let his naked feet touch the floor—and emptied a watering-can over him. Then she soaped under his arms till he was helpless with laughter. Afterwards she fed him toast dipped in lukewarm tea for breakfast, and at night, after his regular dinner, a sweet firni made of rice flour and cream. But then she faded away, the victim of a debilitating disease which a little milk might have cured, and Little Eugene passed to the care of Victoria's ayah (a woman with elbows like rock salt), and Victoria herself. Queenie was now busy with a daughter, Eugenie, a plain, even ugly girl with delicate wrists and vacant green eyes. Once while chasing her he fell into the cesspool outside Victoria's bathroom, a shallow pit of scummy grey water where he lived an eternity of filth until rescued by his Uncle Albert. There was no Sultana to soap him under the arms and rinse him off with a hundred tingling jets of water from the nozzle of a watering can. He had barely recovered when he was sent to boarding school in the hills where there were cold showers. On the first day of the new term he lost a pocketful of marbles to a tall lean Turkish-looking boy; on the last day the same boy relieved him of a top that he couldn't get to spin. But it was the food that decided him: the next year he refused to go back. Life as a day-scholar at St Aloysius's (the school of his middle name) was an improvement, with a lunch-box and fruit trees on the way home—mangoes, guavas, jamuns (*Eugenia jambolana*). Albert, who didn't go to work, showed him where the best groves were, and at night kept him up late with stories of churails, bunyips, yetis, sasquatches, and headless horsemen. "The most scarifying thing, Euge," he said when his nephew looked sceptical, "is not that there are ghosts, but that there are no ghosts." Dulcie the Diva's lessons were just as confusing. Having sacrificed a career in singing for one in education, she hoped to train young Trotters to venture farther, but with Eugene her techniques proved impracticable. The theory thrashed out, she toyed with vocal lessons for a week before suggesting an instrument and turning to Eugenie. Little Eugene forgave her her artless envy because of her largesse out of shiny floral toffee tins after their visits together to the dreaded dentist, Dr Chew of Hazratganj. Curiously, where the quondam diva failed, Victoria, gross amateur, helped bring out the boy's voice.

She sang outside the bathroom too. Towards the end she insisted that the whole family worship in the chapel together on Sundays. It was the beginning of the regime of prayer, all the inner Trotters being required to attend. The Kahn- and Alexander-Trotters, who were pious and had many singing voices besides, came readily, making up a choir. Among them was a young woman the colour of jamuns (*Eugenia jambolana*) whose clear soprano and doll-like face drew Little Eugene early to every service. Young Paul, who had a gravelly bass and didn't mind airing it, was also there early with his mother: often the choir would fall silent while together these two pushed back the frontiers of music. When he heard them—Victoria shrilling in the language of the great whales, deep calling unto deep, and Young Paul growling richly into the upper air like some future jet—the half-deaf Eustace would hang his head in a mist of pain and shame. He was easily embarrassed, believing that if a thing was done it should be done well, but he was also pained by his embarrassment and prayed for forgiveness. Eugene, however, saw things differently: he saw the singers transported beyond the limits of their rough gifts, one cruising through the stratosphere, one ploughing the briny deeps as they nosed serenely toward their God. And shyly, his round face glistening, he lifted up his own voice in a high clear descant. When he first heard himself he stood rapt and afterward stayed behind in the chapel to test the gallery echo. It came back high and sweet, a timbre which stayed with him through his childhood and which, when threatened, would lead to the night of blood.

Eugene grew up half with Victoria, Albert, and the Maiden Aunts in the Begam Kothi, and half with Queenie and Eustace, who had decided to occupy the New Armoury near the Ice Gate. The arrangement worked well: he fed at both tables—a trick Victoria discovered early and encouraged. Even in her old age she could abstemiously divide a large fish down the backbone and then forget and eat both sides. And it did not escape the boy's notice that while the old lady who was a constant eater had never cooked a meal, Queenie who cooked constantly ate like a bird. From them Eugene learnt to respect the great division between cookers and the cooked-for: there was enough to be learnt about the art of eating to prevent one from ever approaching the science of cookery.

From Victoria, Eugene learnt that curries might be eaten at lunch, but at dinner never, dinner being, for all Trotters of the blood, a formal affair. That lunch was of India (or India Britonized), while dinner was of Britain (or Britain Indianized). That lunch was not a light meal but a heavy one, dinner being, however, no less heavy. That curry, wet or dry, is eaten with a dessertspoon, dessert being eaten with a teaspoon. That mulligatawny soup might precede lunch, but at dinner the soup must be clear, a consommé perhaps of trotters; that a pigeon might swim in chilli gravy at noon, but at night must be roasted; that pickles might accompany the first, but chutneys were for the second; that gulab jamuns might be eaten after the first, but a British pudding must follow the second. That Crumble Custard was a corruption, howsoever apt, of the cook's for caramel custard. That bed-tea was an excellent invention for those who did not go to work, for afterwards one might doze again or chase one's waking dreams until chhota haziri or the small breakfast, which preceded the greater breakfast as the morning star the sun. That spices in the morning were offensive, except for the nutmeg in the sugar-pot. That toast was eaten and toasts were drunk (a lesson later Trotters forgot). That butter went with toast, not toast with butter, the same law applying to marmalade (a law Little Eugene later forgot). That Smarmite was holy and must be applied sparingly, being English and expensive, but that no Trotter household should be without a bottle. That toast must not be dipped in tea. That eggs were eggs on weekdays but on Sundays became omelettes. That fruit in the morning was gold, in the afternoon silver, but at night lead. That stomach disorders were put right by a dose of effervescent salts in warm water taken in the morning.

Every morning after prayer Victoria took her opening dose of Kruchell Salts. The bright sun-yellow cardboard box stood open on the peg-table beside her as she sat on the porch in her battered wicker chair. The chair was of the same vintage as the Maiden Aunts' mondhas but, subjected to greater wear, it was coming apart more or less musically, springing every now and then a coil of wicker that trembled like some withered tendril on the vine. On the wicker table in front of her was the great black family Bible, the bottom corner of the verso page curling wetly where her moistened fingertip had pinched it. The lesson read, Victoria measured out a dose from the brown bottle and poured it into the lukewarm water in her tumbler. Then the submerged tinkling of a teaspoon against glass would go tripping across the morning air as she stirred, a tiny impatient matins bell, and a dome of sparkling effervescence rose up out of the tumbler, the only vapour in the air for a thousand miles. And looking up into the blue she took a sip and sang in her undersea voice.

(VERSE)

Merciful showers,
Heavenly showers,
Showers of mercy from Heaven above;
Dewdrops on flowers,
Raindrops on bowers,
Send us O Maker Thy torrents of love;
Torrents of love,
Currents of love,
Send us O Maker a cloudburst of love.

(CHRONICLE RESUMED)

In a little while Queenie would come by on her way back from the rain-gauge (she kept up the records as a kind of penance for a slip she confessed only to her friend Mavis), and the two would hold hands and smile tenderly at one another. Victoria was pleased with her granddaughter-in-law. The girl was an anchor for that restless Eustace, making children for him and feeding him up nicely.

"Happy, Granny?"

"Yes, child. Where you been?"

"Oh, just to the gate."

Then the roar of a monstrous Triumph would shatter the calm as the Sixth Trotter, Fated Trotter, hurtled up the Trotter Road, waving goodbye in a flash of khaki on his way to work. In the pantry of the Begam Kothi his son Eugene was starting on the day's first tin of sweetened condensed milk. He punctured the top in two places with an instrument from a rusty Globe geometry box and began to suck, glaring over the rim at his wretched sister, Eugenie. After a little while Victoria passed by on her way to the throne room and patted Eugenie's head. Then she bolted herself in and was not seen for half an hour. Encouraged, Eugenie competed fiercely for the run of the pantry, but invariably slunk off to the far corner with a pale blue tin of powdered milk which she ate dry without a spoon. Lately, not long after the sound of the motorcycle died down there came another sound, a new sound like rolling thunder. It did not come out of the sky, which continued blue and cloudless, but it echoed there and tumbled back down to the flat dusty plain where it had begun. It was a rumbling hollow sound that came in waves, like a thundersheet being shaken, and in fact it was the sound of steel. Barely audible in the old days, in recent years it had swollen into a plangent booming.

In which I introduce literary echoes

I wish to introduce literary echoes. For a long time I have wished to introduce literary echoes. I have yearned and yearned to introduce literary echoes, but have held back for fear of ridicule or misunderstanding. Now I have found courage, but I will do it quickly and limit myself to three. They follow:

DA!
DA!
DA!
—*The Waste-Land*

BOUM
BOU-OUM
OU-BOUM
—*A Passage to India*

SUNYA!
-NYA!
-NYA!
—*The Titar-Nama*

This is what I wished to do. Now it is done and my heart is eased. The echoes swell my chronicle and immensely increase its prestige. Praise Him. Praise Him. Praise Him.

(*CHRONICLE RESUMED*)

All over Sans Souci, steel trunks were being packed. You could hear them grating on the floor as they were pulled out of storage, a hollow booming sound, *bou-oum, ou-boum*. DA!—the lids cracked as they swung up, releasing bitter draughts of naphthalene and nim leaves. -NYA! -NYA!—the hinges might have found it all grimly amusing. The booming was muffled as clothes went in—mid-calf frocks, church hats, double-breasted suits—growing duller as the level rose. Then the trunk was full and the next one was pulled out, and *boum, ou-boum*, the thunder started again. The Trotters were getting ready for Independence.

Not all were packing, and not all believed that the British were really going to pull out of India. Of these, some actually brought out full trunks and proceeded to unpack ostentatiously, to their neighbours' annoyance. The uncommitted limited their bravado to political debate: the Congress party couldn't possibly manage on their own; it was a bluff; the British had too much at stake here; now that the war was over, both sides would see sense; each would see how much it depended on the other. Unconvinced, the packers packed on. The unpackers turned to making almirahs. Caught in between, the ditherers compounded the noise by pulling out their trunks one minute and pushing them back the next. The thunder was loudest over the railway colony, which had long been where the majority of Trotters lived. It was a rare Victor who could be seen digging in the garden now—and yet in days past the railway homes boasted the neatest row of gardens in the city.

Nowadays if people were not at home they were at the institute playing housie. The ditherers, who might spend Tuesday packing and Wednesday taking everything back out, were especially grateful to be relieved of thought when the cry came: "*Eyes down!*" The game was played with a ferocity never before witnessed: in the one year since the war two persons succumbed to heart seizures while the last numbers of the day were being called. Victoria, who had once sat aloof on her rare visits to the institute, now had herself dropped there early on Saturday evenings, taking with her her lucky yellow pencil stub. Three years after Mr Montagu's death (*God is just*) she discovered the thrills of housie. She had a run of beginner's luck, winning a jaldi five, two houses, and a jackpot, but frittered away the hundred and twenty rupees on coupons that brought her nothing however much she kissed and chewed her pencil. She promised herself that if she won again she would stop—it did her heart no good—and come out ahead. She didn't win, but still bought two coupons for each round. For the jackpot she bought three. There were some who played six at a time, people were getting so restless.

One Saturday the jackpot was three times the usual size. The Trotters were celebrating their leader's birthday, though Young Paul was away in Calcutta. Victoria sat there working her pencil halfheartedly as the caller called: "*One and six, sweet 16; all the sixes, clickety-click; four zero, for-tay.*" Her numbers were filling up but she seemed hardly to notice. Elsewhere in the institute hall people were starting to sweat. The caller called: "*Top of the house, 90; one fat lady, number 8; hockey sticks, 77.*" A few pencils scratched and were still. Then: "*One and nine, 19;—*" and somebody called: "*House!*" A huge sigh went up, but when the coupon was examined it was found that the excited Fonseca-Trotter, a guest no less, had overlooked a number in the corner. He apologized, holding up his hands, but there were glares and boos and cries that it was no joke, men. One woman had torn up her coupon in disappointment; another recommended an eye specialist. The false player was debarred from further play and the caller rapped out: "*Eyes down!*" Victoria already had hers down when she noticed that the third coupon in her hands needed only one number to win. The last number, 19, had been scored out with a single bold stroke. She went over it a couple of times with her pencil while she waited. The caller shook the bag again and smiled maliciously. There were ladies who could have eaten his heart, raw. One to go. Victoria's blood was pounding at the extremities of her body—which seemed a longer way off than usual as she swelled. The 19 was obliterated as her pencil stub went over and over it. Her breath came and went in rapid moans. The lady in front was also waiting on one number: she was rigid and hissing like an engine. Around the hall handkerchieves were gripped uselessly in fists as the sweat ran unchecked into Trotter eyebrows. Victoria, whose eyebrows were almost gone, ignored the salt and hung unblinking over the last number on her card, an 89. The man called: "*Next year, 47,*" and the lady in front let out a shriek that turned into a whistling rush of air that went on and on like the Howrah Mail coming up to the level crossing at the Lower Trotter Road, trailing off into an incredulous whisper: "Home!" She meant "House!" but nobody corrected her. They knew what she meant and looked enviously at her when the caller and the judge agreed that the coupon was shipshape. In a way she was right. It was a big purse, the biggest on record, and it would go a good way towards a P&O ticket to Southampton.

Victoria took the 47 to heart, seeing in it a kind of omen. There was not much time left, then. She began to prepare herself, giving up housie for a start. Next she gave up those little shots of Maxwell's Compound that she took once in a while. She gave up fish. Lastly, she stopped using Mr Montagu's ceiling fan. She spent the time saved in prayer in the attitude of the woman in the painting on the wall. The woman had a cascade of red hair, dove grey eyes, and a heavy jaw, all done in the gelid Pre-Raphaelite fashion. Bands of soft light sloped down onto her face through a high stained-glass window, touching the skin and hair with purple, ruby-red, and blue. In her hands she folded a prayer book. She had all the vitality of a piece of wax fruit. Not that Victoria imagined herself. "That's you!" she would say to her granddaughter-in-law, loving her. In a way the woman was not unlike Queenie (except that Queenie was paler, with a touch of Burmese gold at the temples, and smiled more), and because the comparison sank in, Queenie's hands came more regularly to be folded around a book of prayer. They knelt together, the three of them, praying long and earnestly for a better Sans Souci, a better country, and a better world. "And grant our leaders wisdom in this hour of peril," was their petition as 1947 drew near. "And lead thy flock safely into the fold." And one night towards the end of December, Victoria decided that she had no wish to see the year of omen. She said simply: "Queenie, I'm going Home," and she closed her eyes and crossed herself and went.

"Such a lovely death!" Queenie sighed when they had prepared the body. There was a dignity to Victoria's vast expanse of flesh, the dignity of a beached whale, a massive unreachable presence, palpably there and yet inscrutably not. They buried her at one end of the Tank near where the bathing machine stood, filling in a good portion of the artificial lake in the process so that it was now neither fleur-de-lis nor fish but some new shape without an assigned meaning and only a virtual dimension. (By the monsoon it might have been a frog.) Because it was winter, Victoria's remains could lie in state for a day while the inhabitants of Sans Souci paid their respects. Fey Eugenie, who saw the old woman laid out, could not understand how death could possibly be lovely. Now *she* was called pretty by everybody ("Such a lovely girl!" Queenie would sigh) and she looked nothing like the woman on the bed. But the new year had scarcely begun when she was laid out like a china doll on the selfsame bed, the victim of choking.* And so farewell, Eugenie!

The Lord giveth and the Lord taketh away.—Book of Common Prayer

Winter had nothing to do with either death, but Queenie fortified her surviving child against chills with oranges and Vicks and refused him peppermints. The fact was, the tip of her own nose had suddenly grown numb, as if it had been pressed against a pane of ice. And strangely, it grew more uncomfortable as the winter retreated, being less and less in touch with the rest of her body. It was as though it needed a cold climate to feel at home in once more.

That spring, the Maiden Aunts looked in the mirror and found themselves grown old—all except Dulcie. Dulcie had decided to stop at middle age, and such was the strength of her resolution that she succeeded. Love helped, certainly, for she was in love with someone she had met at Queenie and Eustace's wedding in the cantonment church. It was the army chaplain from Pembrokeshire who read murder mysteries in paperback. The Rev. Percival Reese, red and stout, with a woman's mouth half covered by a moustache,

---

* Little Eugene was in the pantry at the time, but (*let it be recorded*) at the far end, and, being absorbed in his own affairs, did not hear his sister's silent inhalations of powdered milk *until it was too late.*—E.A.T.

was several years her junior, but now he could catch up. When he did, Dulcie decided, they would marry, though she had not yet declared her love. Meanwhile she continued to sit in a row with Faith, Hope, and Prudence, her mondha drawn slightly apart from theirs as they looked out together across the Sea of Tranquillity. When she first confessed her passion to them they blinked at the desert's changing colours and asked:

"Do you—"

"—really—"

"—think it's—"

"*Recitative!*" snapped Dulcie in a rare display of bad temper, and drew her mondha further away. But the bond between them held. Together they invited the reverend over for lime juice and biscuits.

When he came, one April evening, with his grey cassock hitched up, its ends tucked under his broad bottom so they wouldn't foul the bicycle chain, the older sisters met him at the Begam Kothi gate. They fussed over him, taking old-maidish liberties while Dulcie darted inside to do her face and to stir an extra spoonful of sugar into the lime juice in the jug. Another mondha was brought out to fill the gap, so that Dulcie sat on the reverend's right and the others on his left—Prudence, Hope, and Faith, in ascending order—as they faced out across the painted desert. Albert, who happened by, said it looked like the Great Trotter and his four wives, but the joke appealed only to Faith. The visits became a regular feature after that, and in time the mali learnt without being told to put out five mondhas instead of four when he had finished damping down the dust with his watering-can. The Rev. Percival Reese was met at the gate by the older sisters; Dulcie ran inside to do her face; the others said flattering things about her; she came out with her lips bruised watermelon red, balancing a jug of lime juice with five glasses and a plate of ginger biscuits on a tray. And then they sat and gazed out across the Sea of Tranquillity, feigning interest in arsenic and butlers and blunt instruments and listening patiently to minute accounts of daily life in Pembrokeshire while the earth steamed around them. Plainly the Maiden Aunts were not among the packers-and-leavers.

With Victoria and Eugenie gone to their heavenly home, Queenie felt she would like to move back to the Kothi. Eustace, expecting a transfer any month, said it would be silly to move twice: they would soon have to set up house in another district altogether. All the more reason why, Queenie answered. The Begam Kothi felt like home, while the New Armoury—even though the guns were long gone—had bars on the windows. They moved back. Sitting in her old room again, with bougainvillea burning crimson in one window and festoons of quisqualis in the other, she took out her embroidery and breathed contentedly. As she worked (it was a scene called HOME

SWEET HOME) she turned the word *home* over in her mind, slowly, deliberately, wondering what it concealed. A label under the snow-globe said: *Made in Japan*; what was under the word *home*? Did it mean simply the place where things were the right side up and familiar-looking? But what was familiar? Could you be familiar with what you had never touched—like the inside of the snow-globe—even though you felt you had breathed the air in there? (It was water, really, but you knew what was meant.) Was home the place where one was born? Or the place where one hoped to bury one's bones? Was a lodger at home? How long did he need to stay before it happened, before the change made itself felt? Was home the place where your ancestors lay dead? Or where your grandmother-in-law and your little daughter lay buried? Was it simply where you happened to be at the moment? Or the place in your mind where you weren't? The place of your deepest sleep? The place of your waking dreams? The place of your father's fathers (where was that)? Or your mother's mothers (was it Mandalay)? Could you have two homes, like the Begam Kothi and the New Armoury and come and go forever between them? Was the Siberian goose at peace in his winter home? "Not within Young Paul's range!" Queenie laughed softly, the first time since Victoria's death. "Such a lovely bird!" she sighed, and realized that Little Eugene was at her feet.

"Let me see," he demanded, brusque because he had thought she was going to say: "Such a lovely boy!" (*Blind Mother, Imperfect Aesthete*)

She held up the tea-cosy, her needle in a black swan of a kind never known to visit India. The bird had a blood-red beak and yellow eyes. There was a stone bridge, a thatched cottage, bluebells, a lady in a wide skirt and a bonnet, her head turned away. Queenie was working from a transfer, but it might have been Philippa's pattern from a century ago, when such skirts were actually worn. It was magic, neatly worked in colours intimately known, but Eugene turned it inside out with a malignant grin.

"Listen!" Queenie took out her spotted darning shell from her workbox— one of Dulcie's floral tins—and pressed it to her son's ear. "Listen to the sea."

A thousand miles from the ocean, he never tired of the game.

"A trunk-call," she explained professionally, plugging in imaginary wires. But now another word distracted him from the sea. *Trunk-call*: it echoed in his afternoon dreams, a distant trumpeting, wild sonorous and louring; the earth might have trembled under mother and son.

It was Eustace, home on his motorcycle. He came into the room, instinctively turning his good ear towards them. From his pocket he produced a wad of fresh rupee notes.

"Not worth holding up the bank nowadays," he said with a low chuckle. The only time anybody had ever heard him raise his voice was when a quarry owner brought him a bribe. Eustace flung the basket of mangoes with its fringe of interleaved ten-rupee notes over the lantana hedge, abused the man in two languages and came close to assault and battery (*Hasty Father, Wasteful Cop*). "Look!" he said now, and ran his thumb down one edge of the wad to show Eugene how the numbers danced. It was the payday treat. Then he handed the money over to Queenie and went off to change out of his starched khaki which smelt of sweat and vanilla. He spent the evening sawing and planing and hammering; he could drive in a two-inch nail with four strokes, but he liked planing best.

At night, after he had done his rounds with the Three-in-One oil can, oiling every hinge and bolt and latch in the house, and all was quiet as they lay on their beds under the stars, he found he could hear the smallest sounds. He heard Little Eugene repeatedly smooth out his bedsheet; the least wrinkle held heat, the slightest breeze brought relief. The breeze came, out of the east, riffling the tree-tops.

"Listen to the trees," he whispered.

Eugene listened. He fell asleep with the sinister murmuring in his ears, a sound they called high treeson. From the Tank the frogs were calling: *Frogmore, frog-more!* Just before dawn a sudden shower sent the three of them clattering into the verandah carrying beds, bedding, and mosquito nets tied onto bamboo poles. The small rains broke early over Nakhlau that year; the big rains, when they came, would sweep away the Ice Bridge.

> *And now, Cup-Bearer, fetch me some vinegar, or failing that, gall—yes I am in my senses.*
> *There is only wormwood, Narrator.*
> *Then fill the cup. It must be endured. Hear what the pigeon told me.*

(*CHRONICLE RESUMED*)

As August drew near, the peace left Sans Souci. The British had fixed a date for handing over power, and the rumble of the packers-and-leavers drowned out the monsoon thunder. Eustace, still waiting on transfer orders, brought home news of rioting in the city. All police leave was cancelled, and he might shortly be required to live nearer the barracks to be on call.

"What's happening there?" Queenie asked.

"Same thing. H's and M's killing each other. This country." Hindus and Muslims were never so called at the Begam Kothi, in case the servants understood. Eustace looked tenderly at the girl he had married, still young and fresh while he had gone stiff like an old boxing glove.

"Maybe," he said, in his quiet precise way, "we should go."

"Go?"

"You know."

The bougainvillea in the window blazed up on Queenie's cheek. Suddenly she felt that this room, with Pearl's dressing table, and the next room with the picture of Prayer, and all the other rooms made up a satisfactory home. But the chill in her nose was still there.

They compromised by packing half their trunks; the other half could be quickly done—or the first half leisurely undone—depending on the state of general law and order that the fifteenth of August ushered in. The caramel custard would be the test: if it crumbled on Independence Day that would be a sign.

Ruby was also bringing back tales from the city. "This is what your friends do!" she taunted Albert, who was regularly to be found in the company of Boy-Girl and Zafar, another *Nuntio* journalist. She had stepped out of the Civil Hospital one morning after the night shift and tripped over a brass lota that spilled out what looked like leeches. They were Hindu foreskins. Next day there appeared on the hospital steps a clay ghada full of revenge. "Nice sort of friends you have, men."

She sipped the cup of hot tea Dulcie had made her. Albert twisted up his lip infuriatingly. That did it.

"You ever heard of an Anglo doing those kind of things?" Ruby shouted. "*Tell me!*" Her hand shook and she brought the cup down on the saucer. "Even a *third* class one?" She had worked for thirty-six hours with a ward full of Trotter nurses sewing up Hindu and Muslim knife wounds.

When she went home to the old Elephant Wing, Thomas Atkins-Trotter, cashiered private, said: "Why do you think we're 'ere, luv? To keep the peace." He meant the British army, though its troops were now almost all through the Suez Canal on their way home.

Home. Eustace thought about it as he kicked his Triumph to life and raced the engine a few times before getting on. He put a stick of chewing gum into his mouth, turned out of the gate, and roared off up the Trotter Road. The Hindus wanted theirs, the Muslims wanted theirs, the British were going back to theirs. What about us? He had never taken seriously Young Paul's Nicobar homeland idea—an island reserved for his people. A place for those who were neither Indian nor European, who spoke English and ate curries with a spoon. Like the Muslims carving out their holy Land of the Pure, and the Hindus dreaming of a once and future Aryan homeland. But why stop there? Sooner or later the Sikhs would want their own Land of the Pure. And what about the Malabar Jews? Or would they go off to their promised land? There was talk of a new state to be called Zion over there. So many purities! And yet he too wanted a home. He was only half at home here. Could one have a home that one had never been to, that filled one's chest with a prickly longing, like the plainsman's longing for the mountains he has never known? Once when touring on duty Eustace had caught an unexpected glimpse of the mountains. Out of the plain there rose in the distance—quite without warning because the foothills were hidden by a belt of hot green forest—the Himalayan wall entirely covered in snow and gleaming in the clear sunlight. Eustace stood still, breathing so gently he might have been a plant. The miracle hung there, cool blue-white and unreal. At length he turned away and stepped heavily down onto the earth, having floated up an inch or so above the grass. The white wall was not home, he knew, but it was a vital place to which his thoughts would go back again and again. It went deeper than the ordinary longing for a sense of quiet rootedness—it was the sense of a source or spring, maybe one that had to be invented. Like the Hindu's dreaming, or the Muslim's forgetfulness of all that went before the Prophet. What was the reality of the country's past? He had kept his good ear cocked in the history class, taking in the endless invasions, conversions, and climbings up and down the ladder of caste. The latest incursion had produced him, and already he was busy looking for another home. Or did he simply need that healing vision of another place?

He took the long westward curve of the Upper Trotter Road at sixty miles an hour. The sky was still grey after having rained all night. On either side of the road were muddy lakes where the water had collected. A diffused early morning light seemed to come from nowhere in particular, lighting up from underneath a nim tree where the Sagarpaysans prayed on certain days, glowing on the fresh monsoon-green grass, feeding the lakes, slicking the tarred surface of the road. He passed a dhobi's donkey loaded down with hanks of wrung clothes walking, patient and unattended, towards Trotter-purwa. On the other side of the road were three village women going the other way, barefoot and with their saris pulled up to their knees. A little further on were two angels with wings, looking like the marble figures one saw in the cemetery, only they were walking. In the distance by the Ice Bridge, a small crowd of early morning people was spread across the road. Eustace cut the ignition as he approached, making out the ragged figures of day-labourers, a milkman, two electricity workers with a long bamboo ladder hung between their bicycles, a night-soil carter, an ancient speckled eggman, and a traffic constable. The constable saluted as he came up and reported that the bridge had been declared unsafe: last night's rain had raised the level of the Ganda Nala and eroded the foundations on either side. Eustace could see where the bridge had sagged on one side, straining the arch and causing the road to buckle. Two cracks in the surface, about a motorcycle's length apart, ran right across the road and up the containing walls on either side. Even as he looked, bits of plaster and brick came loose and fell into the swirling stream, and the section between the cracks grated and sank a little further. At any moment the mid-section would go and the whole bridge would collapse. On the other side another small crowd watched and waited. It was something to do, and it brought strangers together. The cantonment bridge further up the canal was safe, the constable said, pointing.

Eustace started up his motorcycle and made in the direction of the road that led along the canal to the second bridge. On the spur of the moment he changed his mind and made a wide turn, bringing his machine around so that it pointed at the Ice Bridge again. Fifty yards away he stopped, as precise in rest as in motion, racing his engine to alert the crowd. When he made up his mind, nothing could deflect him. The people on either side hurried out of the way, and Eustace twisted the accelerator as far as it would go. The machine leapt forward. The most important thing was to get to the other side. It was suddenly more important than home.

A further note, very brief, on the crocodile of Hindoostan

His tears are not to be trusted, being the marks not of sorrow but of joy long suppressed. He sheds them when a meal approaches, but often he is disappointed and they turn bitter. He is rarely to be found in swiftly flowing water.

(CHRONICLE RESUMED)

The bridge shuddered as Eustace, Sixth Trotter, went over. As his back wheel crossed the second of the two cracks, the mid-section caved in and fell through. It took with it another chunk at the Nakhlau end, and for a moment— as Eustace spat out his gum—the motorcycle seemed to be going upwards instead of down the farther slope of what had been the Ice Bridge. But the power of the machine carried him across and he roared off without looking back. Behind him a fountain of water rose to the height of the missing arch and fell back. The men at either end, momentarily stunned by the narrowness of the escape, began to cheer. If Eustace had stopped, they might have hoisted him onto their shoulders; instead, they lined the banks and peered into the muddy torrent. Eustace reached the Police Lines just in time to hear the double fall-in. It was a minor scuffle somewhere in the old city, quickly attended to.

Later in the afternoon the bugle call went on and on. This time the trouble was serious.

Boy-Girl had to cross by the cantonment bridge to get to the city. Coming through the cantonment bazar he found the shopkeepers closing their shops instead of opening them up for the day. Those who had started early were dragging their sacks and crates back in. Nearer the city centre the streets were practically empty. Instead of the army of cyclists—bank clerks, accountants, peons, shop-assistants—who converged on the city at that hour, there were two or three men riding in the opposite direction. They looked furtively at him as they rode by, pedalling hard, one man's chain scraping against his chain-guard. Boy-Girl's own pace was leisurely as usual, his radiant kurta and his long hair flowing behind him. He came up silently beside a pedestrian who leapt away, startled. "What's happening, bhai?" he asked. The man scrutinized him without replying and crossed the road, from where he called: "Trouble!" There were none of the usual vendors selling roasted corn; the roadside barbers were gone. The cycle repair man who sat opposite the masonic lodge from early morning till after dark surrounded by pink inner tubes was not at his post. So. "Another riot brewing up," Anil announced to nobody in particular. "Miscreants committing nuisance." When he needed cheering up he spoke in the phrases of Nakhlau journalese. On an impulse he took the road that went by the Council House and saw lying against an unused gate the day's first piece of nuisance. It was the body of a man with knife wounds all over. He was clearly dead. The killers had pulled down his pyjamas to check his religion.

Boy-Girl rode on, his kurta flapping audibly now. He was thinking of his friend, Zafar. When he reached the *Nuntio* offices there were several journalists there—Zafar among them, he was relieved to see. The familiar hum and clank from the print room was dead, and the night-shift typesetters looked ready to go home if they could only find the courage. "Better wait," Boy-Girl suggested. "There must be some food in the canteen."

Edgy speculation took up the morning. In the general quiet, shouts carried from a distance, but there was no gunfire or chanting. Men came in with rumours of looting and burning and killings, but no one would risk going out again to investigate. The telephones were dead, including one that kept up a haphazard ringing. Twice a police truck went by along Station Road using a loud-hailer to advise people to stay at home, but as far as the journalists knew (and they were usually the first to hear) Section 144, prohibiting the assembly of four or more persons, had not been declared in the city. Among the *Nuntio*'s employees there was no sign of mutual suspicion, no danger of their splitting into sides. The men knew each other well, and Hindus and Muslims could be heard loudly denouncing troublemakers of both faiths.

"Let a single troublemaker come through those gates," a Hindu warned, "and we will show him."

"Let *twenty* come," someone risked, "we will show."

"*Fifty!*" came from Zafar.

At noon Boy-Girl brought around cold samosas from the canteen. Day-shift men took out their tiffin-carriers to share their lunch with night workers. Some were too nervous to eat; one or two were afraid of pollution and complained of stomachaches. (At the railway station there were still two sets of tea men who ran up and down the platform calling: "*Hindu tea!*" and "*Muslim tea!*") Strangely, no one had sat down all morning. There was one steno-typist, a small man with a modest moustache, who had been pacing the verandah since nine-thirty. By one o'clock the men began to tire of being cooped up. The editor had not appeared, and it seemed unlikely that the *Nuntio* would come out tomorrow. The night-shift men were getting restless; their families would be wondering. It was then that Boy-Girl had his idea. "We will go out together under a banner of unity!"

The idea caught on because the alternatives were less attractive. A couple of bamboo poles were produced, and ink from the print room. Across a tablecloth the *Nuntio* cartoonist painted the slogan: HINDU-MUSLIM BHAI-BHAI! The banner of brotherhood was raised and the staff of the *Nuntio*, keeping close together, stepped out into the streets. They began to chant their message, growing bolder as they went. "This way!" Boy-Girl yelled, and the procession followed him. No point in wasting their breath on the empty Council House; they turned left into a residential street. "Where are we going, bhai?" asked the little steno-typist. "To set an example!" Boy-Girl answered, and the chanting grew louder as the procession was joined by the curious and the brave, as well as others who simply wished to make their way home. They progressed, gathering support, towards Kaiserbagh, did a round of the Circle, took the narrow road past the Marris Market to Aminabad, whose residents came out to greet them, marched chanting past the park where there had once been a notable bonfire of British fabrics, turned right along the old Cawnpore Road towards the Residency, right again along the road that led back to Kaiserbagh and the Roshan-ud-daulah, in through one Mermaid Gate, past the last king's white throne room, out at the other Mermaid Gate and along a narrow curving street that led to the Lalbagh Circle. By now their numbers had multiplied many times over as windows and then doors opened in houses along the way to let out men shouting: *Hindu-Muslim bhai-bhai!*

At Lalbagh, just short of Hazratganj, the procession was stopped. Boy-

Girl had been wondering for some time what to do with the crowd he had gathered, and now the decision was taken out of his hands. Across the radial road leading to Hazratganj was a cordon of riot police, three deep, armed with steel-tipped lathis. Behind them was a platoon of constables armed with .303 rifles. Their orders were to bar the way to the city's main shopping centre and disperse the procession. Eustace, Sixth Trotter, was the senior-most officer present; with him was a city magistrate. They had waited for the procession at first at the head of China Bazar Road and then at the head of Ruttledge Road until it became clear that the Lalbagh Circle was its destination. After that they drove their three-ton trucks to the Circle and blocked off the two critical roads leading north and east from it.

Boy-Girl was euphoric as he marched hand in hand with Zafar and the other journalists at the head of the procession. The march had succeeded beyond all expectations, and it had been a spontaneous affair led by no political party. In fact, a Congress party jeep had just pulled up and tried to seize the initiative, but no one paid them much attention. Hindus and Muslims were walking amicably together for the first time after months of fear and mutual suspicion. It was raining lightly, but nobody minded getting wet: the rain brought the temperature down and a fresh breeze had sprung up, adding to the general elation. A few young men had clambered over the railing around the island where two or three ragged oleander bushes ringed a dry fountain. One of them climbed up on the fountain and began to sing, waving his fist.

(VERSE)

> *My shoes they are Japani*
> *These pants are Englishtani*
> *My red hat is Russi*
> *But my heart is Hindustani*

(CHRONICLE RESUMED)

The crowd took it up. Every Indian knew the song: it had served in the old days as a marching song. Three days before independence it was a pleasing reminder of a battle almost won. In the Lalbagh Circle it was a mistake. The crowd, brought to a standstill by the police cordon, began to tramp once more. It marched on the spot at first; then it began to make forays here and there. The word *Hindustani* had little appeal to the Muslims: *Bharat*, not *Hindustan*, was to be the name of the new country. Noticing that some of the Muslims refused to join in the singing, a group of boys at the edge gave a mischievous twist to the unity slogan. They began to chant, softly, giggling among themselves: *Hindu-Muslim bhai-bahin!* Their elders turned on them wrathfully, but already the Muslims in the crowd were looking around. After that things happened quickly. A few late-joining Muslims split off, one of them throwing a stone at the offenders as he went. "*You* are the sisters—" they shouted. "We'll be the sister-fuckers!" The chanters, suddenly indignant, picked up stones and threw them back. Around them, others were already looking for stones. Some of the stones began to fly towards the police. A half-brick went through the windscreen of a three-tonner. Another, flung by a man with a grudge, went through the painted glass sign of a sweet shop (*Communal Element, Miscreant*). From the surrounding rooftops boys began to pelt selected targets, aiming either at skullcaps or at topknots. The *Nuntio* group held together, hoarsely chanting *bhai-bhai!* The two men carrying the banner, Zafar and the Hindu who was against troublemakers, climbed into the island garden and dug the poles into the rain-softened earth around the oleander bushes. Through the hubbub the city magistrate was reading his prohibitory order under Section 144 over a loud-speaker. Meanwhile Boy-Girl leapt onto the fountain, pulled the singer off, took his place, and began to harangue the crowd.

"In three days we will be independent, my friends! Let us keep calm. We are all one! When we are one we cannot hurt ourselves. We have shown what can be—let us show what will be! There is still much to do. But for today we must go home in peace. Let us disperse in peace. Go home, my friends! Go home, my brothers! But remember the battle is not over. It is just beginning."

An order was given. The police lathi-charged the front-rankers. Several journalists and typesetters went down, including the little steno-typist, who had his head laid open. Hemmed in from the back, the crowd surged outwards at the sides, the bulk of the marchers fleeing home while a few looked willing to test their strength. Others ran off, smashing windows as they went in search of reinforcements. Already the composition of the crowd was changing. When the police withdrew, the newcomers replied with a shower of stones and bottles. The police charged again; the crowd fell back and returned with more stones. In the broad curving verandah that ran along the shops on the Circle, a small band of looters had stationed a lookout and were working industriously, concealed from the police by the arcade of pillars and almost oblivious of the melee. On the other side the battle had become a ding-dong affair, with the police charging further each time but losing control of the ground as soon as they withdrew. More young men came up, darting out of lanes with fresh ammunition. A few country-made guns went off, aimed at close range and not only at police targets; old scores were being settled. Eustace, who had been waiting on reinforcements, gave orders for his men to fire into the air.

The stoning continued. Boy-Girl had come down from the fountain and kept up his harangue from the slight eminence of the traffic island. The rioters made one last mad rush at the police. "Fire above their heads," came the order. There was a volley, not scrupulously aimed, and two men fell. The rest retreated, panicking for the first time. Boy-Girl fell back against one of the bamboo poles, then fell forward across the railing, spitting blood. Where the blood fell, there opened a deep rut that would never heal. Zafar and a friend ran up and dragged him away. His clothes showed no marks of a wound but from his mouth he conjured an endless ribbon of blood. He was already dead. His ghost flapped swiftly up above the Circle in the shape of a pigeon, loth to abandon its theme.

A sermon—cut short

My friends, the struggle is only just beginning. [*Flutters above the scene*] That was a victory, no doubt—the march today. Until all this. [*Wobbles head*] And now we are back to the old game. That tailor is my enemy because he wears a skullcap and a beard, this clerk is your enemy because he has a foreskin, and so you produce your knife and I have my petrol can ready. And when we have glutted our revenge we look around us and see what is razed and what is still standing. My hut is flattened, your hovel is smoking, and across the road behind the high wall with jagged glass along the top is sethji's mansion where the chauffeur is polishing the imported car. And we start to rebuild, but our houses look more like the old ones we knew than sethji's mansion. I do not resent that, because some day I intend to live like him, with my own jagged glass to keep you out. Perhaps this is why I celebrate this thing called Independence. Because it sets me free to do as I please. [*Flaps to another perch*]

Celebrate it by all means—no, perhaps not by *all*. It is no small victory. We have waited a long time for it and there are still one or two of our leaders whom we can trust. They have plans for us. Yes, from up here I can see a little further than you. The First Five-Year Plan. [*Coos*] That is good. A man can wait five years. After that there is another plan. It is called the Second Five-Year Plan. Well, it can't be helped. A man who has waited five years learns patience. The shortfall in the Second Plan, it is announced, will be made up in the Third. This is a comfort. By the Fourth Plan a man is getting on—and the old leaders are dying off. So are the old freedom fighters. The young ones, who wear their uniform, are fighting for something else altogether. Something has happened to their khadi—it's gone very white and fine. The old socialism too is changing. Like the risen sun it's gone from red to pink to gold. Wait a little longer. By the Sixth Plan there will be hotels in this country where in one night you can spend what you earn in exactly one year. There will be a people's car—it will take one Five-Year Plan to appear—that costs what the average Indian earns in exactly one hundred years. This is exactly sixty more years than he can spare, considering the average life expectancy, but there it is. There's no pleasing everybody—except, that is, with song-and-dance and dishum-dishum from the Bombay talkies. Independence from Britain, yes. London is finished, my friends: the day after tomorrow we are free and there is no more Westminster. But the day after that you must make room in your hearts for Los Angeles. Bombay–Los Angeles and Delhi–Moscow. And between these borrowed stools we will fall. And even our fall will be a parody. It has happened before. And here in Nakhlau we will imitate the imitators.

It's confusing, so be ready for confusion. But don't confuse the confusions, theirs and yours. Theirs is easy to identify but still confusing. The Plans will go on, Seven, Eight, Nine. Then, to complicate matters, there are the Programmes. A Twenty-Point Programme. A Five-Point Programme. And then the Fronts, the Schemes, the Operations, the Drives. It's hard enough for an educated man to unravel. He hears the claims, reads the statistics of progress, and looks around him and has his doubts. Then he wants forgiveness for his doubts. He hears more claims, is shown evidence, and he believes. He thinks: the colonial heritage. Teething problems. Development is not a tea party. And he is ashamed of his abstractions, his expectations. He says: When you consider the odds against us, what is astonishing is not that we have achieved so little but that we have achieved anything at all. Progress is always uneven. One thing at a time. He has been won over to their confusion. And the irony is that the progress is there. Everything has changed and nothing has changed. But to show that the change is for the better is their confusion.

Yours is still harder to see because you will want it confused—the old business of the tailor with the skullcap and the clerk in the dhoti. Here you see its results. Look hard. Tomorrow on the trains to Pakistan it'll be worse. And even after Independence it'll haunt us. Who adulterates hospital medicines and sells them to illiterates? That little man in the blue shirt, he's the villain. Shit on him. But you blame his foreskin. The Second Plan dam develops cracks by the Third Plan. Who is the villain? That contractor with the race-horses and his own five-star hotel. Shit on him. But you blame his turban. Who keeps the pensioner waiting fourteen months for his pension of forty rupees because he cannot afford a bribe? You. Shit on you. Shit on that famine-year hoarder—it is a kindness (*Lax Boy-Girl, Lenient Bird*). Independence! You have my sympathy, my friends, those of you who will live to see the mockery of it. Better to have died two days before, like me. And the quality of your rulers will not improve. Or will you get the government you deserve? This very Legislative Council [*points*]—it will become the Legislative Assembly—will be clogged with men whose only redemption is that the man in the next seat is still more vicious and deceitful and corrupt. Perhaps that is why such buildings are circular. Shit on them, my friends. This boy you see looting here will be Minister of Self-Help one day. He will charge the state exchequer two hundred thousand rupees for medical expenses *in one year*—and for travel *in the same year* he will charge twice that amount. So much travel makes a man very sick. Let us shit on him now, in public. [*Swoops down from perch, does so*] Freedom fighters will ride free on buses: very good. But these men will ride free in Mark 4 Ambassadors (if imported cars are not available) with sirens and flashing blue lights, scattering pedestrians before them. The pigeons of this world know what to do with such men—they always have known. If you live to see one of these cars, look quickly as it tears through the traffic and you'll find our mark. The chauffeur wipes it off—it's there again. The pity is that there is not enough to go around. This in a town noted for its pigeon-fanciers.

Never mind all this firing. One or two are always killed—sometimes more, when the Commander is Dyer. But I too am a dyer-and-dhobi by caste—look, this arm is blue. [*Holds up blue wing, wipes beak*] And maybe there is a little of this dyer business in you too. At least he and his men were foreigners—now you will want to blame the pinkness, the yellowness. But wait. The same weapons, the same laws, the same powers of detention, the same curbs on the *Nuntio* will be useful when the government is our very own. Then your fight for freedom, for simple ordinary rights will no longer be a patriotic act. Why? Because freedom has already been won! Then—

(*CHRONICLE RESUMED*)

What happened next Boy-Girl saw in a flash. He broke off his sermon and swooped down to warn Eustace, but it was too late. Down below, the crowd had dispersed, the battle over, the Circle bare except for a litter of stones, shattered glass, half-bricks, and bits of clothing. The rioters had carried away their own, while a three-ton truck (the one with the hole in the windscreen) was being sent back with police casualties. The truck backed towards Eustace, who stepped aside to let it turn and was momentarily cut off from his men. In that space three men slipped out of the nearest lane and came up behind him, as fate would have it, on his deaf side. It was too late for Boy-Girl to intervene. Already Eustace, Sixth Trotter, had one foot on a golden ladder that had appeared in front of him. The three-tonner passed through the ladder, its massive differential lobe making no dent in the rungs. A head-constable in the back of the truck half saluted, then looked away and frowned.

Eustace, already on his way up, acknowledged the salute with a preoccupied air. The wounded men looked puzzled at the sight of three angels in the Lalbagh Circle. The gold ladder was also strange, standing as it did in an evil drain whose only cover was a narrow slab for wheeling bicycles across. "Well, that's all right, then," Boy-Girl said as Eustace climbed higher and higher, his face shining. His khaki uniform fell away, with its dark patches of underarm sweat that smelt of vanilla and three new stains at the back, on the right. It was replaced by a radiant surplice spun out of molten glass and stuck with feathers. A few steps higher and one might as well have tried to look at the sun—though the ladder simply sloped up into the low grey clouds. On the way it passed through the telephone wires on the other side of the street, narrowly missed an upstairs surgical goods warehouse, and hung swaying over the rented barsati on the roof where a row of damp underclothes was hung out on a line. After Eustace disappeared, the ladder remained, like the rut in the road a permanent fixture of the Lalbagh Circle, though the gold came away and the bamboo was splintered once years later when a chief minister's motorcade went by at high speed in Free India.

> *And now, Mr Speaker, what is this age we have entered?*
> *First, something moist and fruity, Citizen Cup, for my mouth is dry with grief.*
>   *Rooh-Afza—my sweet Cup-Bearer! Come, trade sip for sip democratically as*
>   *I tell you of the age of diaspora.*
> *Diaspora, Narrator. That is a cure for headaches?*
> *Dunderhead Cup! It is the cause of headaches. Now listen to what the grouse*
>   *told me.*

(CHRONICLE RESUMED)

DA! There was a clap of thunder, and it rained for three days without stopping. The rain brought cooler weather so that the caramel custard at the Begam Kothi did not crumble. Eustace (*Translated Father, Martyr Pater*) was not there to share in it and Queenie, who had made it automatically, remembering a pact, simply sat and stared at nothing. Never one to waste, Eugene, Seventh Trotter, took a spoon to it out of duty. Meanwhile the other thunder continued, *boum, ou-boum*, as the leaving Trotters packed. Some were already gone without waiting to celebrate Independence Day, some left shortly after. Over the months the rumbling grew fainter, but it never quite died away. The Trotters would always live out of trunks; even those who had built almirahs did not know what to do with them. There would always be packers-and-leavers at Sans Souci, even when there was nowhere to go.

Shortly after independence there was another bereavement in the family.

It was Young Paul, getting on for seventy. For some years he had been losing weight and had suffered from HighBloodPressure and hardening of the arteries. He had missed his knighthood and that was good for him (it had gone to that Gidney-Trotter), but he felt disappointed for his wife, the whilom Belle of Bangalore. Towards the end he would complain of dizziness when he came over to call on Queenie, a disorder, he said, of the oblongata—which Little Eugene took to mean either a constriction at the calves or a new order of decoration. His tilt had corrected itself; he had been reading about what was found in Germany. Albert said, with a roll of his pawky black eyes, that he had gone so far to the right that he had come round on the other side. That may have been so, but he had cause to regret his drollery, because the next day Young Paul simply toppled over, forwards, and died. He left a note in his lizardskin wallet which said: *I shd prefer cremation*. This came as a surprise to everyone, including his wife, with whom he had apparently never shared his views on the corruption of the flesh. She decided bravely that the note was to be respected, and the Maiden Aunts volunteered to select an urn for their brother. Lacking the necessary experience, they came up with a shallow pottery vessel.

"*That?*" Suchi demanded. She had dropped in to comfort the bereaved wife. "That's an ashtray!"

"Well?" Faith wanted to know. She had never been very close to Young Paul. Dulcie offered to go back to the shops and returned with something larger.

"Oah-foah! Now they bring a sugar-bowl."

It wasn't, but Suchita was growing impatient. "He was *big*," she reminded them, as if she alone knew how big. The whilom Belle of Bangalore looked witheringly at her, but Suchita went off to buy the urn herself. She found a massive brass jardiniere and brought it back in a tonga. Young Paul was then cremated Tankside, on the farther shore, and his ashes were placed in it on the mantelshelf between a pair of boar heads. It proved too heavy and came down two weeks later, shelf and all, one afternoon when his son Marris was alone in the room wondering about the future. Marris was shaken, but took courage when a flock of house sparrows flew out of the urn and fluttered crazily around the room until they found an open window. There was no trace of ash in the jardiniere. That decided him. The doubts that had begun to gather in his mind about following his father into politics were cleared away, and as he would recall on many an occasion: "*I flung myself instanter into the fray.*" He was elected without opposition—or none that he couldn't crush with a battery of *whereases* and a ready stock of legal phrases weighted, *as per consuetude*, with italics. And years later when he had consolidated his position and was the unchallenged leader of the community, with his own magazine and a seat in Parliament, he would speak with a kind of mystic awe of that moment when *"the mantel descended on me."*

Her husband no more, the whilom Belle of Bangalore gathered up her daughters and left for England. If Marris wanted to stay, that was his business; he was a grown man now. He had the reputation of being one of the ablest lawyers in the new country, and perhaps he had a better future here. For some weeks the thunder emanated from the Comb, *boum-ou-boum*, and then they were gone, including Mavis, Queenie's best friend and confidante. They left behind them all the hunting trophies, more than three hundred at the last head-count. Marris, who also fancied himself a shikari, was happy to stay on among the antlers and glass eyes. When he was bored with a case he fired at the wall from the hip and brought down a tiger, left-barrel or right-, already stuffed and mounted. After he got married, however (to a delicate Fonseca-Trotter crooner at the Uberoi's Coral Gables), his wife, whom he never again let work, grew house-proud and put an end to the practice.

Next to go was half the Olympic hockey team; only they went the other way, Down Under. The result was that India's hockey supremacy was lost while Australia would become a team to reckon with. Australia took Trotters by the thousand, provided they were no less than seventy-five percent white. Notwithstanding the percentage, Perth was the beginning of the end of the White Australia Policy: liners from Calcutta to Black Perth were usually full going out, and once the good ship *Cimmerii* was held up off Freemantle because a forty percenter had wangled his way on board. Some went on to other cities, turning Welsh and Spanish along the way. But the bulk of Trotters went Home, to England. Every second house in the railway colony echoed hollowly, its former inmates somewhere past Gib on the way to Southampton. Those who remained to see other Indians move in next door complained about the state of their neighbours' gardens. "All bhuttas and brinjals in the front, men. No nice flowers, nothing." The Railway Institute shows were not what they used to be. People came, but there was a new loneliness in the old ones' eyes. Once a cow was found grazing on the badminton court. In the first decade five out of ten Victors and their families went; by the end of the next decade eight out of ten were gone. Outside the railway colony the pattern was much the same. And although nobody in the old Elephant Wing declared himself for leaving, there was a small persistent *boum* that kept sounding in some elusive corner until one day Ruby woke up with a cry to find Thomas Atkins gone. In the dusty corner where his trunk had stood was a clean floor-coloured rectangle. One of the Victors reported having seen him go through the gates of the Charbagh Station to no send-off at all. Just before independence his fellow soldiers (the last British regiment to leave Nakhlau) had had a very different farewell. Trotter girls had lined the platform to wave their fiancés

off, and there were streamers and bunting. "Write soon!" they cried, and their
lovers promised to send for them without delay. And then hankies were
fluttering as the train pulled out, Britain withdrawing, and the soldiers were
singing in their funny foreign accents, "Bye-Bye Blackbird."

After the first shock, Ruby took it well. The boys, educated on Pearl's
Hollywood dollars, were grown up, already officers, Thomas in the army,
Richard in the navy, and Harold in the air force. Ian was talking about
mechanical engineering. The girls were teachers in Dulcie's school and other
Trotter schools around the country. "You're better off without him," they
told their mother. "Nothing but a loafer he was." And Ruby stayed on as
matron at the Civil Hospital where the nursing staff was also changing. "Half
our girls gone," she would come back and weep, her starched cap wilting,
but she never missed a day. Her eyes were often red nowadays, set in dark
purple hollows that made her look older than she was. Each morning as she
returned from the night-shift Queenie greeted her with a cup of tea—served,
since the accession of England's second Elizabeth, on a coronation commemorative tray. The two ex-wives sat in the pantry of the Begam Kothi and
talked about the way things were going.

"Sometimes I wonder if there's any future for us here, Queen."

"I don't know, Mrs A. We can only pray."

"Don't call me *Mrs A.*, men. That *wicked* man. You can call me *Ruby*."

"Sorry—Ruby. It sounds funny."

"What you mean, funny?"

"I don't know. Me so young calling you Ruby."

"Well, everything's changing." A pause. "And you're not *so* young."

"No."

"You're not packing, are you?"

"Half our things were packed when—"

The widows sat in silence, considering their variously departed husbands.
Then Ruby said: "It's for the children's sake that I would want to go."

"But your children are doing so well, Mrs A. Sorry. Ruby."

"Yes, men."

"In the army and all. Thom must be going to be a major soon, no?"

"Yes. Richard too's doing well in the navy. And Harry could become a
squadron leader easily."

"Such nice-looking boys. And the girls too."

"The girls too."

"So why you worrying?"

"I don't know, men."

"Now *us*. I—sometimes I—"

"Oah ho, Queen. It's all my fault, complaining away. Here, I'll make you a cup."

"All right."

"There!"

"Thanks."

"You want a hanky? Go on, blow your nose."

"Thanks. It's just that the little chap—well he's not really little any more—I suppose he was never little (*Truthful Mother, Grail of Grace*). He doesn't seem to be doing—I don't know—he's just—all he does is eat and sleep. And he's not, I mean—he's thirteen. Never studies or anything, and if you shout at him he hides and sulks. And, oh my, the tantrums when he was a little chap—I mean when he was younger. Remember once we bought him a yellow gas-balloon at that St Thomas's fete? Well, coming home he accidently let go the string. Oh my. What a shindy. Ready to burst he was. And his poor little sister—what to say? *You* know what happened. In this very room. Now he says he wants to be a singer if you please—and not nice numbers—you know, our sort of songs. Funny-funny numbers from old books that Aunty Dulcie gave him. The trouble is—even she says—he can't even—" (*Slanderous Mother, Mater Traitor*)

At which point Eugene declared himself from behind the pantry whatnot and ambled across to the doolie for a consolatory snack.

How the doolie is made

I wish to shew how the doolie is made. The adept must set aside his motorcycle because not much time is left him before he is translated. Best that he leave behind some memorial or memento of his invention. If he is a handyman a doolie is best to make. It is especially necessary if the art of ice-making has been lost or abandoned, for leftover foods must be stored somewhere. Not every family can afford a refrigerator. It is here that the doolie finds its justification. The plans may be drawn up on a sheet of Trotter paper with a piece taken out of one corner (there is such a piece in the glasshouse). Wood, wire mesh, tools, nails, hinges, hasps, clasps, and the like are all at Uberoi's in Aminabad, but the adept may not wish to go so far. This side, in Narhi, Teli Mahesh used to stock such things but now he has reverted completely to oil. But next door there are ironmongers and the like. Start below, honest adept, with a platform of mango-wood perhaps three feet square such as the Great Trotter (*Path-Treader*) may have left behind. Attach four uprights to it so that it has legs perhaps six inches below and corner posts extending three feet upwards. On the uprights clap a top which corresponds exactly with the base and insert one shelf, likewise corresponding, half-way up. Stretch the wire-mesh around on three sides and place a twin-leaf door, also meshed, in front. This is called a *doolie*, no Trotter home being complete without one. Food of every description may now be placed in it. Such as: last night's fish curry (but never in months that have no *r* in them), boiled milk in dekchis (not to be confused with deck chairs), yesterday's cream in a bowl, today's cream in another bowl—both covered (even in the doolie) with a beaded doily—a chop or crumbed cutlet from dinner, a round of guava cheese with a wedge taken out of it, mango paste in amber layers, a quarter-plate of curry puffs or mince patties, fried peas in a saucer, a crock of vindaloo or else Irish stew, an enamel bowl of curds, Horlicks jars of tiny onions rusting in malt vinegar, tomato jam, guava jelly, stuffed chilli pickle, mango chutney, kal-kals, gujiyas, a jug of sweet rum punch (made with milk), cold sweet potatoes, spiced collar, mustard, barley-sugar, an aluminium tin which holds chapatis folded in a napkin, a bottle (i.e. a jar) of pure ghi, but never the Smarmite bottle, which goes on the what-not between two candlesticks. Take then four large tins of cheese, swiftly empty them and fill with water. Stand the doolie with one foot in each, perhaps on a smaller cheese tin inverted. Thus is a moat formed around each leg, and ants are made blubbering fools. Do, gentle adept, not forget to nail a little catch that swivels up and down keeping the doors doubly secure. It is a silly plectrum-shaped lobe of wood made by whittling. This is what I wished to shew. So do that. Do it quickly. The double fall-in is already sounding. Praise Him.

(CHRONICLE RESUMED)

Time ran out on Eustace before he could put the catch on the doolie. As a result the doolie doors would swing open at the least vibration, the front door blowing open perhaps, or a chair falling back as Eugene left the table. Whenever she found the doolie open Queenie believed her husband had come back. As a test she placed a small cut-glass bowl of freshly ground mint chutney on the upper shelf every day, though now that Eustace was gone no one in the Begam Kothi cared for it. And sure enough, every night the smooth golf-green surface of the chutney was broken, a single hole showing where the ghostly finger had been dipped in. It was proof, all right, but she misread the golf-course omen.

Assured about the next world, Queenie began to worry about flies in this. "Just make a little catch for it," she pleaded with her recumbent son, for whom the doolie was a second home (*Upright Trotter*). But Eugene had his voice to train. At such times Queenie would wish out loud that there were a man about the house. Dulcie, she claimed, spoilt the boy. The sometime diva, who had taken him up again after Eugenie's death, thought rich tea cake might help and experimented on him with excellent results. "One last palely loitering slice," she would declaim and push the Fonseca specialty toward him. Even he, after eight wedges, was forced to put up his hands. "Go on," she urged. "Start with the thin end." It always worked. And the good woman sat beside him, fondling him with her eyes and sighing as he picked up the crumbs with a moistened fingertip. Lipstick apart, it was the same look that came over her when she sat beside the Rev. Percival Reese, dreaming of the many ways in which she would feed him after they were married. And one day she said inconsequentially to Queenie: "You know, my deah"—after all these years she still had her Royal Albert Hall accent—"you should consider marr-aying again." (*Arch Temptress, Unspeakable Aunt*)

Queenie looked up, her eyelids rising in three quick strokes. She felt a sudden chill in her nose as she lowered the duchesse-set she was appliquéing. These days the chill was almost a pain—except when she bent close over her thatched cottages and bluebells. It was worst—like frostbite thawing—on days when the weather was hot. Today it was hot enough to melt the wax in her ears. The throbbing she could bear. Once her fingernail had been drawn under the needle of the sewing machine and stitched through twice. It was vivid blinding pain, but she had only gasped and bitten her lip. What was unbearable with the nose was the sense of being divided, of one part needing to be somewhere else, in another climate. Since Eustace's translation she spent much time praying, having taken down the picture of Prayer from Victoria's bedroom and transferred it to her own. Installed there, it confronted her kneeling figure like a mirror. She remembered Victoria's saying: "That's you!" and couldn't help a small flush of pride. She meant to devote the rest of her life to prayer and contemplation. In the early morning, when God was most evident in his creation, she would wake before anybody else and steal out for a walk. The cool fresh air and glassy light made her tremble with joy as she stepped softly toward the ruined Gunpowder Gate. "Lonely as a rain-gauge," she murmured as she took the day's reading, and turned to find Eugene standing behind her with a devious smile. His lips were stained purple with jamuns. "You've got up early," she said guardedly, knowing he had not yet gone to bed. Other days he slept for forty-eight hours with the violet night light on, and woke ravenous. Maybe he did need a father, she thought. There was something else. The other day in the market a man had called out as her rickshaw went by: "*You!* Go-home." In fact she was on her way back to Sans Souci, but she felt that was not what he meant. A husband would be useful at such moments. So, when Dulcie dropped her half-considered remark, Queenie looked up from her needlework and said, ponderingly, "Maybe."

"It's never too late," Dulcie said, her eyes wandering off.

"But who's left, Aunty?"

"Who!" Her aunt almost blurted out: "Percy," when she remembered it was for Queenie. "Well, there's Albert."

"But isn't it—?" Queenie had once thought about Albert and immediately asked forgiveness as a page from the Book of Common Prayer flashed upon her mind. Wasn't there something about *A woman shall not marry* and then a long list that included *her husband's brother*? Anyway, Albert wasn't the steady sort. He had still to find a job. And although he was much nearer her own age than Eustace had been, he—

"He's not really spiritual," Queenie decided.

"No, I suppose not," said Dulcie, quickly. She had a soft spot for Albert. "A pity about Marris, now." She meant the crooner; she detested crooners. "But I suppose that's that."

"Yes." The relief was Queenie's, now. She was actually a little awed by Marris's italics and his seat in Parliament, and had been shocked when he threw himself away on a crooner.

They considered the other options. The railway Victors were almost all gone; those who had stayed on were family men. Ruby's sons were married, the three military ones as well as Ian who had a technical bent and was threatening to do something about the ice factory. The only single Fonseca-Trotters were bandsmen or billiards players, and Queenie didn't want that— even if one would go on to become the world snooker champion. She had had one Olympian; now she wanted a settled life. The boy had enough late nights as it was. She shook her head over the lean spiritual pickings. There was of course that church-mouse, Daniel, a small shy sober man who smelt of Glucose biscuits and was a clerk with the municipal corporation. He was steady—he had never to anyone's knowledge taken a day's leave—but he was far too mild to handle the boy. He looked carefully at the world but kept his counsel. Then she thought of the Kahn- and Alexander-Trotters in the Rib. Now there *was* a certain man about her age, Reuben by name, the ex-actress Suchita's grandson, who was a lay reader preparing for ordination. He had smiled at her once in the chapel, baring all his teeth but none of his intentions. Still, he associated with American missionaries so he must be reliable.

O Mother beware the Foul Fiend's snare!

He was possibly a year or two younger, and he did wear his hair in a gigantic beetling pomade-stiffened puff, but his clothes were decent and he looked the sort who wouldn't spare the rod (*Old Testament Monster, Philistine Clod*). Someone said he had once been a finalist in the Nakhlau badminton tournament; he had the wiry build. His cousin, Soma, Suchita's other grand-child, sang in the choir. Such a lovely girl!

(VERSE)

Sweetest of Aunts, Dark Moon;
Dearest of Plants, Jamoon. *

(CHRONICLE RESUMED)

Soma was a soprano. Ever since he was as high as a pewback, Eugene had watched her in church, in chapel, and before and after, outside. During prayer he stared solemnly at her through the cracks in his folded hands. She was tall and slender and black; in some lights her edges shone purple. Her nails, which grew to extraordinary lengths, were carefully buffed but never painted; against her skin they looked yellow. Repeatedly Eugene found his eyes drawn up the slope of her praying hands to those steady flamelike tips that lit up a perfectly oval face framed by straight glossy hair that grew down to her waist. A pair of wide deep-set indolent eyes looked out from above a long broad nose, grazing impartially on the world's surfaces, storing up food for rumination in private. Soma never turned those eyes on Little Eugene; nor did she ever turn them on anybody else. She kept to herself, singing for the pleasure of it, not caring about the words, and afterward gliding back to her room without waiting to exchange the usual civilities. She did go for walks by herself, though never beyond the ice pits, and although she had a ladies' bicycle, bought in imitation of the heroine of one of her favourite novels, she could not find the energy to learn to ride. On weekdays she typed invoices for the Alexander Cooperative Milk Enterprises (Grams: ACME) whose offices were just above the dairy in the Rib; on Sundays she sang in the choir and returned to her room.

At thirteen Eugene was at last admitted to the Trotter choir from which jealousy and factions had hitherto debarred him. By an unimaginable stroke of luck, he found himself seated beside Soma. He sued immediately for her help with the descant in "The Lord's My Shepherd," a part that he saw required application and frequent rehearsal. Soma, at thirty-nine, thought differently. She found the descant straightforward, even a little vulgar, but submitted sulkily to this importunate cousin who called her Aunty, who was obviously backward and who needed encouragement. She helped him across the highest notes, at *ri-igh*-teous-*ness*, and patted his head absently when he stumbled onto the right note. She would rather have been in her room, sucking Extra-Strong peppermints and reading proletarian novels. Her room was next door to the

* *Eugenia jambolana*—Ed. The best jamuns are ten rupees a kilo.—E.A.T.

ACME office adjoining on the other side what had once been the Great
Trotter's hall of inventions. One end of the hall had been walled off as the
office, while at the other end another wall had been run up to form a boxroom
for the Kahn- and Alexander-Trotters, among whom there were few packers-
and-leavers. This room, where empty trunks were stored, Soma had made
her own as a girl and kept as she advanced into mature womanhood. Here
she spent her fiercely private Sundays, answering no calls and admitting no
callers. She even missed her Grandmother Suchita's funeral (an event attended
by the entire Sagarpaysan population who had not forgotten the skipping-
rope trick) because it happened to fall on a Sunday. "And here I am," she
grumbled, "stuck in the chapel because a minor cousin can't hold a high C."

There was something about the boy. He exuded a slavishness that was
deeply unsettling. His eyes—one blue, one brown—crawled over you, leaving
a shiny viscid snail-track where they passed. You decided to go home and
found yourself unable to move, bound to him by those silvery links. You
found yourself turning from Janice Smalley's heroine—Jenny of the bicycle,
with a rime of mill cotton on her hair—into the loathsome boss, gold-buttoned
and cigar-scented. You threatened to lock him out, but where were you without
him? If you crushed him, a tempting but hardly feasible proposition, you were
lost. And yet soon he would invade your office, or worse.

That year the monsoon broke early. After the first shower, cool winds
flapped across the Tank, jamuns glistened on the trees, fat and purple and
beaded with rain, and throughout India poets turned to writing love poems.
At the typewriter Soma caught herself capitalizing her *E*'s. *DEar Sir*, she
tapped, *May wE rEmind you that your milk bill for thE month of FEb.* For the
next Sunday practice session she took along a store of Extra-Strong peppermints which of late she was in the habit of sucking two at a time. Because
Eugene had made progress with his part, she gave him one. He smiled his
unctuous smile and gave her a jamun in return. It was sweet—he knew where
the best tree grew—but afterwards her mouth went dry and she wanted
another. But there was only one. She had forgotten that jamuns did that to
you; every year the choirmaster warned his younger wards about how you
couldn't stop and what they did to your voice. The next time Soma gave her
young cousin two peppermints, but he gave her one jamun in return. The
time after, she put a fistful of Extra-Strongs into his hands—she no longer
cared for them—but she got one jamun in return. It was exquisite on the
tongue but afterwards her mouth was like a desert; on peppermints it was a
desert in winter. Her descant blew across it in stinging gusts that did the
throat no good. She gave up Extra-Strongs altogether, bringing him her entire
stock, but the jamun habit was set—and still he brought her only one. In
another month the season would be over: her mouth went dry at the very

thought. The next time he brought her none at all. When she complained, there was a smugness in his smile which she smacked off his face before she knew she had struck him. He looked at her, wounded at the heart, and again without thinking she bent swiftly and kissed him. A tiny lens of ice came away on her tongue: he had been sucking the last of her peppermints. To his astonishment, she bent again and gave it back, lingering this time with her eyes shut. Then she turned and glided out of the chapel. He sucked it thoughtfully until it was a minute grain of sweetness which he crushed between his front teeth.

The next Sunday he was not in the chapel. Soma waited an hour, flipping through the hymnal. Finally she returned to the boxroom full of boding. She slipped into her kimono and settled down on the two empty steel trunks that, pushed together end to end with a mattress laid along them, served as her divan. She took down *Lancashire Jenny Fights Back* from the shelf but found she couldn't concentrate. Another year gone. Forty-one, she decided, was worse than forty, the way the second gray hair caused more gloom than the first because it confirmed what might otherwise have been a freak or an illusion. There was a knock at the door. Soma never answered knocks. Then there sounded a C sharp sweetly held. It was Eugene with a basinful of jamuns. At evensong that day the principal descants were missing from the choir, and the singing was not the same. There was also a distracting roll of thunder— *boum! ou-boum!*—that seemed to come from the boxroom in the Rib, which was strange because the Kahn- and Alexander-Trotters were not packing to go anywhere.

Nightly, till the end of the season, Eugene made his pilgrimage to the box-room with his basinful of jamuns. Soma was waiting with a replenished jar of Extra-Strongs, and the thunder rolled—*ou-boum! bo-oum!*—and at the end it was like breathing on peppermints and jamuns, hot and cold and moist and dry and sweet and crying out: *Aunty! Aunty! Aunty! Aunty!* Afterwards he fell asleep, his hand resting like a plump white spider on her breast. When he woke up he found her stroking him as if with a feather. He looked at her hands, touching them for the first time. "How do you type with such long nails, Aunty?" he wanted to know, his boyhood fascination returning. She touched a run of imaginary keys on his back: *Dear Mr Trotter, I think I'm in love.* He felt nothing but her fingertips; and yet when he touched them himself they were like knives. And so each night the thunder rolled in the Rib and Eugene cried out and Soma typed lightly on his back. Then, just when it seemed their world was complete, that labour and capital would live in united bliss, nature intervened.

At the end of the jamun season Eugene's voice began to break. It was not the jamuns or the peppermints but the simple onset of adolescence. He was banished from the choir until the pieces settled, and the Trotters, who had all along suspected something, pounced on the order. There was now no reason, they decreed, for the cousins to practice together any more, certainly not in private. "Come back when you're a counter-tenor," the choirmaster sniggered, a debonair Alexander-Trotter whose eyes regularly returned to Soma. Soma was unselfishly despondent, and forced herself to say: "There *is* a way of keeping your soprano if you really want to. But you'll have to choose between your voice and me." She whispered the medieval Italian remedy in his ear. Eugene already knew, and had chosen: he loved his voice. He would do what had to be done. That night, whistling Scriabin to keep his spirits up, he went to desecrate the grave (*Forgiveness, Great Trotter! Mercy, Fat Man!*). He didn't get very far because it was dark in the Audience Hall and he was nervous. But it was far enough, and a few drops went down the crater through the grill that Mr Montagu had placed there.

He woke in the Civil Hospital. A man with his hair done in a glittering puff was standing over him. It was Reuben. Queenie was there too, the tragic mother, and Soma, and Ruby on the night shift and two very pale American missionaries. "You should be grateful to these good people," was the first thing Reuben said when Eugene opened his eyes. "And give thanks that they have a Land Rover." He went on in that vein until Ruby, as head matron, led him away. Queenie followed shaking her head, and then the pale missionaries. Before leaving, Soma bent and whispered affectionately in his ear: "It's not *all*—you know—gone, the doctor said. And anyway *you* could afford—" The nurse drew the curtain. Left alone, Eugene tried his voice, but it was neither one thing nor the other, and he saw that he would always linger in between. After a week he was transferred to the American Mission Hospital, where they took out his tonsils for good measure and brought him ice cream and an OT paintbox.

(INTERPOLATION)

OT

All this bloody business about genius and creativity. All balls. Painters are made, not born. Now, singers, that's another matter—though some used to be made. But with paint you start with a box. Paper, pencils, something to rest on, something to copy and you're off. So the first few efforts are miserable and the next fifty hardly worth preserving, but the habit is formed. Simple OT. That's Occupational Therapy—in case you've not been in an American hospital. Not the Old Testament—we'll soon have enough of that from Reuben, that is, until his Baltimore conversion. So. OT makes a painter of you since you're obliged to switch professions. A great singing career cut short and you end up with a squirrel-hair paintbrush and a box of OT water-colours and time on your hands. Fat fingers help, naturally, the shorter the better when you come to miniatures (not yet) where the strokes are controlled and your scope limited. So you scribble away and before long it happens— the first adequate mimetic version of the real. A vase over there: a vase on paper. A lady over there: a lady on paper. A picture of a lady over there: a picture of a lady on paper. A miniature over there—no, not quite so soon. Before you know where you are you can copy anything (miniatures apart) that's put in front of you without resorting, like old Henry Salt—remember him?—to the camera obscura. Pictures are easiest of all—they're flat, the copying already done for you. You simply copy the copy. And can we here and now and once and for all abandon the fetishism of the Original? All art is imitation—the point is to make the imitation sing. And sell. The museums of the world are filled with copies, and copies of copies. Call them fakes if you like, but they fool a lot of fakes too. I should know. Because, oh my, the wrath, the tantrums, the vindictiveness, the sheer *ill grace* when they find out! Threats, intimidation, Interpol. Advance blood money to hounds like Carlos. Why won't they simply accept the facts, these dealers, auctioneers, curators, and—lowest of the low—art historians? The point about a copy is that it *improves* on the one that went before, edulcorating, dissolving the old imper-fections, the contradictions of the original, so-called. All the sly designing of the first copyist is reproduced, but filtered through the guile of the next man, so that what you have as your copies multiply is a progressively better product. You learn that right at the start with the hospital life studies. Nurses aren't prudish, praise the Lord. Your work gets better and better and soon there are enough improvements to warrant speaking of an epistemological break—a painting with no allusions to the past. A new painting—not an original one— just one that has no direct link with the world. And when you first learn to dispense with the world—or squash it—you're on your way to becoming a miniaturist. Not quite home yet. A little more OT. All the pretty staff coming to take a peep. Ice cream, hospital food (why do people slander it?), the scales every day—not the musical ones, not for a while—weight back to normal, then going up by leaps and bounds, and all the while your paintings getting smaller. The thing, as I've said before, is to prepare the *artist*. The art takes care of itself. You fatten the fingers, they do the rest.

(*CHRONICLE RESUMED*)

Discharged from hospital, Eugene spent his days in the Begam Kothi, in bed. He reminded Queenie that the doctor had advised complete rest and lifted all dietary restrictions (*Noble Physician, Healing Touch*). Of a morning he discovered the pleasures of chasing dreams while the little sounds of the workaday world filtered through to the bedroom: the *thap, thap* of a dhobi washing clothes somewhere, the sputter of fried eggs from the kitchen; head-mistress Dulcie's hairbrush crackling as she prepared to face the school; a tap running in the bathroom; the tender bleating of the ACME buffaloes from all the way across *Sungum*; the lid of the teapot lifted; a knife in the marmalade jar (that would be Albert). He dozed on till eleven, ate a large breakfast, then slept again till lunch. On her lunch break Soma would come to see him. One day she said: "My goodness, Yev, if you don't stop eating you'll become a proper—" He turned his eyes on her with quiet dignity and stared, unsmiling. She saw her mistake and added: "I mean—you know . . ." but relations between them were strained for some time. Even when he returned to the choir that winter, walking unsupported to the chapel past the crater with the grill, he sat in the second row, behind his cousin. He sensed a reproach between her shoulder blades (she had gone and cut her hair) but he was now dedicated to another art. Rebuffed by the choirmaster, he stopped going altogether and sang for himself in the sitz-bath.

Soma's cousin was also a frequent visitor at the Begam Kothi, only he didn't come to see Eugene. Reuben Massey came daily to ask if there was anything he could do for Queenie. He implied, with a toss of his puff, that his visits concerned her convalescent son, but only once looked in at the boy. "You call me Reuben *Uncle*, you understand?" he growled when Eugene made free with his Christian name. He turned to smile at Queenie, who had come into the room. Then he said a prayer for the sick and the dying and set his hatchet face for the door, touching Queenie gently on the elbow as if to say: *We mustn't disturb the patient.* And he took his goatee and pencil moustache and dark glasses away to the drawing room, where a cup of tea was waiting; he liked it hot. The dark glasses he wore at all times, even indoors, in case he should be taken for a pork butcher. Queenie, whose tongue was always loosened by sorrow, was glad of a listener. These days Ruby was a bit abrupt. By contrast, Reuben held his head at an angle and looked directly at her, although his responses, usually in the form of scripture, with chapter and verse, had no bearing on the subject and came either too late or too soon. His mind might have been running up and down a thumb-index. One day Queenie moaned: "What to do, Padre?" (She already called him Padre, though his collar was not due for another six months.) "He just lies there all day feeding his face and drawing pictures. And some of the pictures—" And Reuben answered: "*A boil breaking forth with blains.* Exodus 9:10." Queenie began to have her doubts. Could you live with a man who issued scripture by indent? Reuben's quick appraising eye saw the flicker at once. He leaned forward and said, dropping his voice very low: "You know, I don't know what it is, but there's something *spiritual* about you." He looked ready to weep.

They were married in the cantonment church by the Rev. Percival Reese. There was a moment of anxiety when it seemed the bride might not turn up. Reuben stood at the front of the church with his best man, the debonair choirmaster, both men craning around, one to look at the church door and the other to look meaningly at a certain soprano. On the altar, sprigs of white and pink acacia wilted. The congregation shuffled and coughed and mopped their foreheads. (*Turn back, Mother! Shun this midsummer madness!*) But then the Maiden Aunts swept up the aisle with Queenie in train. The bride's dress was in a shambles. Large damp half-moons had appeared under her arms. It transpired that the hired car had broken down on the Lower Trotter Road at the level crossing and they had had to wait for rickshaws. Ill temper marred the ceremony, infecting everybody except the celebrant and Dulcie, who seemed rapt away in a rite of their own. The Trotter choir ground out a nuptial hymn with a reduced descant, and then the organ thundered the Mendelssohn march, a hot blast of sound which ran on ahead of the couple and scattered the flies at the door. Afterwards there was a Fonseca cake in the Spur with cool drinks from the Glacerie. (Ruby's technical son, Ian, had not only got a degree in engineering from Roorkee and set the ice factory going again in a modest way, he had opened a small aerated water plant next door in one of the old kitchens.) Then there were photographs which the groom took himself with an American box camera: he couldn't trust anyone else to handle it satisfactorily, and so was missing from his own wedding pictures. Also missing— though indubitably present at the wedding and smiling bravely at the camera— was Eugene. The greyest of grey Trotters was, quite simply, and quite unlike Pearl, unphotographable in black and white.

A few months after he was ordained, Reuben was able to return the Rev. Percival Reese's favour. Not that there was a shortage of clergy in Nakhlau. In the Civil Lines there was a young English minister and his family who drove a Morris Minor. Then there was another English reverend who wore a dhoti and rode a bicycle seven miles a day from his village ashram. His wife wore a sari and they ate rice with their fingers, sitting on an immaculate clay-and-cowdung-washed floor. Of the true church there was a broad gentle Italian Franciscan who had worn the same cassock for (it was said) thirty-seven years. He had thick glasses and went everywhere on foot. His Keralite understudy read Teilhard de Chardin and rode a scarlet motorcycle. Then there was an American Indian, Mr Elkhorn, who carried a green felt board and cut-out Biblical figures in Hollywood-Palestinian garb. But he was not ordained, and so couldn't have married the Rev. Percival Reese and his bride.

Nor could Reuben's missionary friends who gave away powdered milk and medicines and made donuts in an automatic stainless steel machine. The Baptist pastor was an Anglo-Indian who wore a solar topi and was looking forward to the Third World War: it would bring humanity to its senses, he said. The Methodist minister from Ypsilanti looked like Rock Hudson (it was said) and quoted Robert Frost. And there were two Jehovah's Witnesses, an Indian and a Canadian who dressed identically and spoke in stichomythia. Reuben kept all but the Americans at bay, and when Prudence and the Rev. Percival Reese expressed a desire for a private ceremony in the chapel, he discharged the debt promptly. He hated being beholden to anyone. Dulcie was there, wearing an aggrieved look, but there was nothing she could do because she had never declared her love. When the elderly pair went off to live in the New Armoury, taking with them several crates of paperback murder mysteries, she resumed her old place in the diminished row of mondhas that looked out across the Sea of Tranquillity. Her watermelon-red lipstick was no longer carefully applied, and her mouth looked more than ever like a wound. But she refused to close the gap between herself and Faith and Hope. There were times when she felt like packing and leaving, but there was nowhere she particularly wanted to go. It was many years since she had sung a line or even played on the rat-fati school piano that leaned up against three huge clay jars of water in the dry months but got more and more out of tune.

As head of a dwindling community, Marris was harsh on packers-and-leavers. "*Go and become bus-conductors in London if you want,*" he warned. "*But don't come crying back to me.*" Or he might scoff: "*Melbourne is all very well, but can you get mangoes there?*" He favoured the Nakhlau dasheri personally. For those who stayed he had words of comfort and advice: "*This is your home; serve it and it will serve you.*" And just in case the Home should forget to serve Trotters, he lobbied for a new lease on the special concessions that the British had allowed Trotters: job quotas in the railways, the post and telegraph service, police and customs, and grants for the continuation of Trotter schools across the country. The government of independent India was gracious. The jobs, it decreed, would be reserved for another decade; the grants would be contingent on the admission of other Indians to Trotter schools. The schools, moreover, had a constitutional right to teach in English, since that was the mother tongue of a recognized Indian community. Thanks to Marris's efforts, there were appointed representatives in the legislatures both in Delhi and in the states to protect the interests of Trotters—appointed because there were not enough Trotters left to elect a single member by due process. Marris's legal acumen had won him respect among the framers of the constitution; afterwards, during his long, tumid, and eventually dateless career as Representative-in-Chief of Trotters and their kin, he had the ear of the highest power in the land. Except for a brief eclipse along with his favourite prime minister, he bored Parliament for a longer spell than any other member in the history of that boring institution. Because he was appointed and not elected, he had an unusual handicap: he was not corrupt. Thanks to the constitution, Trotter representatives would never need to bribe, cheat, wheedle, lie, deceive

—or forge, Narrator?—

or break promises or—*beware Cup-Bearer*—bones, or even kill to get into Parliament. Marris was clean. Nor was his capacity for work the abiding envy of his fellow parliamentarians, but as a result his achievements mounted year by year. They were recorded in a magazine called *The Sans Souci Reminder*, a slight review edited by Marris himself with a two-colour cover in curry-yellow and indigo. Inside were grey photographs, usually of Marris and invariably hazy because Trotters (Pearl always the exception) fared poorly in black and white. When it came to the text, a technical problem presented itself. Since Marris spoke only in italics and the *Reminder* regularly printed or quoted him, how to distinguish between those portions of text which emanated from him and those that were the work of lesser men eulogizing or quoting him—which was frequently the case? Besides, it was sometimes necessary to emphasize passages in Marris's own contributions that were *already* in italics. Did one return to common print—a font Marris secretly despised as plebeian? The problem was resolved with **BOLD FACE**, a head which came to be so frequently used that between it and the italics the sight of common print was at first startling and then a relief. The result was that people read only those refreshing snatches and took to cherishing inconsequentialities while important announcements concerning the leader simply brought on a glazing of Trotter eyes. At first the magazine was free, but it refused to move. "Put a rupee on it," Ian the ice-and-soft-drinks maker suggested. Marris did, and the *Reminder* sold out. And soon it was being billed as the most widely circulated magazine in the country, not unjustifiably, since there was bound to be a Trotter somewhere in Kashmir and another at Cape Comorin and not a few between the jungles on the eastern frontier and the marshy Rann of Kutch in the west. But the *Reminder* was not the only medium that kept far-flung Trotters in touch.

The Commercial Service of Radio Ceylon (31m)

. . . That was Cliff Richards singing the old favourite, "Summer Holiday," for all the girls of Maqbara, Nakhlau. And next we have a number that I know yo'all are all going to like because it's a great favourite, a favourite of mine as I know it's a favourite of yours, and it must be someone else's too because it's sold a million copies

and it's pure gold, and I'm talking about that great hit, "Please Release Me," by the oneandonly . . . Englebert Humperdinck, and Engels is going to be singing his song for a very special bir'day girl, Tina McKenzie of Madras, who is seventeen years old today—my, oh my—and this wish comes to you, Tina, from Mummy, Daddy, Martin, Roberta, Patricia, Kenneth, and little Rosie, boyfriend Patrick, cousins Valerie and Trevor in Cawnpore, and Uncle Archie in Baihar, and not forgetting Uncles Victor in Mughalsarai and Jhansi and Asansol, may you keep an even keel through life, and may you weather the storms of adversity and anchor in the harbour of success. Bir'day greetings also go out to . . .

(CHRONICLE RESUMED)

Every day the radios of Sans Souci were switched on, already tuned to the short wave 31-metre band. The bad girls near Free School Street preferred the evening show because they slept late, while many working Trotters listened to Ceylon in the morning during breakfast. Queenie, Ruby, the Atkins-Trotters, the Fonseca-Trotters (except for the bandsmen), some of the-Alexander- and Kahn-Trotters, and all the remaining railway Trotters listened to both. Nobody except Albert and the Maiden Aunts and a handful of Alexander- and Kahn-Trotters, including Soma Aunty, listened to All-India Radio. The atmospherics on short wave were a sore point with Ceylonists—at times it seemed that the Shadows had fled leaving Cliff to fend off a Martian orchestra whose whistles, drones, hoots, beeps, and blips poured intemperately out of the upper air—and Albert never failed to rhapsodize over the clear medium-wave reception from Delhi. "Much closer than Colombo, you know," he said, bringing the tips of his fingers together. He still hadn't got a job. Ruby struck back: "All Indian music, men. The only time they ever play English music they play Beethoven. No nice tunes, nothing. And hoity-toity accents and all as if they've all been to Oxford: *A-this is All-India Rhay-dio!*" Dulcie looked as if she might say something but held her peace. Where would you begin? her look said. In the New Armoury, old Prudence and Percival Reese-Trotter tuned in to the BBC World Service. But there was one man who had no time for either India or Britain, much less Ceylon. Reuben Massey-Trotter had new ideas, though at times it seemed his wife stood in the way. True, Queenie had promised to honour and obey her new husband, but when it came to the Commercial Service of Radio Ceylon she refused to yield the old Philips valve-set. Reuben was obliged to borrow a transistor radio from his missionary friends; of all Trotters he alone had an ear for the future. His slim-line battery-powered set, which he polished twice a day with a soft yellow shoe-cloth, faced out across the Ice Court toward the Philippines so it could pick up, with a minimum of disturbance, the Voice of America. And it irritated him that Eugene, whose room was next door, listened to a little of everything, twiddling the tuning knob every few seconds with the volume turned up high. Mostly, however, Eugene listened to the sound of his own voice, which he liked to think of as the Voice of Sans Souci.

Once installed in the Begam Kothi, Reuben began his campaign of harassment (*Vicious Stepfather, Vindictive Ogre*). He declared that Eugene had rested long enough following his accident, and that even complete excision would not have merited such a lengthy convalescence. It was time Eugene found a job instead of being a burden on his mother. Other Trotters of his age were out learning to weld or working in schools and banks and offices. "Or you want to become like that ne'er-do-weller, Albert Uncle?" he sneered.

Eugene would not be moved. "I am working," he insisted, drawing himself up in bed so that he sat with his back up against the pillow and the drawing board in his lap. To avoid getting up to fill his water-jar he simply sucked a brush and dipped it in the paint box.

"Working!" Reuben scoffed. "*Go to the ant thou sluggard: consider her ways and be wise.*" He left the room because the blank thumb-index look had come over his face. A little later he poked his head back in and said thickly: "Proverbs 6:6."

No one could fault Reuben for sluggardliness. Even when he was doing nothing he moved from room to room organizing business in his head. He made exhaustive lists of things to do and the precise time at which they should be done. Almost the first thing he did was to plant a guava tree in front of the Begam Kothi. The Maiden Aunts complained that it was a flower garden and that the tree would one day block off the view of the Sea of Tranquillity. But guavas were Reuben's favourite fruit (*Insipid Cleric*) and that was that. Queenie thought she would make guava jelly and guava cheese (*Sapid Wife*), but her husband said: "Let's see," meaning if there were any left. He watered the plant punctually, applied controlled doses of fertilizer to hurry it up, and measured its height at the end of the month as if it were a child. His movements were precise and economical. If you asked him the time he looked carefully at his Grandfather Alex's watch and said: "3:17," or "10:32," sometimes adding, to be on the safe side, "almost" or "not yet" or "and a half." On Friday evenings at six sharp he started writing the sermon for Sunday. If it was an important Sunday he started a day early. His texts were from the Old Testament because he felt there was more thunder there. But he also worked in improving stories from the *Reader's Digest* to which he subscribed annually because it was cheaper that way. "That's two free copies," he beamed, a Moses coming down from Sinaii. You could always tell if a sermon was going well. He strutted about the house smirking, gave Queenie a kiss for nothing, and was unbearable at dinner. On those Sundays Albert made it a point to go to church to distract him by sitting just below the pulpit and pretending to nod off. He would totter slowly to one side, then sit up with a jerk and look around in measured disbelief. Reuben stumbled and glared at his persecutor, but picked up again and went on. The only time he ever failed to recover was with the YAHWEH sermon.

He started it on a Wednesday and by Friday Queenie was pushing him rudely away. On Saturday Albert felt he couldn't face dinner, but on Sunday he was seated in his place below the pulpit. Reuben read his text and spoke convincingly for fifteen minutes in his neighing voice. It was one of his better sermons, a little high-flown for evensong, and the congregation sat woodenly in their pews. But the message told on Albert, wearing down his antics. Instead of swaying and looking around, he found himself gazing earnestly at Reuben and hanging on every word. Unprepared for the transformation, Reuben became unnerved and lost his thread. "And this YAHWEH," he neighed, "is the . . . is the I AM." He had already said that. "It is the *original* I AM." The blank thumb-index came into his eye. "It is the . . . the *one* I AM. And the *only* I AM. And the I AM . . . the I AM is the . . . is the . . . the great YAHWEH." He paused. "The *original* YAHWEH." Another pause. "The *one* YAHWEH . . . the *only* YAHWEH, my friends." He looked down at his notes for the first time, but his eyes refused to focus. He frowned savagely at Albert and made a little brushing-off motion with his jaw. But Albert was too caught up to notice. "The YAHWEH of the Hebrews, my brothers," Reuben sang, "*that* is the YAHWEH I mean. Let us never forget . . . this YAHWEH. This I AM. And this I AM"—he went in deeper, reckless now and drawn in in spite of himself—"this I AM . . ." He leaned over the pulpit and whispered urgently to Albert, but Albert's stare grew more earnest. He looked pleadingly at the congregation, but the congregation did not easily forgive abstraction after dark. He started again: "And this I AM . . ." There was a silence which must have lasted a minute. Then inspiration came: "—is the I AM." He spun on his heel and faced the altar, but it was all a hot watery blur.

The next day Reuben kept his eyes down and spoke to nobody. The day after that, shame turned to anger and he took up a stick. He couldn't punish Albert, but there was always Eugene. He came into the invalid's room and announced: "*He that spareth the rod hateth his son.* Proverbs 13:24." And he began to belabour Little Eugene out of love, the tuffets of fine hair quivering on the back of his fingers. "How long you think you're going to lie there getting fat on your parents' bread?" Eugene had memorized Proverbs 9:17 for just such an occasion. He repulsed the attack with a few well-placed mounds of flesh, answering: "*Stolen waters are sweet and bread eaten in secret is pleasant.*" And he gave the authority. Reuben made freer with the stick and brought in Ecclesiastes. "*Cast thy bread upon the waters,*" he advised, prophetic in a way he could not have foreseen. "Tomorrow," he went on, "you will go out and start to look for a job. You wait." It was not an idle threat.

On Wednesday (*Day of Woe, of Adam's Banishment*) Reuben had Soma's unused bicycle standing outside the Begam Kothi. He stood over Eugene while he dressed, ignobly curious, and when he was ready presented him with a pair of secondhand stainless steel bicycle clips. Then he led him to the gate and waved cheerily. "It's a ladies' cycle," he called, "so you don't have to worry about anything." Each morning the routine was repeated. It didn't work, but Eugene learnt to ride the bicycle. He used his OT talent to make foolproof cinema tickets and came back after the matinee show looking haggard. He was starting to duplicate banknotes when fate and Reuben intervened once more. An advertisement had appeared in the *Nuntio* for a clerk in the Nakhlau waterworks. Reuben took him there himself. The interviewer, Mr Mathur, a handsome man with a slight onset of leucoderma, said without raising his eyes: "But what is this *Trotter?* It is not an Indian name." It was the standard response. Nowadays if you were a Trotter you might as well not bother applying. But then Mr Mathur looked up and saw Eugene. "All right," he smiled. The rapport was instant. "It is a sitting job." And he took up the pen with his short plump fingers, dipped it in the inkwell, and wrote at the top of the application form a memo to his superior: *Negi Sahib, this young man is most suitable.*

The job was Eugene's. His office, perched on the roof of the main accounts office, was a tiny dark-blue-washed addition that overlooked the first of the settling tanks. There were two rows of these open pools like swimming baths. Beyond were the filtration tanks and then a pump house into which ran several wide-gauge steel pipes, and finally the cylindrical purifying tanks made of riveted steel and painted silver. The office was reached by an external stair that went up the side of the building. Up this stair Eugene, Seventh Trotter, climbed every morning, having ridden his bicycle all the way up the Trotter Road and right across the city, his five-tier tiffin-carrier sliding from side to side on the handlebars and gleaming in the early sunshine. At the top of the stair was a door which opened directly into the makeshift office, a room he shared with Mr Mathur and two other men in sleeveless pullovers and toothache mufflers. Mr Mathur's desk was farthest in, hidden from view behind a cabinet that was turned so that its back faced the door. Next there were the other desks partially concealed in the same way by shelving almirahs. Eugene's desk was nearest the door in a narrow space left by the last of the almirahs. He sat with his back to a window, facing a wall which ran the length of the office with an assortment of ancient filing cupboards stood up against it, reaching to different heights. They had serial numbers painted across the top and were packed with water-supply files tied with faded red tape. Squeezed in there, the Seventh Trotter slaved from morning till late at night (when the sun was virtually hidden by the purifying tanks) with a short break for tiffin. Had it been summer, he might have been hard put to last three months on that roof. As it was, he saw December in.

"So." Mr Negi rocked on the balls of his feet. "This is what you are doing." He was an athletic-looking man with short cropped hair greying at the sides. "*This* is what." Chance had led him to the precise file where Eugene kept his drawings. He picked up one, held it at arm's length, and looked critically at it. "*Lady at Toilette*, Accounts Received. *The Princess Awaits Her Lord*, Accounts Payable. *The Gond's Dream*, Accounts Received. *Samoan Idyll*, Accounts Payable . . ." He went on in that vein a while, raising and lowering himself on his toes. Then he turned to Eugene, standing in the door.

"Naked ladies, *han*?"

Eugene said nothing.

"We are paying you to make naked ladies?"

"It's art."

"Oho. Art. We are paying you to make art."

"I do it at home on Sundays."

"So. You are making art at home. You are making art at home on Sundays. You are making art at home on Sundays on government paper. Then you are putting art in your attachy-case. Then you are putting your attachy on your cycle. Then you are bringing this dirtiness here. For purification."

Except for the motive, Eugene could deny none of this.

"On *Sundays*, Mr Trotter."

A vision of poor Mrs Negi came to Eugene. Like her, he preserved a wretched silence.

"*Now!*" Mr Negi yelled. There was a collective start in the next section, and nibs began to scratch on government paper.

"Now." Mr Negi's voice dropped to a moral whisper. He scooped up an armful of drawings. "Now Mr Work-thief, you can be doing these dirty things on *Monday*"—he flung a handful out of the window where the wind caught them up—"and *Tuesday*"—another handful—"and *Wednesdayandthursdayandfriday*." The drawings streamed through the air above the settling tanks, a pair of kites swooping down inquisitively among them. "*And*"—he tore a sheaf down the middle—"half of Saturday!" The wind spread the last consignment out against the sky until the afternoon was dark with broken ladies. Mr Negi leaned out of the window triumphant, defying a single immodest reentry. The last sheet ended its crazy zigzag dance and lay on the surface of the settling tank. From behind, Eugene watched with a pang the ink of the first sketches bleeding a little. In the distance Bahadur the tank attendant was racing for his fishnet.

Eugene pedalled slowly home. Just past the Ice Bridge he stopped at the ruined shell of the old hunting lodge to eat his tiffin. He sat on a doorstep which led nowhere and ate parathas with mango pickle, a potato dish with cumin seed, a brinjal puree, suji halva with raisins. As he ate he reflected on the truth of Reuben's last prophecy about casting bread upon the waters. He felt a balloon of pleasure swelling inside him. Now it was for him to fulfil the rest: *and thou shall find it after many days.*

Queenie said nothing when she saw him return early; she left the disciplining to her husband now. Today he happened to be out with his missionary friends. Soma, who was over from the Rib on her lunch break, listened sympathetically, her hand on Eugene's knee. When he finished his tale her eyes, usually no more than half open, were wide and sparkling as she stared straight over his shoulder. "Strike!" she hissed, gripping his knee painfully till her knuckles stood out a pale grey. When she saw he was happy to be free, something like scorn flared in her eyes, but it was snuffed out as soon as it appeared and her heavy eyelids slid back down. She patted his thigh and chuckled: "At least now I can have my cycle back." She still hadn't learnt to ride. Eugene grinned, letting the years of misunderstanding melt away.

"There's no more invoices left today," Soma said. "Come have a peppermint."

But Eugene looked away and spoke of Platonic love and how he was married to his art.

"So you're going to paint for a living?"

"Yes. Let him say what he wants."

"You'll go away. Artists are always wanderers."

"Not yet."

"You'll forget your old Soma."

For the first time Eugene felt her knives.

"Aunty!" he blinked.

Surprisingly, Reuben said very little. He decided that perhaps he did hate his stepson and could afford to spare the rod. "*Let him go for a scapegoat into the wilderness.* Leviticus 16:10," he said to Queenie loud enough for Eugene to hear. There was something else on his mind. It looked more than likely that his missionary friends were going to land a scholarship for him at a Bible school in Baltimore. He was in fact half packed already, only his was not a booming black trunk but a flat American suitcase of the kind you took on a plane. He might have to pay his own fare, though, and he was wondering about ways and means. A loan from Ian Atkins-Trotter, whose ice and aerated drinks were doing well enough in spite of competition from the Uberois? But Ian was notoriously tightfisted. He wore his rubber slippers down to lucent wafers and went vegetable shopping late in the evening when greens were cheaper. Reuben crossed him off. Should he sell the grazing rights for Sans Souci to that prosperous Yadav from Trotterpurwa? But the ACME managers (his cousin worked for them) would never allow it. Eventually he called a kabadi-wala and had him assess the contents of the many subterranean go-downs in the Begam Kothi. The ragged old man's eyes glittered when he saw that everything in the world was there, gathered no doubt by some neurotic magpie of a woman in the large old days. He said: "Sahib, fifty rupees."

"Ten thousand, take it or leave it," Reuben answered.

"Sahib. Do I look as if I have ten thousand rupees?"

"Yes."

"Sahib, I will have to make two trips."

"Ten thousand," Reuben insisted, but he sold it for four because the man would go no higher. It was the fare to America.

The next day the old man was about to leave when Reuben called him into the pantry.

"What will you give for these?" He pointed at a row of books on the whatnot, just as Queenie came in.

"Two rupees, Sahib."

Reuben laughed. "One hundred and fifty."

The old man produced fifty. It was Reuben's foreign exchange allowance. Queenie found her tongue. "My recipe books! You know how old that one is? It's the original one from England, not Calcutta." She pointed to *Mrs Beeton's Cookery and Household Management Book*. But Reuben had pocketed the fifty (*Brazen Manager, Household Crook*).

Queenie went on for two hours after the old man had gone. Secretly she was relieved that Reuben hadn't sold her coronation tray. Reuben continued with his packing in silence and afterwards filled the empty space on the whatnot with his badminton trophy. When Queenie had talked herself out he turned to her and said: "Why you worrying? When I get there I'll send you the *latest* edition *Betty Crocker Cookbook*. It's got colour photos and it's *this* fat."

He kept his word (*Stern Justice, Even-handed Man*). Altogether he was gone two years and a few months, but it seemed much less to those who stayed behind (*Wingèd Time, Greasèd Lightning*). Even his cousin, Soma, whom he sent a bottle of Southern Belle Hair Dye in a sea-mail parcel along with the book, remarked on how quickly those years had passed, and she was not looking in a mirror at the time. Also in the parcel were a couple of Betty Crocker cake mixes—Angel and Devil's Food, the former carefully marked with Queenie's name and the latter illegible—sealed pouches of instant wine crystals, tiny packets of Californian raisins, quickset jellies, instant puddings, instant mashed potato, American mustard, and a packet of marshmallows. The parcel was delayed somewhere along the line, possibly at customs in Delhi, where it was opened and samples were taken. Fourteen months later it was delivered. The cake mixes had spilled out and mixed together into a greyish weevil-ridden sand, the instant wine was a chunk of purple semi-precious stone, and the raisins were crystallized. The remaining mixes had come open and run together with the instant potato to form a kind of plasticine the colour of mustard, and the marshmallows had expanded and worked their way around the other contents where they stiffened into a snug protective styrofoam mould. Only the hair dye was serviceable. Queenie used the new cookbook, but she was usually half-way through a recipe, something bubbling on the stove, when she had to run to the lantana hedge and call across it to Ruby: "What's allspice?"

Eugene bore the loss philosophically. An American parcel ruined was a small price to pay for having Reuben safely lodged at the other side of the planet. Besides, America had already arrived intact in the bookstalls of Hazrat-ganj. The gentry of Nakhlau, adults as well as children, were agog for the new offerings, but it was the children who did the buying. When he was tired of painting, the Seventh Trotter would amble across to the Elephant Wing, where there were piles of dog-eared Dell Comics. And a whole New World was opened up. But usually it meant being headed off at the gulch on the way back by a posse of young Atkins-Trotters with their bushwhack lariats and six-guns and silver bullets.

> *Howdy Narrator!*
> *Howdy Cup-Bearer.*
> *Goin' somewhere?*
> *Nope.*
> *I thought maybe you was goin' somewhere.*
> *Nope.*
> *You sure?*
> *Yup.*
> *Waal, I guess I'll just mosey along then.*
> *Yup.*

(CHRONICLE RESUMED)

During those years when Eugene went nowhere, he was perfecting the art of the miniature.

(INTERPOLATION)

The Kirani School

What's the first thing you do when you find a cache of old miniatures? Hide them? Hoard them? Burn them? Frame them? Display them? Sell them? Wrong. First you copy them. Then you can do all those other things and still have your cake sitting there. Twice as much is twice as good.

So you're sacked from your accounts clerkship at the waterworks and you've made up your mind about your career. OT's finished—now the serious painting begins. Heavyweight stuff, in keeping with your growing dimensions, only inversely so. That is, the *paintings* get smaller and smaller. What Reuben once indelicately called my caponization actually helps when it comes to sitting on the world and flattening everybody in it to essentially medieval proportions. Along with your prodigious skills of course you need a little luck. (To start with, you need Sans Souci.) It leads you to a glasshouse full of rubbish and illusions—but also a set of perhaps a hundred passable miniatures of Sans Souci and its inhabitants, illustrations evidently of a fusty Persian volume by Qaiyum-i-najum, that comely courtier of the Great Trotter's. Next luck leads you to the top of the North Tower, quite a climb, where you find a quantity of eighteenth-century paints and pencils and brushes laid up. And finally it leads Soma to investigate a lingering cabbagey smell beyond the roughcast wall of her room. The boxroom, she discovers, was once a paper factory; there, under an overturned hand-press, is a stack of Trotter paper, yellowing with age but wrapped in a protective layer of dust. Now all the essential ingredients are present—all perfectly authentic.

You start by copying a few of the old miniatures—they're good enough for practice—on a sheet of Trotter paper that's lying on Eustace's workbench, a piece taken out of the corner. No need for tracing paper after years of OT apprenticeship. The lines go on crisply, confidently, expertly. The colours take a little longer. You learn about grinding, mixing, blending, steeping, testing, applying, waiting. About two parts of zinc with one of lime, a pellet of charcoal steeped in writer's ink and dried and crushed; the three sieved together through mosquito netting into the white of an egg to which have already been added powdered sago, chalk dust, frog spawn and tincture of isinglass; and finally the secret ingredient, which should be apparent—all for a single shade of grey in a patch of sky above Justin in *The Great Trotter Subdues a Rogue Elephant.* You go to exhibitions, talks, displays at the State Museum where Prudence worked, and the Red Throne Room opposite the Umbrella Palace which became the State Fine Arts Gallery; you make forays into the library—around the edges—for old illustrated *namas*, copying all the time, learning from the errors of smaller men. You learn from unfinished works about sequence and scale, from overworked ones about fuss and strain and opacity. You study strokes, stippling, washes, suffusion, hatching, shading, tonality, values, recessive reds, the green threshold, the ochre effect. About planes, panels, borders, angles, multiple perspective, the floating farther eye, the works. And all so that some day there will hang in the great museums of the world—and in many a modest one—exquisitely crafted miniatures with plaques underneath that say, say, "*Girl with a Bird of Paradise*, Nakhlau, Kirani School, circa 1825, Artist Unknown (Charles Pote Trotter?)." *Charles* Trotter! A-Trotter! That fibril! No. The very best galleries do not allow themselves lewd conjecture of the de Soto sort, letting the matter rest at "Artist Unknown." Fullstop. Thank you. Misattribution hurts: far better a distinguished anonymity.

This Kirani School. More luck. The way has already been smoothed for you by that great American critic-and-aesthete, Coomaramungulum. This noble-hearted generously proportioned man argued, in a series of controversial but exact and incisive articles that appeared between the Wars, the existence of a hitherto unnoticed niche in the world of Indian miniature painting. In addition to all the other identifiable schools—the Mughal, the Rajput, the Buddhist, the Kangra, the Nepali, the (East India) Company, and so on— there is, said Coomaramungulum, a Kirani School or style, in Nakhlau. He might have specified Sans Souci, but then he had never been to India, much less to Nakhlau, and had to ground his judgements on a few specimens sent him by a dusty historian-and-would-be-aesthete. His fellow critics were sceptical. "Company School," they said. "One and the same thing." Not so, answered Coomaramungulum, and proceeded to show why in three articles. They're there for all to see in the journal *Oriental and African Art*. What has emerged, he concludes, despite a specious resemblance to the Company School, is a new style in its own right—the Kirani. He might have come right out and said Cranny, but once again he was a long way from Sans Souci. He does not name his source (who preferred to remain anonymous, apparently) but he lists and describes the paintings sent him, and cites others on the same authority. At his death the specimens pass, through various hands, to the Clancy and Avril de Soto Museum in Philadelphia to remain a source of controversy. At the close of the last of his articles Coomaramungulum struck a prophetic note: "It is not without the bounds of probability that some day there will be released into the world of art a collection of miniatures whose beauty and authenticity will establish beyond a shadow of doubt the autonomy of the Kirani School." (*Voice in the Wilderness, Vatic Sage*)

So there you have it. From the horse's mouth. And Eugene, when he comes upon this passage, is not so dense that he will fail to underline it at once and in red.

Meanwhile he's skilled enough to begin to improvise now, to improve on his models, adding perhaps a yellow balloon where before there was a bland expanse of sky, a dish of ripe purple fruit where before there was none. Inchmeal, he introduces Cranny elements into his work—or rather he allows free play to those elements in himself that he has held in check till now. And as liberties multiply, his spirit takes wing and soars until suddenly there's no longer a blend of Company and indigenous elements but something altogether new, the transition visible only in *Feringhee Priests Casting Out Devils*. Talent, practical genius, and gumption are what it takes. In the end you could even lead one of your connoisseurs by the hand into your studio and show him your pile of paper and your inks, brushes, paints and half-finished work and he'll go back with his faith unshaken, convinced that *The Great Trotter Subdues a Rogue Elephant* is not of this century and scarcely of the one before. *Mundus vult decipi*. Human nature is on your side. Can he *allow* himself to believe that the painting he's paid $11,000 for is not authentic?

(CHRONICLE RESUMED)

Reuben brought the rain with him. He came back in early July when people were beginning to wonder whether the monsoon might not fail for the second year running. An hour before he showed up at the Gunpowder Gate there was a cloudburst over Nakhlau. The rain drilled into the earth, sending up fat pink earthworms. It fell in sheets on naked children who sang and danced, churning up the mud with their feet. Lizards appeared from nowhere to gobble up the flying ants. Reuben made the tonga-wala back right up to the verandah of the Begam Kothi, but his luggage got wet all the same. His cassock was already spattered from an accident in the Lalbagh Circle when the tonga had lurched in a rut and thrown him out. He had put on a little weight in Baltimore, which made him look younger, Queenie noticed with distress. Beads of water slid down his puff and up and over his new ducktails; his hairstyle now suggested a roller coaster. He exclaimed over how tall his guava tree had grown. "You know what I missed most in Baltimore?" he asked. "That there tree!" Next he asked whether his parcel had arrived, and satisfied on that score, rambled on about sidewalks and freeways and elevators and plumbing. The thing that impressed him most about America, he said, was the plumbing. "Where it's visible it shines, where it's not it works. That's grace for you. If I were dictator of this country, I would have every Indian issued with a private bathtub and shower. A hot shower." Dulcie, who was sitting in the verandah with Faith and Hope, looking out between the guava leaves at the Sea of Tranquillity, had a sudden vision of that vast yellow plain covered with rows of gleaming porcelain bathtubs, a fellow citizen in each. Her face grew sad and she asked, to change the subject, "How was the Bible School?" But Reuben had gone to bathe, out of a bucket, and change into a fresh cassock.

He came out with a few humble gifts. There was a slim pamphlet for Eugene which said in front, *The Art of the Job Interview*, and on the back, down below, "Department of Labor, 25,000 copies, Not for Sale." For Queenie he had the latest Sears mail-order catalog in full colour and about the size and weight of a large Bible. "Everything in the world," he said, rapping it with a knuckle, "is in there." It was heavy enough, and Queenie was delighted. For years afterwards she would sit in her room when she had nothing to do and pore over it, discovering a page she hadn't turned, exclaiming over a dress pattern that had escaped her eye. Zuhur Ali, Tailor Master (Trotterpurwa), could copy any pattern you showed him. True, there were some things in the catalog that you couldn't get here, but it was enough to look at them: the Snowflake flannelette jamarettes, the bronze-finish praying hands that lit up, the Empire-style fitted ecru bodice lined with sheer nylon or white lace (please state bust size), the Snow White and the Seven Dwarfs cookie jar, the Dopey toothbrush holder, the soft vinyl bootees with dyed-to-match shaggy cuffs of acrylic or shearling lamb. The book proved popular with all Trotters of the blood, but it was in still greater demand outside Sans Souci. Overnight Queenie became a favourite among civil servants' and senior policemen's wives (whose husbands also flipped through the pages, while their sons were casually interested in the lingerie section). The catalog came back ever more thumbed and dog-eared as people marked off their fantasies. Then someone discovered that the book was free and wrote off for his own copy. And soon everyone was sending for mail-order catalogs until the men at Sears finally got wise about India. It didn't matter that you could never send for anything out of the catalog because the government would not release the foreign exchange; it was enough to have the book. In some ways it was better than having the things themselves. For himself Reuben had bought a watch, because Grandfather Alex's had stopped working in Baltimore, and a single-lens reflex camera to replace the old box. For the house there was a high pop-up-action four-slice dual-control toaster—it made dark and light toast at the same time—with a handy snap-out crumb tray and chrome body (*Fairy Stepfather, Family Man*). Breakfast was still an important Trotter meal.

The rain continued every day for the rest of the month. By the end of August the rivers of the north were in spate. The Moti Ganga overflowed its banks, and its tributary, the Cranny river, which had for weeks been a lake rather than a stream, began to edge towards Sans Souci. It swallowed up the flat Sea of Rains overnight, submerged the lowest of the old indigo baths till the ruined aqueduct looked like a bridge, and filled in again the amphitheatre by the music pavilion. To the east the marsh was a sheet of glass which had joined up with the Tank and was encroaching on the Water Gate. A week later the floodwaters were half-way up the Grand Steps and lapping at the Ice and Indigo gates.

"We must move to *Sungum*," Reuben decided, and the next morning a strange procession snaked out of the Begam Kothi, carrying mirrors and chamberpots, aluminum dekchis, candles, coal, cups, kitchen knives, brinjals, hairbrushes, pillows, and a clay firebucket found in the glasshouse for cooking on. Reuben, Queenie, Eugene, Albert, and the Maiden Aunts found shelter in the pillared arcade surrounding the huge Audience Hall. Ever since the collapse of the West Tower the roof of the hall had developed cracks; with the falling of the bell, the problem had worsened. In the winter rains it leaked, in the monsoon it poured; now, since the cloudburst, the water came through in torrents. "Better to have got our feet wet in the Begam Kothi," Dulcie mourned. She was still vain about her hair, and preferred floods to rain. The cold in Queenie's nose got worse, but she was not one to complain about pain. The Begam Kothi lot were joined that evening by Prudence and Percy Reese-Trotter, whose crate of murder mysteries had floated away. Prudence was secretly grateful for the loss because she felt that literature had come between them. If they ever got out of the flood alive, she vowed, they would buy two copies of every mystery and read them side by side, turning the pages together and exchanging glances so that neither one should know more than the other by running on ahead. Ruby and three generations of Atkins-Trotters came up the slope the next day, bringing a quantity of firearms, real and imitation. On the other side there was a commotion as the Kahn- and Alexander-Trotters herded their buffaloes upstairs. A despairing Ian Atkins-Trotter shut down the Glacerie and came flapping up the slope in his gauzy rubber slippers. A few railway Victors and their families waded across the Sea of Tranquillity with their possessions on their heads, looking like villagers. The institute billiard table borne on a quirky current floated right past them, the one remaining ball tracing a random geometry upon the green baize until it slipped through a pocket and plopped into the water, the nets having rotted away. And all through the early days of the flood, a shippie Fonseca-Trotter retired from the merchant marine—he had for years been building a boat in his backyard—rowed around picking people up. Nobody called him Loco Luis any more.

The waters crept steadily up the Grand Steps. Every morning the marooned Trotters gathered in the Water Court to check the new level. There were two more steps to go, after which the water would spill over into the highest of the Sans Souci courts and threaten *Sungum* itself. A foot above that and it would inundate the Audience Hall and pour back down the crater into the crypt below. Already the tomb was submerged by the risen water-table. On all sides the flood lay in a mud-brown sheet which stretched as far as the eye could see. The tops of the larger trees were green islands and the slender curving toddy-palms picked out the pattern of a hidden Tank. Some days the bloated corpse of a cow might come floating by, followed closely by a drifting palm log. Into the wide blue silence above would break the chatter of a typewriter from the upstairs office of ACME, where it was business as usual. Apparently stores of fodder had been laid up in the old Hall of Inventions. Once or twice there came the harsher beat of an army helicopter doing its rounds dropping sacks of cold puris on high ground.

Reuben took charge without waiting to be appointed. He was every-where, giving orders, advice, and consolation, repeating to himself: "*Feed my sheep.*" He no longer quoted from the Old Testament. When the first helicopter came over, he bawled: "Get inside! Do you want to . . ." But the rest of his words, profanity according to Albert, were drowned out, and rather than risk injuring anyone below, the tiny model soldier in the helicopter door heaved the sack out over the water. It fell with a smack just short of the Steps, sending up a fountain of spray that reached a very junior Victor who was standing at the edge. "It splashed me here!" he announced, showing the spot on his cheek, and he became something of a hero among his friends. "You see?" Reuben scolded, heaven's vengeance on his side. "If it fell on you we would have had one extra puri. Next time you hear a chopper coming you get inside double quick, see?" And after that sacks of puris thudded down like divine sanction onto the Water Court where the grass was beautifully green from so much moisture. The water was up to the top step now. Reuben insisted on treating all drinking water with potassium permanganate until it was purple as church wine but bitter (*Perverse Shepherd, Vintage Crook*). He organized rope teams to wade out and catch any branch or tree that floated by for firewood. If it was too far out the shippie was sent after it in his boat with a lasso and an assistant. The furniture—an old marquetry desk with barley-sugar legs, a couple of almirahs with attached cheval glasses, pews from the chapel—would be saved till the last. All matches, even those in smokers' pockets (Reuben didn't approve of smoking), were to be surrendered to Control. Control would also handle rations. It sternly rebuked a gang of exuberant young Fonseca-Trotters who were conspiring to haul in the next pig that floated by for a vindaloo (*Worthy Pastor, Levitical Cook*). "Do you know what cholera is?" Reuben said, frowning over his dark glasses. Later that week one of them did find out, no doubt from eating pork. He was isolated at once in the North Tower where he turned grey in the face and died with his eyes open and a yellow froth on his lips. Reuben sealed the door and said a prayer on the outside. "That will have to be our moratorium," he said darkly. "Mortuary," said Hope, who was lingering nearby. "Same thing," Reuben snapped, and put up a sign to that effect. He made it an excuse for instituting prayers at night in the chapel and was pleased at the response; nobody wanted to pass through that dreaded door.

Reuben's sermons were from the New Testament now, and invariably from his favourite epistle at the Baltimore Bible School: 2 Timothy. He spoke so consistently from that brief letter that Albert chaffed him publicly about it and began to call him 2 Timothy. When the name looked like sticking, 2 Timothy responded with a sermon from the Acts of the Apostles. He was on unsteady ground there but decided to dress it up in the way he had learnt to at the BBS where he read *Time* magazine on the day of issue. He said: "My friends. A long white Cadillac is speeding down the highway to Damascus. Suddenly a blinding light dazzles the driver. He brings the car to a screeching halt on the shoulder. UFOs from Venus? James Bond in trouble? U.S. Army manoeuvres? No, my friends. It is Saul the heathen, Saul the persecutor, Saul the hit-man. Soon to become Paul the protector, Paul the apostle, Paul the martyr. The greatest letter-writer of all time." He wondered whether he shouldn't give them a for-instance, but decided against. Instead he swung his Bible up and brought the other hand down on it with a clap that echoed in the vaulted ceiling. "Struck *blind*, my brothers and sisters, blind. But only momentarily, my friends. Because when he has seen the light and heard the voice, he climbs back into his car and without battering-an-eyelid does a U-turn on the highway. Now I know what you're thinking, my friends. You're thinking, that's against the law." He paused for laughter, but twelve thousand miles from America he drew only perplexity. It was to have been the softener before the message: a U-turn in your lives. The rest of the sermon vanished from his head, and he was forced to deploy another BBS technique, free association, ranging across the New Testament and invoking equally the paraclete and the Gadarene swine. At the parable of the swine he looked hard at Albert, but Albert was up to his old tricks. In the next pew, the old Rev. Percival Reese actually was asleep, while Queenie, who usually sat supportively still was chafing the tip of her nose, which had suddenly gone very cold. An old Kahn-Trotter woman got up and shuffled out. "Parakeets and gabardine swine!" she scoffed. After that 2 Timothy never strayed from his eponymous epistle, returning regularly to a particular verse, 2 Timothy 3:13, which he liked to tell people was inexhaustible. "Stories," Albert prompted him, with a nod at the youngest Trotters. "Never mind your bloody letters." He had become a champion of the Old Testament, which he claimed stored the Trotters' only available myths. "Faith is sufficient," 2 Timothy answered. "Wait and see."

The next day it was found that the waters had gone down one step.

2 Timothy fell on his knees and worked the prayer of deliverance around to 3:13. As the news spread, cheers went up from the Trotters, who had been marooned for more than a month. After the first week there had been no fresh vegetables, except jakfruit from the tree at the bottom of the slope, and no meat, while milk from the ACME buffaloes was selling at prices guaranteed to make enemies. Only Eugene regretted the end of the flood, which had brought him next door to Soma's, a short walk along the roof of the Rib with its jumble of stepped arches and truncated pyramids where there had once been an observatory. While the Audience Hall echoed with the whoops of the saved, the Seventh Trotter, who had his own food hoard and access to ACME cream besides, was content to paint *Sungum Defies the Flood*. "Calmly, my friends," warned 2 Timothy, but nobody heeded him until a very junior Victor was drowned when he fell out of the tub in which he had been boating. That sobered the revellers in the Water Court. "It's going to be weeks before we can return to our homes," 2 Timothy explained practically, and set about assigning duties, the harshest reserved, by Control, for Albert. But Albert simply smiled and spoke of lilies and the absence of toil and spinning. Or he might quote Milton: "They also serve who only stand and wait." In purely secular moments he might point out that Rome was not built in a day and that all work and no play made Jack a dull boy. "So how come you're not brilliant?" 2 Timothy asked. He went in himself, without stopping to take off his new watch. The branch swept by just out of reach and he clambered back up the submerged Steps tight-lipped and dripping. Albert was watching. "*Their strength is to sit still,*" he called. "Isaiah 30:7." A little later another branch floated up and lodged against the Steps. Albert yawned and ran his thumbs around the armholes of his singlet and went to haul it out. Afterward he gathered a group of young Trotters around him and performed disappearing tricks with a handkerchief, a coin, a pack of cards, a cigarette, and a matchbox he hadn't surrendered to Control. During the next few days 2 Timothy could be heard asking the time of anyone whom he passed on his rounds. His American watch had stopped. Albert was his least reliable informant, from his habit of rounding off time to the nearest hour. But there was one afternoon when he was able to turn to Control and answer, truthfully, "2 Timothy, 3:13." Even Daniel, the mousy municipal clerk, risked a giggle.

Actually, Albert had of late been thinking seriously about work. He let a line of dirt gather under his fingernails because he thought it looked workerly. He had been borrowing novels from the ACME secretary, the girl with the extraordinary nails. "A mechanic," he brooded, chewing his lip. The idea of lying under a car for hours on end was appealing, but it would mean, he saw, leaving Sans Souci to work in the city. Next he buttonholed Ian Atkins-Trotter to ask about whether the old post of Ice Manager of Sans Souci was likely to fall vacant. Ian said no at once, horripilating all over at the thought of another salary to be paid out. He liked to think of himself as owner, operator, manager, and foreman all in one. Disappointed there, Albert decided he would like to start a small factory of his own making something light and clean. "A nice factory," he sighed.

Ian jumped. "An *ice* factory!"

Albert ignored him. "Light industry," he murmured wistfully.

"How about pencils?" said Dulcie, encouraging him. She was now In-spectress of Schools for the state, though well past retirement. "The demand is limitless. Think of all those teeming classrooms. By the end of the century you could be a millionaire."

But the thought of limitless demand was exhausting and Albert looked unhappy.

"Paper clips," said Daniel, who was itching to be back at work.

"Shuttlecocks," put in 2 Timothy, on his way to somewhere else.

"Toothpicks?" suggested Eugene.

"Thermos flasks," said Queenie.

It was a kind of game as they sat there on the parapets waiting for the floodwaters to recede. They knew all about Albert's plans, the lawn mowers for Arabia, the ice for Alaska (he had documentary evidence that that state had imported five times as much ice as it exported in 1910), an armchair fitness book for inveterate readers, yesterday's papers at half price, the Craft cheese scheme, the Winks shirts that would one day outstrip the more famous Wings. At the time of independence he had proposed a toilet-paper factory and a factory for Western-style seats, but people were content with the old ways. Now he was ready to consider lotas and squat toilets just when people were starting to change. "We lag behind as a nation," he complained to Eugene. "Or maybe . . ." he looked thoughtfully at his spatulate fingernails, "maybe I'm just ahead of my time." He stared down into the toffee-coloured water. "You know what?" he said presently. "Tell you the truth, I can't swim. That's why I didn't go in after the branch. Don't tell him, though." There was a silence. He looked at Eugene's reflection in the water and addressed it. There were only two of them left on the parapet. "Can you see yourself? Yes? Clearly? Sure? Mine is all funny. You know what? Yesterday I looked down and it wasn't even there. I almost jumped in. Jokes aside, men."

The following day the roof of Victoria's old bathing machine was visible. 2 Timothy would have liked to release a dove, but it smacked of the old dispensation. By the end of the week the outlines of the Tank, such as they were, could be made out and the low humps of the Water Gate reappeared looking sodden and sorry; the old red wafer bricks showed where chunks of plaster had come away. One of the dolphins was gone. The tamarind trees, English and Indian, had a divided look, fresh above and bedraggled below where the lowest branches hung limp and rotten. Half-way up the toddy-palm trees was a water line beneath which the wood was dark with wet; knobs of black hairy bark came away easily in the hand. The earth remained spongy underfoot, the grass a strange yellow alien fungus which was unusual enough for old Faith to take a sample. She never got around to examining it because the next day a parasite carried her off; she had grown very feeble during the flood from a lack of vitamin C. Reuben planted her in the cemetery by the railway track where many of the graves lay open, the tombstones overturned, the coffins carried off. The sample of yellow grass lay forgotten on Faith's dressing table like a tuft of underarm hair, until one night it took root in the wet wood and began to spread. While *Sungum* had escaped the floodwaters, the outer buildings showed the mark of the flood level, khaki below and white and damp above. Even on the ceilings the lime-wash had flaked and crumbled into a fine powder with bald patches showing through. When Albert walked along the empty corridors he heard a soft dry rain of plaster falling around him. Holes appeared in the walls before his very eyes; his shadow crept silently beside him like a cloud of grey mould. He had to hold his nose, the stink was so bad. It was everywhere, a dank clinging fishy smell that would take weeks to go away. When he stepped outside onto a smooth-looking patch, he sank in at once up to his shoelaces. It was like walking in batter, and he was glad to reach the Steps, where he scraped the mud off his soles as he climbed. Half-way up he began to walk along the length of the perron. When he reached the middle he sat down. The Tank lay before him, a middling muddy green, with the marsh to one side, the colour of army camouflage, steaming peacefully. Beyond, the earth was silt brown, and the fields in the distance were painted with the same brush. Then he saw something that was more frightening than having no reflection at all.

It was a reflection, but not of him. Just beyond the Tank his eye caught a glint of something unusual in that neutral expanse. He stood up. There it was again. It was actually several glints, a kind of swift rippling. He climbed up another step without turning his head, shielding his eyes with one hand and squinting. He ran to the top step to make sure. Then he ran back down again, crossed another pool of batter, and hurried along a ridge of grass between the Tank and the oozing marsh. His shoes went in all the way but he didn't care now. He didn't stop until the Tank was behind him and would have run farther if his way had not been barred. He stood aghast, disbelieving his eyes. There at his feet, its ripples glinting in the sun, chuckling softly at some sombre cosmic joke, was a river.

After two hundred years of travelling ever further east, the Moti Ganga had changed its mind and swung back twenty miles to flow at *Sungum*'s doorstep.

When he heard about the river, Marris flew in by the first plane from Delhi, where Parliament was in its monsoon session. It was incredible that the Trotters should have lost four fifths of Sans Souci overnight. But when the plane circled around Nakhlau while waiting for permission to land, it banked over the river and Marris saw that the telegram was not one of Albert's practical jokes. The Moti Ganga had indeed changed its course.

He began to prepare a speech. Nobody could rally Trotters the way he did. Their faith in him was complete, and the more touching as he knew it was not misplaced. He found the damage worse than he had feared. The Gunpowder Gate was a token: the only part of it left standing was a stump to which the Trotter postbox was fixed. (From the front it looked as if the postbox was holding up the gate, and Marris made an inspired mental note.) The rain-gauge stood like a smug sentinel on its plinth, but its prim green finish was daubed with slime. The minaret was gone, the mock ruined round-house was a heap of stones, the fallen white columns near the ice pits had been whisked under like stage props (the one visible capital was wreathed in money plant, and Marris made another note). The mehndi-hedge maze had been torn up for the most part, the umlaut bushes washed away. All the Chinese orange trees were gone from the orangerie; only the stunted custard-apple remained. Now that the river flowed just beyond the Sea of Rains, its tributary, the Cranny, was a very short stream. All the mango topes on the new left bank of the bigger river were lost; only Munnoo's tope on the banks of the Cranny and another one just inside the Gunpowder Gate remained. Marris was glad his father, Young Paul, hadn't lived to see this day. The dank smell struck him as his rickshaw came up the drive. He flinched when he saw the blotchy walls of the Spur, the scabrous Glacerie, the strange yellow grass growing out of a window in the Begam Kothi. The Trotters were assembled in the Audience Hall, expecting the consolation he was bound to give. When he finished his famous Adaptation Speech there was not a dry eye in the place. The echo gallery above took his fricatives to heart and made a revolving motto of his opening words: *Fate is fiction, fitness is fact.* The future, Marris said, lay ahead of them, the past was left behind. They must do what was to be done, and forget what could not be undone. They must meet the challenge bravely or else be cowards. They must survive or else they would perish. And last, but not least, Marris wished to congratulate Reuben Massey-Trotter on his part in the recent emergency and to promise him a seat in the state legislature. But 2 Timothy had other designs.

In spite of the Adaptation Speech, there was another wave of packers-

and-leavers. 2 Timothy ranted against them from the pulpit—his bull-pit, the backbenchers had begun to call it—but the thunder drowned him out even though the old booming sea-trunks had generally given way to suitcases with a forty-four-pound limit. Most departures were by air now, usually Qantas, heading south. More of the Indian hockey team packed away their sticks and made for Australia; Australia's Tokyo bronze became a Mexico City silver. But Queenie's nose, which was colder than ever at the tip, pointed resolutely west, to England. It was not so bad in winter when the rest of her body was also cold, but summers were a trial. Some days she would go and sit in the Glacerie godown among the huge books of ice stored in sawdust, inhaling deep draughts of the cold healing vapour. But Ian didn't encourage visitors to his factory, and he looked suspiciously at her bag when she left. What was to be done? Should she pack the other half of her trunk? Sometimes when she passed by it, it gave a negotiable *boum*, like an appeal. She decided to ignore it. In any case one could hardly take a trunk like that on a plane. 2 Timothy told her it was all in her mind: she needed something to occupy her thoughts. His were presently occupied by the Condensed Bible he was working on. "A capsule version," he said, shucking admiration, and proceeded to explain about thumb tabs and underlined verses and three colours of print. There would be no Old Testament, and the gospels would be conflated into one since there was no point in telling the same story four times. Some of the epistles would have to be dropped; there was only one that was short enough to be featured in full and it was not 1 Timothy. He was having trouble with the text, though. Now that, as textual editor, he was reading closely for the first time, he saw that the italics in the original didn't seem to have any logic to them: "Now a certain *man*, Lazarus *by* name, *was* . . ." he read and shook his head. The problem haunted his dreams, and he began to talk that way.

"*Oah* foah!" Albert chivvied him one day. "*Between* you *and* Marris we'll all *go* mad."

2 Timothy gave him a shrewd look. He said levelly: "How come you're looking so bright-eyed and bushy-tailed these days?"

It was true. A change seemed to have come over the sardonic and so recently suicidal Albert. He was smiling rather a lot, a smile quite free of mockery, and he carried himself like a courtier of old Nakhlau, never once turning his back on you. The eternal singlet was gone, or covered over by a shirt which he wore all the time, and he was regularly to be found in the back verandah of the Begam Kothi with his hands in a bucket of soapy water. Twenty minutes later there would appear on the clothes horse the old singlet with some new marks on it; despite all the scrubbing it showed on the back transverse streaks of what could only have been blood. It looked like the property of a flagellant, and there were indeed times when Albert smelt of Dettol and seemed to be in pain. And yet he was smiling. It was very strange.

> *Narrator, just one minute, before you get carried away. The* grouse *told you all that about the* flood?
>
> *No, it was the duck.*
>
> *Then why you didn' tell me?*
>
> *Because you have been adulterating the wine.*
>
> *Me!*
>
> *With crystals of permanganate. Or that American instant formula—same difference.*
>
> *What to say, Narrator. You want the whip?*
>
> *Fetch me a cola and I will tell you more.*
>
> *The cola is adulterated, Narrator. In this country everything is adulterated.*
>
> *Then make it tea. Warm, with seven sugars. Now listen. Here is what the painted partridge told me.*

(CHRONICLE RESUMED)

Eugene had finished a century of miniatures. Nowadays he rose later than ever because that way he didn't need to share the *Nuntio* at breakfast. 2 Timothy got the paper first and left it folded crisply just as delivered. He was an early riser, earlier even than Queenie (he claimed to have been born in the early hours of the morning, but that was typical of his boastfulness). Queenie read the *Nuntio* next, leaving it in several gatherings folded any old way except that the front page was always cunningly concealed. Eugene read it at random, starting with whichever page his mother happened to leave uppermost. He spread it on the tablecloth to catch the crumbs and ate his breakfast off it, sliding the toast rack or the butter dish up and down or sideways as he read. Today there was an article by Elgin the journalist-and-broadcaster. Where other Trotters were fleeing India, Cedric's son had decided to return to his father's country to take up a job with All-India Radio. According to the article, in the last war with Pakistan seven out of sixty-three medals for gallantry were awarded to Trotters, a figure out of all proportion to the community's microscopic size. Further, the only Indian woman decorated for supreme gallantry was also a Trotter. And yet there were those, Elgin complained, who questioned Trotter loyalties. Eugene picked up another section and lazed through it. Most days there was little enough of interest.

Groundnuts stiffened. Kanpur cotton was looking up. There were narrow movements in Bombay edible oils.

Then his heart skipped a beat.

An engagement

MR IVOR BRYDGES, F.R.A.
Artist in Residence at Grant University
will speak on
The So-called Kirani School of Miniature Painting
in the Lal Baradari (Red Throne Room)
on Friday April 11, at 5 p.m.
Sponsored by the British Council
ALL WELCOME

(*CHRONICLE RESUMED*)

"And you say there are more where these came from?"

Mr Ivor Brydges, a weedy man in his early forties, sat with Eugene's portfolio open on his lap. He wore a white summer suit and smelt of Queenie's cologne. From time to time he took off his steel-rimmed glasses and wiped them with a rose-coloured handkerchief. Without the spectacles a look of utter incapacity came over him; it might have been world-weariness—the world-weariness of a precocious child—or simply very short sight. His nose preserved the impression of the plastic bridge as faithfully as wax, and when he put the glasses back on he pressed them deeper into the rut. Eugene sat beside him, a little nervous, but fascinated by the rose handkerchief that sprang from a different pocket each time. Was it the same one, or several?

"Sugar?"

The lady he thought of as Madam British Council bent over Eugene's cup. Earlier she had risen to thank the speaker just as Eugene came in sweating from his ride.

"Five spoonfuls, thank you, madam." Eugene sometimes listened to the BBC.

She showed no surprise but simply measured out five teaspoons for the well-made young gentleman who seemed to interest her speaker. Eugene saw he might have asked for his usual seven and this graceful lady would have proved unflappable. He made a mental note: show no surprise.

"I'm sorry you missed the talk," she said. "I saw you come in at the end."

"I was . . . a bit late, madam. My cycle——"

"Oh, don't tell me. The roads are awful, aren't they. Of course when you consider the problems the country faces." She was a slight sylphlike woman with a small smooth chin. Her face grew solemn when she considered the problems of a developing country.

Eugene made rapid notes: drop exclamation marks, question marks; slow down, don't finish. Apologize for your guest. Consider the problems India faces. He had never imagined his considering them might help.

"Astonishing! Why, I don't, quite know what to say! And these have lain in your library for what, close on, it must be, almost two hundred years?" It was Mr Brydges again. His translucent fingers plucked a fresh silk rose that he sniffed and discarded. "They're obviously by the same hand as the de Soto four. So this is what old Coomaramungulum was on about."

"Coomaramungulum? You mean *the* Coomaramungulum?"

"Yes, of course. That's what the talk was all——oh, but you came in late. Well, he went on about a whole school to be found in these parts. I met him once in the Museum when he was a very old man. Pathetic, really, quite sad, quite sad. But wouldn't budge an inch. This is what he meant, I suppose. I'm afraid I must take back all I said about the de Soto ones being Company. This certainly is proof, of, of, something new. To think that these——" He broke off to remove his spectacles, blinking helplessly into a luminous void. All the innocence in a corrupt world was distilled in those liquid forget-me-nots. "You realize," he continued, pressing the glasses back on, "my university would pay handsomely for these?"

"You haven't seen them all yet."

Eugene produced one of his copies. He had included a few among the originals.

"Ah, yes. Unmistakable. This, this, this treatment of the mango leaves. Those curlew in the river. Some flaking here——but very well preserved. Ah, now, this would be the, the companion piece to the de Soto *Boatride*. Beautiful!" He shook his head, a man overcome. "Retouched, surely?"

"Yes. But ethically." Eugene had learnt the value of a little truth, and he had read about presale restoration. He produced his pièce de résistance.

Ivor looked up reluctantly. He had not had enough of the *Boatride* companion, but when he saw the newest offering his peaked jaw dropped.

"Well, I never——this'll be——well, I never . . ."

He looked enquiringly at Eugene, his heart full. Eugene held the gaze evenly a space, his brown eye misting over. He nodded slowly.

"Yes."

"Whell, I never!" Ivor's eyes returned to *The Great Trotter Subdues a Rogue Elephant*, feasting there as one does for the first time upon a city whose name one has learnt to cherish from earliest childhood.

"But your tea must have frozen over."

Madam British Council was back from shepherding away the last of the guests. She had gathered that her speaker wished to be left alone with his discovery. Released, she came and leaned on the back of Ivor's chair. Eugene made a note: tea is never just cold; it freezes over, even on a hot day. Aloud he said: "I like it warm, madam."

"Madam!" she repeated, with a smile. She leaned nearer Ivor, and Eugene felt his advantage draining away. He stirred the sugar up from the bottom of the cup.

"I have one other set here," he said, addressing Ivor. "They're duplicates, virtually. I suppose the artist wasn't satisfied with the first."

He held out two general views of Sans Souci, one found in the glasshouse with the rest and the other an improved version of the same with a few additions, chiefly a yellow hot-air balloon in the sky.

"Superb!" Ivor said, glancing at the first. He was actually interested in the *Rogue Elephant*.

"And *this* one."

Ivor looked at the other.

"What do you think of it," Eugene pressed him.

"Mm-m. A bit of a p-pastiche, wouldn't you say?"

Eugene swallowed. "What would you give for the lot?" Enough of indirection, then.

Ivor smiled at him. "You mean my university. *I* could hardly—" He broke off and looked away. His eyes, hugely magnified by pebble lenses, swam out a short way. The future had suddenly spread for his inspection a bright little sequence of possibilities. The rose blossomed in his hands and disappeared again, blown and sick. Ivor sat back and made a steeple of his fingers.

Eugene was also thinking. He hadn't meant to rush in, but now here he was. He did some rapid calculations. Delhi-London. How much had Queenie said? Three thousand rupees? Plus a liqueur on the plane. Heathrow bus fare. Tube. Misc. A vista of jewelled panels opened before him: nothing so exciting had met his eye since he first looked through the eyebath. He folded his hands on his knees. Ivor was coming around.

"What would you say was, oh, *fair*?" The steeple came apart briefly.

"Six thousand."

Ivor regarded his stigmata sadly.

"I would have said, two."

Eugene stood up. "You've seen the paintings. The *Rogue Elephant* alone is worth two."

"True enough, true enough, Eugene, is it? Look . . ."

Eugene sat down on the edge of his chair. Ivor sat in silence for a few moments, his eyes skimming over the paintings. He found his voice.

"You say there are, more where these, these came from. Well, I'll tell you what. There *is* another one that Coomaramungulum mentions—or says his anonymous correspondent mentioned. It's called *The Great Trotter Hunts the Boar*, or some such thing. Perhaps you've, seen it."

"I may have."

"It's said to have a ruled margin decorated with fish or something and dusted with silver—like the *Rogue Elephant*—and there's no signature. Now, if you could, find *that*, we might settle on, oh, say, what? maybe, ah, let's say four thousand rupees?"

"A ruled margin with fish. And, say, fleurs-de-lis?"

"Splendid!"

Eugene inclined his head. It went against the grain to do a boar hunt, but he scribbled lightly on a slip of paper—"dusted . . . with silver"—the dignified bespoke tailor who has just heard, amid the welter of measurements, a very reasonable offer.

Ivor Brydges was also pleased. For a mere two hundred pounds a treasure trove was being turned over to him. He said: "I have to be in Delhi for a Lalit Kala Akademi symposium this weekend but I can be back on Monday. No, Tuesday."

"You can have these now. For an advance."

"I'm afraid I wouldn't have that much on me. But let me see, you could, you could, you could come over to the Deanes' now. I'm staying with them." He turned to Madam British Council. "Would that be all right, Sarah? Good. Well, in that case you could, you could, you could have, what? two thousand? now? and bring the *Boar Hunt* over on Tuesday. Elevenish, say? Are you sure that's all right, Sarah?"

"Yes, of course. Stay for lunch, Mr Trotter."

"Thank you, madam."

"Splendid, then, it's settled. Tuesday." For a man who had not two hours ago doubted the very existence of the Kirani School, Ivor seemed supremely confident that the *Boar Hunt* would be found. "Now let's see. How many of these are there? One, two, threefourfive, six—that yellow one I think you could, you could, keep—seven, eight. Eight. Tuesday, then." He held out his hand like a gift. "Oh, but you're coming back with us now, of course. Very good. But what a find!"

He turned again to Mrs Deane, a changed man. She leaned still closer and breathed on him. It was plain that the find was Ivor's; that Eugene, the glasshouse, Sans Souci, all Nakhlau, why, the entire benighted continent had been waiting centuries for the impress of Ivor's lotus foot.

(INTERPOLATION)

The Great Trotter Hunts the Boar

I don't know whether you've tried painting a miniature over the weekend. It was said that Basawan the Elder, working with an assistant, finished a portrait of Akbar's musician Tansen in twenty days. And that was straight portraiture. But a whole boar hunt (*Vicious Practice, Unnatural Sport*)! Pure fiction, naturally, even if Charles Pote Trotter did do one with that title. It's inconceivable that Justin Aloysius would have trotted about the countryside of Tirnab sticking pigs for fun. But a customer is a customer and your first one's especially valuable. After all, you tell a tailor: buttons down the left, and if you're paying him enough he bites his lip and puts them there. You learn to obey when the price is right. So mount up, lance down.

You start with a high horizon. You might think masses of sky are simple but the plain truth is that masses of earth are simpler still. A low horizon means the trees stand higher and stand out, and trees take time. Besides, the boar is hunted (if at all) in open country. And grass, as every schoolboy knows, is quicker than trees—broad generalized strokes, no fussing with knotty trunks and individual leaves. A bush maybe—twelve leaves in all— from behind which the poor boar darts. One boar will do. And just one assistant huntsman, not a whole horde (or is it herd) of hunters. You can cannibalize *The Great Trotter Spots the Leopard* for an assistant huntsman. And quarry *The Great Trotter Leaps a Broad Stream* for some useful rocks. Boulders, really— nothing like a mass of rocks to fill up half the middle ground. A large boulder is a fine thing. Save the peeping lynxes, the wild asses, the leaping fish for another time. Concentrate on the boar and the Great Trotter's horse—the Great Trotter himself (*Portly Master*) you could do blindfold in an hour. All the same, three days is three days, not Basawan's twenty. It means missing meals (breakfast is hardest, but Soma brings a tray of sorts), sleeping eight hours a day or even less, straining your eyes, your back, your fingers. But by midmorning on Tuesday you're done with the panel as such and putting in the well-spaced fish and fleurs-de-lis along the border. True, the bush is not quite finished, but the pencil lines are a talking point. Nothing more convincing than a slightly laid-bare, unfinished look. Now all that's left is to apply a thin transparent solution of gum arabic and rice water to the margin

and dust lightly with silver scraped off jalebis or amirti or barfi or some such
delight from Mansoor & Boy, Confectioners of Renown Since (circa) 1776.

(*CHRONICLE RESUMED*)

"Not a word, not a word. The *roads* these days. And the *bicycles* they're
building. Of course, when you consider the problems a poor country faces."

Madam British Council's face grew sad for a moment, but she recovered
and invited Eugene in and showed him where he could leave his portfolio.
The table in the next room was set for four, he saw out of the corner of his
eye. He remembered Queenie's admonition: "*One* helping, and don't disgrace
us." Aunty Hope had croaked from her bed: "Make sure you call her Madam."
Aunt Dulcie said: "The fish fork's on the outside—but of course you may
not get fish. *Chicken à la Egyptienne* probably." 2 Timothy said: "Chew each
morsel thirty-two times, now. And say your own grace if they don't." He felt
sure he would have made a better guest. "Keep off the hard stuff," Brigadier
Thomas Atkins-Trotter Jr winked. He was home on leave. Ruby shushed her
son: "Don't joke, men. You'll give him ideas. You know how those people
drink, diplomats and all." "They call dessert a sweet," Albert put in, and
acknowledged Eugene's grateful look. Only Soma said nothing as she watched
him fold over his best grey terry-cot trousers at the cuff, snap on his bicycle
clips, and push her ladies' cycle to the gate and around the corner. Eugene
never mounted the saddle when anyone was watching.

"I'm afraid it's I who have to apologize," said Madam British Council,
"on their behalf."

She waved towards the table, but Eugene was barely listening. He stood
taking in the air-conditioned colour-magazine room with its curios from many
parts of the world: a black wooden shield with feathers stuck in it, a painted
ikon, a Chinese paper dragon, a brightly coloured rug with rows of llamas
on it hanging on the wall, not spread on the floor. But it was predominantly
Indian brass and ivory-inlaid wood of the kind he had seen in shops on the
'Ganj. So you could furnish a room with all that. He shut his eyes and saw
the Begam Kothi drawing room with its three wooden ducks going up the
wall. He opened them on a telegram Madam British Council had handed him.
It said: IVOR DELAYED ON ACCOUNT NATIONAL MUSEUM STOP HOME TOMORROW
STOP APOLOGIZE MR TROTTER LOVE STOP MALCOLM. Or something of the kind.
She took the telegram back, folded it once, ran her nails sharply along the
fold, and slipped it under the telephone.

"It arrived just before you did. They found they had a lot in common,"
she added with a touch of bitterness. "Oh, he'll pay. I'll see he does. 'LOVE

STOP MALCOLM.' He'll pay. I'm sorry you had to bring it all this way for nothing."

"Pay?" Eugene was coming out of his stupor.

"You know, for the *Great Boar* or whatever it is. You've brought it, haven't you." She looked at the portfolio.

"Oh, the painting—yes, madam. It's there."

"Very good, then. But do sit down. Oh, that's all right. The furniture they're building these days. Of course when you consider. Try the next one, it's alleged to be teak. Would you like a glass of mango-fool before we have lunch? Yes? You must be hot after that beastly ride. Look at your poor shirt. It was silly of Ivor to have got you out during the day. But he doesn't know India. Thinks the sun's marvellous. He'll find out. I never step outside till after six-thirty in summer. Now, Malcolm's used to it—goes marching off under the midday sun. So long as you don't bring your mad dogs home with you, I say to him—*used* to say. Now, will you look at that. I *told* that cook of ours to put the jug in the fridge. Yes, memsahib, yes, memsahib, and of course he goes and leaves it on the table. It's no good warm, is it— mango-fool."

Eugene had to agree. At Sans Souci the ice went in the jug. Only the Atkins-Trotters had a fridge. With Thomas a brigadier and Harold almost Wing-Commander, Ruby could afford one of those new split-level two-door models like the ones in Queenie's Sears catalog. Turning where he sat, Eugene saw one very like it.

"You could put it in the freezer for a few minutes." The jug was one of those tall narrow-necked tooled-brass ones out of the Arabian Nights or some extravagant fantasy. It had a familiar look: where had he seen it before? Hundreds of years ago, it seemed. He shook the nonsense out of his head. He had seen it in one of the state handicrafts emporia and thought it strictly ornamental. At Sans Souci they used a plain glass lemonade jug.

"Yes, why not. And we can eat in the meantime, if you're ready. Unless you'd rather wait. Good. I'm afraid it's not much chop. But you won't mind a simple lunch, will you. A rather grizzled *Chicken à la Egyptienne* and a sweet."

How ice cream is made (these days)

I wish to shew how ice cream is made, these days. Fair adept, make the mango-fool in the usual way. Then forget about it. This is easily done. Some use knots on the finger, some not. A lemonade jug will do to forget it in (such as may be had from Uberoi & Uberoi on the 'Ganj) or else a tall brassware jug, not unlike a gypsonometer, from the UP Handicrafts Emporium also on the 'Ganj just where the road turns away. The other element in the recipe is a split-level two-door refrigerator of foreign manufacture which may be had from the Hudson's Bay Company which supplied ice tools in the old days. Alternatively, one may apply to the Sears mail-order department, or else Selfridges direct. Customs will present a problem to the ordinary adept, but the adept of adepts has a diplomatic container or access to one. When she moves on, to Malta or New Guinea, she will have no trouble disposing of this machine (or any other consumer durables and appliances of foreign manufacture). The natives of Hindoostan will pay the price three times over with what is called black money, such is the craze for white goods. (These days, the pale yellow, from Japan, will also do.) Very much they are loving foreign. The three essentials for making (mango) ice cream are now present and accounted for: the mango-fool, the jug, and the refrigerator-and-freezer.

Let the guest arrive on a hot day. Follow his instructions closely. Turn then to the *Chicken à la Egyptienne*, which the adept may eat with her fingers while the guest perseveres with his knife and fork. Let there be small talk. A Greek salad, perhaps, with tinned olives, vile with salt. Let the sweet be served. Let it vanish, having made no difference, like ice on a hot day. Let the raga *malhari* as interpreted by Ravi Shankar play itself out in the background. The meal over, return to the drawing room where there are rugs, mirrorwork cushions, Nakhlau taqiyas, and long peppermint-stick bolsters. Examine together the *Great Boar*—or is it *The Great Trotter Hunts the Boar*? It is in truth a great bore. Tell the guest this when he has spent long enough expounding its virtues. He will smile and preen himself. Ask him if the lunch was enough. His face will fall, but he will say, *Certainly, madam*, like a BBC receptionist. It is then, fair adept, that you remember what was forgotten. The jug is painful to the touch, its contents frozen solid. The guest offers to heat it. This a great joke, which at length he grasps. Thus is the ice broken—he is such a *silly* boy—butter melted in the mouth, scorching kisses exchanged, and revenge on the husband made sweet. A long spoon or else patience are the only further desiderata. Patience is better, there being no hurry. There is only one flight a day from Delhi. This is what I wished to shew. So do that. Do it slowly. Give praise.

(*CHRONICLE RESUMED*)

Eugene stopped twice for breath on that tremulous ride home. The old landmarks slid by unnoticed as his quaking legs worked the pedals. The slower he rode, the faster his brain churned the afternoon's sensations: when she said of Ivor, He lives off the fat of his head—but don't we all, and he made a note: live off the fat of your head; when her elbow dug him gently; his mouth going suddenly dry; the string of rich hesitations; her paperweight chin become delightfully mobile, sweet as a water-chestnut with one tiny prickle she had missed; his crying out at the end, *Madam! Madam! Madam! Madam!*; his hand like a plump black spider on her breast; his mortification at finding his bicycle clips still on afterwards; her saying, What's it *like*, tell me; her story of Mrs B. Meer Hasan Ali, an Englishwoman married to an Indian of this city a hundred and fifty years ago, who left a full account of everything important except her name, so that the world must remember her simply as B; his saying it was like falling; her saying you're the hyphen in Anglo-India and then smiling at something; the moment of panic before lunch when she said, Not much chop; her explaining the Indian derivation to him later; the button she sewed back on his cuff; the cup of tea she brought him with five spoons of sugar already in it, and, when he confessed, her shriek, *Seven!* My dear *boy*!

> *I say, men, Narrator! Narrator! Where you been all day?*
> *What the hell, Cup-Bearer? You gave me a start, men. Here I am thinking nice-nice thoughts and you—*
> *Guess what, men!*
> *What-thing?*
> *Cellar's empty, men. Nothing left down there.*
> *Nothing!*
> *Just one bottle. Here, take. Someone must have been down there.*
> *Someone, eh? Just bring me that whip one second.*
> *Narrator!*
> *If I have to get it myself it'll be worse.*
> *Look, men, Mexican Kahlua and all. Sweet as hell. You finish it. And might as well finish the story. How long you going to go on and on?*
> *On and on, eh? Just bring that whip—*
> *Narrator. If the bottle breaks don't blame me.*
> *Sweet Cup-Bearer! Listen. I have heard from the crow that it happened in this way.*

(*CHRONICLE RESUMED*)

The ticket to London was bought—Ivor paid—but it was not Eugene who used it. The change in plans had to do with guavas.

Ever since his return from Baltimore, 2 Timothy had been especially careful of his guava tree. It was a monsoon tree, not a winter one, and it bore good fruit every other year—if the monsoon was a satisfactory one. For the past few years the monsoon had been more than satisfactory. In fact there were few rooms in the Begam Kothi which did not leak, with the result that every empty vessel in the house from a basin to a cheese tin was used to catch the drips. The old roof was not what it used to be. Saucepans, Quaker Oats tins, dekchis, kerosene canisters, buckets, biscuit tins, cake tins, urns, ashtrays, and chipped soup plates were pressed into service. The only likely vessel that was spared was 2 Timothy's badminton trophy, an electroplated cup that stood on the whatnot. The rest lay about the floor of the Begam Kothi, a constant hazard to the unwary. Each had its own note, depending on its shape and size, and each drip its own tempo. The result, backed up by the kettle-drum roll of the rain, was music to 2 Timothy's ears: he could *feel*, he said, the monsoon plumping his guavas. Only the thunder spoilt his peace, that and the lightning. When a storm threatened he went from room to room covering all mirrors that might reflect lightning into the house; when the storm passed, he peeled off the towels and tablecloths and stepped outside to give thanks for deliverance—and for his swelling guavas. With the sun, however, came the birds. 2 Timothy hated them with a lively helpless vengeful hate. "I will make shuttlecocks out of you!" he raged. But it was no use. No sooner had a guava begun to turn from dark to pale green than the crows and mynahs and seven-sisters were there before him. Where the green was palest, verging on yellow, they pecked a conical hole and went on to the next guava.

2 Timothy declared war. In most fruit groves he knew, the chowkidars hung empty kerosene canisters in the tree-tops and tugged a rope attached to a clapper inside to scare the birds away. In the Begam Kothi the kerosene tins were all used to catch drips from the many leaks in the roof. 2 Timothy glanced at his trophy. Upside down it would have made an excellent bell for scaring crows—if it had been someone else's. The only other likely object on the whatnot was Queenie's coronation tray. He hesitated, but when he marched off towards the tool room it was in his hands. The next day when the sun came out he was waiting for the birds. He had a choice of mondhas to sit on in the verandah because the Maiden Aunts no longer sat there; Faith was gone, Prudence lived in the New Armoury, and even if Hope and Dulcie had wished to sit there, the view of the Sea of Tranquillity was now completely cut off by the guava tree. 2 Timothy sat down on the first mondha in the row. In one hand he had a book, in the other a rope which swung in a long low curve to the top of the tree. If a bird alighted on the tree, he waited till it was poised to peck and then gave the rope a sharp tug. The clapper—an old ladle—rose and fell with an almighty clang on the coronation tray: DA! It worked well.

Coming back from church the next morning Queenie noticed in the distance something unusually festive about the Begam Kothi. Then she saw it was the guava tree, not the house that looked pretty, crowned with what looked like a tinsel star. As she drew nearer her eye picked out the various royal seats, strangely familiar, surrounding the portrait: Balmoral, Holyrood-house, Windsor Castle, Buckingham Palace. She smiled dreamily. It might have been a proper Christmas tree with snow on the ground and a robin on the fence. It was only when the portrait spoke—DA!—that she recognized it. She scraped the mud off her shoes on the front step and went in without a word to 2 Timothy and bolted the door to her room. Moments later there sounded a short *boum*: Queenie had begun to pack the upper half of her trunk. She knew about Eugene's ticket. When she was finished she went to him with a promise: as soon as she got a job there she would send him out his fare. Hardly a week later she flew out from Delhi, her trunk to follow by sea. At the end of the month there came a Horse Guards postcard to say she had arrived safely and was staying with Mavis and the whilom Belle of Bangalore. There followed a letter from Willesden in which she said the kitchen was lovely, just like in *Woman & Home*, and the air was so fresh and sweet. The cold in her nose no longer troubled her, she said; it had gone away about half-way on the air trip, somewhere over Constantinople. There was a job in the telephone exchange that looked likely, though the technology was all new. If she got it, she could send messages to Nakhlau, to her friends. The interviewer seemed a nice man, nice-looking, dignified, considerate and soft-spoken, in short, a thorough gentleman.

The barb went home. When 2 Timothy read the letter (which was ad-dressed to Eugene) he went out and gave the rope a vicious tug even though the guava season was well over. He decided that if he was not a gentleman there were other options open to him. In fact, this not being a gentleman rather liberated one from all kinds of finicky constraints. And much later, when he was secretary to the Bishop of Nakhlau and gunning for the bishopric himself while selling off the huge empty church properties of North India with his committee of henchmen, 2 Timothy would stop and give thanks for the day when Queenie first opened his eyes. But to start with, he sold the grazing rights of Sans Souci to the Yadav from Trotterpurwa. The sale sparked off a feud with the ACME people in the Rib, who carried on grazing as before, and every now and then a buffalo on either side would swell up like a paper bag from having eaten something left lying in the grass. To add to his ex-chequer 2 Timothy rented the same ground to the local bourgeoisie as a golf course. And there were months when he allowed the Great Grand Indo-Chinese Circus to pitch its tents on the old Plain of Cannonballs this side of the stupas. On some days in November there was extreme confusion on the green as acrobats jostled against industrialists, milch cows left steaming brown pats on the first tee, and a bewildered human cannonball flew across the Upper Trotter Road through a hail of golf balls. "It just goes to show," said Aunty Hope, who was now bedridden and spat quantities of yellow bile into an aluminium chamberpot between her slippers, "that it's better to scold a man than to shame him."

Dulcie, round and seventy, took the golf course less philosophically. The doctor had recommended long walks for her, and since she liked to have the downward slope coming back, her route lay along the Upper Trotter Road. She was convinced that she would meet her death from a wayward golf ball and whenever she saw one lying unattended she picked it up and slipped it into her bosom. She met several managing directors in this way, and not a few major-generals, but neither threats nor blandishments would persuade her to yield up the ball. "A *ball!*" she would ask, with a flutter of her eyelashes and a heavenward turn to those eyes that were green as a brace of fig-pigeons. "Really! When?" Her hair was still bright-red and freshly sprung from curlers; her mouth was watermelon-red and wore an irregular smile. When she got back from her constitutional she gave her bosom a shake to release the day's catch, and ate, standing up, a potful of spongy rasgullas from Mansoor & Boy, Halvai and Confectioner, Estd. (circa) 1768. Mansoor's rasgullas were the envy of Hindu halvais, drawing devotees from all over Nakhlau. When, in the interests of prestige, Mansoor moved to the 'Ganj, Dulcie simply extended her walk, sustained by the vision of a potful of spongy white rasgullas at the end, swollen with heavenly syrup to their fullest—or about the size of a standard golf ball. When she was finished, she would ease her acres of dimpled white flesh into a special chair and sit there dreaming of a vanished night at the Albert Hall. In retirement her routine seldom varied: the morning run through florid passages from her repertory with stops for breath and a green julep to clear her throat; the evening walk, because she had faith in Dr Ahmed, followed by the shedding of golf balls and then her treat. Over the years the golf balls, at first only ankle-deep, came to reach the level of her bed and threatened to fill up the room. They made going in and out difficult since one either ploughed through them or—theoretically—walked over the top, a dangerous exercise because the movement of a single ball set all the others in motion, causing whispering avalanches in the corners of the room. Although she lived surrounded by the little creatures, Dulcie never lost her fear of them in the wild. Once she decided to take Eugene walking with her for protection, but he dragged along behind, the only person in Sans Souci slower than herself. "You should go to the Swiss Alps," she called over her shoulder. "You would enjoy watching the glaciers whizz past you." After that she went by herself, gleaning lost balls in the twilight and slipping them into her bosom. Eugene was content to join her when she got back; Dulcie still enjoyed feeding him as much as ever. It was brave of her to go, because one of her recurring nightmares was of an interminable walk along the Upper

Trotter Road. She would wake out of it sweating in the middle of the night convinced that a murderous general had shouted "Fore!" behind her.

It was not a ball that killed her, as it happened, but the great blotting paper scandal. The scandal rocked Nakhlau, and for years afterwards people used a special lower register when they talked about it. It put an end not only to Dulcie (and nobody knew how many other rasgulla connoisseurs) but to the establishment of Mansoor's, Confectioners of Integrity Since (circa) 1757. It started when a single sheet of blotting paper fell into Mansoor's vat of scalding milk and disintegrated, instantly and wonderfully thickening the cream. When the white spongy balls were shaped that night, it was found that their texture and mass were distinctly improved while the flavour remained, to the untutored tongue, unchanged. Once they were immersed in syrup there was no appreciable difference between a rasgulla made of pure cream and one with the new additive. After that discovery several sheets of blotting paper fell into the milk vat, and before long it was an arguable point whether blotting paper was being added to the milk or milk to the blotting paper. What was certain was that the stationers next door to Mansoor's on the 'Ganj began to turn away students and office workers and that that year the letters, documents, and copybooks of Nakhlau were the worse for it. Not to be outdone, other confectioners began to mix sawdust in their suji halva and chalk dust with their barfi. The adulteration idea, always popular in India, assumed new proportions. Grocers, encouraged by Mansoor's enterprise, reversed the usual proportions of charcoal and black pepper, pea flour and gur shakkar, beef tallow and vegetable oils, until it became impossible for the ordinary citizen to buy unadulterated food. When the rasgulla scandal broke, Dulcie was aghast at the thought of so much paper in her. She, who had in her sea trunks a collection of menus from the restaurants of Europe, who in her prime had kept a diary which recorded in rapturous detail every meal eaten out, began to stutter and went off food altogether. A week before she died a white owl came and stationed itself above her window, spreading its wings only at dusk when it was relieved by bats and swallows and other crepuscular companions of her abandoned walks. "A-at least I'll never have to give myself i-injections," she said to Eugene, who like her was terrified of needles. It was a sort of warning. Through the night of her death the golf balls kept up an agitated whirring until the spirit had left her body, whereupon they fell silent. Just before dawn they burst out of her door and rushed like lemmings across the Ice Court and into the Tank, which was ever after the repository of lost golf balls. The owl spread its snowy wings, hooted once, and glided away, leaving a silent alp upon the bed.

Next to go were Prudence and Percy Reese-Trotter. They went together, under circumstances that would have interested a private investigator: they were found slumped in their respective chairs (which faced each other), with a copy each of the same murder mystery in their laps, open at the end. Their eyes were wide open and on the pupils of each was the image of the other in miniature down to the last detail of the wide-open eyes. 2 Timothy said it was usually the butler, but that this time there seemed to be no motive and no hard evidence. Albert reminded him that there was no butler either; the Reese-Trotters had lived alone. Finally it was decided that the murder mystery they were reading might hold a clue. Albert read it out of a sense of duty— ordinarily he could never stay with a book for more than twenty pages—and found the answer by perseverance: the last page of both copies had been torn out. The Reese-Trotters had died of vexation. Eugene, who favoured the textual approach, read the novel and reached his own conclusions. It was about a couple who marry late and live peaceably together reading murder mysteries in duplicate. One day, after a tiff—their first—they exchange identical gifts, the latest novel by their favourite author, and sit together as before, reading. When they come to the end they discover simultaneously that the last page has been torn out, and they look up at each other in mortal disbelief. The doctor's report on the Reese-Trotters said simply: *Heart failure* (which by a further coincidence happened to be the title of the novel), but Eugene put it down to the shock of recognition.

Of Victoria's older children only Hope remained, determined not to die. It had taken her all her life to rid herself of the liverishness brought on by Victoria's unnatural craving during her fourth pregnancy, and nowadays she hardly spat bile at all. One morning she brought up the whole liver, such as it was, and was glad to be rid of it. It lay there at the bottom of the aluminium chamberpot that served as her spittoon, a small squashy maroon wallet worn down over the years. She lived happily after that on her pancreas alone, a bright old woman, brown as a rusk, with keen black eyes hugely magnified and split across the middle by luminous bifocals. It was she who organized socials for the young Trotters, had the Spur opened and aired, and put up with the loud electric guitars played by a villainous group called *Chris and Alan and the Miranda House Babes*. "Louder!" she would call from the stage wings to which she had herself transported. "You *men* or what, men?" Or: "Faster! Oh my, the girls these days, I'm telling you. If I could only get up." She saw that the dancers didn't get too close or (lately) too far and lose their partners; that there was a slow number every now and then for the middle-aged—who were half her age and called her Granny. The catering was her preserve: samosas and chhole bature on contract, pink-and-brown iced cakes that the Uberois called pastries (they had bought out Fonseca's on the 'Ganj), and vermilion soft drinks that she forced Ian to contribute. By common consent these socials were held on Marris's birthday and ended at midnight. Hope said: "In the good old days, my God. We went on till two and three, isn't it?" But there was no one of her generation left to confirm the truth of it. Some of the middle-aged had heard that in the old days Hope never went anywhere near the Railway Institute, being too highbrow and liverish to dream of dancing. Today it was a different story. "If they don't enjoy themselves now, then when?" she wanted to know. But sophisticates from the city came to sneer, and there were undesirables who gate-crashed with knuckle-dusters and vernacular abuse. Once a knife flashed in the night and a young air force Trotter marched across the dance floor dripping blood. After that the day of the annual social was kept secret and Marris's birthday was made a movable feast.

The next year 2 Timothy sold off the forest to independent woodcutters and charcoal-burners and bought a fleet of taxis. He sold blocks of the Sea of Rains to speculators-and-developers and then auctioned squatting rights on the same land to displaced villagers. That done, he contracted to build a slum on the site and paid gangs of goondas to threaten the new owners with pukka houses and the squatters with eviction. He stripped *Sungum* of its remaining furniture, including a couple of pier glasses and a chandelier that had escaped destruction in the first sack. In the Spur he removed all the brass fittings and sold them by weight to be melted down. If *Urban* had not been immovable he might have sold it as well; as it was, the great gun was embedded in cement blocks that had been hardened with jaggery. Like the revolted sepoys of old, he missed the turning to the military museum, but he knew the way to the chapel well enough. As his congregation dwindled, he sold off the front pews; then he sold off the back ones and spread a bright dari on the floor, but by that time there was no one to sit on it. He turned to the plate and got a good price. Meanwhile, on the strength of his foreign diploma, he got himself elected secretary of the Amalgamated Churches of Northern India (Grams: ACNI). At home he moved from room to room, penetrating ever deeper into the heart of the Begam Kothi as he looked for an office that was dark enough for his designs. The light hurt his eyes, he complained, even with his dark glasses on indoors. By sheer persistence he found a room in the very centre with a single door and no skylight. In it he installed a desk with an infrared desk lamp and a fridge which stood on a mango-wood pallet which he had got from breaking up the doolie. For twelve months he sipped cold water with ice cubes in it and studied the deeds and titles of every church property in North India. He came out knowing something to the discredit of every district committee, and did a tour to let them know he knew. The next year he was elected bishop, and as if he knew that his term would be the shortest on the record of that hitherto blameless office, the spoliation of the churches began at once. Sometimes the land to the very edge of a church was sold, so that when a building went up next door (belonging, say, to a lawyer named Light) the stained-glass window above the altar no longer caught the morning sun. From there it was a short step to rezoning the cemeteries. When a group of parishioners objected, 2 Timothy waved them off with his crook and a French phrase of his manufacture: *l'histoire est bonque* (*Good Shepherd, Timid Sheep*). "The enemies of progress," he announced with episcopal disdain, "will be dealt with in one foul swoop." And Marris, sitting in Delhi, refused to intervene in church affairs because he was only the secular leader. "In any case, men," one of his deputies said, "these chaps aren't even Trotters. They can't even speak proper English."

Letters, in proper English, continued to arrive from Queenie in England, but their tune had changed. The job at the telephone exchange hadn't come through. Instead she was working in a dry-ice factory where the men were coarse and the work was hard. And strange to say, her nose, the tip of which had once been unbearably cold in India, was now unbearably hot. Only when she held it close to her embroidery (she worked tablecloths with flame-of-the-forest and hibiscus and laburnum) did the pain subside. There had been a period in between when it adjusted wonderfully to the new climate, but over the past year it had gone from warm to hot, and now it looked as if only a tropical climate would bring relief. There was something else which Queenie had to admit. A few days after she arrived in England, she had found herself turning brown. In fact, the process had started in the aeroplane when she went to powder her nose about half-way between Delhi and London. Now she was dark enough that one Sunday when she thought she'd worship in another suburb the verger said kindly, meaning to clarify, "This is an Anglican church." In short, Queenie was ready to come back home. She suspected that the process would start all over again in reverse until she once again stuck out in India, but what was one to do? There was no ideal solution short of becoming an air-hostess, and it was too late for that. Even they didn't remain forever suspended in the air over Constantinople.

2 Timothy was waiting at the Gunpowder Gate to meet her. He looked older, gaunt, and unforgiving, pleased to have his wife back only for the sake of appearances: it hadn't looked right for the bishop to have his wife living in another country. So it was not Queenie's fault when, shortly after she returned, her husband was relieved of his bishopric by an investigative committee under court order. 2 Timothy bore up. There was in any case little that he had left undone in his term of office, and he turned from his scorched pasture without regret, a man who has sensed a new calling. He had decided to become an educationist.

It was simple enough—everyone was doing it. So great was the demand for English education that any citizen who cared to might have set up a school and made his fortune in a year. But the Trotters were a little late: most of the new English-medium private schools were run by Hindi speakers. Not that the established government-recognized Trotter schools, where Ruby's daughters taught, suffered any depletion. "Hypocrites!" Ruby snorted. "Why don't they start their own kind of schools, with prayers to the sun and all? Just see how they shove their daughters into our schools." It was true. In modern India, where children were bought and sold for marriage through the newspaper, a girl's chances of a wealthy match improved sharply if she had been to a convent. The scramble gave a new word to the language. A matrimonial ad in the Sunday paper, after describing the bride-to-be as *very fair*, *beautiful*, and *homely* (meaning house-trained), clinched the business with *convented*. Naturally, convents multiplied all across the country, most without any trace of a nun, and one of them named, memorably, BLONDIE CONVENT. Others, less fastidious, settled for plain *School*, but since recognition was important their signs said: LOVELY SCHOOL, English-Medium (Recognized by the Petroleum Corporation), or SAINTLY HEART SCHOOL, English-Medium (Recognized by the Pulp Mill), or, with disarming modesty, NICE SCHOOL (English-Recognized).

Eventually the Trotters joined in, as if sensing anew their historic role as mediators. For three hundred years their kinsmen had set up little verandah schools throughout the country in which English and other subjects were taught. Now several small schools sprang up across Sans Souci, each with its own prescribed uniform and matching particoloured signboard. In the early morning, thousands of schoolchildren in green-and-white or navy-and-white or black-and-white or ordinary khaki flowed eastward out of the city like confused armies. They came, to the annoyance of early morning golfers, in an endless stream along the Upper Trotter Road, crammed eight to a cycle-rickshaw, calf-eyed innocents bowed down with bursting satchels because their parents demanded homework. 2 Timothy watched them come with an inky glitter in his eye. He saw the green-and-whites split off towards the railway colony while the rest poured on, some bound for the Rib, where Ivan Alexander-Trotter, a cousin of Soma's, had opened a fine academy, some for the Elephant Wing whose ground floor one of Ruby's daughters had converted into a junior school, some to other parts including the old indigo shed where Ian Atkins-Trotter had a tutorial centre. One day, 2 Timothy vowed, all these schools would be united under him, just as he had once headed the Amalgamated Churches of Northern India. Queenie, who had picked up a teacher's diploma during the long London evenings, contented herself with one student. "Each one teach one," she quoted the national slogan. But her husband had a grander scheme; already he was fitting out the Spur with a battery of desks set very close together. In the old cock-fighting days fortunes had been made and lost there. "You wait," he said, "we'll soon be gathering golden eggs in this cockpit."

Not everybody at Sans Souci was teaching, though there were times when it seemed so. Soma still worked in the ACME office, while the other Alexander-Trotters looked to the diversifying dairy industry: the butter plant, the cheese division, the milk residue, the plant from which every day forty striped cream-and-chocolate pushcarts went out under the blazing sun, the vendors calling mournfully as their mouths filled with flying sand: *Tar-tar Ice Kream!* Over in the Glacerie, Ian Atkins-Trotter continued to look after the ice and the aerated drinks himself, the tuition being irregular because he didn't trust the parents to pay their dues. His older brothers were koi-hais, posted somewhere important and loaded down with stars—Thomas a Major-General, Richard a Rear-Admiral, and Harold an Air Vice-Marshal. Their sons and daughters were also in the armed forces, gathering medals for every Pakistani jet they shot down. There were one or two nurses left in the Civil Hospital, the occasional mail driver or ticket-collector in the railways, the odd customs officer home on leave. Out towards the second bridge, the bazar-side Trotters played caroms and cards and waited for their mechanic friends to stand them a drink. The bad girls still listened to Ceylon in the evenings and plied their trade at night. In the respectable suburbs Trotter stenographers, almost as numerous as Trotter teachers, turned up their noses at the self-employed, but dreamed of Australia and hated their bosses for the passes they made. On Sundays after church they could afford to go to the pictures and eat chow afterwards at Lu Wing's, where a little Miss Wing played "Chopsticks" on the piano. Daniel, the mousy municipal clerk, went regularly to his office in the city; he still looked mildly at the world and kept his counsel, and had yet to take a single day's leave. In the Begam Kothi, Albert was still dreaming of the ideal job. Hope Granny, who kept good health, titubations apart, said she was past drawing her pension, so why didn't Albert do it for her? "You can have a cut," she told her nephew, and for a moment Albert wondered whether he might not have found the answer, but he rebuked himself and continued to look. These days he had no trouble seeing himself in the mirror; he could even bring himself to like what he saw. Obviously someone else did too, because one day Eugene surprised him singing in the verandah as he washed the stripes out of his cheesy singlet. His back, yellow as a pear, was as delicate too—it was scored with ten fresh scratches that started at the backbone and petered out at the edges. Eugene painted with a fierce concentration that day, wishing he were ten thousand miles away. There was nothing else for him to do. Madam British Council was two postings away in Ghana.

If fate would only send him another buyer like Ivor Brydges! Queenie's savings had been used up on the ticket back.

Fate obliged the painter. Two days later there came a letter from Ivor, apologizing for long silence with a prolix archness that Eugene overlooked because it enclosed a cheque. "If you should find," were Ivor's words, but the specifications were rigorous enough. It was a virtual commission for a further series of paintings. Looking back, Eugene often wondered whether he hadn't sensed the man's connivance at the time, but at the time he bent professionally to his task. The cheques came back with a regularity that might have alerted all but the slowest of the Trotters, and they didn't bounce. His bank account swelled, and by the end of the series he could have travelled around the world if he had wished, leisurely by sea, taking with him Queenie's steel trunk. The trunk already had two sets of addresses on it, the first painted over but still visible in bare relief under the new black skin. Eugene gave it another coat, this one of many colours. When it was dry, he began to pack, *boum-ou-boum*, putting in the tools of his trade: a pile of eighteenth-century paper, forty brushes, and the original colours transferred to condensed milk tins. But even after the paintbox was packed he hung on at Sans Souci, because of the haunting.

It started when Queenie disappeared. She was last seen kneeling in her room under the picture of Prayer, snivelling from a particularly luscious cold, and then she vanished. Her going had an inexplicable finality to it, so that people didn't look seriously for her around Sans Souci. Everybody knew she would not be found, and her presence was so strongly felt in the Kothi that the inner Trotters were sure she was no longer encumbered with a mortal body. There was other evidence. The woman in the picture had changed, and not subtly. Gone were the pink cheeks, the undisciplined cascade of golden-brown hair, the rapturous blue eyes, the thread-of-scarlet lips, the piece-of-pomegranate temple, the slender translucent fingers. In their place were cheeks of medium beige, dark, orderly hair—the hair of an older woman who took care—quiet grey eyes, a bluish-red snivelling slightly upturned nose, a lower lip full enough to suggest the need and the act of prayer, and deft, reliable telephonist's fingers that looked as if they had just put through an important trunk call. That was not all. The picture—or the portrait, as Eugene now thought it—moved. It was not the woman in the frame who moved: she remained fixed in an attitude of prayer, her eyes uplifted (though when you looked away they turned on you). The whole picture, frame and all, seemed unwilling to remain on its nail in Queenie's old room. Eugene would be painting from his box in the studio when he would hear a sniff in the next room—and there, just visible through the door was the picture with its imploring eyes. He shifted to a room at the far end of the Begam Kothi, but when he lifted his eyes from his work, there she was in the next room on a new nail. Once after a long session with a single-hair brush (he was painting the brocade on a bedstead canopy), he felt a prickling in his back and turned to find the picture come up close behind him. It fell back with a clatter as he leapt out of his chair.

"Eye strain," Albert advised. "Take a holiday." He waved suavely at the world.

Eugene was inclined to agree, though he suspected the picture would follow him to Ultima Thule and back, those mute eyes fixed on him when he turned aside but flicking upwards when he looked back. Was it forgiveness she wanted? But for what crime? Was it a request? But what for? For release? An heir? A sitting? He went to Hope Granny. Nowadays the call was a pilgrimage in itself. When you had hacked your way through the spreading yellow funguslike grass outside Faith's room, you had to tackle the wild lantana thicket outside Hope's. The old hedge, always unruly, had entered by a window and spread its brittle thorn-hairy tentacles around her door. One had to squeeze through a forest of interlocked stems sprouting fuzzy serrated leaves and pink-and-yellow clusters of tiny neat foul-smelling flowers, each cluster a severely symmetrical posy. Dead leaves and the corpses of small birds carpeted the cement floor. A passage had been worked through the tangle by Hope's ayah, a woman almost as frail as Hope herself, who emptied the chamberpot and fed her rusks dipped in warm sweet tea. For larger visitors the journey remained an ordeal.

"So you've come," his great-aunt said to a scratched and shaking Eugene. She had an ancient grey-green cross-stitch counterpane, the colour of dust and mould, pulled up over her bones. On the other side of her bed stood an anthill across which large black ants darted distractedly. A vein of mud led across the floor from the doorjamb to the nearest leg of the bed, showing where unseen white ants were at work. The chamberpot was there but the slippers were gone. Eugene told his tale of the portrait's visitations. There was a sound of sand running out as his great-aunt shifted. She turned her head towards him and he looked into those luminous black eyes, wide as her lenses and split across the middle.

"Mavis—" she rattled. She cleared her throat of the past and swallowed. "Mavis would know. That Bangalore beauty's daughter. She and your mother were good friends. She's somewhere in the Midlands, or maybe London. Go on. What you waiting for? Here. Give Granny a kiss." She pointed to a satiny spot on her cheek. "Now go. Don't worry, men, I'll still be here."

Eugene was at the door again surveying the lantana. The path he had broken through it had closed up. He would have to bulldoze through again. He put his head down.

"And don't—"

He looked back at her without unbending.

"—don't come back alone." One of Hope's eyes narrowed to a black slit that ran along the hairline of the bisected lens. Eugene was halfway through the lantana jungle when he realized that his great-aunt had winked at him.

The Air India jumbo lifted off, juddering and flapping its wings. For sixty seconds Eugene was pressed back into his seat by a sickening numbing gravity. Then the force eased and the plane tilted slightly. He saw the earth of India flatten and fall away into a miniature painting bordered with blue and indigo and dusted with gold. Clouds of fish and fleurs-de-lis swam past the window. Fields, houses, huts, rivers, tanks, mango topes, shrank under his eye into tiny formal shapes, the symbols of themselves. He found he was using the brown eye, the one nearer the window. To get a better view he had to lean across the window seat, which was occupied by a middle-aged but snowy-haired man, a journalist from Manchester. His own seat was the aisle seat, while the one in the middle was technically free. He leaned, gaping at the

"Do you mind."

"Sorry, men. Sorry."

perfect miniature, executed in two, maybe three, minutes. Although they were soaring over a dwindling Delhi, he saw Sans Souci in the landscape below. It was after all an extension of the same silt plain, the greens, the blues, the khaki, identical. Could those be the indigo baths down there or was it a factory? Were those the ice pits? What was that yellow blimp in

"*Do* you mind?"

"Sorry, men. *So* sorry."

the air? Eugene sighed and settled back in his seat. Better to use the blue eye. He felt under him where something bit into his thigh. It was the buckle of his safety belt. The man beside him made a joke about seat belts to make amends and began to talk as Eugene's blue eye swept the future. His voice drummed at the Seventh Trotter's reverie, breaking through in parts so that Eugene learnt that his name was Jonquil, that he had been in India to do a story on the Anglo-Indian remnant, that he had been. Eugene saw a dark old woman in a shabby print dress, her hair grey and fine as spidersilk hanging in damp strands as she moved through the crowd outside a Nakhlau cinema hall, men's eyes dipping briefly at her bare legs.

The stewardess brought breakfast, her sari silk swishing along the aisle carpet as she put a tray of miniature food in front of each passenger. Mr

Jonquil leaned back in his seat and gave the stewardess a nod. The Seventh Trotter got an identical tray.

"And one for the middle," Eugene heard himself say. "He'll be back." And he craned expectantly down the aisle at where the toilets might be.

The stewardess put a third tray down in the middle and passed on. Mr Jonquil looked curiously at Eugene and went on too. He said he had been to Calcutta, Madras, Bombay, the Kolar Gold Fields, Bangalore, Clement Town— but no, not Sans Souci—why?

"Well—" said Eugene. His mouth was full of toast dipped in tea.

"A strange sad monadic people," Peter Jonquil went on.

"Nomadic?"

"Monadic. They live in a kind of bubble—or many bubbles. They speak a kind of English."

"I say, men, you're not eating your jam?" Eugene reached across gratefully.

"They fantasize about the past. They improvise grand pedigrees. It's like a Raj novel gone wrong."

How the Raj is done

I wish to shew how the Raj is done. This is the play of children, good adept, rest easy. You must have the following ingredients. (It matters little if one or another be wanting, nor is the order of essence. Introduce them as you please, and as often.) Let the pot boil of its own.

An elephant, a polo club, a snake, a length of rope, a rajah or a pearl of price (some use both), a silver moon, a dropped glove, a railway junction, some pavilions in the distance, a chota peg, a tent peg, a learned brahmin, a cruel king, a chapati (or chaprasi), a measure of justice, gunpowder (q.v.), equal portions of law and order, a greased cartridge, a tamarind seed or else a cavalry regiment, a moist eye, some high intentions, two pax of Britannica, Glucose biscuits, an ounce of valour, something in the middle, a Victoria Cross, a soupçon of suspense (q.v.), a bearer, a dhobi (or dhoti), a chee-chee, a dekchi (or deck-chair), a pinch of dust, a trickle of perspiration, a backdrop with temples or mosques (some use both), a church pew, a little fair play, a boar, some tall grass, a tiger, a rain cloud, a second snake or a mongoose, a flutter of the heart, a sharp sword, a bared ankle, walnut juice or burnt cork (some use both), a boy of British blood unsullied, a locket.

The sharp adept will notice that all the above ingredients are present in my book—except the last but one. Some will quibble that this last (but one) lack is sufficient of itself to disqualify my book, and I admit the lack is grave. I begin to wonder, but it is too late. The fault is mine alone.

The sharpest of adepts will note another lack, namely, something in the middle. In my *nama* there is nothing in the middle.

This is what I wished to shew. Now I have shewn it and I am undone. I must fly. So do that. Goe litel boke.

(CHRONICLE CONCLUDED)

Eugene had started on the second tray. He saw Hope Granny, bedridden but bright and ever-watchful—she slept with her eyes open—suddenly get up and walk; he saw 2 Timothy's school prosper in the Spur, where baskets of golden eggs were stored in the Room of Gilt Cages; he saw Ian Atkins-Trotter's soft drink factory fold under competition from bigger companies, and the bigger companies succumb in turn to a cola that was red-white-and-blue; he saw the Glacerie continue to supply ice to the city and to the ACME dairy and the Trotter Ice Cream plant; he saw Soma swell up like a balloon; he saw again the stripes on Albert's back that would never heal; he saw the Atkins-Trotters, army, navy and air force, decorated with medals for service to the country; he saw Ruby turn into a grande dame casting away pearls; he saw Thomas Atkins-Trotter Jr and Richard Atkins-Trotter in handcuffs and leg-irons for selling military secrets to the CIA; he saw Ruby's heart crystallize, turn a pomegranate red, and shiver into a thousand fragments; he saw Harold Atkins-Trotter become Chief of Air Staff and Ruby recover; he saw a portrait with a nose-drip of indigo; he saw a ladder of gold in the Lalbagh Circle and a red ribbon in a rut across the road; he saw dances where railwaymen with pale sharp features steered thin brown girls wearing pleated skirts and open faces; he saw a block of ice melting away in the sun; he saw silver winged pencils carrying Trotter teachers to Kuwait and beyond; he saw black boxes carrying waxen Trotters slip from their ropes as they were lowered into the ground near the railway tracks; he saw those who stayed never forgive those who went; he saw a girl in white play a piano and a neighbour's daughter in saffron play the sitar, after which they made a sort of hesitating music together; he saw the orthodox block their ears; he saw silver tears shed when one of Our Girls married out; he saw coins of blood when a Trotter boy eloped with one of Their Girls; he saw Marris, M.P., grow snowy wings to match his hair, and name half a dozen public schools after himself; he saw Trotter schools burst at the seams and run like honey to the edges of the peninsula; he saw 2 Timothy, more gaunt than ever, look beyond the Spur and discover in the sky above *Sungum* a constellation of five stars; he saw him break the seal of a scroll which decreed that *Sungum* would become a luxury hotel; he saw armies of workers arrive with Italian marble and red Agra sandstone, teak, crystal, aluminium, and stainless steel; he saw Albert turn to 2 Timothy one day and say: "You know, I read somewhere—I think in the *Reader's Digest*—that by stylometric analysis 2 Timothy is not Pauline. That means you're apocryphal"; he saw the rain-gauge near the mango tope overflow with petrol; he saw 2 Timothy grow five horns and stir himself in the depths of the Begam Kothi; he saw him yawn and stretch and swallow and decide that he would lie in bed a little longer; he saw him lie with his hands folded under his head staring up at the ceiling fan which spun directly above him; he saw his muscles contract and his legs swing out of bed at the thought of moneyed tourists pouring in through the restored Gunpowder Gate; he saw him get up just as the fan fell where a moment ago he had been stretched out contemplating its harpoon centre; he saw him look in an un-covered mirror and fall on his knees and give thanks; then he saw him run outside in his pyjamas to the guava tree propelled by the need to confide. What he did not see—but then neither did 2 Timothy—was the thunderbolt.

DA! -*boum!*

It left a neat smokeless hole where 2 Timothy had been standing, a narrow hole about the width of his shoulders, perfectly round and smooth like the bore of the big gun, *Urban*, but bottomless. If you sang into it, it answered with a brassy echo. If you rapped its sides you set up a fathomless tintinnabulation, -NYA -NYA -NYA. If you dropped a pebble down it, you waited in vain for the report. You could see only a short way down it; with a torch you saw a little farther. If you stared hard enough at it, it was a fullstop expanding to infinity and drawing you down into its vortex so that it had to be covered with a grill. At the rim was a flange of fulgurite where the earth must have resisted the impact for a fraction of a second. Below that it was unscored by the slightest imperfection—or for that matter perfection—neither black nor white nor grey, devoid of all qualities, unless lightlessness and emptiness were significant attributes of a window onto nothing.

NAMA

Hey nonny no nonny,
Ho ré, ré ho,
Oah men, ah men,
And a featherless cranny.

—CATCH

Hallo hallo, where you been, men? Yeah yeah it's me—Eugene, same chap. Stop looking like you seen a ghost. Just lost a bit of weight, that's all. Wondering where you'd gone. So how was the wedding and all? Missed it! Reading, han? Damn sad. Never mind, men. Happens. Shouldn't read so much—bad for the eyes, like painting.

Bloody hell! Here, just come in front of me one sec—

OK, he's gone. No, no, I'm OK. Just thought I saw that Carlos bugger. Keep seeing him everywhere. So. Reading what? What bloody chronicle-fonicle? Trotter-Nama? Oh that. Liked it? So what you did with it? Lost it! Which storm—oh that. Ya we had it here too—worse even. So it's all gone, hé? Never mind. Bit late inventing the paperweight, hé? Not that it matters now. Wait till you hear.

Anyway come on now I'll show you where I live. Not Soosee-foosee, men—just here in the city. You see that lane? See that butcher's next to where the sign says HEM BECAN SOUNCES? Down that lane and left. There. Come have a cup of tea.

Here we are.

So. What to say. I was there, now I'm here—finished.

Working as a sort of agent—just a mo—

Eunice darling bring something to drink for the guest. No, no, not that stuff—just a cup of tea. Maybe a piece of cake too—went and missed a wedding.

Nice-looking girl, no? Lives upstairs with her mummy, so they let me have this room for fifty-sixty chips a month, tea included. Sometimes I can't pay and Ma says, Never mind, next time. But tots it up, the old girl. Incidently she's doing a wedding tonight, that's why this place is all chockablock like a madhouse. Does a bit of catering, but not like the old days, she says. Nowadays the showcase is half empty. Just a couple of dummy cakes—cardboard and silver-paper and icing. Waste of sugar, if you ask me. See—through that curtain, there. Used to be full of cakes—fruit cakes, plum cakes, big-big wedding cakes, Christmas cakes, birthday cakes, pastries, patties, don't know what-all.

That's Lassie. Don't worry she doesn't bite unless you try to pet her. Like that. Come here, Lass, never mind, girl. Not Lassi—Lassie. Yeah yeah we know all that but we prefer Lassie. She does too, don't you, girl?

Thanks, Eu. Darling, chain up Lassie. Just while the guest is here. You brought the cake? Good. Bit stale, never mind.

How many spoons you want? Two! I tell you, the price of sugar these days.

So. I was saying—yeah, working as a agent. But let me tell you from the start. Listen. You remember Feejee—that guy on the plane? Pen in his pocket. Wanted dry white wine and all? Yeah. Well, when you went off with the manuscript I heard him saying to the taxi driver: Sungum Hotel, but I didn't connect it. Didn't strike me, you know? And taxi driver gives him a real five-star salute.

So I got into a tonga—thin skinny bloody horse—but glad to be back so in no hurry or anything. Told the tonga-wala, you get me there in one hour I'll give you ten rupees, you get me there in two hours I'll give you twenty. Flushed with money in those days. So the guy gives the horse a hell of a crack and starts off in a great bloody hurry, then suddenly he frowns and looks around at me and laughs and slows down. Nice and slow. Lovely trees going by, green-green rice fields all flooded. Koel singing in the trees—my God that sound after so many years! Pulls your bloody heart up like a radish. Then near the city all the buildings looking familiar but different. Tell you the truth the only way to keep it the same is to stay away. And the same with other places too. You just keep moving to a new place and all the old ones stay the same. So why I came back? God knows.

Anyway, there I was in the tonga. All the places looking the same but changed. You know—more filthy, more flies and all. Puddles everywhere, drains overflowing. I mean, just look outside. These people. Not like your south. Anyway, so listen. Rolling along in the tonga, horse going chickchock-chickchock. When I was a boy I used to like to go at night so you could see the sparks near the horseshoes. Anyway, so in the Lalbagh Circle the stupid tonga wheel goes into a rut and throws me right out. Pants all wet and hands scraped all over. Just as well the ladder was still there near the button shop. Pulled myself up, and saved one of the duty-free wine bottles.

Anyway, got to Soosee and I see the place completely changed. Then I realized. My God! Sungum Hotel. New gate, parking lot where the maze used to be, mango grove gone, builders putting finishing touches, guests already coming in. One busload of smart Italian tourists. Couple of soft-soft brigadiers' wives in chiffon saris with Archie comics and Ayn Rand and a Pekinese. And Feejee in the lobby getting damn worked up about something.

So I walk in like I own the place—what the hell, men, I thought I did. Anyway I knew it better than anyone there, even though they'd gone and put carpets and rubber *plants in the Audience Hall and a new fountain copied from King's Cross in Sydney. All confusion in there. Furniture still being moved around, chaps coming and going. I go and stand near the counter looking around like this-like this.*

And Feejee says: Are you the manager. Not: Are you the manager? Just: Are you the manager. Doesn't recognize me. So I shake my head maybe yes maybe no. And he starts off. But this reservation was made three weeks ago. And I telephoned from the airport precisely to——. Going on like that, la-di-da. Hoity-toity accent and all. So I say: Just one moment till my assistant gets here. And I point at any girl in the confusion. You know, carpenters here, bearers there, hostesses everywhere. Then he says: I would like to lodge a formal complaint. Serious-serious. Have you a complaint book. Not: Have you? Just: Have you. So I turn to another girl and say, not too loud, Darling, go get the complaint book. And all the time Feejee's looking around like he's writing in his head: three men to carry one bedside lamp. Six hands. India. His nose going like this-like this. Then he looks at his watch and says, Well. Not: Well? I tell him, She's going for it, men. He looks at her, says, She's going nowhere. Then these four chaps go by carrying a stool, so I say, Sit, men, have a seat. It'll come. And I shout at the chaps: Here! What is this. (Not: What is this? Just, What is this. Eugene picks up damn fast, I'm telling you.) You can see a sahib here and you don't have the courtesy to give him a chair. The men jump. Petrified. Put it here, I say. They put it down. Feejee looks up slowly to the ceiling like this. Ignoring the stool. So I sit down. And just to pass the time I say, You got any cheese. Any what, he says. Cheese, men, cheese, I say. And I cut a slice in the air. Stuff's damn hard to get here. You know—— pretending I haven't just come back from there. He just looks away like he's bitten a lime or something. About to have a conniption. What the hell, men. OK, so the air conditioner isn't working yet, and the fancy fans are just barely moving (ruined the bloody ceiling, by the way). It's a bit hot for everybody. What to do? Work's going on slowly-slowly. Other tourists asleep in chairs, but not chum. Stands there like he's being crucified or something. Then suddenly he slams his hand on the counter and turns around and walks out shouting: Cheese. Cheese! And some Americans coming in shrug their shoulders like this and point a camera at him. Obliging chaps, Yanks, isn't it?

By then the real manager comes and says to me, Sorry, no room. Only the Purple Suite at a thousand rupees a night if you want it. Otherwise the whole second floor seems to be leaking. Poor chap all harassed. So I said, Yes, it always leaked, but never mind I got a room. And I went around to the Rib to see Soma. You know, still thinking she's waiting there and everything's the same. But the box-room was all empty and when I asked one of the Alexander-Trotters where she was he said, Where you been, men? She's in the Kothi. Still I didn't twig on.

So I went all the way across the Steps and around to the Begam Kothi, and there were some kiddies playing outside Albert's old room. Albert sitting scrubbing his vest in the verandah. Looks up and says, Eugene! You didn't send us a card. We sent you an invitation. I said, I didn't get it. I didn't know. Sinking in. Anyway, congrats and all. And Soma comes out just then and says, Thank you, in the old silky-silky voice. Still no grey hairs. Suddenly started to feel damn lonely, men. So I said, to cover it up, What's all this hotel business? Voice going all funny. As if I didn't know. They said, You didn't know? And they told me about 2 Timothy selling Sungum off. You heard what happened to him, no? Albert said. I had to say, No, men, what? Couldn't say I saw it happen long before it happened, you know. Then they took me to the other side of the Kothi near the guava tree and showed me the hole. Sort of a round circle where chum must have been standing. For all his bloody verilies, Albert said. Had to put a grill on it because of the kids.

Albert looking a bit pulled down. You haven't got a job or anything? I said, getting worried. Where, men, he says. This is full time anyway. Pointing to the kiddies. Then he says, shy-shy, And I'm writing a book. A Short History of Ice, it's called, but already it's six hundred pages. Damn funny stuff ice, when you come to think about it, he says. Just like you and me. Comes in in a pipe and goes out in a crate. And in between what a bloody tamasha, blowing hot blowing cold, waiting waiting, then suddenly it all goes still and you're left stiff and cold.

Same old Albert. Then I asked, How's Hope Granny? They said, She seems to be all right. Ayah's the only one who can get in to see her. Sends out messages now and then if she wants anything. Asked for you once.

So I went to her room, but the bloody bathroom flower—you know, the lantana— and the yellow fungus grass had joined up and the door was completely blocked off. Ayah must have got damn thin. Called out, Granny, Granny! Eugene here. No answer. Then just when I was getting ready to push off she says in a thin-thin voice, You alone? What to say, men. So I said, No, Granny. And she sounded happy.

So I went back to Albert's place—same place, other side—and said, Listen, I've got a special dinner for Sunday night, just for coming home and all. Learnt how to cook while I was there—you got to. Brought most of the stuff with me but we can borrow one or two things from them. Pointing to the five-star buggers in Sungum. Glacerie's still ours, no?

So, Sunday night in the Glacerie at the big table. A few Trotters from close by sitting there. Some Alexander-Trotters (not the rich ones—they all in fancy houses now), couple of Kahn-Trotters, Ian Atkins-Trotter, still running the ice factory alone, still wearing his thin-thin rubber slippers, couple of teacher nieces of his and a smart young Fonseca-Trotter. Looking at me damn strangely, all of them. So I handed out the menus that I had made up, and they started to read. One of Albert's little ones saying, Ugh! chickens en lezards. So I said: Mesdames et masseurs—you know, putting on a bit of kanni—first we have a gazpacho to which I have taken the liberty of adding crotons. One of the teachers, nice-looking girl, said: Sippits, men, what crotons-fotons! And when she tasted it: Cold soup! The other teacher said: It's meant to be cold, and tilted her plate nicely away from her. Then everyone complaining, Not enough salt in the fish. Where are the chips? No ketchup? Soma eating the sweetbreads in walnut sauce with her fingers. When I tried to take away the dessertspoons and keep them for the dessert Albert gave me a hell of a look. Anyway after the flan au miel—*sweet as hell*—I brought out the cheeses. An old Kahn-Trotter said, Why you didn't serve them first with the salty things, men? I said: All right, you wait till you try this, and I opened the wine. Second teacher said: Mm, bouquet! Ian says, Not enough fizz, and takes out an orange drink. Still had a couple of crates left. He was sorry he did, because everyone started saying—except for the second teacher—Yes, yes, give us one, Ian. Little ones mixing the wine with the orange. So afterwards when I put on a record—we went across to the Spur—they ask what the hell is this? No Bocherinni-Focherinni. What's this? Haydn—where's he hidin'? And the first teacher went and got a Boney M and started dancing with the smart Fonseca-Trotter. Albert takes me out and says, Come off it, Eugene. You grew up sucking chusni mangoes, men. So I say OK. What the hell. But must have been looking a bit hangdog because Soma came up and asked me to dance. But when I tried squeezing her a bit for old times' sake, she became all stiff and held me out like that, six inches.

So then I asked her, Why's everyone looking at me so funny-funny? She keeps quiet. I said: Why, men? So in the end she says, 2 Timothy told everyone you weren't even a Trotter. Just so he could sell without a conscience. I said: Conscience! 2 Timothy! making a joke because I suddenly felt like my shoes were filled with sand. She said, You want to sit down? You're looking a bit pale. Then when we were sitting—Albert dancing with the nice-looking teacher and making her laugh—she said, You know, Mavis came back from England. I said, So that's why I couldn't find her! Went everywhere looking. Willesden, Weed in California, Perth. And she's back here all the time! Was, Soma says. She passed away in June. I said: She knew the truth. Queenie used to tell her everything. That's why I went looking. She told you anything? Again Soma becomes all quiet. Come on, men, I said. So she looks at me straight and says: Just something about Boy-Girl. You remember that man with long hair who used to come on a cycle when—?

Did I remember.

So that night I dreamt, when I fell asleep—morning it was actually—about 2 Timothy and Mavis pulling my teeth out and asking, What's your real name? What's your nama? And when all the teeth were gone they gave me a letter addressed to Mr Eugene DAS, and inside was a piece of paper with one corner torn off and nothing on it. And I woke up laughing and crying. Lightning and thunder all round— kraaak-boum. That was the night of the storm. Ya, ya, same one. Little bloody cloud about as big as a split pea and raining all over the north for a week.

Rained and rained. Bloody roof like a Swiss cheese. You got any? Raining in Sungum too. All the guests left. Must have gone to the other big hotel, the one that looks like a bloody Holiday Inn. Full of lalas and smugglers and dirty MLAs. Even the Trotters evacuated Sans Souci—whole place deserted except for me. And a couple of red-bum monkeys.

Don't know what I was thinking or doing in those days. Just remember one or two things. Water came up over the Steps so I took the lift in the new West Tower. Kitchens all flooded downstairs but found a couple of rusty tins of condensed milk in a cubbyhole where I used to paint sometimes. Slept in a different bed each night. New Dunlopillo mattresses and all. Damn posh, but leaking everywhere. Water just kept rising all round. Up the Steps and over and into the Audience Hall and out on the other side filling up the sunken garden near the tea-house. Glacerie must have got full, because I saw the dining table come floating out. Then big-long blocks of ice like coffins all in a row. From the Begam Kothi side, beds, dressing-table, pictures, sitz bath, a mango-wood pallet, whatnot. Leaves, branches, trees, a couple of ACME buffaloes all swollen up. Everything floating past the oval where Urban *was and turning down the drive because the land slopes that way. And then out toward the rain-gauge and the Gunpowder Gate. So when I saw everything going past like a parade I ran across to the military museum. All shipshape there. Put on the Great Trotter's jacket, faded again but buttons still shining. Must have shrunk after all those years. Stockings, shoes, sword. Then ran downstairs and went out to the cannon, walking through the water. Slashed a couple of jakfruits on the way. Got to* Urban *and fired—DA! DA!—across the ice and all. After that went back up and drank a few tins of condensed milk and slept in the Purple Suite—thousand chips a night—for don't know how long.*

Woken up by one of their chowkidars. River must have gone down so they sent a couple of buggers to make sure no one had pinched their five-star stuff. Five-star! You should have seen it. Anyway so then I came to the city and trying, trying, found this place. Sick for hell of a long time but Ma and Eunice looked after me. You could call it a breakdown, but not a Noor Manzil case or anything. Nowadays sometimes Albert and all come and say, lots of room in the Kothi, Eugene, but I say, No thanks. No more Soosee-foosee.

Working in a hotal—no, no, hotal—*round the corner, not far. Sort of a agent, travel-and-general. Sometimes a bit of a mater-dee. Come—you finished your tea? Cake also? Never mind. Come, I'll show you round. Free, men, free—no charge. We'll come back and gate-crash the wedding this evening and have a motherless chew.*

There. See? Fancy signboard, no? Actually it's Ajanta Hotal, but the painter got a bit carried away. Made the capital A so fancy it looks like flowers and leaves and janta Hotal. *Can't trust these painter buggers.*

Who me? Softly, men, you don't know who's listening. Gave it up as a bad joke. Bad for the health painting with chaps like Carlos around. Still, he's just doing his job. Now that bugger Ivor. Selling my stuff at six hundred percent. Told me he knew right from the start. And then squealing when the Great Boar *was found out. So I had to run from bloody country to country. And what really cheesed me off was that he could paint himself. Could've painted the bloody fingernails on the* Veenus dee Meelo. *But letting me do all the work. Cunner. Like those artists in the olden days at Akbar's* court—*laying it out and then letting some sidey finish it off. But those sideys knew their stuff, I'm telling you. You look hard at the red in one of those paintings and you can feel the fire in the bugger's eyes who was bending over it. You look hard enough, and your eyes start to water and you* become *the poor bugger. I still got one of a woman with a watermelon and you should see the red in the middle of that, my God— a slice like a ice boat with a red sail—burning like it's on fire for hundreds of years. Tell you the truth, though, I remember doing one just like it of Naomi, and now I don't know whether this one is mine or not. Ivor would think it was hell of a joke. Still. Can't blame him fully. I started it. You piss into the wind you get wet. Piss into a crater and see.*

Come inside. See, this is the dining room here for the guests. That's just a rag. Nice rooms upstairs. In fact why you don't stay here? Come on, come on, I'll fix it up. Forget about Soosee, men. Place still wet and stinking ever since the flood—even if they put fifty coats of whitewash on. And you pay through your nose just for an American mattress and air conditioning. Here you get a table fan. See? OK we'll get a guard for it. In any case you can't hurt your toes—it goes slowly-slowly. Voltage. See the mossie flying in and out the blades, quite safe. OK so it's not a Dunlopillo pillow, but nothing wrong with silk-cotton. You can play with the seeds till you fall asleep. And you wake up right in the city, not miles out. Toasts, butter—not margarine-fargarine like those five-star dieters want—two eggs fried in vanaspati, bit of tallow, who cares, ketchup, picture house round the corner just over there where the rickshaw stand is. Showing Bruce Lee and James Bond. Quality's gone down a bit. In the old days you could see The Ten Commandments, Matinee Show *Ben-Hur,* Coming Soon *King of Kings. Good Cecil dee Meele stuff. Now it's Coming Soon—King Kong—but the bugger never comes.*

That? That's just a back lane. You don't have to look at it. No, no garden- farden—but then no snakes. OK so the water's not ice-cold, but who the hell needs ice? All right, all right, you want ice I'll get it. Baraf-wala friend of mine just down the gully. Gets it from Uberoi's in blocks and breaks it up on the pavement for you. For mango shakes they put it in a truck tyre-tube and smash the hell out of it.

All fixed up? Come I'll show you the city. Free, men, free.

See, they give me a bit of commission for every guest I bring. So most days I go to the railway station and wait for the tourists. Train comes in from Delhi at nine- thirty. Bit early but what to do? Passing through on their way to Kathmandu, about ten years late. So I bring them here. If it's busy I put on a white jacket and take orders for lunch. Nice chap the owner. Khan Sahib. I mean most places once they find out you're an Anglo—bas, finished. All the donkey work you get. And you apply for leave, they say: O-ho-ho, next week Narain is taking, take it after Raksha Bandhan. And after that Choubey is going for his cousin-sister's wedding. Like you. Or they come and say, Happy Good Friday! Waiting for sweets. But not Khan Sahib. You want a couple of days off he twists his hands like this and says, Take! And doesn't boss you around. Just comes now and then and says: Working hardly, Mister Eugene? And you say: Very hardly, Khan Sahib. And he goes off. Smiling.

Come I'll show you round. No charge, men. Not tombs-fombs—though I do that sometimes. Agent-and-guide. What to do. People want to hear stories about places so you make them up. I mean they've all heard about Lakhnau—what's that? Oah, Nakhlau-Lakhnau, same thing, men. You can even call it Luck-now if you want— not that I've had too much of that lately. So if they want all that bloody past-fast rigmarole I give it to them. All the monuments, Imambaras Big and Small, Friday Mosque, Turkish Gate, Chowk, Clock Tower, Kadam Rasul, Residency, Moti Mahal, Martinière, St Aloysius's, Dilkhusha. But not Soosee. Not that there's nothing there. I mean, I could show them the Black Hole near the guava tree and make up a hell of a story, but you got to draw the line somewhere. Tell you the truth I made up the whole line—I mean joining up all those Trotters like that. Funny bloody story, more holes than a cheese in it. In fact, there's a hole right in the middle. You remember the Middle Trotter? Well he wasn't even an Anglo like I thought, I mean one of us. Some people said he was, so I used him, but afterwards I looked it up. British. So what to do? Change the whole bloody story? No thanks. All finished anyway. Never found out whether he was guilty or not. Ran and ran all the way to the British Museum, where they had the last copy of his second book, The Verdict. *Filled out the form, waited, waited, and what do they say? Sorry. Book was bombed to nothing in the war. So much for the bloody past.*

Anyway the present is tricky enough, just watch your step. Potholes everywhere in this city. Now if they let them all join up, the road would be nice and smooth. But no, they keep patching, bit here bit there. India, men. Feejee's right.

Here, you want to have a bit of a snack? Puri-tack? I know this chap An-joy Rest-au-rent. If I bring him a couple of tourists, he gives me a glass of special tea— once in a while—called khadachamcha. So much cream and sugar in it the spoon just stands in the middle like this. Have something? No? Smell the rice? Real genuine basmati from Dehra Dun. They make good firni, sort of a rice pudding. No? Never mind, there's another chap I know who's got a tea shaap further along. Actually he's better than this chap. Not that this chap's bad. In fact tell you the truth they're better than the janta *for meals. Think about it. No hurry.*

Come on we'll turn left here. If you want a biryani, the best biryani in Nakhlau is at a stall next to those tombs over there. Nawab Saadat Ali and Mrs. See where the eucalyptus row ends? There. One-one grain rice cooked in stock and no skinching on the oil and meat. Some days you even find a raisin in it. Chap across the road where you can get a glass of sugar-cane juice afterwards. As for kulfi. Forget about Mansoor, that circa 1700 rasgulla-wala on the 'Ganj who blotted his reputation—ha! blotted his reputation—hm, anyway he opened up again after paying off the health inspector. His kulfi's not bad, but for the best you just go straight down the 'Ganj away from him and towards the tombs—same tombs—only you turn right. And just before you get to the Monkey Bridge there's a chap on the right. Chap from Kanpur. My God, his kulfi! Fust class, he says himself. Pure cream and real pistachios and sweet as hell. Sells pearly-pearly laddus too that just melt in your mouth. Come why don't we eat something quickly?

No? Anyway, we'll get free tack at the wedding. Want to go back? No? Come I'll show you a couple more things.

See that's our cathedral there—ya, I changed back—new one designed by some Italian fellow. Damn snazzy, no. Nice modern look plus old-fashioned statue stuck on top. New hall next door where we play housie. Ma won a pressure cooker last time. Opposite there is the British Council Library. Downstairs is the Fanfare picture house, upstairs the library. Lovely and cool in there—six air conditioners and nice watercooler—cold-cold water. And peaceful and quiet. Just the air-mail Times *rustling, phr, phr. But when you come* out*!*

I tell you, you try it sometime. First you're inside with the nice big smooth books by—who those chaps done a hell of a lot of nice books together? Thames *and* Hudson. *No, no, not Tems—Thames. I know, men, I was there. I remember reading about them—Hudson was the fat chap. Nice thick-thick books always with pictures, cool green fields and stone fences and all. Anyway, first you're in there with the green fields and the fat-fat cows and olden days and then you step out and it hits you. My God! Hazratganj, I'm telling you—hot, bloody flies, thin-thin cows waiting for the green light, Ambassador cars, mopeds, popcorn boys, lottery sellers, ice cream carts, cycle stand blocking up the verandah, loafers, lepers, heart-cake sellers, cold-water carts, tempos, bullock-carts, cyclists, tongas, scooters, lorries, fifty poor skinny bloody rickshaw-walas calling out to you, shouting, Sahib, I called you first, don't listen to this man, Babuji, I'll take you there for less, give me anything, anything, whatever you want, I'm new, I don't know the rates to there but whatever your worship will give. I tell you sometimes you want to sit down and cry.*

You want to take a rick back? No? OK we'll walk. Which way you want to go? No, that way's the Lalbagh Circle. Come we'll take a shortcut through the Maqbara lane.

I tell you sometimes I have a dream—what sometimes!—many times, same dream. A funny city, could be here, could be there, could be both. Narrow crooked mixed-up lanes on one side and on the other side long broad new straight roads. On the old side of the city there are ruins, old-old buildings you know with domes and things like that and plaster coming off. Brownish walls, bit overgrown, jungly like, thick grass. A graveyard with graves, some small some big like houses. One big one has funny foreign words on one side like Chinese. Other side is blank. I say, Tomorrow I'll see whose grave it was. The other side of the town all modern tall clean grey houses new with glass. Clean greenshaven lawns, broad roads like Los Angeles, with buses, not tinny thud-class buses—solid long shiny ones new with glass and computer numbers flashing on and off on and off. No pushing shoving, nothing. A lady pulls the cord and the bus stops. She gets off with her parcels. I say, Tomorrow I will follow her and see how she lives. Bus keeps going, keeps going, till it comes to the other side, the old side of the city. Suddenly it stops and there's the same big tomb. I get off and see a lady standing there with her parcels trying to read the stone. I say, Can't you see it's blank, men? And she turns towards me and my God her face is also blank. And I start to run till I wake up and my heart's going like a bloody tabla at a potter's wedding.

Anyway, talking about weddings if you want some free grub we'll get some now. Going to be a big show. Ma said let the whole street come. Feeling rich. So all sorts of types will be there don't mind. Barbers and eunuchs and tanners and honey-gatherers and cotton-beaters and KG teachers and ear-cleaners and scooter-drivers and waiters and knife-grinders and rice-pounders and compounders and bread-slicers. Hear the crackers? The becan-wala too, though that's going a bit far I told Ma. Even a bloody bird-catcher—in fact I think it's his wedding. That's what Ma was saying. Anglos of course from here and there—not many left. Albert and Soma and all—but none of those damn hoity-toity ones who think they're the cat's whiskers just because they got a car and a TV and all. You go to them and say, Just help me out a bit, men, not much, just thirty-forty chips and a cup of tea and they start to give you a sermon. And gossiping, my God! Gossip, gossip, gossip, like bloody scissors in a barbershop. Not just the rich ones, everyone. Forever yakking about each other—this one's this and that one's nothing but a that, on and on nothing better to do. Favourite Anglo pastime—smile at you then stab you in the back.

You saw that cracker! Where you keep your eyes, men? Green and like a flipping corkscrew. Might be a bit of something nice to drink there. You got any liqueurs or anything, I say? Never mind.

Anyway, I was saying, not too many of us left and half of those waiting to leave. And we're not the only ones. They want to go too. You read their matrimonial columns. American Green Card holder preferred, only doctor or engineer settled in U.S.A., Canada, Australia. But what to do?

Me? Where to go? I don't know. Here, you look into my eyes. See? Tell me now. Where to go?

I was saying to Eunice—nice-looking girl, no?—I was saying to—Who? Me? Marry her! Oah no. I've already got four waiting, men. One nice brown plump one over that side, one damn risky one just down the road, skin like a black swan. Then a German one, bit cold at first. Used to stay in the janta actually, but she's just gone on a short trip Nepal side. And the youngest one, pink like a I don't know what. Cries all the time, but she'll grow up.

So. I was saying to Eunice, go see Londin, girl. Her brother's gone. Married a Hindu girl. My God, what a bloody fuss the parents made. Wanting to kidnap her back and all—that's the way it is up here. Same down there? What the hell—it'll change slowly-slowly. Let the old fogeys die. Anyway they went off to Londin, never regretted it. So I said to Eunice, go girl. Save up and go—she works in the bank. You won't regret it, I said. Just have a look anyway. My God, the first time I went I just stood there. Shops like Christmas in September, and air so sweet. Everywhere you look chocolates. And apples right on the trees like mangoes, only they're bloody apples, men. She says, You come with me, Eu, and I say no, Eu, you go, I been. Anyway that bugger's waiting—how to explain about Carlos and all? At least here I'm safe. Safe and free.

You hear the brass band now? "I Am a Disco Dancer." Only tune they know. We're almost there, I brought you another way. Funny damn music—all dhoom-dhaam. Don't know why they don't just switch on Ceylon. What? Sri Lanka, Ceylon, same thing, men—same old records anyway. We like the old tunes.

There's the band now, see? Gold epaulettes and barefoot. Typical. What to do? This chap's my photographer friend from Kaiserbagh. Can never get his flash to work. Either it's two seconds too soon or two seconds too late. See? Smile, men. Cheese.

Hallo, Eu! Looking damn sweet, darling. Where you got that veil?

Come we'll go get some grub. Free, men, free!

Hallo, Ma. When this bird-catcher going to get here?

ACKNOWLEDGEMENTS

I would like to thank my parents, Irwin and
Dorothy Sealy of Dehra Dun, for a recipe; my wife,
Cushla, for the name of a dog; my sister, Janet, and
Jim Harwood, for a fixed address; and two friends,
John Cline, for a trade name, and Krishna Acharya,
sometime of Baihar, for an extended metaphor.